Methods in
Hormone Research

SECOND EDITION

VOLUME IIA

Bioassay

Methods in
Hormone Research

SECOND EDITION

Edited by

RALPH I. DORFMAN

Institute of Hormone Biology
Syntex Research, Stanford Industrial Park
Palo Alto, California

VOLUME IIA

Bioassay

1969

ACADEMIC PRESS · *New York and London*

ACADEMIC PRESS, INC.
111 Fifth Avenue, New York, New York 10003

United Kingdom Edition published by
ACADEMIC PRESS, INC. (LONDON) LTD.
Berkeley Square House, London W.1

LIBRARY OF CONGRESS CATALOG CARD NUMBER: *68-23496*

PRINTED IN THE UNITED STATES OF AMERICA

LIST OF CONTRIBUTORS

Numbers in parentheses indicate the pages on which the authors' contributions begin.

VIVIAN L. BEACH (481), *Department of Physiology, Warner-Lambert Research Institute, Tabor Road, Morris Plains, New Jersey*

WILLIAM W. BROMER (415), *The Lilly Research Laboratories, Indianapolis, Indiana*

RALPH I. DORFMAN (121, 151, 221, 251), *Institute of Hormone Biology, Syntex Research, Stanford Industrial Park, Palo Alto, California*

C. W. EMMENS (3, 61), *Department of Veterinary Physiology, University of Sydney, Sydney, New South Wales, Australia*

NORMAN KIRSHNER (287), *Biochemistry Department, Duke University Medical Center, Durham, North Carolina*

ROBERT L. KROC (481), *Department of Physiology, Warner-Lambert Research Institute, Tabor Road, Morris Plains, New Jersey*

K. L. SMITH (365), *Boots Pure Drug Co. Ltd., Nottingham, England*

BERNARD G. STEINETZ* (481), *Department of Physiology, Warner-Lambert Research Institute, Tabor Road, Morris Plains, New Jersey*

R. H. THORP (435, 457), *Department of Pharmacology, University of Sydney, Sydney, New South Wales, Australia*

C. W. TURNER (301, 515), *College of Agriculture, Department of Dairy Husbandry, University of Missouri, Columbia, Missouri*

* Present address: CIBA Pharmaceutical Co., Summit, New Jersey.

v

PREFACE

This volume is, in part, a successor, once removed, to "Hormone Assay," which was edited by Professor C. W. Emmens in 1950 and published by Academic Press. I had the pleasure of contributing to that work the chapters on androgens and adrenal cortical hormones. In 1962 "Hormone Assay" was incorporated in "Methods in Hormone Research" under my editorship. Professor C. W. Emmens kindly contributed two chapters to the first edition of Volume II of this treatise, and by contributing to this edition continues his association with this publication.

Since the expansion of the field in many areas is such that all bioassay procedures of hormonal agents cannot be adequately described in a single volume, Volume II (Bioassay) of this second edition will be published in two parts, A and B.

I would like to express my appreciation to all the contributors who have been particularly cooperative and thoughtful. As always, my deep thanks are due to Mrs. Iola Graton, who made such valuable contributions to this revised volume.

All of us, I am sure, remember the important role the late Mr. Kurt Jacoby played in initiating this work. His memory lives on in many books.

Palo Alto, California   RALPH I. DORFMAN
March, 1969

CONTENTS

Part I: Statistical Methods

1. Statistical Methods

Part II: Steriod Hormones and Related Substances

2. Estrogens

3. Antiestrogens

8. Thyroidal Substances

9. Insulin

10. Glucagon

11. Parathyroid Hormone

CONTENTS OF VOLUME I
Second Edition

PART I

Statistical Methods

Chapter 1

Statistical Methods

C. W. EMMENS

I. Introduction

A. THE BIOLOGICAL ASSAY

Since the first edition of this volume in 1962, there have been rather few additions to statistical methods in biological assay, so that much of this chapter remains unaltered. The foundations of the subject were laid in the 1930's, refinements of various kinds referred to in the first edition were added in the late 1940's and 1950's, and have not been much augmented since. This is probably because the fundamentals have been fairly well explored, and biologists in general are not interested in exploiting more sophisticated techniques such as within-animal quantal responses and do not wish to indulge in complicated designs for assays. In addition, no very long time has elapsed since the chapter was considerably expanded from the original version in Emmens (1950).

In a biological assay, animals are used as though they were test tubes, as a convenient way of observing a reaction, usually called the response. This response may be the death of the animal, or changes in its growth rate, blood constituents, or other tissues. Sometimes each animal can only be used once, sometimes it can be used in repeated assays. Whichever is possible, groups of animals are usually employed and their mean responses are the basis of the subsequent calculations. This is because, unlike a set of test tubes treated alike, animals usually show considerable variation in response, and little reliance can be placed on individual observations.

A satisfactory assay must give an unbiased estimate of potency, and of the range of potencies within which the mean estimate lies, to a given degree of probability. It has become conventional to regard a probability of 1 in 20 as satisfactory for ordinary purposes, but sometimes 1 in 100 is demanded. These are usually referred to as the 95% and 99% limits, respectively (sometimes as the 5% and 1% limits), and imply that in repeated assays of the type under consideration only in 5% or 1% of cases will the stated limits fail to include the true potency. It is also usual to center the range so presented on the mean estimate of potency, so that 2.5% or 0.5% of each tail of the calculated distribution is cut off.

To perform a satisfactory assay, certain elements of design must be fulfilled, and a potency determination will be valid only if they are. Essential requirements are as follows:

1. The substances compared must have similar actions on the test material. This is usually checked to some extent by determining the parallel nature of the individual dose-response lines, and rejecting any assays not showing parallelism.

2. The assay must be balanced in time, all responses being obtained simultaneously or so balanced that secular variation may be discounted in analysis.

3. The living material is allotted to dosage groups in such a way that variation in response will not bias the result or the estimate of error.

4. An estimate of error must be available from the internal evidence of the assay itself, although a homogeneous estimate gained from a series of assays may ultimately be used in calculations of limits of error.

These are restrictions that must be placed on any assay of whatever form; in addition, there are other highly desirable points that should be adhered to if at all possible:

5. The assay should be completely balanced, with equal numbers per group and equal numbers and spacing of groups on whatever scale is used (often a log scale).

6. A standard preparation should be employed as a routine, either a substance carefully calibrated against an international standard, or a local standard if no international standard exists.

Many of these considerations have been ignored by investigators in the past, but it is fortunately becoming more frequent to pay careful attention to them. Perhaps the second requirement for a valid assay, simultaneity or temporal balance, has been the most often ignored, but it must be closely followed by the fifth. However, lack of attention to any of the first few points leads to invalidity; lack of attention to point 5 leads to tedious calculations and less precision than could otherwise have been gained. This requirement is less important, however, as electronic calculation becomes available.

Most assays in this volume are based on a log dose-response relationship, i.e., equal increments in response are produced, at least over the working part of the dose-response line, by equal increments in log dose, not in the dose itself. This relationship leads to straightforward methods of calculation, and since there is almost never any point in failing to keep the numbers of test objects per group and per substance constant, only this case will be treated in detail. In assays where some degree of mortality before the end of the test is likely, it is still possible to keep group numbers effectively constant either by replacing missing observations as described in standard texts or by reducing group numbers to the minimum encountered in any one group. This is done by random rejection of surplus observations in the other groups. Except when first investigating the characteristics of a dose-response line, it will usually also be pointless to do other than a 4- or 6-point assay, with 2 or 3 groups each on the standard and the unknown. A 6-point assay checks for linearity, and a

4-point assay is the least that gives any running check on similarity of action. In special circumstances, when a very limited amount of a preparation is available, as in some clinical work, a 3-point assay with only 1 group on the unknown and 2 on the standard may be forced upon the investigator, but this should never be regarded as really satisfactory.

B. BIOLOGICAL STANDARDS

The need for a standard has been mentioned above. It arises because of the great influence of changes in technique, in the animal material itself, and time-to-time variation in response on the estimate of potency obtained. In a satisfactory assay a standard must be included so as to discount these effects, which are the cause of the failure of various types of animal unit so frequently used in the past in comparing activities. The same group of animals responds differently from time to time, and different animals within the group have different levels of response at any one time. Even stocks of animals kept under apparently constant conditions show these phenomena. Thus Burn (1937) found that the frog unit for digitalis varied during a year from 1310 units/gm to 2940 units/gm, and Emmens (1939) found that the mouse unit for estrone varied during a similar period from 0.064 μg to 0.150 μg.

Recognition of this source of error has led to the establishment of international and local standards, kept under conditions designed to preserve them unchanged and to enable their use as stable reference materials on which to base potency estimates. International standards are available for many hormones, and other widely circulated preparations exist, such as the purified pituitary preparations of the National Institutes of Health at Bethesda. These are distributed to various laboratories, in which it will usually be desirable to establish carefully calibrated substandards for everyday use.

If the unknown and the standard preparations act in a similar manner, so that one may in fact be regarded merely as a dilution of the other, an estimate of relative potency should be independent of the particular test method employed. Very careful safeguards have been found necessary in practice to ensure that this is the case, and different assays will often be found to be extremely sensitive to different impurities or inhomogeneity in either preparation. Such difficulties led Emmens (1939) and Pedersen-Bjergaard (1939) to conclude that, in estrogen assays, only pure characterized substances could be meaningfully compared with the estrogen standards by biological assay of the types then available.

C. DESIGN AND ANALYSIS

Emphasis has been placed above on the design of valid assays, and minimum adequate types of design have been indicated. However, assays may be designed of a far more complex nature than this, sometimes with great advantage. In addition, in the exploration of new methods of assay, it is frequently advantageous to use factorial or other advanced types of design in order to gain as much information as possible in a limited time and with limited animal stocks. These methods will be treated in greater detail below. It is, however, usual, once an assay method has become established, to use it under rigid conditions, so as to help preserve continuity in results. This may not necessarily be wise; it depends on the findings from more complex investigations such as have just been mentioned. If it is found that wide variations in technique do not change relative potency estimates significantly, it may be best to arrange assays on a factorial basis and to gain all the added information available. The fact that this is almost never done in practice should not stop us from contemplating doing so, particularly since it is becoming apparent that animal material frequently gives few or no significant interactions in complex tests (Emmens, 1960). The stability of a potency estimate over a range of test conditions should add to the confidence placed in it.

Within certain limits, the design of an assay dictates how it must be analyzed if all the information is to be salvaged. Within these limits, however, we are free to make use of various so-called models upon which to base calculations. It is usual to assume log-normality in distribution or log-linearity in dose-response lines, and the fact that no dose-response line is log-linear over the whole range of doses, or that log-normality of distribution is rarely proved, should not worry us unduly. It is better to choose a log-linear segment and to work within that, than to try to cope with a wider range of dosage by adopting less convenient statistics, and better to assume log-normality than to try to make calculations on some less likely basis or on no such assumption to all—which may give very wide and almost useless estimates of error. It has been shown in several instances that various "reasonable" methods of calculation (or models) all give virtually the same answer, so that it is usually a question of choosing, from an infinity of possible functions, that which while giving an acceptable fit to the data is the easiest to use in computations. Thus Finney (1952) shows that the same data analyzed by four different methods gave practically identical estimates of potency and limits of error (Table I). In discussing in detail comparisons between these transformations of response, Finney (1964) concluded that all but the rectangular $(P = Y)$ are very nearly the same between responses of 2% and 98%. Biggers (1951) came to exactly the same conclusions.

The importance of appreciating this position will be more apparent when quantal responses are discussed below, where it will be seen that some methods of calculation, notably those using such transforms as the probit or logit, lead to very tedious or impossibly complex calculations, while others which give the same answers are simple to handle and permit experimental designs of a much more complex nature. This may be important to the investigator who wishes to make the most of his material, and to the routine worker who is faced with many assays to compute in a short period of time. The growing possibilities of using automatic computers in this field have served to emphasize the importance of

TABLE I

RELATIVE POTENCY OF DIGITALIS IN FROGS[a]

Transform	Relative potency	Limits of error
Probit	2.09	1.70–2.65
Logit	2.09	1.69–2.67
Angular	2.08	1.70–2.62
$P = Y$	2.06	1.72–2.53

[a] Injected by two different routes, and calculated on different assumptions. Table adopted from Finney (1945).

alternatives to probits, for instance, since although a medium-sized machine can handle the requirements for probit analysis on a considerable scale, it may not do so as rapidly as desirable and the costs are likely to be high. The large, high-speed computers now becoming available do, however, enable us to envisage a stage in the very near future when it will not really matter which model is adopted.

Since an assay is not complete without an estimate of error, and approximate methods of calculation do not yield unbiased estimates, or yield none at all, these are to be avoided. If a rough idea of the results is to be obtained for immediate use, a simple graphical estimate is best, to be followed by the calculation of fiducial limits of error as soon as necessary. These were investigated by Irwin (1943) and take into account uncertainties in the slope of the dose-response line when small numbers of animals are used. If this slope does not exceed about 8 times its standard error, the fiducial limits will appreciably exceed the approximate limits calculated prior to Irwin's work. If the slope is known with high precision, the approximate limits are good enough. These calculations do not affect the estimate of potency, only the limits of error.

D. COMPUTATION AND COMPUTERS

Various types of computation are discussed in the next sections; these are basic to bioassay whether the calculations are made longhand, on a desk calculator, or with an automatic computer. Only the latter, however, can offer the rapidity necessary for either large-scale assay of many substances or the use of really complex investigations involving, perhaps, factorial analysis with the exploration of many possible ways of measuring and expressing responses. Otherwise, investigation may be held up while calculations are in progress, and the next step in a research or screening program may have to await days of computation. Avoiding this means the availability of a high-speed computer with adequate programs and staffing, so that results are known, if necessary, within a few minutes of preparing the data. This is only slowly being realized, and most of us must still contemplate desk computation and this may limit the scope of experiments so that we can deal with them. Bioassay programs for computers are not usually available, and they are difficult to write, even for programmers experienced in other fields. It is thus pleasant to see some useful publication emerging in this field (cf. Thorslund and Paulsen, 1963), but it is sparse and does not present the full scope of modern methods either in statistics or computation. Biologists must impress those who help in this regard with the urgent need to publish their program or methods of writing them.

II. Terminology and Procedure

A. SAMPLING AND RANDOMIZING

The statistical discussions in this chapter assume that the samples of test material used have been obtained and allotted to dosage groups by a process of randomization. This means that of all possible test objects that could have been selected for use, those taken represent a sample in which each individual object was independently chosen by a process which made it equally likely to be selected as any other. It means additionally that in allotting test objects to dosage groups, each, independently, was as likely to fall into any one group as into any other. The word "independently" has been introduced into these definitions to ensure that it is clearly understood that allotment of groups of animals together by one act of selection is not permissible unless each group has been formed by the individual random selection of test objects.

Completely unbiased sampling from a population in an animal house or from other stocks is often impossible, but every attempt should be made to achieve it or to approximate to it. Failure to take care in this direction may lead to inconsistent estimates of slope, of variability, and even of potency from one assay to another. Sometimes there is a very restricted choice, or no choice at all, of the test objects to be used, as when all of the animals of a certain age or weight available must be used. When this occurs, care must still be taken to see that random allocation occurs to the dosage groups, and notice should be taken of time-to-time differences in population characteristics and response.

Any bias in the allotment of test objects to dosage groups or to any other integral subdivision of the assay will invalidate conclusions. Bias in the selection of test objects to be used may not invalidate an individual assay, although it may invalidate the combination of a series of assays. The allotment to dosage groups must, therefore, be strictly at random, by a process analogous to writing the number of each object on a card, shuffling thoroughly and then dealing into the various groups. In practice it is usually easier to use a table of random numbers such as those of Fisher and Yates (1963) or Snedecor (1956). Common errors in randomization are discussed by Emmens (1948) and include such procedures as taking animals from a large cage or run and allotting them by hand to dosage groups. Such a procedure will usually select the tamest or the largest first, and therefore not be random. Even more subtle errors may creep in if such a process is left to an assistant who does not understand the object of randomizing, and may try to balance out groups in in a nonpermissible manner, thereby reducing the real error, if he is successful, but increasing the estimate of it.

However, random allocation to dosage groups is often practised within various restrictions in design, examples of which are discussed below. Thus, several litters may be available for use in an assay, and we may wish to take advantage of the greater similarity in response usually exhibited by littermates in comparison with the general population. If one member of each litter can be placed into each dosage group, again at random, then in the subsequent analysis appropriate steps are taken to segregate the variation attributable to differences between litters and to base the estimate of error on differences within litters. The same procedure may be used with any classes of test objects that are believed to react alike to a greater extent than the population from which they are drawn. If the assumption is wrong, no harm is done unless an unusually few degrees of freedom are available for the eventual estimate of error.

B. DISTRIBUTION

Fuller discussions of appropriate statistical methods in assay than is possible here have been presented by various authors. Emmens (1948) and Finney (1964) may be consulted for an elementary and more advanced and comprehensive treatment, respectively. The basic principles of bioassay do not change, although detailed methods are always changing. It is still felt, however, that a useful purpose is to be served by introducing the nonmathematical reader to the basic concepts and to the elements of statistical procedure, without which he will fail to realize the need for various measures in design and analysis. It is still true to say that the biologist's reading of statistical papers is often spoiled by his being plunged into unfamiliar concepts with little or no

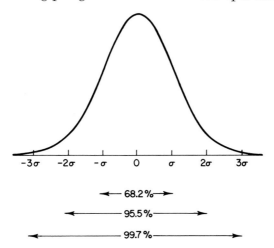

FIG. 1. The normal distribution. (From Emmens, 1948.)

explanation, even when these papers are addressed to biologists. The usual cause is that it is not possible to include the elements of statistics with every paper published, and it is quite reasonable to expect the biologist to familiarize himself with at least the basic ideas and procedures involved.

There is an infinity of ways in which a set of observations may be distributed about their mean or average value. It has been shown, however, that the expected distribution of a series of estimates such as the height or weight of the same object is a bell-shaped curve, shown in Fig. 1. This was called the *curve of error*, or *normal distribution*, and has the equation

$$y = \frac{n}{\sigma \sqrt{2\pi}}\, e^{-x^2/\sigma^2}$$

with points of inflexion at $x = \pm\sigma$. The same distribution has been encountered when measuring attributes of a population, such as heights or weights, with the proviso that so-called outliers, extreme individuals at one or either end of the scale, tend to be a little more frequent than expected. Note that the distribution of repeated measurements of the same object is to be distinguished from that of one measurement each (or a mean of several measurements) of a population of objects. Each may be normal, but the first arises from errors of measurement and the second from errors of measurement plus natural variation. Errors of measurement are often unimportant, as in weighing animals for a test or organs after it, and the distribution is then effectively that due to natural causes alone.

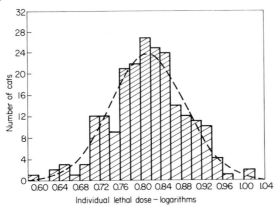

Fig. 2. A normal distribution of individual effective log lethal doses of digitalis in cats. (From Bliss, 1944.)

It is quite unusual to have sufficient observations in any one bioassay to confirm normality of distribution in the responses to drugs or hormones. It is assumed that the distribution is normal unless evidence is presented to the contrary, and it may be shown that this assumption will cause no trouble unless it is rather widely wrong. It is also a useful property of any distribution that the distribution of means of samples tends rapidly to normality as sample size increases. As it is with means that the statistician is often primarily concerned in bioassay, any tendency to departure from normality in the basic data is often eliminated by using units derived from the combination of observations. This may not be so, however, and the assumption of normality may occasionally lead us astray. The small likelihood of this is demonstrated by Table I.

Normality of distribution is nevertheless inherent in the assumptions of probit analysis, in that the individual responses are assumed lognormally distributed. This has again rarely been demonstrated, but Fig. 2 shows an example from Bliss (1944) in which individual cats were slowly injected with digitalis until death occurred. In a few other cases, it has been shown that the overall distribution is not log-normal, but in the great majority no decision is possible, and in the absence of any definite contrary evidence, it is usually assumed that log-normality holds. The consequences of this in relation to advanced design of assay and other investigations are discussed in more detail below, where it is shown that the log-normal distribution may lead to difficult or impossible analyses, and that substitutes for it are to be preferred.

It should be noted that it is not necessary to assume *any* distribution to estimate relative potency, but that methods for doing this, and particularly for assigning limits of error, are only under development. Sen (1963) should be consulted for examples of a method useful in dilution assays, although these are not considered in detail in the present text.

C. MEANS, VARIANCES, AND STANDARD ERRORS

A *variate* is something that varies, like the response of a series of animals to a drug, which may assume a normal or other distribution. There are two variates which appear in all assays, the *independent variate*, or dose of drug, so-called because we determine what it shall be, and the *dependent variate*, or response to the drug, which has to be measured. Other covariates, such as body weight of animals, may also be measured and entered into the analysis. The dose is usually denoted by X and the response by Y.

The *arithmetic mean* of a series of observations is indicated by placing a bar over the appropriate symbol; thus the mean of several responses is $\overline{Y}$, and

$$\overline{Y} = SY/n$$

where S is an operative symbol implying the sum of all values of Y, and n is the number of values summed. The arithmetic mean of the logs of a series of doses (or anything else) is the log of the *geometric mean of* these doses, the geometric mean being defined as the nth root of the product of n numbers. This enters into calculations where response is related to log dose.

The sum of the deviations of all values of Y from $\overline{Y}$ is zero. These are frequently denoted by small italics, i.e., y, hence $Sy = 0$. The sum of the squares of these deviations from $\overline{Y}$ is less than that which results if they are taken from any other point, hence Sy^2 is minimal.

The *variance* (or *mean square*) is the sum of squares of y divided by one less than the number of observations in the group concerned, and is usually denoted by V, hence

$$V = s^2 = Sy^2/(n-1)$$

where s is the *standard deviation*, the square root of the variance. The divisor, $(n-1)$, is the number of *degrees of freedom* or independent comparisons on which the estimate is based. For each statistic calculated from a group of data, one degree of freedom must be subtracted in subsequent computation, thus having calculated the mean, the variance must be allotted $(n-1)$ degrees of freedom. Another way of looking at it is that a measure of dispersion must be based on the $(n-1)$ differences which exist between any observation and the rest. Any subsequent comparisons are not independent of these and can be derived from them.

The variance is a measure that is independent of sign, and includes all positive and negative deviations squared. The standard deviation, s, is not the average deviation, and about two-thirds of all deviations fall into the range $\pm s$ in a normal distribution. It is more informative to think in terms of variances rather than the standard deviation when considering the sources and meaning of variation in experimental work. Thus, the inverse of a variance, or *invariance*, is a measure of the amount of information conveyed by members of a sample, relevant to the point at issue. A member of a group with unit variance supplies one unit of information; a member of a group with a variance of 4 supplies a quarter of a unit.

The *variance of a mean* is $1/n$ of the variance of the group supplying that mean, and thus the mean conveys n times the information that any one observation supplies.

$$V\overline{Y} = Sy^2/n(n-1)$$

where $V\overline{Y}$ is the variance of Y.

The *standard error* of a mean $s_{\overline{Y}}$, is the square root of the variance of the mean; thus $V\overline{Y} = S_{\overline{Y}}{}^2$. The term standard error distinguishes this quantity from the standard deviation of the individual observations.

D. Analysis of Variance

The more completely balanced an assay or experiment, along the lines indicated above, the easier it is to analyze it, particularly in the form of an analysis of variance. As one of the simplest examples of such an analysis, consider the data in Table II, from Emmens (1948). This table shows measurements of blood sugar in milligrams per 100 ml in groups of seven examples each of four breeds of rabbit, as used in the biological assay of insulin. We wish to know, among other things, whether these breeds differ in mean blood sugar level and thus to decide how assays using them should be planned. If the rabbits appear homogeneous in this respect, no advantage may be gained by keeping breeds separate.

TABLE II

BLOOD-SUGAR LEVELS IN MILLIGRAMS PER 100 ml OF FOUR BREEDS OF RABBIT

				Breed			
Y_p	$(Y_p - 100)^2$	Y_p	$(Y_p - 100)^2$	Y_p	$(Y_p - 100)^2$	Y_p	$(Y_p - 100)^2$
117	289	137	1369	135	1225	109	81
116	256	136	1296	122	484	108	64
128	784	121	441	135	1225	117	289
104	16	113	169	138	1444	118	324
121	441	145	2025	131	961	101	1
100	0	123	529	134	1156	134	1156
123	529	113	169	140	1600	113	169
SY_p 809		888		935		800	
$S(Y_p - 100)^2$	2315		5998		8095		2084
$n_p(\bar{Y}_p - 100)^2$	1697.29		5049.14		7889.29		1428.57
Sy_p^2	617.71		948.86		205.71		655.43

Total sum of squares, $SSy_p^2 = 2427.71$

Before performing an analysis, the following identities must be known:

$$Sy^2 = SY^2 - n\bar{Y}^2 = SY^2 - \bar{Y}T = SY^2 - T^2/n,$$

where T is the total of all observations (SY). Also:

$$Sy^2 = Sn_p\bar{y}_p^2 + SSy_p^2$$

where n_p, y_p, and $\bar{y}_p$ refer to the observations in group p (any group). This means that the sum of the squares of the deviations from the grand mean, $\bar{Y}$, can be calculated readily without subtracting each from the mean; and that this sum may be split into two portions. The portion $Sn_p\bar{y}_p^2$ represents the sum of squares attributable to the departures of the group means, $\bar{Y}_p$ (of which there are four in this instance) from $\bar{Y}$, while the portion SSy_p^2 represents the sum of squares attributable to the departure of the individual observations from the group means. These are the *between groups* and *within groups* sums of squares, respectively. The symbol SS means "the sum of the sums of."

Further, the variance of $\overline{Y}_p$ about $\overline{Y}$ is $Sn_p\bar{y}_p^2/3$, and that of the individual observations from their own group means is $SSy_p^2/4 \times 6$, there being six degrees of freedom within each group available for the estimation of error.

These calculations are made in Table II. For convenience, in all but machine calculation, the actual observations have each had 100 subtracted from them before taking squares, a form of *coding* which does not alter the results.

TABLE III

ANALYSIS OF VARIANCE OF THE DATA IN TABLE II

Source of variation	Formula	Degrees of freedom	Sum of squares	Mean square
Between groups	$n_pS\bar{y}_p^2$	3	1799.14	599.7
Within groups	SSy_p^2	24	2427.71	101.2
	Sy^2	27	4226.85	

$$F = 5.93; P < 0.01$$

We then determine Sy_p^2 separately for each group, and find that their added total is 2427.71. In addition, the value of $Sn_p\bar{y}_p^2$ is determined from the calculated means, or, more easily, from the identity:

$$Sn_p\bar{y}_p^2 = Sn_p\overline{Y}_p^2 - n\overline{Y}^2$$

and is found to be 1799.14. These quantities added together should equal the total sum of squares, Sy^2, or $SY^2 - n\overline{Y}^2$, which may be calculated as an independent check and is found to be 4226.85. In practice, it is often more convenient to calculate this total and then to subtract from it SSy_p^2 in order to obtain $Sn_p\bar{y}_p^2$, but in hand calculations it is often a good idea to make the full check. The quantities $n_p\overline{Y}_p^2$ and $n\overline{Y}^2$ are often called the *correction factors* for the respective means.

If there are no differences in mean level of blood sugar for the different breeds of rabbit, the within groups variance should, on a per item basis (per degree of freedom) equal the between groups variance, since the only contribution to the latter is from the former. If, however, there is a difference between breeds, the between groups variance will exceed that within groups by an amount determined by the difference that exists.

The comparison of these data leads to an analysis of variance as in Table III, where the mean squares, or variances attributable to these factors, are compared. It is seen that the mean square between groups (599.7) is much greater than that within groups (101.2), but we have yet to discuss how to determine the significance of this. Note that on the basis of the variance of *means* we would estimate the expected variance of any individual mean as $101.2/7 = 14.46$ on the *null hypothesis*, that breed makes no difference, whereas that observed is $599.7/7 = 85.67$; quantities in the same ratio as above.

E. THE VARIANCE RATIO

To estimate the significance of such differences in variance as are discussed above, tables of a function, F, the *variance ratio*, have been prepared. F is equal to the larger variance divided by the smaller one; in the above case it is $599.7/101.2 = 5.93$. From F tables, it is seen that, with 3 and 24 degrees of freedom, respectively, a variance ratio as high as 4.72 would be encountered only once in a 100 trials, and from this we conclude that the observed figure of 5.93 is highly significant and that breed differences exist. If the estimate of the within-groups variance had turned out to be the larger one, we should conclude immediately that no difference exists between breeds because the within groups variance cannot in reality be the larger of the two, unless some undetected bias has entered the assay. A *significantly* larger within-groups variance should lead us to suspect the whole assay.

F is a general function of which two other common ones, t^2 and some types of χ^2 are particular cases. If it is desired to test only two groups, so that there is only 1 degree of freedom between them, tables of F are often replaced for convenience by tables of t, which is the square root of F with one degree of freedom associated with what is usually the larger variance. Tables of t itself cover cases where the single degree of freedom may be associated with the smaller variance and also include various levels of significance. The statistic χ^2 (Chi-squared) is used when the measurement of Y is discontinuous, particularly when it is quantal. If percentages of reactors can, for example, be calculated the homogeneity of these is tested by χ^2, which is in some circumstances $n_1 F$ when $n_2 = \infty$. The number of degrees of freedom associated with the within-groups sum of squares is in this case infinite, because we calculate a theoretical variance based on some hypothesis, usually the binomial. If χ^2 exceeds a certain value we conclude, as in the F test, that the groups are heterogeneous.

F. Small Samples

When dealing with large samples from a normally distributed population, samples of several hundreds, the standard deviation may be used with sufficient exactitude to predict the proportion of the sample that will fall within specified limits with the mean as a center. Thus, about 68% of all observations will fall within the limits $\overline{Y} \pm s$, where s is our estimate of σ, the true standard deviation. About 95% of all observations will fall within $\overline{Y} \pm 2s$, and 99.7% within $\overline{Y} \pm 3s$. When small samples

TABLE IV

Values of t and Limits of Error of a Mean ($\overline{Y} = 100$)[a]

| Sample size | Sy | \multicolumn{4}{c}{Limits of error and t for:} | | | |
		t	$P = 0.95$	t	$P = 0.99$
2	7.06	12.71	10.3–189.7	63.66	−349.4–549.4
4	5.00	3.18	84.1–115.9	5.84	70.8–129.2
8	3.54	2.57	90.9–109.1	4.03	85.7–114.4
16	2.50	2.37	94.1–105.9	3.50	91.2–108.8
32	1.77	2.04	96.4–103.6	2.75	95.1–104.9
64	1.25	2.00	97.5–102.5	2.66	96.7–103.3
∞	0.00	1.96	—	2.58	—

[a] Population variance of 100, derived from small samples.

are dealt with, s is a very approximate estimate of σ and the limits must be widened at each level of probability. The effect of this is shown in Table IV, which gives values of t and the limits of error of a mean, assumed to be 100, with a population standard deviation of 10, when derived from small samples. The limits of error are given for the 5% ($P = 0.95$) and 1% ($P = 0.99$) levels of probability, and it is seen how wide these become when sample sizes are small.

It will be noted that in all these calculations it has been assumed that the within-groups variance is homogeneous, even though the means for groups may differ significantly. Fisher (1954) has discussed the likelihood of obtaining misleading values of t because of heterogeneity in this variance, and finds that it is very unlikely to be a source of practical trouble. However, when any doubt arises it is possible, and advisable, to test the assumption. Thus, the analysis is not applicable if variance is correlated with response to any marked degree, and it may be necessary to transform the response so that this is no longer the case. A transform frequently used is log response, which may then be related to log dose in the usual manner. Any transform which equalizes variances may be employed, although it may then be necessary to confine experimental observations to a particular linear segment of the dose-response line.

G. QUANTAL RESPONSES

It has become conventional to analyze assays involving all-or-none responses in quite a different way from those in which continuous variation is measured. The usual transform employed is the *probit*, based on the *normal equivalent deviation* of Gaddum (1933). At an earlier time of writing (Emmens, 1950) it was possible only to remark that, apart from such observations as those of Finney in Table I, nothing seemed to have been done about the possibilities of using simpler techniques. It was remarked also that the angular transformation (cf. Fisher and Yates, 1963) might prove useful, having the advantage of a constant variance at all levels of response, which the probit has not.

Since 1950, a greater effort has been made to explore the possibilities of other transforms, a project which has in particular been stimulated by the difficulties of probit analysis when attempts are made to use factorial or other complex designs, and its virtual inapplicability to cross-over or repeat tests of a quantal nature when the same animal can be used more than once. As it stands, probit analysis cannot usefully be applied to the calculation of *within-animal* variation (Claringbold, 1956; Emmens, 1957; Claringbold and Emmens, 1961). The substitution of logits (Berkson, 1949) is no help in this regard.

On the assumption that the distribution of individual effective doses is log-normal, the appropriate theoretical transform is indeed the probit. Finney (1952, 1964) has described the operations of probit analysis, taking it as far as simple factorial tests, when calculation commences to be especially tedious. The probit corresponding to a given percentage of reactors is

$$5 + Y = 5 + (X - X_0)/\sigma_x$$

where X is the log dose causing the percentage of reactors in question and X_0 the log dose causing 50% of reactions (it being assumed that nil dose causes no reactions). The quantity 5 is added to keep the probit positive in all ordinary circumstances.

In practice, however, we do not know X_0, and the equation,

$$P = \frac{1}{\sqrt{2\pi}} \int_{-\infty}^{Y} e^{-\frac{1}{2} Y^2} dY$$

is employed. It derives Y, the normal equivalent deviate, or probit minus 5, from P, the percentage of reactors. After fitting a dose-response line, or lines, to the responses expected on the hypothesis, the adequacy of the transform is checked by a χ^2 test, a "goodness of fit" test, to see whether the points fit the calculated line well enough. Unfortunately, the inconstant variance of the probit, which is least at 5 and greater the farther from 5 one goes, makes calculations very tedious if many are to be done, of if a test is complex in deisgn. Analysis of variance is inapplicable, at least in theory, but in fact it may be used as a short cut if extreme percentages are not frequent in the data, perhaps finally to be rounded off with a single cycle of probit operations. Otherwise, cycles of calculation have to be repeated until successive estimates agree within reasonable limits. With few points, this may involve several repetitions, but, fortunately, estimates for larger assays usually settle down rapidly.

The angular transformation was investigated by Claringbold *et al.* (1953), who showed that transformation of *observed* responses (Eisenhart, 1947) leads to a rapid, noniterative, but approximate solution. Transformation of *expected* responses (as is usual in the probit method) leads to an exact, iterative maximum-likelihood solution. In practice the two methods gave almost identical results, and with the addition of one cycle of the maximum-likelihood solution following the method of Eisenhart, this method is fully adequate. To overcome difficulties with regions of 0% or 100% response, parallelogram designs were introduced for assays or experiments, in which the *region of useful observation* was covered by dosage groups, avoiding expected responses of less than, say, 10% or more than 90%.

Despite the advantage of the angular transformation, it is still inadequate for some types of work. Claringbold (1955) showed that the within-animal variation, over a period of 5 weeks, was only 29% of the between-animal variation in the response of ovariectomized mice to estrone, which is quantal. He then proceeded to investigate the possibilities of within-animal bioassays with quantal responses (Claringbold, 1956) and confirmed that a 4-point cross-over design had about 25% of the variance seen in standard designs of the same type. But in such an assay, solution in terms of probits would imply a group size of unity, since a constant must be fitted for each individual (Finney, 1952), and in the standard maximum-likelihood solution, estimates of more parameters would be needed than there were animals in the test. Estimation with the angular transformation would be very awkward also, because a working angle would have to be computed for each observation with a "group" response always of either 0% or 100%. Instead, the simple

approach was made of scoring each response as either 0 or 1, and performing an analysis of variance. Although open to some theoretical objections,
this method gives reliable results.

A comparison of the angular transformation; $(0, 1)$ or $(0, 1, 2)$ scoring
was made by Emmens (1957), again in cross-over tests with ovariectomized mice and is used as an example below. In these tests, a repeat smear
from each mouse on each occasion made the $(0, 1, 2)$ score possible, so
that a semiquantal assay was also performed. This test was over an
extended period of 16 weeks, but still showed a 2-fold gain in information
as a result of within-animal estimates. It also demonstrated how $(0, 1)$
or $(0, 1, 2)$ scores make possible the estimation of slopes and relative
potency in the presence of heterogeneity, when either probits or angles
in a typical assay would demand the use of a heterogeneity factor and an
estimate of error based on very few degrees of freedom. The analysis of
complex tests is feasible only with such methods, while that of simpler
tests is very much facilitated, with a possible gain in information as well.

We are, therefore, faced with a choice of methods in presenting the
results of quantal assays. There is no doubt that very complex designs
can in practice be analyzed only by other than probit methods, unless
automatic computers are used, and that the same methods are useful in
simpler cases, either on their own, or, if desired, as a basis for a cycle of
probit calculations for those who feel the need of reassurance about the
agreement between methods.

H. Semiquantal Responses

The methods just outlined can clearly be extended to any number of
numerical classes of response, and would probably give satisfactory
results, but it should be noted that the instance of several outcomes of
treatment, instead of strictly 2 as in the quantal case, has been examined
by a number of investigators. Statistical approaches have been made by
Aitchison and Silvey (1951), Ashford (1959), and Gurland et al. (1960).
Gurland et al. have particularly considered the efficiency of using
multiple response classes and described general procedures for dealing
with any number greater than 2. The statistics are not simple, and the
original references should be consulted.

Van Strik (1961) gives an endocrine example of the above, but
analyzes it differently. The response of the rabbit uterus to progestogens
can be graded into as many classes as the observer feels able to distinguish,
which could then be handled semiquantally. In such an example, this
author ranks the uterine reactions (in rather small assays) and then
analyzes them with the rank numbers as responses, or by transformation

to corresponding normal scores (or *rankits*), obtaining similar results whichever method is used. The latter method is independent of the number of observations per assay and is clearly to be preferred for general use and comparison or combination of results.

III. Measuring Responses

A. Graded and Quantal Responses

Since graded (continuous) responses, such as organ weights or blood sugar levels, give more information per observation than do quantal responses, they are in general to be preferred. As is apparent from above, it is also easier to apply the full possibilities of modern design to graded assays. It may be shown that a graded response gives about twice the information per test object that a quantal response gives, over the range of about 20–80% of reactions on the quantal scale, but in addition to this, graded responses can usually be measured over a more extended scale, and thus their usefulness is likely to be even greater than is implied.

When there is a variety of ways in which a response may be measured, it is often difficult to decide between them, and experiment may repay the trouble involved. The ideal response is easy to measure, has a small error, changes rapidly with dose over a linear segment of a dose-response line, which is wide enough to make assays practicable without much difficulty in finding the useful response range on each occasion. These desiderata are rarely found all together. A simple measurement is as likely to give good results as a complicated one, and it is usually best to avoid subjective decisions wherever possible.

There is sometimes justification for expressing responses in relation to such measures as body weight of the animals, such as crop-gland weight in grams/100 g body weight in the pigeon assay of prolactin. It should never be assumed that this is so, however, and the technique of *covariance analysis* should be used to decide whether it is applicable, or whether some other adjustment should be made. It will also be apparent that the arbitrary decision to give doses in terms of so much per 100 g body weight is open to the same objection. It is usually best to keep dosage as simple as possible until adequate information is available from which any necessary adjustment can be made.

Covariance analysis extends the methods of the analysis of variance to include estimates of the influence of one or more variables that were not rigidly controlled in the assay. A frequent covariate is body weight, as previously mentioned. It is often impossible or inconvenient to select all animals of the same body weight, or if such selection is made they may differ by the end of an assay. Any regular influence such a factor may have on response can be eliminated in the analysis by entering it as a concomitant variable, usually on the assumption of a linear effect, but this is not essential. By this technique, assumption about the nature of the dependence of response on the concomitant variable is avoided, and correction is made from the internal evidence of the test.

When it is possible to measure changes in the test object, such as a gain in body weight, blood sugar before and after insulin injection, or comb size in a capon before and after hormone treatment, it is often assumed that such measurements of differences must be better than final body or organ weights, or final measurements of any kind, unrelated to some initial measurement. This point has been discussed by Emmens (1948), who showed that there must be a sufficiently high correlation between initial and subsequent readings to compensate for the additional variance introduced by the initial measurement. The variance of a difference (or sum) of two uncorrelated observations is their added variances, and thus an assay may have a substantially increased error if little correlation exists. The variance of a ratio is also greater than that of its components, and similar arguments apply. Data of Marks (Emmens, 1948) showed that, in the assay of insulin by the rabbit blood-sugar method, final blood-sugar readings at the second hour after injection gave as precise an assay as the far more complex procedure usually employed. This involved measurement of blood sugar before and several times after injection, the postinjection mean fall was then expressed as a percentage of the initial reading and then corrected by covariance for the initial reading. The introduction of initial blood-sugar measurements in the manner described served only to increase error, but the increase was removable by covariance analysis, bringing the error down again to that of a final reading, or group of readings.

The commonest qualitative data are quantal, occasionally more than two grades can be used in an assay, as with estrogen determination. If there are several grades it is possible to give them scores, other than purely arbitrary scores, by discriminant analysis (Fisher, 1954), but this has rarely been done. The estimation of anaphylactic effects by Claringbold and Sobey (1957) provides an example. There is, however, no guarantee that a dose-response line based on scores assigned by such a technique will be linear, unless this condition is imposed in their estimation; but this may be done, or a sufficiently linear segment of the line is likely to be found.

Sometimes quantal data may be avoided with a little ingenuity, for example, employing reaction time instead. If it is feasible to measure time to death, for instance, a more accurate assay may be performed.

This is done in the assay of adrenal hormones with adrenalectomized rats or drakes (Bülbring, 1937). The assay of melanophore-expanding hormone, based on the time required for the melanophores of hypophysectomized frogs to return to the contracted state (Calloway *et al.*, 1942) also uses a reaction time. In such assays, either time or log time has been successfully used as the dependent variate.

B. TRANSFORMATIONS

Whatever response is measured, attention must be paid to attaining linearity of a sufficient segment of the dose-response line for useful assays, either with the response as measured or a transform of it, to attaining a constant or near-constant variance at all levels of response employed, and as steep a line as possible in relation to the magnitude of the variance —i.e., the quantity s/b should be minimal, where b is the slope of the dose-response line. Transforms to bear in mind are as follows:

1. *Log response*—useful when the standard deviation is a constant fraction of the response, whereupon the standard deviation of log responses will be constant.

2. *The square root* of the response—useful when the response is dependent on a factor like a cell count, when the square root should have constant variance.

3. *Angular transformation*—useful not only in straightforward quantal assays, but also in responses dependent on enumeration or estimates thereof, such as a percentage live sperm count.

If no transform can be found which at least approximately equalizes variance throughout the dose-response line, the fitting of the line should in theory follow a series of successive approximations resembling probit analysis. Fortunately, in balanced assays, when the potency of the unknown has been well judged and responses to it and to the standard are much the same, quite large inequalities in variance may safely be ignored with little or no bias in the assessment of relative potency. This may not be true with more complex designs, such as a Latin square, where equality of variance is particularly important to avoid bias.

The amount of information per test object is b^2/s^2, and the quantity s/b mentioned above, often called λ, is a direct guide to the precision of assays. The value of λ differs greatly from one method to another, and it is generally felt that if it exceeds 0.4 the assay is not likely to be very useful.

In quantal assays, equality of variance is not expected, unless the angular transformation is used. That is the great advantage of this transform over the probit, but, as has been discussed above, simpler scoring still, although involving inequality in variance, offers great advantages. In such assays, s has either a theoretical value (probit, angles) or an experimental one (0, 1 transform) according to the method of analysis. If probits or angles are used, the steepness of the dose-response line alone determines the value of λ when comparing various techniques.

If the response is found to be linearly related to dose (*not* log dose) other techniques may be used. Such a response seems hardly ever to occur in hormone assays, but if it does, the papers of Finney (1945), Wood (1946), and Wood and Finney (1946) should be consulted, and also Claringbold (1959) for more recent methods of analysis.

C. BETWEEN- AND WITHIN-ANIMAL VARIATION

Whenever the same animal can be used in repeated or simultaneous tests, or the same test object or its parts, such as strips of gut, can receive simultaneous or successive treatments, the advantages of planning within-animal assays should be considered. Examples of this method are given by Bliss and Marks (1939a, b). Bliss and Rose (1940), and Bliss (1940), who did much of the pioneer work in this field. Another possibility is the use of within-litter variation, which is also usually less than otherwise encountered. Curiously, the use of inbred lines has not been found to give regular gains of this nature (Emmens, 1939; Biggers and Claringbold, 1954), apparently because genetic homogeneity is often accompanied by instability in response to small environmental changes. Instead, first crosses of inbred lines frequently give more stable and useful stocks for experimental work, including bioassay. The use of within-animal assays frequently gives a 4- to 6-fold gain over those between animals, and within litters a corresponding gain of 2- to 4-fold. Examples are given by Emmens (1960). An assay based on quantal responses between animals tends to be at one extreme of precision (or imprecision) and one based on graded responses within animals at the other.

IV. Assays Based on Graded Responses

A. BALANCED DESIGNS

The simplest valid assay, depending on its own internal evidence for a check of parallelism of dose-response lines and for an estimate of error, is the 4-point assay, with 2 groups on the unknown and 2 on the standard. It should have equal numbers in each group, and equal log spacing of doses for the two compounds (i.e., if the standard is given at doses of 1 mg and 2 mg; the unknown must be given in doses of x and $2x$ units). In such an assay, the calculations are minimal (Irwin, 1937; Bliss and Marks, 1939a,b). If there are n_p test objects in each group, the estimate, s, of the error of the assay, is based on $4(n_p - 1)$ degrees of freedom, and on the within-group variance. If the totals of responses in the four groups are S_1 and S_2 for the low and high doses of the standard preparation and U_1 and U_2 for those of the unknown, the remaining three degrees of freedom can be isolated as follows, and are the components of the *between-group* variance:

1. The difference between the overall potencies of the substances is represented by the total difference in response:

$$(U_1 + U_2) - (S_1 + S_2) = 2D \tag{1}$$

2. The slope of the combined dose-response line is represented by the total difference in response between high and low doses:

$$(S_2 + U_2) - (S_1 + U_1) = 2B \tag{2}$$

3. The difference between the individual slopes for the standard and unknown is represented by the difference between the corresponding estimates:

$$(U_2 - U_1) - (S_2 - S_1) \tag{3}$$

This is a simple example of *factorial analysis*, in which each individual degree of freedom for the sum of squares between groups has been separately examined in a meaningful way. To each of the quantities (1), (2) and (3) can be attributed a standard error derived from s, by which their significance is evaluated. If (3) is significantly large, the two preparations cannot be supposed to have the same dose-response relationship, and thus no valid assay is possible on the evidence available.

The slope of the combined dose-response line, b, is such that:

$$b = (S_2 + U_2 - S_1 - U_1)/2In_p \tag{4}$$

where I is the log dose ratio, or difference between log doses, necessarily the same for each substance. The precision of the assay λ, depends on b and s as usual.

The log ratio of the potency of the unknown to that of the standard is represented by M, such that

$$M = (\bar{X}_s - \bar{X}_u) + (\bar{Y}_u - \bar{Y}_s)/b \tag{5}$$

where $\bar{X}_s$ and X_u are the mean log doses of the standard and unknown, respectively, and $\bar{Y}_s$ and $\bar{Y}_u$ are the mean responses to the standard and unknown, all groups combined. This relationship is true whatever the number per group or the number of groups. With a 4-point assay, the value of M reduces to ID/B. It is then assumed that one unit of the unknown equals one unit of the standard, and the expression for M is very simple. The antilog of M (the relative potency, R) is the number of units of the standard required to give the same response as one unit of the unknown.

The standard error of M, s_M, is approximately given by the equation

$$s_M{}^2 = VM = s^2 I^2 (B^2 + D^2)/B^2 \tag{6}$$

This quantity is used in conjunction with t, based on $4(n_p - 1)$ degrees of freedom, giving as the limits of error of M

$$(M + ts_M) \text{ and } (M - ts_M)$$

where t is taken at any required level of probability, usually $P = 0.95$ or 0.99 (or 0.05 and 0.01—the two ways of expressing the probability level; both mean that there is about a 5% or 1% likelihood that the true value lies beyond the stated limits). These are log limits, just as M is a log relative potency, and the ordinary arithmetic value R and its limits of error are obtained by taking antilogs. The lower limit is, therefore, always nearer to R than is the upper limit.

This method of fixing limits of error is not sufficiently accurate unless the assay has given a value of b/s_b exceeding about 8, where s_b is the standard error of the slope. Methods for examining b/s_b and the procedure for calculating limits of error (fiducial limits) when it takes a lower value than 8 are discussed below.

When more than 2 doses are used per substance, the arithmetic remains simple, but requires modification. If 3 doses are used per substance, there are 5 degrees of freedom associated with differences between groups, so that in addition to the components isolated above, two additional components may be isolated so that (4) the possible departure of the combined dose-response line from linearity, and (5) the possible opposed curvature of the two separate dose response lines may be examined. Details of such isolations are given by Bliss and Marks (1939b), Emmens (1948), and Finney (1964), together with full computations.

It is unusual to employ more than 3 dosage groups per substance in an assay, as apart from the exploration that may precede the establishment of an assay method, but where it is desirable an extension of the same methods may be used. Equation (5) is not affected, but Eqs. (1) (2), (4), and (6) are modified to take account of the large number of groups. As long as components (3) or higher are insignificant, the modified forms of (1) and (2) are always used to form estimates of D and B, when Eqs. (4) and (6) become

$$b = B/In_p Sk^2 \qquad (4a)$$

for an odd number of dosage groups, and

$$b = 2B/In_p Sk^2 \qquad (4b)$$

for an even number of dosage groups, where Sk^2 is the sum of the factorial coefficients (Bliss and Marks, 1939b) used in analysis. Then,

$$VM = s_M{}^2 = s^2 K^2 I^2 (B^2 + D^2)/B^2 \qquad (6a)$$

where K is a constant depending on the number of dosage groups. The limits of error are calculated exactly as before.

An example, previously given by Emmens (1950) and modified from Bliss and Marks (1939b) is repeated here, as it remains as good an exposition of these methods as is available. Eight rabbits were used per group in the estimation of the potency of a sample of insulin in terms of the standard; 3 dosage levels were used per substance and each dose was twice the preceding one. The response is the mean percentage fall in blood sugar over a 5-hour period following injection and has been remarked on above. The basic data are given in Table V, and an analysis of variance in Table VI. From the latter, it is seen that a highly significant dose-response slope was obtained and that the doses of the preparations as given may have differed in mean potency. Departures from linearity and parallelism are negligible; in fact, they are somewhat smaller than might be expected from the magnitude of the error term, but not significantly so, as the value of F with 42 and 1 degrees of freedom for the larger and smaller variances, respectively, has to be very large for significance—greater than 250, even at the 5% level.

The modification of Eq. (5) to be used in determining M when there are 3 dosage groups per substance is

$$M = \sqrt{8/3} \, ID/B$$

$$M = \sqrt{8/3} \times 0.3010 \times \sqrt{790.9}/\sqrt{1673.3}$$

$$= 0.336$$

Hence the log of the potency of 3.2 mg of the unknown, which was assumed equal to 1 unit of the standard in setting up the test, is 0.336, antilog 2.17. Therefore 3.2 mg is equivalent to 2.17 units of the standard and 1 mg = 0.68 unit.

TABLE V

ASSAY OF INSULIN POTENCY BY RABBIT BLOOD-SUGAR METHOD[a]

	Standard (units)			Unknown (mg)		
Dose	0.25	0.5	1.0	0.8	1.6	3.2
Percent fall in	11.2	16.5	32.7	19.8	37.7	45.4
blood sugar	21.2	23.2	14.0	21.7	40.7	28.6
	18.7	25.6	28.9	26.1	29.3	50.4
	2.8	12.7	40.2	32.2	48.1	47.7
	27.2	39.8	35.1	28.5	45.6	50.0
	25.1	28.4	36.2	20.2	35.3	12.4
	25.8	40.0	37.8	35.7	14.2	39.0
	2.2	2.4	39.4	26.1	7·9	38.1
Mean fall	16.8	23.6	33.0	26.3	32.4	39.0

[a] Adapted from Bliss and Marks (1939b).

TABLE VI

ANALYSIS OF VARIANCE OF THE DATA IN TABLE V

Source of variation	Degrees of freedom	Sum of squares	Mean square	F
Between samples	1	780.9	780.9	6.2*
Slope of D/R line	1	1673.3	1673.3	13.3**
Departure from parallelism	1	25.9	25.9	0.2
Combined curvature	1	6.8	6.8	0.05
Opposed curvature	1	3.0	3.0	0.02
Error	42	5286.8	125.9	—
	47	7776.7	—	—

* $P < 0.05$.
** $P < 0.01$.

The standard error of M is approximately as in Eq. (6a), where $K = 8/3$, whence $s_m = 0.167$. The value of t for 42 degrees of freedom at $P = 0.95$ is 2.02; the limits of error of the determination of potency are thus the antilogs of $0.336 \pm (2.02 \times 0.167)$, or 1.00 and 4.71 units, approximately, per 3.2 mg; 0.31 to 1.47 units per milligram. The percentage accuracy at $P = 0.95$ is therefore 46–218%, approximately.

If an assay like this had unbalanced dosage groups, and/or unequal spacing of doses, the calculations would be tedious and the total yield of information less. It has been stressed above that this can normally be avoided, and even the loss of one or two observations does not prohibit the application of the methods just employed. Missing values can be supplied from the internal evidence of the test, allowance being made for the loss in precision in the estimation of error (Snedecor, 1956; Emmens, 1948).

B. INCREASING PRECISION

Various ways of increasing the precision of assays have already been mentioned—care in randomising, selection of the response and perhaps of a transform of it, the use of concomitant variables, use of balanced designs, and the use of within-animal or within-litter estimates of error. We are usually concerned with trying to guarantee the homogeneity of the biological material entering assays, or to take such measures as covariance analysis to reduce the effects of measurable heterogeneity. The same is achieved by segregation of possible sources of heterogeneity in the design of assays; some types of which may allow quite heterogeneous material to be used if there are no interactions with dosage levels.

Whenever the test objects can be subdivided into several groups believed to be more homogeneous than the whole, or whenever a test object can be used more than once, various *restrictions* in the design of assays become possible, which will usually contribute materially to the reduction of error. It may also be possible to give different doses to different animals in the same subclass, after preliminary knowledge of individual response levels (Bliss and Marks, 1939b; Claringbold, 1955).

A simple instance is provided by littermates. If it is possible to place one littermate into each dosage group in an assay, then a series of litters may be used to build up a test in which differences within litters are used in the estimation of potency and error. Each litter may be regarded as a complete assay in itself, since every dose is represented, but there will be no estimate of error from each individual litter, since only one animal is in each group. However, the degrees of freedom which represent overall response differences between dosage groups may be examined separately, leaving other degrees of freedom associated with *litter-dose interactions*, which it will usually be profitable to use as an estimate of error. The interaction measured is that concerned with the extent to which different litters reacted differently to the various doses, irrespective of the general level of response of each litter. An example may make things clear, as in Table VII, which gives the responses of eight litters of ovariectomized rats to estrone, which when injected causes uterine enlargement. There were three levels of estrone in geometrical progression. These data are not an assay, but half of an assay, showing only responses to a standard (adapted from Bülbring and Burn, 1935).

From Table VII it will be seen that litter 1 gave a much greater mean uterine weight than litter 7, but the changes caused by differences in dosage level are much the same—an increase of 39 mg in litter 1 from 0.2 μg to 0.8 μg of estrone, and one of 45 mg in litter 7. The other litters give a similar picture, and when this occurs, the elimination of the mean levels of response of whole litters is required to reduce the estimate of error, which would otherwise be artificially inflated by the very procedure designed to reduce it. The form of the appropriate analysis

TABLE VII

RESPONSES OF LITTERMATE RATS TO INJECTED ESTRONE

| | Dose of estrone (μg) | | | |
Litter No.	0.2	0.4	0.8	Totals, T_l
1	106	116	145	367
2	72	88	135	295
3	42	68	115	225
4	64	111	136	311
5	70	111	133	314
6	56	68	85	209
7	42	63	87	192
8	65	70	150	285
T_p	517	695	986	2198 (T)

[a] Adapted from Bülbring and Burn (1935); uterine weights are given in milligrams.

is shown in Table VIII, where the 23 degrees of freedom available in the assay are segregated into 7 associated with differences between litters, 2 with differences between doses, and the remaining 14 with variation within litters. The variation between litters is significantly greater than that within them ($F = 7.1$, $P < 0.01$), and a gain in information has thus been achieved. Had littermates been ignored, the sum of squares for error would have been 10,904.2, with 21 degrees of freedom, and a mean square of 519.4, three times as large as the proper term for error. This failure in segregation could occur at either of two stages: (1) by omitting to allocate littermates properly in the design of the assay, or (2) by failing to segregate the appropriate sum of squares in analysis.

In the assay of insulin, as described above, the same rabbits may be used repeatedly, and differences between individuals are commonly segregated in analysis. In one example, Bliss and Marks (1939b) found the mean square between rabbits to be 845 and that within rabbits, 41.4.

TABLE VIII

ANALYSIS OF VARIANCE OF THE DATA IN TABLE VII

Source of variation	Degrees of freedom	Sum of squares	Mean square	F
Between litters	7	8509	1216	7.1**
Between doses				
Linear regression	1	13748	13748	80.3***
Curvature	1	266	266	1.6
Within litters (error)	14	2396	172	—
	23	24919	—	—

** $P < 0.01$.

*** $P < 0.001$.

The between-rabbit sum of squares was 9296.9, associated with 11 degrees of freedom; that within rabbits was 3149.5, associated with 76 degrees of freedom, so that an estimate ignoring the structure of the assay would have associated 9296.9 plus 3149.5 with 87 degrees of freedom, giving a mean square of 143.1—three and a half times the real error of the assay.

The *Latin square* is a popular example of the type of restriction under discussion; it was first used extensively in agricultural research, where it had a physical application. If a square or rectangular field of crops is subdivided into a number of smaller rectangles (plots) like a chessboard, the yield per acre will be more uniform in any one plot than over the field as a whole. Then if experimental treatments are so allotted to these plots that each falls into one row and one column, as in Fig. 3, any regular gradients across or down the field may be eliminated in part or whole by segregating sums of squares in analysis which represent differences between rows and columns. The 36 plots in Fig. 3 yield 35 degrees of freedom, which may then be subdivided into 5 between rows, 5 between columns, 5 between treatments, and 20 for the estimation of error. These 20 degrees of freedom represent complex interactions between rows, columns, and treatments, and the design will succeed in its purpose of reducing the magnitude of the error term only insofar as these are smaller than the fertility differences over the whole field. If *replicates* (repeat measurements) are possible from within plots, a true estimate of error is available from which to assess the magnitude of the interactions.

In assays, the physical layout of rows and columns may be represented by positions in an animal house, but will more often be replaced by litters, times of injection, etc.

Such an arrangement must retain randomization, but within the restrictions imposed by design. It will still be true that each test object is as likely to receive any given dose as another, and the appropriate square would be selected at random from all possible squares by such methods as described by Fisher and Yates (1963). In an assay, a 4-point design could be accommodated by a 4×4 Latin square, with 4 test objects per dose, a 6-point design by a square such as that in Fig. 3, when the three doses each of the standard and unknown would be allotted at random to the letters A–F, if rows represented, say, litters and columns order of injection. When the same test object can be used repeatedly, it may form a row or column of such a square. Greater numbers of test

```
C   F   A   B   E   D
B   E   C   F   D   A
D   B   F   C   A   E
E   D   B   A   C   F
F   A   E   D   B   C
A   C   D   E   F   B
```

FIG. 3. A 6×6 Latin square.

objects per dosage groups may be desirable, if so, several ways of doubling-up or more are available. As just mentioned, each plot may receive more than one test object, or further squares may be added to the first as in the example by Bliss and Rose (1940) of the assay of parathyroid hormone in dogs. These authors used a series of 4×4 Latin squares in 4-point assays, so that 12 dogs in all were used, each at every dosage level on different occasions. In the general run of biological tests interaction is minimal, often completely absent (Emmens, 1960), and a design like the Latin square succeeds frequently in achieving the desired control of error, even without intraplot replication.

C. UTILIZING RESTRICTED MATERIAL

When the maximum number of test objects which fall naturally into a homogeneous group, such as a litter or twins is small, it may be necessary to balance an assay in a different way from those already discussed. *Incomplete blocks*, none of which contains the full range of doses, may be used, so that in sum they provide the necessary information because of the balance in design. *Symmetrical pairs* form a special case of a balanced incomplete block design, and were described by Bliss and Rose (1940). Table IX gives an example of the layout of an assay using symmetrical pairs, where twin pairs of animals were used in a

4-point assay. Any pair, used once only in this assay, could receive no more than two doses of the standard and/or unknown, but the arrangement in Table IX of the 6 pairs of animals is such that every possible combination of doses is given to a pair. Table IX also gives a similar scheme for using trios of animals. Symmetrical pairs must be used in multiples of 6, and trios in multiples of 4. The analysis of these designs is not simple, and if they are employed it is recommended that professional assistance be sought.

TABLE IX

Assay Schemes: One Complete Replicate of
Each Symmetrical Pair or Trio is Shown

Pair No.	Doses		Trio No.	Doses		
1	U_1	U_2	1	U_1	U_2	S_1
2	U_1	S_1	2	U_1	U_2	S_2
3	U_1	S_2	3	U_1	S_1	S_2
4	U_2	S_1	4	U_2	S_1	S_2
5	U_2	S_2	—	—		
6	S_1	S_2	—	—		

Cross-over tests were first used in the assay of insulin, which still provides the neatest example in the twin cross-over test of Smith *et al.* (1944). The neat feature of the test is the confounding of differences between rabbits with departure from parallelism of dose-response lines, in a test in which the slope of the dose-response line is known with virtual certainty to be the same for both substances, both being pure or nearly pure insulin. A more accurate estimate of the value for the combined slope and potency differences is available from the within-rabbits sum of squares, while a difference in combined slope on the 2 days of the assay does not affect the results. Table X illustrates the layout of such a test.

TABLE X

Scheme for a Twin Cross-Over Test

Group	First day	Second day
1	S_2	U_1
2	S_1	U_2
3	U_2	S_1
4	U_1	S_2

Four groups, each of 3 rabbits, receive doses as in the table, the high dose of the unknown and the low dose of the standard are crossed over in 2 of them, and the reverse cross is made in the other 2 groups, the test occupying 2 days. Differences between days are then eliminated in analysis, but a difference in the number of animals per group does not affect the working in a particular test.

Comparisons that can be built up from differences between successive responses from the same group are *within-animal* comparisons, those built-up from the sums of successive responses from the same group are *between-animal* comparisons, with a lower precision. For rapid calculation of the sums (Y) and differences (y) are determined and given suffixes corresponding with their group numbers in Table X. Then:

$$M = ISy/y_2 + y_3 - y_1 - y_4)$$

where I is the log dose interval as usual, and Vy is estimated from the differences for individual animals within groups, with $(Sn_p - 4)$ degrees of freedom.

Departure from parallelism is measured by the quantity,

$$(Y_1 + Y_4) - (Y_2 + Y_3)$$

and has a variance $(VY)S(1/n_p)$ based on between-animal sums of squares; also associated with $(Sn_p - 4)$ degrees of freedom. Limits of error are calculated as follows:

1. F for 1 and $(Sn_p - 4)$ degrees of freedom is taken from the table of F at the required level of P.

2. $U^2 = (y_2 + y_3 - y_1 - y_4)^2 - (FVy)S(1/n_p)$ at the chosen level of P.

3. $UT = (y_2 + y_3 - y_1 - y_4)Sy - (FVy)(1/n_2 + 1/n_3 - 1/n_1 - 1/n_4)$ is also calculated.

4. The *fiducial* limits of error are the roots of the equation:

$$U^2 m^2 - 2UTIm + T^2 I^2 = 0, \text{ solving for } m.$$

D. GROUPS OF ASSAYS

Groups of assays may combine several estimations of potency of different substances at the same time, serial estimates of potency of the same substance at different times or in different places, or combinations of these. The object of simultaneously testing several compounds is to save time and material, in that one set of test objects on the standard may suffice for all unknowns. Various designs will suggest themselves for this purpose, and if restrictions are to be included in design, as in a Latin square, a suitable type must be chosen so that all dosage levels of all substances contribute equally to the summed totals for various integral restrictions. There is a limit to this, and groups of tests made simultaneously are most often of fairly simple structure.

TABLE XI

PENICILLIN ASSAY BY THE CYLINDER PLATE METHOD[a]

	Dose of solution (ml)		
Sample	0.8	1.0	1.25
Standard	607	673	740
	577	615	645
	605	643	700
	1789	1931	2085
U_1	614	661	742
	582	615	652
	590	630	689
	1786	1906	2083
U_2	608	652	758
	580	611	633
	605	630	684
	1793	1893	2075
U_3	606	661	723
	568	596	637
	562	584	659
	1736	1841	2019

[a] An assay of three samples. From Emmens (1948).

The results of a group of simultaneous tests can be pooled, if they turn out to be reasonably homogeneous in respect of error terms, to give improved estimates of slope and error, or of any departures from parallelism, or curvature, that may occur.

Table XI gives an example from Emmens (1948) in which three simultaneous assays of penicillin samples were made on an agar plate, the drug inhibiting the growth of *Staphylococcus aureus* to an extent depending on potency. Circular areas of inhibited growth of the seeded culture are scored according to their respective diameters. The diameter increases with increasing dose and is linearly related to the log dose over a wide range. The analysis of variance is shown in Table XII, in which the combined linear regression for the standard and three unknowns is shown to be highly significant, but terms representing curvature and differences between substances are not significant. The dose/substance interaction, with six degrees of freedom, is also highly significantly less than expectation, which is the same as the error term. This arises because in actual

TABLE XII

Analysis of Variance of the Data in Table XI

Source of variation	Degrees of freedom	Sums of squares	Mean square	F
Between doses	1	55873	55873	44.2***
Between doses				
Linear regression	1	55873	55873	44.2***
Combined curvature	1	697	697	0.6
Between substances	3	2944	981	0.8
Dose/substance interaction	6	194	32	0.03***
Error	24	30332	1264	—
	35	90040	—	—

*** $P < 0.001$.

fact the different doses and substances were not randomized on the surface of the agar plate, but were placed systematically, so that they sampled the irregularities of the medium more effectively than should occur by chance. However, they were not arranged in a design that allows segregation of the systematic effects, and an error term resulted which is in excess of the value it should have; so that a precise assay has been accompanied by a decrease in apparent precision.

If we assume an unbiased estimate of error, this combined term for all substances would be used together with the combined estimate of slope for determining the potencies and limits of error for the three sustances under test by the usual means, with the advantage that a larger number of degrees of freedom is available for estimation than would otherwise be the case.

In a series of tests made over a period or in different places, a very similar structure may be used if the assays are logically planned, U_1, U_2, and U_3 etc., being replaced by T_1, T_2, T_3 etc., representing different times or places, and consistency of estimates and a combined estimate for all assays are easy to compute. With different places of testing, care should in particular be taken to check homogeneity of variance. Even when such tests are made on different plans, combined estimates of slope and of error may still be justified, with improved overall accuracy. Methods for testing various aspects of homogeneity in combined assays are given by Emmens (1948).

It should also be noted that, for maximal efficiency in simultaneous tests, although not usually for maximum ease of computation with most designs, there should be more test objects on the standard preparation than on each unknown. If N is the number of unknowns, N times the number of observations on any one unknown should be made with the standard. With any but simple or special designs, it is easier to forego this advantage for the others consequent upon more balanced assays. As the screening of drugs of various types is becoming more and more important, and large numbers of assays or contractions of assays are being practiced, techniques such as that of King (1963) are gaining importance and should be consulted by those interested.

E. Fiducial Limits of Error

Until the paper by Irwin (1943), it was not commonly realized that the formula using s_M and t as above is misleading when calculating limits of error of M, unless b/s_b exceeds about 8, when some 5% error is involved at the most. The approximate formula gives finite limits of error at levels of P at which the slope itself may not differ from zero. Accurately calculated limits, which take the error of b into account, are called *fiducial limits of error* to indicate their greater precision. Corresponding *confidence limits* were calculated by Bliss (1946) when referring to factorially designed assays and have essentially the same meaning. These limits must be calculated anew for each value of P, as in the example above dealing with twin cross-over tests.

The calculation of fiducial limits for the assay of insulin on page 29, for which the approximate limits were 46–218%, gives, for example, new limits of 53–374%, which are not only wider than before, but different in range. The estimate of relative potency is not affected, only its limits of error. In this assay b/s_b is only 3.6, hence the big difference. Irwin (1943) gives a table of examples showing how the value of b/s_b affected the comparison of approximate and fiducial limits of error at $P = 0.95$ and $P = 0.99$; these results are shown in Table XIII.

TABLE XIII

COMPARISON OF FIDUCIAL AND APPROXIMATE LIMITS OF ERROR[a]

b/s_b	P = 0.95		P = 0.99	
	Fiducial %	Approx. %	Fiducial %	Approx. %
2.74	19–143	58–172	0–155	49–204
2.76	72–117	85–117	24–127	81–123
3.64	53–128	72–139	29–136	65–155
3.76	80–128	82–123	71–148	77–131
3.90	76–122	82–123	63–131	77–131
3.98	83–119	85–117	75–129	81–123
4.08	83–123	84–119	77–137	80–125
4.05	83–121	85–118	75–131	80–125
4.75	83–116	86–117	76–122	82–122
5.17	88–116	88–114	83–122	85–118
5.36	85–116	87–116	80–123	83–121

[a] The median fertility dose of vitamin E in rats. Modified from Irwin (1943).

V. Assays Based on Quantal Responses

A. BALANCED DESIGNS

Just as with graded-response assays, the simplest valid assay with quantal responses is the 4-point design, again with equal numbers per group and equal log spacing of doses. If probits or logits are then used, the calculations are not so simple as with graded responses, as the variance differs at different levels of response, and the error variance is supplied theoretically; the goodness of fit of the data to that theory is tested by χ^2. If this test indicates heterogeneity, and that the theoretical variance is exceeded in the data, any single assay when so treated is unlikely to give much information, as a heterogeneity factor has to be introduced that not only incorporates the increased estimate of variance, but also the very few degrees of freedom on which it is based (only 2 in 4-point assay).

When probits are used, the following steps must be taken:

1. Two parallel straight lines are drawn by eye, or with the help of formulas (Emmens, 1948), one to fit the data for the standard and the other that for the unknown, as well as can be managed. Allowance is made for 0% or 100% responses, but only by slightly altering the slope if these occur at the end of the dose range.

2. The provisional lines are then used to read off the *expected probit* at each dosage level used. (The observed probits are called the *empirical probits*.) From these two, *corrected probits* are calculated from tables such as those of Bliss (1938) or Fisher and Yates (1963). These are then used in conjunction with corresponding weighting factors, which allow for the variance of the probits concerned, to compute a first approximation to the common slope and separate positions of the dose-response lines.

3. If the provisional slope and the first calculated approximation differ by more than a small amount, which is not usually specified, however, a second cycle has to be computed, and so on until successive approximations agree satisfactorily (a process of *iteration*). It may be necessary to go through 4 or 5 cycles, but fortunately not often. If the data are homogeneous and based on reasonable numbers—say, several groups per substance of 20 observations each—1 or 2 computed cycles are often sufficient.

4. The final approximations to the dose-response lines are then tested for goodness of fit by χ^2 and for the tenability of the assumption that they are in fact parallel. Suitable methods are given in the references above or by Finney (1952).

5. The log ratio of potency is given by Eq. (5), (page 26); $\overline{Y}_u$ and $\overline{Y}_s$ are now the mean probits for the unknown and standard, respectively. With equal numbers per group and the same assumed dosage units, the equation does not simplify, as $\overline{X}_s$ and $\overline{X}_u$ are not the same unless the responses are identical at all corresponding levels, because of the introduction of the weighting factors in step 2. The variance of M is calculated integrally in performing the operations listed above, but it is based on the theroetical variances of the probits and used with infinite degrees of freedom in determining approximate limits of error. Fiducial limits of error should be calculated by the same methods as outlined above.

If the angular transformation is used, calculations are simplified, even with the above procedure, because the variance remains constant at all levels of response. As also indicated above, this transformation (and also the probit) may be used in two ways. Transformation of the *expected response* gives an exact iterative solution, but transformation of the *observed response* (or *empirical angle*) gives a rapid, noniterative procedure due to Eisenhart (1947). Claringbold et al. (1953) have pointed out that the two methods are very similar in practice, and it may be noted that Gaddum (1933) used the empirical probits when first evolving the method. However, if complete assurance is required, a single cycle of iteration by the exact method seems to be all that is required. This at least reduces even the full maximum-likelihood solution to 2 cycles of computation, one of them very rapid. When this is done, exact fiducial

TABLE XIV

COMPARATIVE VALUES OF REGRESSION COEFFICIENTS AND χ^2 FOR GOODNESS OF FIT[a]

Expt. No.	Eisenhart method			Fisher-Bliss method			
				First cycle	Second cycle		
	b	s_b		b	b	s_b	
1	1.6	2.4 ⎱	$\chi_{[16]}^2 = 16.2$	1.8	1.8	2.3 ⎱	$\chi_{[16]}^2 = 14.0$
	12.7	2.1		12.6	12.6	2.0	
	−6.9	2.1	$0.5 > P > 0.3$	−6.4	−6.4	2.0	$0.5 > P > 0.3$
	−11.4	2.1 ⎰		−11.5	−11.5	2.0 ⎰	
2	2.8	2.1 ⎱	$\chi_{[17]}^2 = 7.3$	2.7	2.7	2.0 ⎱	$\chi_{[17]}^2 = 8.8$
	13.7	2.1		13.3	13.3	2.0	
	10.4	2.4	$0.98 > P > 0.95$	10.1	10.1	2.3	$0.95 > P > 0.9$
	−9.1	2.1 ⎰		−8.5	−8.6	2.0 ⎰	
3	−0.3	2.4 ⎱	$\chi_{[18]}^2 = 14.7$	−0.6	−0.6	2.3 ⎱	$\chi_{[18]}^2 = 12.1$
	10.9	2.1		10.9	11.0	2.0	
	−14.6	2.1 ⎰	$0.7 > P > 0.5$	−14.9	−15.0	2.0 ⎰	$0.9 > P > 0.8$
4	7.0	1.5 ⎱	$\chi_{[7]}^2 = 4.6$	7.1	7.0	1.4 ⎱	$\chi_{[7]}^2 = 3.6$
	−7.2	1.5 ⎰	$0.8 > P > 0.7$	−7.4	−7.4	1.4 ⎰	$0.9 > P > 0.8$
5	17.7	3.3 ⎱	$\chi_{[10]}^2 = 9.2$	17.6	17.6	3.2 ⎱	$\chi_{[10]}^2 = 7.8$
	9.8	1.5 ⎰	$0.7 > P > 0.5$	9.7	9.7	1.4 ⎰	$0.7 > P > 0.5$
6	12.7	1.4 ⎱	$\chi_{[10]}^2 = 7.5$	12.6	12.6	1.3 ⎱	$\chi_{[10]}^2 = 7.7$
	3.1	1.1		2.6	2.7	1.1	
	−2.7	0.9 ⎰	$0.7 > P > 0.5$	−2.7	−2.8	0.9 ⎰	$0.7 > P > 0.5$

[a] Six factorial experiments were analyzed by the method of Eisenhart (1947) and followed by two cycles of the Fisher-Bliss method (Claringbold et al., 1953).

limits may be calculated. If the noniterative procedure alone is used, despite its giving almost identical results, exact fiducial inference is not theoretically possible.

Claringbold *et al.* (1953) applied the approximate method with angles in various designs leading to an analysis of variance (not possible with the weighted probit technique), and compared it with other transforms. Table XIV from their paper demonstrates that the approximate method, when applied in six factorial experiments and compared with two *further* cycles of the Fisher-Bliss method, gives very useful results. The table

compares goodness of fit at the three stages of computation, which is
perfectly satisfactory in all. There was no sensible difference between the
two Fisher-Bliss cycles. However, had an attempt been made to start off
with the usual probit technique, fitting complex provisional grids in
several dimensions to the data, no such agreement could have been
expected between the two cycles and difficulties would have been encountered in the calculations, which could not have been based on an
analysis of variance.

The advantage of the angular transformation is thus rapidity and
ease of calculation, applicability of the analysis of variance, and results
that are in practice indistinguishable from those obtained with probits.

B   WITHIN-ANIMAL QUANTAL ASSAYS

These advantages are not enough, however, particularly when cross-
over quantal tests are possible, or tests in which any series of individual
responses may be examined. It is then necessary, if analysis is to be at
all feasible, to pass to the $(0, 1)$ or $(0, 1, 2)$, etc. methods of scoring described above. A within-animal bioassay with quantal responses was
first performed by Claringbold (1956), who determined the approximate
individual sensitivity of his animals (ovariectomized mice) in estrogen
tests. He had already shown that about a 4-fold gain in precision was to
be expected if this were done (Claringbold, 1955). The results obtained in
the 4-point cross-over assay are shown in Table XV. The design was in 6
Latin squares, each 4×4, so that each mouse received all dose levels of
the standard and unknown by the end of the assay, but although the
actual doses were in the same ratio throughout, each mouse was given
an individual set of doses scaled to its own level of sensitivity, as are
rabbits in the assay of insulin. Each mouse, therefore, yielded a total
score which varied between 0 and 4, since it was scored only 0 or 1 on
each occasion. Very few examples of 0 or 4 occurred, however, because
of the scaling of doses, thus making the test more useful than if it had
had many of them.

The data were then subjected to analysis of variance as shown in
Table XVI, using 0 or 1 as the basic variate. Since the dose-response
lines were not significantly different in slope, relative potency was
computed and found to be 1.52 (1.16 to 1.99, $P = 0.95$), whereas the true
figure was known to be 1.414. This assay entailed 96 observations, 4
with each of 24 mice, and was compared with an assay of normal design
using 400 observations, 1 with each of 400 mice, analyzed by probits.
This assay gave an estimate of 1.38 (1.02 to 1.85, $P = 0.95$), fiducial

TABLE XV

FOUR-POINT CROSS-OVER ASSAY WITH QUANTAL RESPONSES[a]

Latin square	Mouse No.	Mean sensitivity $(10^{-4}\ \mu g)$	Order of tests				Responses to doses			
			1	2	3	4	S_1	S_2	U_1	U_2
I	1	4	S_1	S_2	U_1	U_2	0	1	0	0
	2	2	U_1	S_1	U_2	S_2	0	1	1	1
	3	8	U_2	U_1	S_2	S_1	0	1	0	1
	4	23	S_2	U_2	S_1	U_1	0	1	1	0
II	5	8	S_2	U_2	S_1	U_1	0	1	0	1
	6	6	U_1	S_2	U_2	S_1	0	1	0	1
	7	4	U_2	S_1	U_1	S_2	0	0	1	1
	8	4	S_1	U_1	S_2	U_2	0	1	0	1
III	9	3	U_2	S_2	S_1	U_1	0	0	0	1
	10	11	S_2	U_2	U_1	S_1	0	1	0	1
	11	3	S_1	U_1	S_2	U_2	0	1	1	1
	12	11	U_1	S_1	U_2	S_2	0	1	1	1
IV	13	8	U_2	S_2	S_1	U_1	0	1	0	1
	14	16	U_1	S_1	S_2	U_2	1	1	1	1
	15	4	S_1	U_2	U_1	S_2	0	1	0	1
	16	8	S_2	U_1	U_2	S_1	0	0	1	1
V	17	3	U_1	S_1	U_2	S_2	0	1	0	1
	18	23	U_2	U_1	S_2	S_1	0	1	1	1
	19	1	S_2	U_2	S_1	U_1	0	1	0	1
	20	23	S_1	S_2	U_1	U_2	0	1	1	1
VI	21	6	S_1	U_2	S_2	U_1	1	1	1	1
	22	1	U_2	S_2	U_1	S_1	0	0	1	1
	23	3	U_1	S_1	U_2	S_2	0	1	0	1
	24	11	S_2	U_1	S_1	U_2	0	1	0	1

[a] Modified from Claringbold (1955).

limits of error being calculated in each case. The ranges are almost the same, with over 4 times as many animals in the second assay.

The use of this type of score, with cross-over tests, was extended by Emmens (1957), who tested the effect on precision of analyzing the same extensive data from estrogen tests by analyses of variance employing the angular transformation, (0, 1) and (0, 1, 2) scoring, *without* adjustment of dosage for individual mice. As the tests took 16 weeks to perform, and all mice received the same doses, it was a matter for conjecture whether any great advantage would accrue. First, mice might not remain

TABLE XVI

ANALYSIS OF VARIANCE OF THE DATA IN TABLE XV[a]

Source of variation	Degrees of freedom	Mean square	F
Between animals	23	0.12	0.9
Between times	3	0.05	0.4
Linear regression	1	9.38	68.0***
Parallelism	1	1.50	10.9**
Between substances	1	0.38	2.8
Error	66	0.138	—

[a] Claringbold (1955).
** $P < 0.01$.
*** $P < 0.001$.

TABLE XVII

RESPONSES OF MICE TO INTRAVAGINAL ESTROGENS[a]

Test group	Estrogen				Proestrogen			
	1	2	3	4	5	6	7	8
I	9(2)	17(4)	12(3)	2(1)	4(1)	13(3)	17(4)	11(2)
II	19(4)	14(3)	7(1)	11(2)	18(4)	12(2)	12(1)	17(3)
III	8(1)	14(2)	17(4)	11(3)	10(2)	7(1)	20(3)	17(4)
IV	8(3)	10(1)	9(2)	17(4)	15(3)	18(4)	16(2)	10(1)

Test group	Proestrogen				Estrogen			
V	9(1)	20(3)	15(2)	22(4)	19(4)	8(2)	14(3)	7(1)
VI	14(2)	12(1)	21(4)	19(3)	18(3)	14(4)	6(1)	11(2)
VII	15(3)	23(4)	7(1)	16(2)	11(1)	8(3)	14(2)	13(4)
VIII	15(4)	19(2)	16(3)	11(1)	5(2)	5(1)	16(4)	13(3)

Doses	1	2	3	4
Response to estrogen	57	81	98	132
Response to proestrogen	72	113	135	151

[a] Twenty-four animals per group, in cross-over tests, showing group totals only for quantal (0, 1) scores, with dosage groups 1–4 in parentheses. Modified from Emmens (1957).

steady in relative sensitivity for so long a period, although the data of Emmens (1939) indicated that they would, and second, too many 0% or 100% responses might occur. The chance of this was, however, minimized in the design of the test since each mouse was used eight times.

These tests were not assays, because they investigated the slope differences between estrogens and proestrogens (Emmens, 1941), but they were in all other respects of the same design as an assay would be, were slopes the same. The design is shown in Table XVII, with 0, 1

TABLE XVIII

ANALYSIS OF VARIANCE OF ANGULAR TRANSFORMATION[a]

Source of variation	Degrees of freedom	Sum of squares	Mean square	F
Tests	7	44.17	6.31	4.2***
Doses	7	268.45	38.35	25.7***
Groups	7	23.25	3.32	2.2*
Interaction	42	61.29	1.46	1.0
Theoretical variance	—		1.49	—

[a] Data in Table XVII, determined from group responses. From Emmens (1957).
  * $P < 0.05$.
*** $P < 0.001$.

TABLE XIX

ANALYSIS OF VARIANCE OF $(0, 1)$ SCORING[a]

Source of variation	Degrees of freedom	Sum of squares	Mean square	F
Tests	7	6.39	0.91	4.7***
Doses	7	40.77	5.82	29.8***
Interaction	42	8.89	0.21	1.1
Residual (= error 1)	1288	251.85	0.20	—
Groups	7	3.13	0.45	1.2
Animals within groups (= error 2)	₁84	69.74	0.38	—

[a] Data in Table XVII, based on individual scores. From Emmens (1957).
*** $P < 0.001$.

response scoring as an example. Tables XVIII to XX give analyses of variance for the angular transformation, $(0, 1)$ scoring and $(0, 1, 2)$ scoring, respectively.

Analysis with the angular transformation showed that there was indeed heterogeneity in response, differences between groups giving an $F = 2.2, P < 0.05$. This would preclude assay if found in an ordinary test, except with a heterogeneity factor of 2.2 and, in this rather extensive

experiment, only 7 degrees of freedom for error. However, in this particular example, the *interaction* mean square agrees with expectation and
shows that the within-animal variation must be less than that between
groups of animals and presumably between individual animals. Analysis
with the $(0, 1)$ or $(0, 1, 2)$ scores gets over any difficulty about interpretation, in addition to making computation much easier. Because it is now
practicable to use all the 1535 degrees of freedom in the tests, variation
both between and within individual animals, not groups of animals, is
examined. In both Tables XIX and XX, we see that differences between

TABLE XX

ANALYSIS OF VARIANCE OF $(0, 1, 2)$ SCORING[a]

Source of variation	Degrees of freedom	Sum of squares	Mean square	F
Tests	7	17.29	2.47	4.8***
Doses	7	156.04	22.29	43.7***
Interaction	42	22.64	0.54	1.1
Residual (= error 1)	1288	652.66	0.51	—
Groups	7	6.70	0.96	0.9
Animals within groups (= error 2)	184	193.30	1.05	—

[a] Data in Table XVII, based on individual scores, are from Emmens (1957).
*** $P < 0.001$.

groups are associated with approximately the same variance as differences between animals within groups, which in turn is about double the
residual error (error 1 in the tables). The residual error, representing
differences *within* animals and applicable to the within-animal comparisons of primary interest, is usable even in the presence of the
heterogeneity between animals, with about a 2-fold gain in precision,
indicated by the heterogeneity factor of 2.2 and by errors 1 and 2 in
Tables XIX and XX, which give factors of 1.9 and 2.1, respectively, for
the degree of heterogeneity between animals.

VI. The Design of Assays

A. EXPLORING METHODS

When a general method of assay occurs to the investigator as being
likely to prove fruitful, he usually needs to explore the variables that
may be associated with it. The number and spacing of doses, the vehicle

and method of administration, the time of final examination, the age or weight of animals, the effects of body weight, and methods of measuring responses are among the common factors that may need investigation. They often form a large array, complete examination of which may seem forbidding. Many workers have in the past spent up to several years investigating such variables, often in an incomplete fashion because of the methods employed.

If classical techniques are practiced, varying one thing at a time and keeping others constant, it will indeed be a long task to investigate a series of variables, and even then there will be no guarantee that the particular set of conditions chosen as optimal are in fact so. On the contrary, there is usually a greater likelihood that the optimum set of conditions within the system investigated has been missed. Factorial analysis of such situations was advocated by Fisher some time ago, and has been utilized widely in agricultural and some other fields, relatively little in bioassay other than in the restricted sense used above, in the factorial analysis of dose-response lines. What is needed in exploration is factorial planning of reasonable large-scale experiments designed to look into the possibilities of a general technique, varying as many factors as is feasible in each experiment. The advantages of such methods were pointed out by Fisher and many subsequent workers. Standard texts such as Cochran and Cox (1950), may be consulted for details of the methods, but it seems worth while to point out briefly the advantages they convey.

A factorial experiment, whether involving an assay technique or otherwise, explores the possible effects of a number of variables simultaneously, in all possible combinations. Thus, the number of doses into which the material is subdivided for administration, the time over which they are spaced, and the total dose administered, may form the subject of one factorial test. Suppose we decided to try 2, 3, and 4 doses per total amount administered, spaced equally over 1, 2, or 3 days, and totaling 1, 2, or 4 mg. It is usually best to do a few very simple pilot tests, with one or two test objects per group, before embarking on such a factorial experiment, so that we know roughly where the useful regions of response lie. Then such a test would have as a unit component $3 \times 3 \times 3$, or 27 test objects, each receiving a different combination of treatments, and would be referred to as a 3^3 factorial. It is most satisfactory to allot at least two test objects per treatment combination, and so advisable to have not less than 54 in such a test. In certain circumstances, particularly when it seems advisable to crowd as many factors in as possible at the same time, *replication* in this manner may be omitted, and each treatment combination may then be given to one test object only, and

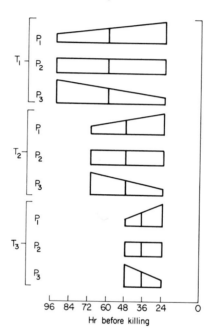

48　　　　　　　　　　　C. W. EMMENS

interaction used as a measure of error. In special circumstances, *partial replication*, which implies the use at any one time of an incomplete simple replicate, may be practiced, with the sacrifice of certain pre-determined comparisons.

In the normal case, however, we shall have every treatment combination represented by several test objects, and the within-cell variation

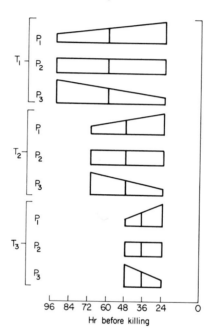

Fig. 4. Diagrammatic representation of the treatments in the experiment by Claring-bold and Lamond (1957). Ordinates represent the proportion (*M*) of the total dose given at any one time.

can be used as error. Since every test object receives one level or another of every factor under test, each factor is investigated as fully as if the test were devoted to it alone, and at the same time its interaction with other factors is investigated. If there is no interaction between particular pairs of factors, we conclude that the test is indifferent to the particular combination of them we choose to use; whenever there is interaction, we can see its effect and decide at which levels to design the assay. We proceed similarly with other higher combinations of factors. Thus, the dose-response line may be steepest when 4 doses are given over 2 days, but had we made 1-factor tests all the time we might have explored the effect of doses over 3 days, and the effect of number of days at 2 doses, and so never have hit on the best combination. Had we built up a complete factorial by such methods, taking a long time and many tests to do it, we should still have confused time-to-time variation with the factors under examination and still be uncertain about the real magnitude of the effects we measured. Factorial experiments are thus more informative and economical of both time and material compared with other tests.

A practical example of a very similar experiment to that just discussed is provided by Claringbold and Lamond (1957), in designing an assay for gonadotropins. This particular test used a secondary response—growth of the uterus subsequent upon stimulation of the ovaries of mice. Figure 4 shows the plan of the test, which involved three ways of giving a total dose in three injections, namely, in increasing, equal, or decreasing amounts, three spacings of dosage, over 72, 48, or 24 hour (T) and three dosage levels (P). The test was made with 4 mice per treatment combination. The mice were killed 24 hours after the last injection in all instances. Since variance depended on the level of response, the uterine weights were transformed to logarithms before analysis, a procedure giving

TABLE XXI

ANALYSIS OF VARIANCE[a]

Source of variation	Degrees of freedom	Mean square	F
Time base			
Linear	1	2532.3	10.9***
Quadratic	1	176.0	0.7
Partition			
Linear	1	93.4	0.4
Quadratic	1	1768.2	7.5**
Levels			
Linear	1	40375.3	170.8***
Quadratic	1	210.0	0.9
Interactions			
$P_L \times L_L$	1	1575.5	6.7*
Remainder	19	134.9	0.6
Error	77	236.5	—

[a] Data from the experiment illustrated in Fig. 4. Adapted from Claringbold and Lamond (1957).

* $P < 0.05$.
** $P < 0.01$.
*** $P < 0.001$.

approximately equal variances. The analysis of variance of the transformed data is given in Table XXI, from which it will be seen that each factor gave highly significant effects. The conclusions were as follows:

1. Administration of doses over a short period (24 hours) gave the highest responses.
2. Three equal doses gave a greater response than either of the unequal dosage schedules (i.e., the quadratic term in the partitioning of doses was significant).
3. The log dose response was linear over all combinations of treatments, but increased in slope as more of the dose was given in the first injection.
4. Only one interaction in 20 was significant, and that only at the 5% level, which could readily have happened by chance.

TABLE XXII

GROUP OF TEN SURVIVAL[a]

Anesthetics	Age (days)	Air temp. (°F)	Glucose?	Surviving mice at 24 hr	48 hr	75 hr[b]
Avertin	18	78	+	4	1	1(1)
(0.01 ml/gm)			−	5	4	3(2)
		87	+	2	2	2(2)
			−	5	4	3(2)
	25	78	+	9	7	7(4)
			−	7	7	7(6)
		87	+	7	7	7(2)
			−	8	8	7(4)
Avertin	18	78	+	9	6	6(5)
(0.005 ml/gm)			−	9	7	6(5)
plus ether		87	+	9	9	8(7)
			−	10	10	10(8)
	25	78	+	10	9	9(8)
			−	9	9	9(5)
		87	+	10	10	10(7)
			−	9	9	9(6)

[a] Hypophysectomized mice after various operational procedures. From Lamond and Emmens (1959).

[b] Figures in parentheses show completely hypophysectomized survivors, upon which analysis is based.

The error mean square in this list was computed from the three degrees of freedom at each treatment combination, minus three degrees of freedom for missing values.

This experiment, therefore, demonstrated that a sensitive assay resulted from equal spacing of doses over a short period, although greater accuracy could be obtained if more of the dose were given early. Further tests showed the advantage of giving only one dose and killing 44 hours later, omitting any later doses, which was the final form of the assay.

Another example of factorial analysis, this time at an even earlier stage of investigating a proposed assay technique, is provided by Lamond and Emmens (1959); in this example, assays using hypophysectomized mice were in planning, but poor results were being obtained at operation, many of the animals dying within the first 24 hours after their pituitary glands had been removed. The factors thought most likely to be affecting survival were the duration of anesthesia, the age of the mouse, the air temperature, and adrenal insufficiency. Since the mice were to be used for pituitary-gonad investigations it was felt that cortical hormone therapy should be avoided, but glucose could be injected. Consequently, the basal anesthetic Avertin was used alone, or in a half-dose plus ether anesthesia, giving a briefer total period of anesthesia; mice were used at 18 or 25 days of age; air temperatures of $78°F$ or $87°F$ were tried; and 0.3 ml of 5% glucose was given intraperitoneally after the operation in half of the cases. This was, therefore, a 2^4 factorial test, the results of which are shown in Table XXII, using 10 mice per group. The figures themselves demonstrate unequivocally that the anesthetic technique was at fault in earlier trials; reducing the period of anesthesia resulted in far fewer deaths over all the other treatment combinations, which did not themselves differ significantly. Summing totals over each pair of factors, we get, among the completely hypophysectomized survivors:

	Living mice
Effect of anesthesia	23:51
Effect of age	32:42
Effect of temperature	36:38
Effect of glucose	36:38

The data were converted to angles to equalize variances, the analysis of variance is shown in Table XXIII, and confirms the conclusions above. The suspicion of an age effect is seen not to be confirmed.

TABLE XXIII

Analysis of Variance[a]

Source of variation	Degrees of freedom	Mean square	F
Anesthetics	1	1853	22.6***
Age	1	251	3.1
Temperature	1	11	0.1
Glucose therapy	1	13	0.2
Interactions	11	84	1.0
Error	∞	82	—

[a] Data in Table XXI (complete hypophysectomy). From Lamond and Emmens (1959).
*** $P < 0.001$.

B. Regions of Useful Response

In factorial tests, or in assays based upon them, one is likely to encounter the difficulty that certain regions of the design are liable to give no response or maximal responses, and to convey little information at the same time as making analysis difficult because of problems concerning equalization of variance. This is particularly acute when quantal responses are in question. To overcome this trouble, *parallelogram* designs were introduced by Claringbold *et al.* (1953). Consider an $n \times m$ factorial design as in Fig. 5, where whole areas are expected to

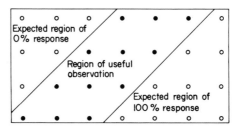

FIG. 5. Region of useful response in a parallelogram design. (From Claringbold *et al.*, 1953.)

give 0% or 100% responses. Then doses of X_1 and X_2 can be given which avoid these regions, as do the solid dots in the figure. The analysis of variance is treated in detail by Claringbold *et al.*, and presents no difficulties; the following example is taken from the same paper (Table XXIV). This table shows the effect of the time interval (X_1) and dosage

TABLE XXIV

EFFECT OF THE INTERVAL OF TIME (X_1) BETWEEN DIVIDED DOSES OF
ESTRONE ON THE PERCENTAGE VAGINAL RESPONSE IN
OVARIECTOMIZED MICE[a]

Dose estrone (10^{-4} μg)	Time interval (hours)			
	0.89	2.67	8.0	24.0
1				20
2				45
4			15	50
8			30	70
16		30	35	
32		55	65	
64	25	60		
128	30	70		
256	60			
512	85			

[a] From Claringbold et al. (1953).

of estrone (X_2) or the response of ovariectomized mice in the vaginal smear test, scored quantally. At short time intervals, a much higher dose is needed than at longer intervals, so that the dosage scale must be ascended as the interval lengthens, in order to obtain useful responses. This experiment, when analyzed by taking empirical responses (Eisenhart, 1947) gave the results shown in Table XXV, below, demonstrating

TABLE XXV

ANALYSIS OF VARIANCE BY EMPIRICAL ANGLES[a]

Source of variation	Degrees of freedom	Sum of squares	Mean square	F
Doses				
Linear	1	1883.7	1883.7	44.7***
Quadratic	1	3.1	3.1	0.1
Cubic	1	23.5	23.5	0.6
Time interval	3	254.5	84.8	2.1
Interactions	9	191.0	21.2	0.5
Theoretical variance		—	41.0	—

[a] From Claringbold et al. (1953).
*** $P < 0.001$.

a highly significant linear dose-response relationship unaffected in slope by the time interval chosen. The position effect has been absorbed by the design of the test, and does not appear in the analysis.

It is easy to extend this design to many dimensions, as in 2^n or 3^n, etc., factorials, or to extend it, should it be necessary, to curvilinear relationships.

C. Mixtures of Substances

A considerable literature has accumulated on tests of joint action of hormones, insecticides, and other substances, reviewed by Finney (1952). Its importance to assay is that methods are offered by which, in certain circumstances, the similarity of action of substances under assay may be examined. If two substances are acting in the same manner, such that one may be assayed in terms of the other, a test involving mixtures of the two should reveal comparable activity to that shown by either one alone. If antagonism or potentiation of any kind is seen, the similarity of their action should be doubted, whereas if like action is indicated the evidence is of a stronger nature than mere parallel dose-response lines. Even so, care must be taken in the interpretation of such tests.

Joint action tests may be quite complex (cf. Plackett and Hewlett, 1963; Hewlett and Plackett, 1964); the principle, however, is simple. If dose A of substance 1 is equivalent in effect to dose B of substance 2, and if the dose-response lines are parallel (as they will be in a valid assay), we may investigate mixtures of 1 and 2 to see whether the dose-response lines remain linear and parallel to the originals. One such mixture could be A/2 + B/2, others A/4 + 3B/4, and so on, where A and B may then take a series of values up the dose-response lines. If substances 1 and 2 act either antagonistically or cooperatively, mixtures giving lesser or greater responses than might be expected, the dose-response lines will curve, or, alternatively, mixtures expected to give a constant level of response will fail to do so. Thus, in the examination of gonado-tropin action on the mouse uterus as in assays cited above, Lamond and Claringbold (1958) found that various mixtures of gonadotropins acted in a purely additive manner, indicating, in this assay at least, similar action. Figure 6 gives examples of two such mixtures, with the responses shown diagrammatically in the form of fitted regression surfaces. In the HMG:HCG mixtures, equivalent doses were misjudged, but this merely resulted in a skew surface, with linearity unaffected.

It is of great interest that other evidence (Lamond and Emmens, 1959) clearly demonstrates the *dissimilarity* of action of some of these substances in a different type of test, also on the mouse uterus, but in hypophysectomized animals. In the tests of Lamond and Claringbold

(1958), intact animals were used, whose own hormone secretions entered the picture, and entirely changed the action of injected substances in some cases. This finding is a warning to be very cautious about accepting even seeming convincing evidence of a purely statistical nature in the hormone field. Parallel dose-response lines and apparently complete similarity of action did not, in this case, guarantee that the pairs of substances act alike on the ovary in all circumstances, let alone that one could be regarded as a dilution of the other.

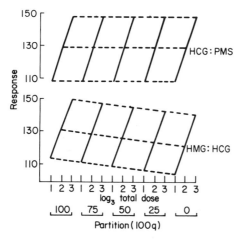

Fig. 6. Regression surfaces fitted to the data of Lamond and Claringbold (1958) by the authors, showing equivalence of action of all mixtures of various gonadotropins in pairs (HCG, PMS, and HMG).

D. Predicting Requirements

When an assay method has been established, the characteristics of the dose-response line may be used to predict requirements in future assays, on the assumption that these characteristics remain constant. It is also necessary to assume that the responses to the doses of the standard and unknown(s) to be given will not differ greatly and will fall within predetermined limits.

The minimal possible error occurs if the mean responses to the standard and unknown are equal, and if the same number of responses are obtained to each. The standard error of M is then

$$s_M{}^2 = 2s^2/nb^2$$

where s^2 is the error variance and n is the total number of responses to one preparation.

The least number of observations required with each substance to obtain a given level of accuracy is such that

$$n = 2s^2/b^2 s_M{}^2$$

where s_M is to be assigned the desired value. The calculated limits of error in an assay which turns out to have the s and b postulated may unfortunately not be as narrow as predicted, unless previous experience is taken into account and lower errors for b, in particular, can be assigned. In an assay with a relatively small number of observations, even s may be associated with too few degrees of freedom to give narrow limits of error when the internal evidence of that test alone is utilized. However, a prediction assuming a constant s and b can validly be accompanied, when the assay fulfills the prediction, by the use of average values based on past experience.

Suppose we require limits of about 83–120% in an assay. This corresponds with a log standard error of 0.04, hence the limits of error of M will be $M \pm 2ts_M$ at $P = 0.95$, or $M \pm 0.08$, approximately, if n is fairly large (say, greater than 20). Then if s^2 is 50, and b is 20, we have

$$n = (2 \times 50)/(20^2 \times 0.04^2)$$

$$= 100/0.8^2$$

$$= 157 \text{ observations per substance, a rather imprecise}$$
$$\text{assay method.}$$

In quantal assays, $s^2 = 1$, if probits or angles are employed, and an average value must be assumed for the weighting factor. This is usually taken as 0.5, the approximate factor for 20% or 80% of responses, intermediate responses carrying somewhat higher weights, up to 0.637 for 50%. The approximate equation for n is then:

$$n = 2/wb^2 s_M{}^2$$

where w is the weighting factor.

Thus, in a quantal assay with a slope of 5 probits and an assumed w of 0.5, limits of error of 83–120% ($P = 0.95$) can be expected if not less than $2/(0.5 \times 5^2 \times 0.04^2)$ observations are made per substance, or $n = 100$.

In assays where littermates are used, the appropriate design and analyses must be applied in any future work, if previous experience is to be used for prediction, when the error mean square as derived in typical tests may, if homogeneous, be used in such predictions. If crossing-over has been done, then similar cross-over tests may also be expected to show the same mean square for error, on the average, but differently designed assays, taking account of other or additional factors to those appearing in earlier work, may have quite different limits of error.

The number of animals needed in practice in various biological assays is very variable. Although an assay with a λ value of more than 0.4 is frowned upon, some techniques such as the intravaginal estimation of estrogen have proved essential as research tools and thus have continued in use despite very poor precision. Such an assay, with a slope of 2 and a λ of 0.5 may need several hundred animals per substance, unless within-animal estimates are used, in which case at least 100 observations will still be needed for reasonable precision, say 80–125% limits (Claringbold, 1956). At the other end of the scale, some remarkably precise assays have been recorded, even without within-animal estimates. Such are the assay of serum gonadotropin, using littermate rats (British Pharmacopoeia, 1948), where about six animals per substance give limits of error of 80–125%, and even without littermates only about 13 per substance are needed (in practice, 12 or 14). Adrenal cortical activity, as measured by the total hepatic fermentable sugar in the rat, requires only about 16 rats per substance for comparable precision, again using random animals. Other assays range between these extremes, more typical values lying between 25 and 50 animals per substance for the limits quoted. It is rare for adequate numbers to be used in the laboratory to give such precise results; limits more like 50–200% are frequently accepted in both clinical and fundamental work, particularly in the former, where limited material often prohibits any attempt at high accuracy. It is unfortunate that high sensitivity (response to small quantities of hormone) seems usually to be accompanied by poor accuracy, so that many test objects must be used in an attempt to gain precision, and thus the total quantity of the unknown required may still be substantial.

REFERENCES

Aitchison, J., and Silvey, S. D. (1951). *Biometrika* **44**, 273.
Ashford, J. R. (1959). *Biometrics* **15**, 573.
Berkson, J. (1949). *J. Am. Statist. Assoc.* **44**, 273.
Biggers, J. D. (1951). *J. Endocrinol.* **8**, 169.
Biggers, J. D., and Claringbold, P. J. (1954). *Nature* **174**, 596.
Bliss, C. I. (1938). *Quart. J. Pharm. Pharmacol.* **11**, 192.
Bliss, C. I. (1940). *J. Am. Statist. Assoc.* **35**, 498.
Bliss, C. I. (1944). *J. Am. Statist. Assoc.* **33**, 225.
Bliss, C. I. (1946). *Biometrics Bull.* **1**, 57.
Bliss, C. I., and Marks, H. P. (1939a). *Quart. J. Pharm. Pharmacol.* **12**, 82.
Bliss, C. I., and Marks, H. P. (1939b). *Quart. J. Pharm. Pharmacol.* **12**, 182.
Bliss, C. I., and Rose, C. L. (1940). *Am. J. Hyg.* **31**, 79.
"British Pharmacopoeia" (1948). Constable & Co., London.
Bülbring, E. (1937). *J. Physiol. (London)* **89**, 64.

Bülbring, E., and Burn, J. H. (1935). *J. Physiol. (London)* **85**, 320.

Burn, J. H. (1937). "Biological Standardization." Oxford Univ. Press, London and New York.

Calloway, N. O., McCormack, R. M., and Singh, N. P. (1942). *Endocrinology* **30**, 423.

Claringbold, P. J. (1955). *J. Endocrinol.* **13**, 11.

Claringbold, P. J. (1956). *J. Roy. Statist. Soc.* **18**, 133.

Claringbold, P. J. (1959). *Biometrics* **15**, 307.

Claringbold, P. J., and Emmens, C. W. (1961). *In* "Quantitative Methods in Pharmacology" (H. de Jonge, ed.), p. 72. North-Holland Publ., Amsterdam.

Claringbold, P. J., and Lamond, D. R. (1957). *J. Endocrinol.* **16**, 86.

Claringbold, P. J., and Sobey, W. R. (1957). *Australian J. Biol. Sci.* **10**, 360.

Claringbold, P. J., Biggers, J. D., and Emmens, C. W. (1953). *Biometrics* **9**, 467.

Cochran, W. G., and Cox, G. M. (1950). "Experimental Designs." Wiley, New York.

Eisenhart, C. (1947). *In* "Techniques of Statistical Analysis," Chapter 16. McGraw-Hill, New York.

Emmens, C. W. (1939). *Med. Res. Council Spec. Rept. Ser.* **234**.

Emmens, C. W. (1941). *J. Endocrinol.* **2**, 444.

Emmens, C. W. (1948). "Principles of Biological Assay." Chapman & Hall, London.

Emmens, C. W., ed. (1950). "Hormone Assay." Academic Press, New York.

Emmens, C. W. (1957). *J. Endocrinol.* **16**, 148.

Emmens, C. W. (1960). *Biometrics* **16**, 161.

Finney, D. J. (1945). *Quart. J. Pharm. Pharmacol.* **18**, 77.

Finney, D. J. (1952). "Probit Analysis," 2nd ed. Cambridge Univ. Press, London and New York.

Finney, D. J. (1964). "Statistical Method in Biological Assay," Griffin, London.

Fisher, R. A. (1954). "Statistical Methods for Research Workers," 12th ed. Oliver & Boyd, Edinburgh and London.

Fisher, R. A., and Yates, F. (1963). "Statistical Tables," 6th ed. Oliver & Boyd, Edinburgh and London.

Gaddum, J. H. (1933). *Med. Res. Council Spec. Rept. Ser.* **183**.

Gurland, J., Lee, I., and Dahm, P. A. (1960). *Biometrics* **16**, 382.

Hewlett, P. S., and Plackett, R. L. (1964). *Biometrics* **20**, 566.

Irwin, J. O. (1937). *J. Roy. Statist. Soc. Suppl.* **4**, 1.

Irwin, J. O. (1943). *J. Hyg.* **43**, 121.

King, E. P. (1963). *Biometrics* **19**, 429.

Lamond, D. R., and Claringbold, P. J. (1958). *J. Endocrinol.* **16**, 298.

Lamond, D. R., and Emmens, C. W. (1959). *J. Endocrinol.* **18**, 251.

Plackett, R. L., and Hewlett, P. S. (1963). *Biometrics* **19**, 517.

Pedersen-Bjergaard, K. (1939). "Comparative Studies Concerning the Strengths of Estrogenic Substances." Oxford Univ. Press, London and New York.

Sen, P. K. (1963). *Biometrics* **19**, 532.

Smith, H. W., Marks, H. P., Fieller, E. C. and Brown, W. A. (1944). *Quart. J. Pharm. Pharmacol.* **17**, 108.

Snedecor, G. W. (1956). "Statistical Methods," 5th ed. Iowa State Univ. Press, Ames, Iowa.

Thorslund, T., and Paulsen, C. A. (1963). *Endocrinology* **72**, 663.

van Strik, R. (1961). *In* "Quantitative Methods in Pharmacology" (H. de Jongh, ed.), p. 88. North-Holland Publ., Amsterdam.

Wood, E. D. (1946). *Analyst* **71**, 1.

Wood, E. D., and Finney, D. J. (1946). *Quart. J. Pharm. Pharmacol.* **19**, 112.

PART II

Steroid Hormones and Related Substances

Chapter 2

Estrogens

C. W. EMMENS

I. Introduction

Naturally occurring estrogens may be assayed biologically or chemically; the choice of methods depends on the particular requirements of an investigation. Synthetic and steroidal estrogens used experimentally will tend more and more to be assayed by labeling followed by such methods as chromatography. Biological assays as such, and experiments of the same character as assays, will still continue in use, sometimes when very high sensitivity is needed, even if preceded by chemical extraction and purification, or in investigations demanding the actual demonstration of estrogenic activity or its potentiation or inhibition. Much new investigation thus demands a biological approach at least in the first instance.

Some biological methods of assay are still very much more sensitive than chemical or physical methods other than isotopic labeling. The most sensitive biological methods described below cover the range 5×10^{-6} μg to 10^{-4} μg approximately, or 5–100 picograms (pg) of estradiol or estrone per mouse. However, a colony of mice must be used in such assays, with an accuracy of 80–125% ($P = 0.95$) attainable with about 12 mice per group. If a mean dose of 30 pg is given, a total of 30×24 pg, or allowing for wastage, of about 1000 pg or 0.001 μg will be needed per complete assay. These sensitive biological techniques are fortunately more precise than those available until very recently. The great drawback of the intravaginal method of assay using cornification as a response (Emmens, 1950a) was its variability, and the need for many animals per assay. Despite this, it was and still is necessary as a research tool, although rarely seeing use in routine assays.

For laboratory research and clinical investigation, therefore, it seems likely that the newer biological techniques will see considerable use, sometimes in conjunction with some of the older methods, and with chemical, particularly radiochemical, methods. They have the advantage of high precision, speed, high sensitivity, and freedom from interference from various steroidal and other substances that may occur in clinical material. These methods can be adapted for the direct or semidirect assay of urinary and blood estrogens with a minimum of extraction, they could contribute a great deal, but have so far seen little application. It is fortunate that we are now departing from the situation which has obtained since Emmens (1939a) and Pedersen-Bjergaard (1939) investigated the assay of estrogenic substances, and concluded that the effects of variation in technique were so great that an estrogenic preparation could be validly assayed biologically only if the chemical nature of the estrogens present were known and each was isolated. This arose because different estrogens were affected quite differently by changes in the medium and the number and spacing of injections, so that while reproducible estimates could be obtained with any one method, unless the nature of the estrogen was known, it was not possible to estimate the amount present. It was easily shown that intravaginal assay is relatively free from this drawback, in that all potent estrogens have about the same activity, and the newer methods employing intravaginal application also have that advantage. This means that a mixture of estrogens may be assayed and that with little margin of error an overall figure can be given for the total amount present, whatever the ratio of each to the others may be. On the other hand, if chemical separation is made, each may be assayed with precision, probably without purification; in terms of any chosen standard.

II. Types of Estrogen

A. Natural Substances

The natural estrogens of animal origin so far isolated are all steroids, possessing the cyclopentanoperhydrophenanthrene nucleus, as in Fig. 1. Some plant estrogens are not steroids, although others are. In contrast to the androgens and progesterone, estrogenic steroids have a phenolic

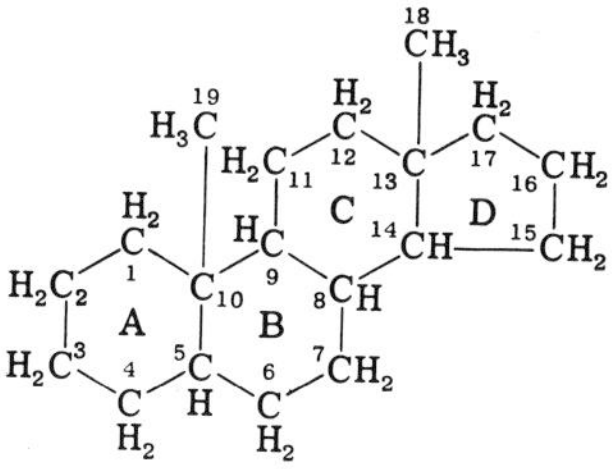

Fig. 1. The steroid nucleus, showing the nomenclature of the rings and carbon atoms. (From Emmens, 1959.)

A-ring, and a carbon atom in position 18, but not in position 19. (Some of the new synthetic steroids, e.g., 19-nortestosterone, possessing a variety of androgenic, progestational, and estrogenic actions, also lack a carbon atom in position 19.)

Estradiol-17β [Fig. 2(I)] is formed by the ovaries and is the most potent natural estrogen by nearly all test methods. It would seem to be the only estrogen produced by the ovaries, and it is also produced by the adrenals, placenta, and the testes of the stallion. Its stereoisomer, estradiol-17α,.is found in the urine of pregnant mares and is much less potent. Some estradiol-17β occurs in human urine.

Estrone [Fig. 2(II)] is found in urine and in the adrenals and the placenta. In most tests involving parenteral injection it is less active than estradiol-17β, but in intravaginal tests of all types it is only a little less active, the ratio of estradiol:estrone potency being about 1.5 to 3.0. The slopes may also differ slightly but significantly. Recent studies (cf. Jensen and Jacobson, 1962) have shown that estrone is converted to estradiol and probably acts in the rodent uterus only after this conversion.

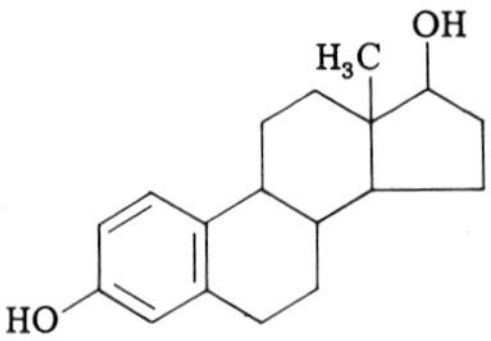

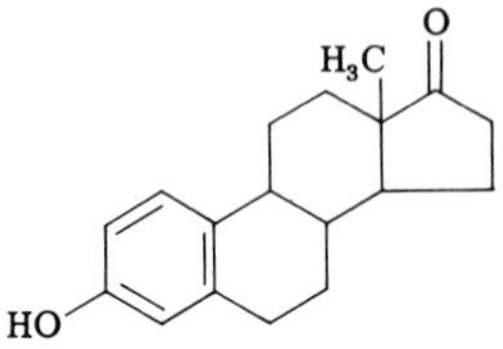

FIG. 2. Four important natural estrogens: (I) estradiol; (II) estrone; (III) estriol; (IV) equilin. (From Emmens, 1959.)

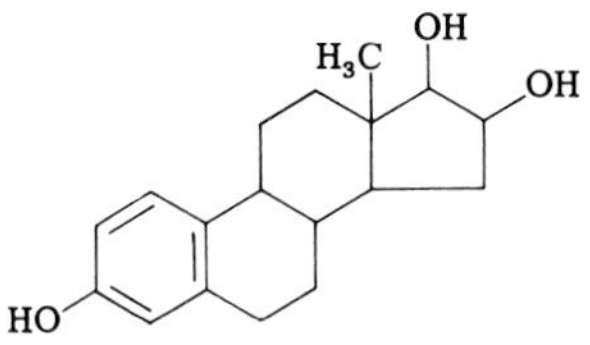

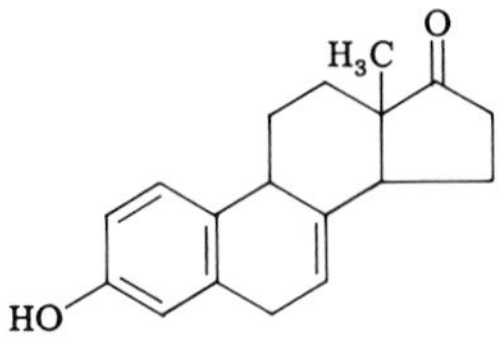

Estriol [Fig. 2(III)] is found in primate urine; it is less active than estrone in all but intravaginal tests under optimal conditions, when the two are of equal potency (Biggers and Claringbold, 1954c; Martin and Claringbold, 1960; Martin, 1960). The potency estimates by older test methods are completely dependent on test conditions and vary between 1.0 and 250 for the estrone:estriol ratio. Both estrone and estriol are formed *in vivo* from estradiol and are excreted in the urine mainly as sulfates and glucuronides (Marrian, 1948).

Various other newly identified steroids, such as 16β-hydroxyestrone (Layne and Marrian, 1958) have now been found in human urine; *equilin* [Fig. 2(IV)] and *equilenin* have been known for some time and are found in the urine of pregnant mares.

Some of the androgens, notably *trans*-androstenediol, 17-methyl-androstan-17-ol-3-one, ethynyltestosterone, and both 19-nortestosterone and 17-ethynyl-19-nortestosterone are estrogenic, but are active only in relatively large doses and almost certainly by virtue of a metabolite (Emmens, 1941b, 1942a, 1943).

B. Synthetic Substances

Dodds and his co-workers first produced a series of synthetic compounds with potent estrogenic activity, and with no apparent qualitative differences in action from the natural estrogens. A very large number of such compounds is now known, although many are far less potent than the natural estrogens and the majority are most probably estrogenic

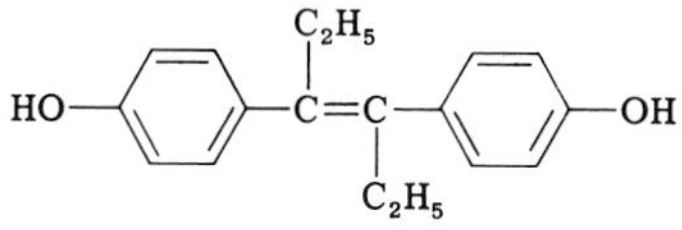

(I) 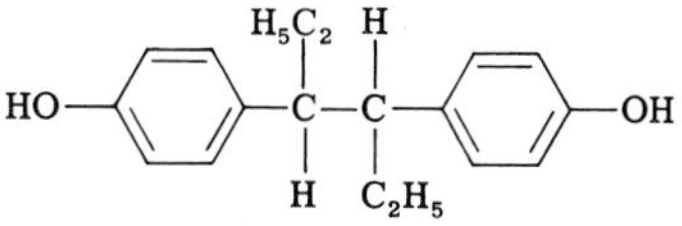   (II)

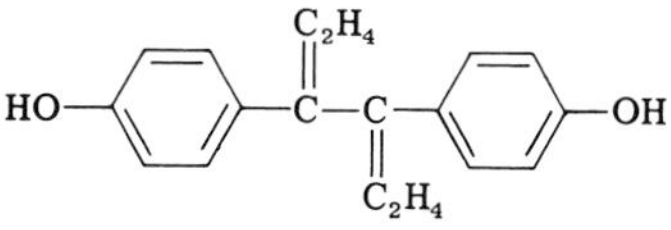

(III)

FIG. 3. Three commonly used synthetic estrogens: (I) diethylstilbestrol; (II) hexestrol; (III) dienestrol.

by virtue of their metabolites. This has not been fully recognized by reviewers such as Solmssen (1945) and Grundy (1957) in otherwise comprehensive accounts of the synthetic estrogens.

Important members of the synthetic series are diethylstilbestrol, hexastrol, and dienestrol.

Diethylstilbestrol [Fig. 3(I)] is active by mouth as well as by injection, in contrast to the natural estrogens which lose much of their potency by mouth unless they are protected by some means. It has a potency, when injected, between that of estrone and estradiol, and a potency equal to that of estrone in intravaginal tests.

Hexestrol [Fig. 3(II)] and *dienestrol* [Fig. 3(III)] are very similar in structure to diethylstilbestrol and share its properties. They are of about the same potency in most tests, but hexestrol seems to be less potent by mouth in the human than is diethylstilbestrol.

The high potency of this type of compound has led to speculation about the structure that must be possessed by a substance if it is to show estrogenic activity. When the proestrogens (Emmens, 1941b) are eliminated, it seems that we are left with substances much resembling diethylstilbestrol, which may be thought to copy the structure of estradiol much more closely than at first appears (Fig. 4).

Studies of the stilbestrol series by Emmens and his colleagues (Emmens, 1957; Emmens and Cox, 1958; Emmens et al., 1959, 1960, 1962) have recently shown that it contains not only proestrogens and estrogens, but also antiestrogens. Some compounds exhibit both proestrogenic and antiestrogenic activity, and the peak of each type of activity is found in one of three adjacent compounds of the series. Thus,

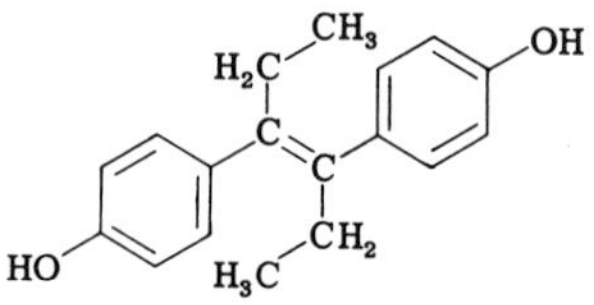

FIG. 4. Supposed configuration of diethylstilbestrol, resembling estradiol.

diethylstilbestrol exhibits maximal estrogenic potency, methylethylstilbestrol exhibits maximal proestrogenic potency, and dimethylstilbestrol exhibits maximal antiestrogenic potency. It is probable that the unchanged antiestrogens in this series are the active substances and that those that are proestrogens may perhaps produce sufficient estrogenic metabolites to overcome their antiestrogenic activity except in special circumstances. It is interesting that, whatever methylethylstilbestrol becomes in the body to account for its quite high estrogenic potency, it is not diethylstilbestrol (Cox, unpublished). The exact relationships between estrogens, "proestrogens," and antiestrogens may involve such questions as duration of action in the target organs, and much remains to be elucidated.

C. Esterified Compounds

It was recognized when setting up international standards for estrogenic activity that, at least in bioassay, a separate standard or standards would be needed for compounds with prolonged action. Estradiol benzoate was at that time chosen, but it was soon apparent that it could be used only for comparison with other samples of the same compound. This is true as long as parenteral methods of assay are under consideration, but the question of the effects of esterification is not a pressing one now that pure characterized substances are usually being handled, except in the parallel case of the natural conjugates. A discussion of the general biological effects of esterification is given in Emmens (1950a).

Estrone sulfate or estriol glucuronide may require assay by biological techniques, and it is unfortunate that no very exhaustive tests have been made to determine whether these naturally occurring substances are potent estrogens when assayed by the intravaginal route. Robson and Adler (1940) concluded that estriol glucuronide is about as effective as the free compound in causing vaginal cornification when given locally, and Emmens (1941b) showed that esterification is almost or completely without effect when aliphatic esters of the natural or synthetic estrogens are tested under the same conditions, but neither estrone sulfate nor estriol glucuronide were tested. Later (unpublished) tests have thrown doubt on the intravaginal activity of these two compounds, but have themselves been the subject of some doubt because of uncertainty about the purity of preparations, some samples giving completely negative results and others partially positive ones. It seems very likely, however, that the two predominant excretion products in the urine are not active locally and that they therefore differ in this respect from the general run of esters; neither is, of course, an ester in the usual sense of the word.

III. Vaginal Cornification

A. CORNIFICATION IN RODENTS

The Allen-Doisy test for vaginal cornification in rodents (Allen and Doisy, 1923) was based on the observations of Stockard and Papanicolaou (1917), who first reported the cyclic vaginal cornification of guinea pigs. In the rat or mouse, used by Allen and Doisy, very clear vaginal changes occur, and these may be initiated in the castrate female by dosage with estrogen. Very many modifications of the Allen-Doisy test have been made, immature animals sometimes being employed instead of castrates, but all the modifications depend on the induction of the characteristic vaginal changes that occur some 60–80 hours after injection and somewhat earlier after intravaginal dosage. Our knowledge of the factors affecting estrogen assays is almost confined to variants of this test, and our decision that many compounds are estrogens (or antiestrogens) has been dependent on it. Detailed discussion may be found in Marrian and Parkes (1929), Emmens (1939a, 1950a), and Pedersen-Bjergaard (1939). Useful studies in addition are those of Allan et al. (1930), de Jongh et al. (1932), and Hain and Robson (1936). These studies are primarily concerned with routes other than intravaginal, in rats or mice.

Much of the earlier work was done with rats, which are still used for the test, but less so than previously. There seems little to recommend the rat unless large amounts of crude material are to be injected. Otherwise, the mouse is easier to handle, requires much less room and less hormone, and can thus be used in sufficient numbers for reasonably precise work. The response of the mouse is also easier to classify than is that of the rat.

B. SPAYING THE RAT OR MOUSE

Ovariectomy, or spaying, is easiest in the immature female, shortly after weaning. A single transverse incision across the midline is made in the skin of the back, with the animal under any convenient but short-acting anesthetic. The incision may be shifted readily from one side to the other so as to lie over each ovary in turn. A small puncture is then made over the site of the ovary, which can usually be seen through the abdominal wall, embedded in a pad of fat. The top of a pair of fine forceps is introduced and grasps the fat around the ovary, care being taken not to rupture the capsule of the ovary itself. In the rat, the tip of the uterine horn is then crushed in a pair of artery forceps, and the ovary, together with the Fallopian tube, is removed with a single cut with a scalpel or safety razor blade. In the mouse, a similar procedure may be followed if desired, but alternatively the ovary plus the tube may be snipped off with a pair of fine scissors and the uterus allowed to slip back into place. There is usually insufficient bleeding to matter, even with the latter technique, which is quicker. In the rat, the abdominal wall may need a single suture, the mouse does not. On completion of the operation, the skin incision may be closed by 1 or 2 interrupted sutures, but with skill, in the mouse, a sufficiently small incision may be made to need no suturing. Aseptic precautions are not necessary, speed and gentle handling are more important. With practice, up to 70 mice per hour may be spayed if sutures are omitted and the anesthetic is administered by an assistant. Age and weight at ovariectomy do not affect responses as much as might be expected (Biggers and Claringbold, 1954a).

C. PREPARATION OF SOLUTIONS

Most estrogens are soluble in organic solvents, and stock solutions are usually made in alcohol and stored cold. These may be added to oil, saline, distilled water or mixtures of water and glycerol or propylene glycol for tests. The final concentration of ethyl alcohol should not exceed

2% by volume for oral administration, 10% for parenteral administration, or 5% for intravaginal administration. It should also be kept uniform in any one test. Although in local Allen-Doisy tests it has not been shown that propylene glycol solutions up to 50% have any effect on response, tests of mitotic responses have been impaired with more than 25% of propylene glycol in the medium (Martin, 1960).

These solutions must be thoroughly mixed, if in glycerol-water media or oil, by gentle warming for a prolonged period over a sand bath or hot plate, with care to adjust the final volume if necessary. Most oils in common use—olive oil, arachis (peanut) oil, sesame oil—will not mix with more than 5% of alcohol. Alcohol stock solutions of estrone were found by Rowlands and Callow (1935) to remain stable for several months, even at 37°C, but Wilder-Smith and Williams (1947) found that solutions of dienestrol and diethylstilbestrol at both 1 μg/ml and 100 μg/ml lost potency when kept at room temperature either in water or alcohol. Estrone, hexestrol, and estradiol were found to be more stable under the same conditions for up to 32 weeks, but still showed a slight potency loss. All five estrogens were little affected if kept in sesame oil at room temperature, or in men's urine in a refrigerator. Aeration, the presence of benzoyl peroxide or hydrogen peroxide increased the rate of inactivation of dienestrol and diethylstilbestrol, while hydroquinone decreased it. Emmens (1950b) found that the very dilute solutions used in intravaginal work may lose potency in a few weeks, but found no instability in more concentrated alcoholic or oily solutions kept cold up to 12 months. It is thus reasonable to keep relatively concentrated stock solutions in the refrigerator for several months, but at room temperature for only short periods, and not to keep very dilute solutions for more than a single test unless they are deep frozen, when they presumably last for a longer period.

D. Preparation of Test Animals

After spaying, the animals should not be used for about 2 weeks, but they may be given a "priming" injection of .1 μg of any potent short-acting estrogen in 0.05 to 0.1 ml of oil subcutaneously before this time. This injection helps to ensure maintenance of sensitivity and greater uniformity of response. It is necessary to prime at about 6-week intervals, unless a particular group has responded positively within that period (Emmens, 1939a), and this makes it advisable to prime at regular intervals in order to avoid heterogeneity in the colony. After positive intravaginal responses (Emmens, 1950b) no priming action occurs, and it is necessary to prime periodically whatever the responses in a colony used for intravaginal work. Palmer (1941) found greater uniformity of response if mice were selected, by priming, then giving a threshold dose a week later and rejecting any mice not responding positively on both occasions. This is a step toward the use of individual dose levels (Claringbold, 1955a). Assays should not follow each other closer than at about 2-week intervals with the same mice, unless one is prepared to make statistical allowance for carry-over effects from one assay to another.

Uniformity of response is worth striving for, particularly when a response must be scored quantally. It is therefore advisable to keep the test animals under as uniform a set of conditions as possible, to minimize time-to-time variation and to maximize the slope of the dose-response line. Randomizing animals, or at least boxes of five animals or some such small number, to dosage groups is essential if heterogeneity is to be avoided. However, the use of inbred lines is questionable. Emmens (1939c) found the one inbred line of mice he used to be more variable than randomly bred albinos, and Biggers and Claringbold (1954b) and others have made similar observations. It now seems to be felt that selected F_1 hybrids are much better for assay work that inbred lines; Chai (1960) working with testosterone or gonadotropins in mice, found that the F_1 had a lower variability in some cases only. Their sensitivity was usually intermediate between those of the parental stocks.

After the above precautions, it is best to test a colony for satisfactory response to a known estrogen by establishing a dose-response line with, say, estradiol. This will check technique and homogeneity, and give a baseline from which to plan assays. The probit-$\log_{10}$ dose line should have a slope of between 5 and 6, in subcutaneous tests, but only of about 2 in intravaginal tests. the χ^2 test for homogeneity should reveal no significant departure from linearity, and in order to test this effectively, the initial dose-response line should comprise at least five or six groups. If the angular transformation is used in computations, the corresponding slopes should be about 100 and 35, and if 0, 1 scoring (see below) is used, they should be about 1.0 and 0.4 for subcutaneous and intravaginal testing, respectively.

E. A TYPICAL TEST

The method now in use for subcutaneous Allen-Doisy tests in the author's department will be described. Solutions for injection are made up in arachis oil (sesame, olive, or other oils can be used) and adjusted so that a volume of 0.05 ml is given per injection. Exceptionally, up to 0.2 ml may be given, but in this amount tends to leak from the site of injection, or even if it does not, to retain some of the estrogen. Also exceptionally, water-soluble material may be given, in distilled water or saline, or in mixtures of water and glycerol or propylene glycol. The same volumes per injection are used, but with such material it is usual to give four injections instead of two.

Injections are made at about 10 AM on Monday and Tuesday, if four are to be given, these are added at about 5 PM on the same days. Smears are taken with a specially ground fine metal spatula at 5 PM on Wednesday and 10 AM on Thursday. Other smears have been found to contribute very little to the final result, although maximal sensitivity may usually be gained by postponing the Wednesday smear to later in the evening if convenient. Precision is not affected. All smears are taken with a saline-moistened spatula as gently as possible, transferred to a glass slide and stained for 10 minutes with 5% aqueous methylene blue solution. They are then washed and scored when dry under a low power of the microscope.

In its original form, the test score records only whether the rat or mouse has or has not responded positively to the dose administered, thus taking several smears merely increases sensitivity so that few positive reactions are missed. In the author's experience, the two smears recommended catch nearly all positive reactions, but may be considered separately in order to obtain more information per animal (see Chapter 1, this volume). This, however, is possible only if quantal scoring and the usual probit or similar type of analysis is abandoned. A positive smear contains nucleated or cornified epithelial cells, and no leukocytes; a full proestrus smear is thus scored as positive. Biggers and Claringbold (1954c) have shown that subdivisions of scoring for individual smears, such as a four-way score of presence or absence of leukocytes plus presence or absence of nucleated or cornified epithelial cells adds nothing to the information obtained—in fact it is the presence or absence of leukocytes that governs the score, as nucleated or cornified cells are nearly always present if leukocytes are absent; if they are not, it usually means that an effective smear has not been taken.

Assays follow standard methods as outlined in Chapter 1 (this volume). Groups containing less than 20 animals are unlikely to give satisfactory assays with quantal responses, and the probability of obtaining 0% or 100% of positive responses rises as group size decreases. If 20 animals are used per group with a dose ratio of 2 with each substance a valid assay will usually result, with fiducial limits of error between about 70% and 140%, or narrower in range if an estimate of the slope of the typical dose-response line is available from previous assays and is found to apply. The position of the line is subject to time-to-time variation, but the slope usually is not.

Even under fairly constant conditions, such as thermostatted rooms, a constant daily period of illumination, constant diet and routine, and the maintenance of priming, time-to-time variation in sensitivity occurs. It is not usually as marked, however, as reported by earlier investigators, nor is it seasonal. Changes in sensitivity are only a nuisance if they cause groups to react with 0 or 100% of positive responses and so tend to invalidate assays. They do not seriously affect the precision of assays when responses within the useful range have been obtained.

IV. Modifications of the Allen-Doisy Test

A. Methods of Administration

Estrogens may be given by mouth, subcutaneously, percutaneously, intramuscularly, intraperitoneally, intravenously, or intravaginally in the cornification test. The last-named method is of considerable importance and will be dealt with below. Peroral administration may be in any of the media mentioned for subcutaneous injection, or even in pure propylene glycol or glycerol. With mice, a metal tube about 1.5 mm in diameter with a blunt end and a side outlet of "organ-pipe" design is best. It is easiest to keep the tube fixed and to thread the mouse onto it than otherwise. Up to 0.5 ml may be given at each administration. An elastic catheter may be used as a stomach tube for rats.

Subcutaneous dosage needs no further comment. Percutaneous administration was shown by Emmens (1941a) to be remarkably effective if in organic solvents. Applied once daily to the shaved skin of mice, estrogens in alcohol or benzene give as sensitive a test as by injection in oil, but there is no merit in the method for ordinary purposes. Oily solutions are not absorbed so efficiently and response is poor. Pincus and Werthessen (1938) showed that the potency of some synthetic compounds is increased 50- to 300-fold if they are injected intraperitoneally instead of subcutaneously. Pedersen-Bjergaard (1939) has reported results using intravenous dosage.

The number and spacing of injections varies in different hands from a single injection (usually employed only with esterified compounds in oily solution) to 6 or even 8 spaced out over 2–3 days. From the studies mentioned above, it is clear that multiple injections increase sensitivity, by making more hormone available over the critical period, but that a peak is soon reached with oily solutions, except in the case of estriol. Little is otherwise to be gained by giving more than two injections. With aqueous media, however, multiple injections continue to give improved sensitivity, and at least four injections are advisable.

Administration may be modified also in a different way, so as to budget for individual sensitivity and to utilize within-animal information. This will usually be followed by a considerable reduction in error. Claringbold (1955a) studied the individual median effective dose in spayed mice, using the intravaginal method of administration which is more fully discussed below, but the same principle may be applied whatever the route. The individual effective dose (IED) is the minimal dose required to cause vaginal cornification at any one time. It cannot be determined, but the individual median effective dose (IMED) can be determined. This is the quantity which causes an individual to respond in 50% of all trials, if it can be tested on several occasions. The IMED is likely to be of use if the variation in response of the same animal at different times is less than the variation in response of different animals at the same time. It usually is; Claringbold's estimate was 29% of the usual variation between animals. Two methods for locating the IMED within reasonable limits are given.

The utilization of within-animal information in a quantal assay was first demonstrated by Claringbold (1956), who used mice for which IMED estimates were available in the assay of estrone. The design was a cross-over, reproduced in Table XV, Chapter 1 (this volume), where it is used as statistical example. It is sufficient to emphasize here that the assay, which was highly successful, gave an answer with four times the precision of ordinary estrogen assays of the same type, using the same number of observations. The method is slow, however, since each animal must be used repeatedly in the same determination of relative potency.

B. Taking and Scoring Smears

The method described above for taking vaginal smears is rapid and convenient. Various authors have felt, however, that a gentler technique is desirable and have used cotton wool pledgets or swabs, or have pipetted a little saline into the vagina and back onto a slide, perhaps after a few sucks back and forth. These methods are both much more time consuming, as new material has to be used for each smear. Even with the swab method, Wade and Doisy (1935) reported that frequent smearing—three times daily for 3 or 4 days—produces 25% of false positives. However, the few smears taken by the spatula in the method described above do not produce false positives. It would nevertheless be wise to check this possibility with any particular method adopted in new hands. Some workers omit to stain smears, but staining is so easy that it seems hardly worthwhile to omit it, as scoring is harder with unstained material, even under the phase microscope. Rat smears may perhaps be handled without staining more successfully than mouse smears.

Some workers have attempted to gain greater precision or sensitivity by scoring smears in one or more of a series of grades between the conventional negative and positive. Mühlbock (1940) used 7 grades, a to g, only the last representing a full reaction. Sulman (1952) has attempted to gain sensitivity by defining a positive smear as one containing more than 50% of nucleated or cornified cells in the presence of leukocytes and mucin. The work of Biggers and Claringbold (1954c) mentioned above, clearly showed that vaginal cornification is a strictly quantal response, that proestrous smears should be classed as positive, and that the absence of leukocytes is a critical factor governing classification. Four sets of data were subjected to discriminant analysis, examining the efficiency of a fourfold classification obtained by a double dichotomy of the usual quantal score. The four classes are listed:

Score

    0—diestrous smear, mainly leukocytes, few epithelial cells

    x—mixture of leukocytes and epithelial cells

    y—proestrous smear, nucleated or nucleated plus cornified cells,
       no leukocytes

    1—estrous smear—cornified cells only

The values of x and y were then estimated for maximal discrimination in analysis, and turned out to be -0.03 and 0.99. Clearly $x = 0$ and $y = 1$ is a valid decision to make, giving only the two classes normally employed and a fully quantal response.

Other criteria of action on the epithelium of the vagina have been suggested, but until the studies of Martin and Claringbold (1958, 1960) and Martin (1960), no effective use seems to have been made of alternative responses.

If the quantal response is used, as seems most appropriate from all the evidence, it is still possible to use the information from individual smears. There are, for instance, at least two components of the reaction —did it take place, and, if so, how long did it last? There is evidence that these factors are to an extent independent. Thus Emmens (1957) compared the information obtained from 0,1 or 0,1,2 scoring in typical but very large tests designed to extract within-animal estimates of error, and found that 0,1,2 scores differentiated more successfully between substances, the F values for the sum of squares for the dose-response relationships of two preparations were, for instance, 84.7, and 149.0 as against 76.2 and 87.4, respectively, with 0,1 scoring and 64.2 and 80.4

with the angular transformation. The 0, 1, 2 score thus has an advantage over single quantal analysis, whether by 0, 1 score or by angles.

V. Interpreting Allen-Doisy Tests

It has been pointed out above that quite different answers may be obtained in vaginal cornification tests when technique is varied, except perhaps in intravaginal tests on mice. There is still little to report in the way of detailed investigation of other than intravaginal tests since the work of Emmens (1939a) and Pedersen-Bjergaard (1939). Tables I and II are reprinted from Emmens' monograph to illustrate the position. They show such wide discrepancies, depending on the author quoted and the particular technique employed, that it is obvious that it is not possible to assay accurately the potency of estrogenic material of either known or unknown constitution in terms of, say, estrone. Studies by both authors of impure urinary extracts from women and mares agreed in showing that with such biological methods, it was impossible to arrive at a trustworthy estimate of the nature or amounts of the estrogens present, and that the two international standards then in use could only be employed for comparison with preparations known to be of identical constitution. Pedersen-Bjergaard found, for example, that an extract of human pregnancy urine assayed at from 158 to 75,900 IU/gm according to the assay method used. It was also shown by Emmens that, in addition to the discrepancies occurring among the different pure estrogens, the responses to impure urinary extracts were modified by the presence of augmenting substances which were present in varying amounts according to extraction technique.

A more recent example (Emmens, 1965), in which the pure synthetic proestrogen dimethylstilbestrol (DMS) was assayed against the pure synthetic estrogen diethylstilbestrol (DES), showed that relative potency varied over a 40-fold range according to technique. With a 2-dose regime as described above, relative potencies in the mouse and rat were obtained as in Table III.

These findings led to concentration by others on chemical methods for identification and assay of urinary and other estrogens, with good success. Since these also necessitate, as things stand, the separation and part purification of the estrogens concerned, bioassay can be used instead of colorimetry or other methods, if so desired. There is usually no advantage in this unless minute quantities must be assayed, or there is a question of checking the estrogenic activity of the substances concerned. There still remains, however, the possibility of biological assay of crude materials, which may give a quick, if approximate answer. If conditions

76 C. W. EMMENS

are used under which the various natural estrogens give much the same response, and if this response is not affected, or much affected, by contaminants likely to be present, it may be worthwhile to have the rapid, approximate estimate available without chemical fractionation and

TABLE I

RATIO OF POTENCIES OF ESTRIOL AND ESTRONE FOUND BY DIFFERENT
INVESTIGATORS WORKING WITH OVARIECTOMIZED RATS
IN THE ALLEN-DOISY TEST[a]

Number and nature of injections	Estrone: estriol ratio	Reference
3 Aqueous	250	Meyer et al. (1936)
3 Aqueous	2	Curtis and Doisy (1931)
4 Aqueous	2	Cohen and Marrian (1934)
4 Aqueous	1	Burn and Elphick (1932)
1 Oily	4.5	Burn and Elphick (1932)
1 Oily	100	Butenandt and Störmer (1932)
3 Oily	90	Meyer et al. (1936)
? Oily	2	Marrian (1930)

[a] From Emmens (1939a).

TABLE II

RATIO OF POTENCIES OF ESTRADIOL AND ESTRONE FOUND BY
DIFFERENT INVESTIGATORS USING OVARIECTOMIZED RATS OR
MICE IN THE ALLEN-DOISY TEST[a]

Animals	Number and nature of injections	Estradiol: estrone ratio	Reference
Rats	3 Oily	6	Schoeller et al. (1935)
Rats	6 Aqueous	7	Schoeller et al. (1935)
Mice	3 Oily	0.8	Schoeller et al. (1935)
Mice	6 Aqueous	3	Schoeller et al. (1935)
Rats	1 Oily	3	David et al. (1935)
Mice	1 Oily	2	David et al. (1935)
Mice	3 Oily	2	David et al. (1935)
Mice	6 Aqueous	2	David et al. (1935)
Mice	5 Oily	5–10	Dirscherl (1936)
Rats	3 Oily (β-form)[b]	12	Whitman et al. (1937)
Rats	3 Oily (α-form)	0.3	Whitman et al. (1937)

[a] From Emmens (1939a).
[b] Modern nomenclature.

TABLE III

Ratio of Potencies of Dimethylstilbestrol (DMS) to
Diethylstilbestrol (DES) in the Rat and Mouse[a]

Animal	Route	Substance	MED (μg)	Relative potency[b]
Mouse	Subcutaneous	DMS	48	0.0029 (0.0013–0.0061)
		DES	0.14	
	Oral	DMS	128	0.0095 (0.0045–0.0225)
		DES	1.21	
Rat	Subcutaneous	DMS	640	0.0004 (0.0002–0.0011)
		DES	0.26	
	Oral	DMS	242	0.0165 (0.0115–0.0222)
		DES	4.0	

[a] From Emmens (1965). In all assays a 2-dose technique in oil and a constant timing schedule for dosage and smearing was maintained.
[b] Fiducial limits of error ($P = 0.95$) are given in brackets.

semipurification. Standard Allen-Doisy tests do not hold much attraction, although useful work has been possible on crude material with their aid, and the modification next to be discussed offers very much better possibilities. This in turn, however, is much improved by changing the end point as in other assays below.

VI. Intravaginal Allen-Doisy Tests

A. Local Application

A summary of the history of local techniques with estrogens is given by Emmens (1950a) to that date. Since then, a considerable volume of work has been done to enlarge the older viewpoint, which will be briefly summarized here. Freud (1939) and Mühlbock (1940) investigated some of the variables of the method and the latter showed that, in the mouse, administration in 50% aqueous glycerol gives·consistent responses of very high sensitivity. Robson and Adler (1940) made the important observation that the natural and (some) synthetic estrogens act locally without absorption in significant amounts, since a separate vaginal pocket formed from the lower vagina was practically unaffected in spayed mice receiving effective doses into the upper vagina. Emmens (1941b) confirmed these results, obtaining almost identical activities for the three natural estrogens to those reported by Mühlbock, who found the

MED for estrone, estradiol, and estriol to be approximately 250, 500, and 750 pg, respectively, in two applications of either saline or aqueous glycerol. Assay by intravaginal administration is thus much more sensitive than by subcutaneous injection, gives more consistent results, and does not show much difference in potency between the natural estrogens.

Further investigations by Emmens (1941b, 1942a,b, 1943, 1947) showed that with the exception of the weakly estrogenic androgens, all the natural estrogens examined, and the most potent synthetic estrogens, are alike in potency by intravaginal assay and are true estrogens, as opposed to proestrogens, which must be metabolized in the body before exhibiting estrogenic activity and which do not show very high intravaginal potencies. It was also established that esterification does not affect intravaginal assays, if the addition to the molecule of an ester chain is allowed for in computations of potency. It was thus concluded that intravaginal assay offered a method that was extremely sensitive, differentiated little between the natural and commonly used synthetic estrogens, and was insensitive to esterification or to the presence of substances that interfere with subcutaneous assays. The drawbacks were a low slope, requiring many animals per test, and uncertainty about the parallelism of slope for different natural substances. In some tests (Emmens, 1941b), the slopes appeared to be different, but in later tests (Emmens, 1950b) these differences were not found to be significant.

Systematic investigation of the intravaginal method was then undertaken by Biggers and Claringbold and reported in various papers cited below. Using aqueous egg albumen as the vehicle for administration, Biggers (1951, 1953a) found that, with a two-injection technique, the potency of estrogens is enhanced. It was thought that the protein bound the estrogen and prevented rapid loss from the site of action, thus maintaining more effective local concentrations. Using bovine plasma albumin, Biggers found erratic responses to estrogens in 0.1% solutions, but an enhanced potency with 0.01%. Biggers and Claringbold (1954c) repeated and extended some of this work to show that the relative potencies of various estrogens other than estradiol under presumably optimal or near-optimal conditions were not significantly different. Their work also showed that multiple intravaginal doses reach a maximal efficiency at four injections spread over 36 hours, more than this proving less effective with all estrogens studied. However, estriol remained less potent than the rest, except with 1% egg albumin, when with four injections as above, it equaled them in potency. The relative activities of a variety of estrogens under these conditions are given in Table IV. It will be seen that estradiol still shows greater activity under optimal conditions of administration; this accords with other evidence presented in the same paper that it differs in slope, and in response to time interval changes between injections, from the other estrogens examined.

Biggers (1952, 1953b) also demonstrated by histological studies that the morphological response of the vaginal epithelium is the same to estrogens administered by either the subcutaneous or intravaginal route, although the response occurs earlier with intravaginal application.

TABLE IV

RELATIVE ACTIVITY OF VARIOUS ESTROGENS, USING ESTRONE AS A STANDARD, WHEN GIVEN INTRAVAGINALLY IN 4 INJECTIONS IN THE ALLEN-DOISY TEST[a]

Estrogen	Solvent	MED ratio	Fiducial limits ($P = 0.95$)
Estradiol-3,17β	Water	1.37	1.04–1.81
Estriol	Water	0.09	0.04–0.21
Diethylstilbestrol	Water	0.76	0.51–1.39
Estradiol-3,17β	1% Egg albumin	1.57	1.03–2.37
Estriol	1% Egg albumin	1.13	0.72–1.76
Diethylstilbestrol	1% Egg albumin	0.82	0.57–1.19
Equilin	1% Egg albumin	0.84	0.60–1.20
Equilenin	1% Egg albumin	0.65	0.37–1.15

[a] After Claringbold (1954).

A number of studies then followed on factors, other than technique, that may affect the intravaginal response. They are of importance in assays only insofar as they demonstrate the need for environmental and treatment stability, as it was shown that the thyroid status (Biggers and Claringbold, 1953), insulin, phlorizin (Claringbold, 1954), potassium cyanide, and the metabolic inhibitors sodium monoiodoacetate, sodium azide, and 2,4-dinitrophenol influence responses (Claringbold, 1953). Moreover, the responses to estradiol were not affected in the same way as those to estrone, leading the authors to conclude that estrone is probably converted in part or whole to estradiol before exerting its action. This surmise has been shown by subsequent studies using radio-isotopes to be correct for the uterus (Jensen and Jacobson, 1962) and vagina (Stone, 1964). The general conclusions from these studies were that estrogens are absorbed at a critical rate from the lumen of the vagina and, in order to initiate the typical cornification response, a threshold level (for each individual) must be present for 36–48 hours. Meaningful studies of relative potency must be carried out utilizing responses to locally administered hormones under optimal conditions of action. The studies with such substances as insulin and metabolic inhibitors indicated the importance of mitosis and active metabolic processes, and led indirectly to the development of other tests.

B. An Assay Technique

Apart from the difference in slope (and activity) of estradiol from the others, assays may validly be performed by the intravaginal method. They have, for instance, been used throughout the work quoted above, even when it has been necessary to compare ED_{50}'s (doses needed to elicit 50% of positive responses) rather than to compute relative potency, because of slope differences. It must, however, be stressed that, in the author's present opinion, many intravaginal assays are much better carried out by the techniques described in Sections VII and VIII, unless for special purposes such as those specifically requiring the particular response of cornification and leukocyte withdrawal.

Applications in 50% glycerol or up to 25% propylene glycol are to be preferred to water or saline, but only because they are better retained in the vagina. Careful technique avoids the preference. The spayed mouse vagina cannot retain more than 0.02 ml, and 0.01 or 0.005 ml is much safer and is recommended for routine administration. This is delivered by a micrometer syringe, such as the Agla, using a blunt-end wide-bore needle with a side aperture near to the end, like a smaller version of the equipment for oral dosage. It is best to withdraw the needle slightly as the dose is delivered, to make room for it. Applications are made at 10 AM on Monday and Tuesday, as with injections; if four are to be given, these are added at 5 PM. Smears must be taken earlier, on Wednesday at 10 AM and 5 PM, two being sufficient. Staining and scoring is exactly as with other tests, and with careful technique the log-dose-response line is straight throughout the whole effective range, whichever transform is used of those mentioned.

Emmens (1950b) showed that mice used in intravaginal tests need regular *subcutaneous* priming; positive responses do not suffice when they are to intravaginal dosage. The slope of the dose-response line is only about 2 instead of 5 to 6 as with subcutaneous assays, and many animals per group are needed for high precision. Thus, in an assay of estrone against itself using 400 animals (100 per group in a 2×2 design), Claringbold (1956) found percentage limits of error ($P = 0.95$) of 74 to 134%, and in the within-animal cross-over test described above, 24 animals and 96 observations in total gave percentage limits of error ($P = 0.95$) of 76–131%.

Mixtures of the natural estrogens may be assayed by the subcutaneous route as if they were one substance—the pure compounds have the same slope and so do mixtures between them (Claringbold, 1955b). However, this is not true of mixtures when given intravaginally, which give lower responses than would be expected from the activities of the constituents. This further complicates the attempted assay of any but pure substances by this technique. In other tests, Claringbold and Biggers (1955) also showed that when a single estrogen is given, partly subcutaneously and partly intravaginally, the response is greatest when most of the effective dose is given intravaginally, but a small portion is given subcutaneously.

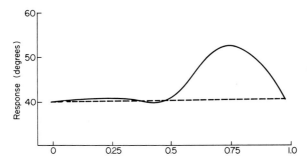

FIG. 5. Diagram showing the increased response to estrone in vaginal smear tests when part of the effective dose is given subcutaneously, but most of it intravaginally. (From Claringbold and Biggers, 1955.)

The amount of subcutaneous estrogen is far below that required to produce responses on its own, and the effect was presumed to be on blood flow to the vagina and perhaps on vaginal connective tissue, producing potentiation of the intravaginal dose by a subthreshold subcutaneous dose. The effect is illustrated in Fig. 5.

The slope of the intravaginal dose-response line may be increased by selection of the mice into more homogeneous groups (Biggers et al., 1954). When this was done by selecting mice into those responding twice, once, and not at all in two successive intravaginal tests, the slope within such groups was 77 ± 7 (by the angular transformation) as against an original slope of 35 ± 11, a highly significant improvement. The higher slope was maintained for 3 months in intravaginal tests, but the corresponding slope for subcutaneous assays with the same mice was unaffected. Converse tests, in which the subcutaneously determined slope improved as a result of selection from 98 ± 8 to 153 ± 14 gave similar results, with no effect on intravaginal slopes, as shown in Fig. 6. This independence of responses to the two methods of administration illustrates that the response to a dose of estrogen may be affected by factors such as rates of absorption, metabolism and effects on systems other than the vagina, which are not the same for the two routes. Other studies in this laboratory have shown that these factors are even independently inherited (Biggers and Claringbold, 1955a).

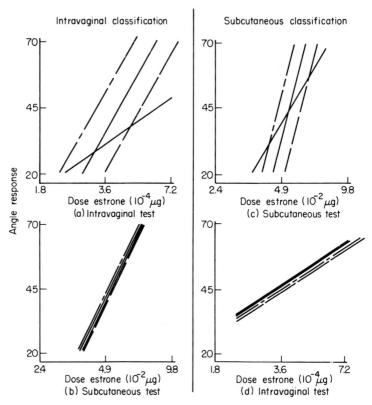

Fig. 6. Schematic diagram of the effects of classification by intravaginal and subcutaneous routes of administration: control (▬▬▬); + + (— — —); + − (———); − (— — — —). (From Biggers *et al.* 1954.)

C. Intravaginal Pellets

Attempts were made quite early to assay blood estrogens by introducing pellets of dried material into the vaginas of spayed rats. Albrieux (1941a,b) obtained positive responses with the blood and serum of nonpregnant women and concluded that the corpuscles contain most of the estrogen. Krichesky and Glass (1947) confirmed the practicability of this method and reported results with rabbit and human blood. A brief account of the technique may be found in Emmens (1950a), which will not be repeated here as little further work seems to have been done, and it was never placed on a fully quantitative basis.

VII. Vaginal Mitosis and Epithelial Thickness

A. EARLY VAGINAL CHANGES

Few studies have been made of the early changes that take place in the vagina after the administration of estrogens. Changes in alkaline phosphatase and cytoplasmic ribonucleic acid were described by Jeener (1947) at 24 hours after injection, and changes in carbohydrate and glycogen content by Biggers (1953) and Balmain et al. (1956a,b). Allen et al. (1937) studied the mitotic activity of the vaginal epithelium with the colchicine technique and concluded that cell division commences less than $9\frac{1}{2}$ hours after a subcutaneous injection of 5 μg of estrone, reaches a maximum at 37 hours and declines by 48 hours. Biggers and Claringbold (1955b) investigated this response when estrone was given intravaginally, finding that mitosis did not commence until at least 18 hours after dosage with 6.4×10^{-3} μg.

Martin and Claringbold (1958, 1960) then made a quantitative investigation of the mitotic rate of the vaginal epithelium 16–36 hours after hormone administration. Randomly bred ovariectomized albino mice were used, of the SW (Sydney White) strain, primed 2 weeks before intravaginal dosage with 1 μg of estrone in peanut oil. Estrone or other hormones were placed in the vagina in 0.01 ml of distilled water as in the usual assay, and 0.1 μg of colchicine was injected 7 hours before killing. After dissection, the vaginas were placed in an automatic tissue processor which carried them overnight through fixative and alcohols to wax. Sections were cut at 6 μ from blocks containing 6 or 8 vaginas in 1 experimental group, and were stained in Heidenhain's hematoxylin and differentiated and counterstained in Van Geison's picrofuchsin. They were ready for examination 24 hours after the mice were killed.

Two types of observations were made:

Arrested mitoses. Each animal provided at least 5 sections for examination, from which 5 fields were selected in as random as possible a manner, and the total number of mitoses were scored in each field at ×720.

Epithelial thickness. The thickness of the epithelium was measured with a micrometer eyepiece in similarly selected fields and expressed in arbitrary units. An increase seen in epithelial thickness during the experimental period is due to an increase in cell size, little or no actual division having occurred because of treatment with colchicine.

Preliminary work showed that at 16 hours the dose-response lines for mitoses and epithelial thickness had slopes differing insignificantly from zero. After 16 hours mitotic rate increases rapidly, lower dosage groups reaching a maximum at 24 hours, higher ones at 28–36 hours after instillation. Similar results were seen with epithelial thickness (Figs. 7 and 8). The effective doses ranged from about 1 to 100 pg, above which

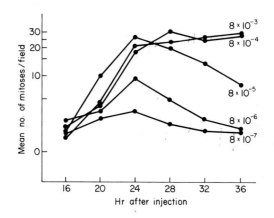

Fig. 7. Increase in mitosis in the mouse vaginal epithelium after the intravaginal administration of estrone in the doses indicated (μg). (From Martin and Claringbold, 1960.)

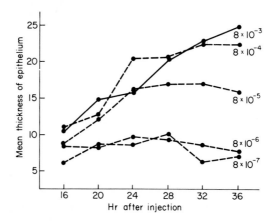

Fig. 8. Increase in epithelial thickness in the mouse vagina after the intravaginal administration of estrone in the doses indicated (μg). The solid line is used only for clarity. (From Martin and Claringbold, 1960.)

no further increases were seen, but rather a decrease. If mitotic rate is expressed in logs, such that the index $Y = \log_{10} (Z + 2)$, where Z is the mean number of arrested mitoses per field, Y is linearly related to log dose in about the range 10–100 pg for periods up to 28 hours, and in about the range 10–1000 pg beyond that time. Sensitivity, however, declines after 24 hours. If epithelial thickness is expressed directly in the arbitrary units used, these are linearly related to log dose over somewhat wide ranges at most times (Fig. 9). The appearance of the epithelium at 24 hours after doses of 4 pg, 20 pg, and 100 pg is shown in Figs. 10–12.

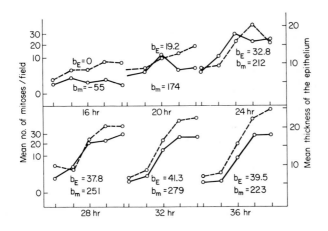

Fig. 9. Dose-response lines for intravaginal estrone in mitotic count (—) and epithelial thickness (– – –) assays at various times after administration. Doses were 8×10^{-7} to 8×10^{-3} μg of estrone. b_m = slope for the interval 8×10^{-6} to 8×10^{-5} μg for mitosis; b_E = corresponding slope for epithelial thickness. (From Martin and Claringbold, 1960.)

B. An Assay Technique

Since sensitivity and slope were both satisfactory at the convenient time of 24 hours after injection, it was decided to base an assay method on this period. It was shown that injection of the estrone in albumin, to delay absorption, did not improve responses, and so a single injection of hormone in 0.01 ml of distilled water was chosen. A dose-response line is illustrated in Table V, based on 16 animals per group, in steps of 5-fold dosage over the range 4–2500 pg. This confirms the falling off in mitotic count and warns against assaying with only one dosage group, which should never be practiced anyway. The epithelial thickness

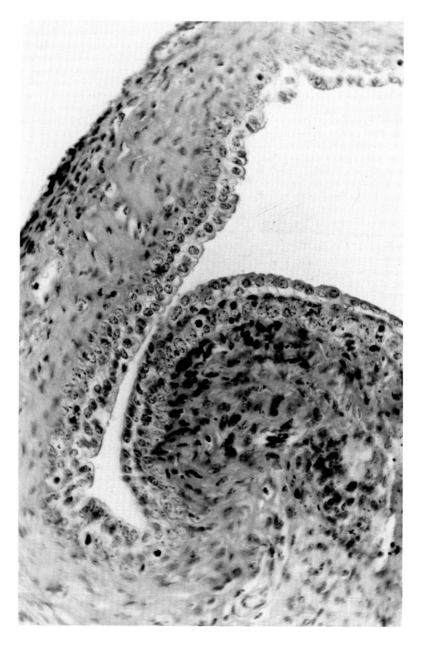

FIG. 10. Appearance of the vaginal epithelium 24 hours after the local administration of 4×10^{-6} μg of estrone in distilled water. (From Martin and Claringbold, 1960.)

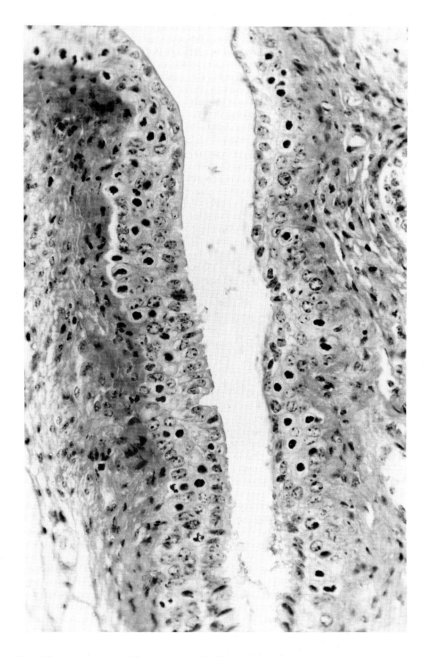

Fig. 11. Appearance of the vaginal epithelium 24 hours after the local administration of 2×10^{-5} μg of estrone in distilled water. (From Martin and Claringbold, 1960.)

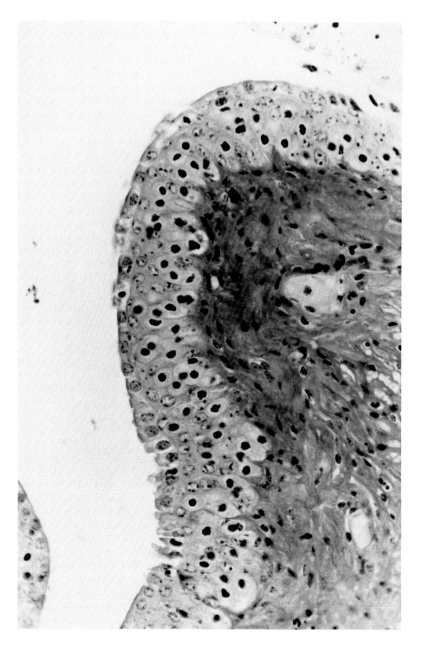

FIG. 12. Appearance of the vaginal epithelium 24 hours after the local administration of 1×10^{-4} μg of estrone in distilled water. (From Martin and Claringbold, 1960.)

TABLE V

DOSE-RESPONSE LINE FOR COUNTS OF ARRESTED
MITOSES AND FOR EPITHELIAL THICKNESS[a]
WITH 16 ANIMALS PER GROUP

Dose of estrone (pg)	Mean number of mitoses per field	Mean epithelial thickness
4	6.2	16.3
20	17.1	23.1
100	22.5	27.9
500	16.4	28.0
2500	12.6	26.3

[a] After Martin and Claringbold (1960).

measurements do not fall so markedly. The cause of the mitotic count decrease is not clear, and it eventually reaches a peak at all dosage levels, but not within 24 hours.

An example of the use of the technique is seen in Table VI, in which a group of tests of various estrogens is shown. The slopes sometimes differed significantly, particularly of the rest from that for estrone, which would appear to be an unfortunate substance to use as a standard.

TABLE VI

RELATIVE ACTIVITY OF VARIOUS ESTROGENS, USING ESTRONE AS A STANDARD,
WHEN GIVEN INTRAVAGINALLY IN ONE INJECTION IN THE MITOTIC COUNT
AND EPITHELIAL THICKNESS TESTS[a]

Estrogen	Test	MED ratio	Limits of error ($P = 0.95$)
Estradiol-3,17β	Mitosis	1.86	1.17–2.96
Estriol	Mitosis	0.99	0.72–1.36
Dienestrol	Mitosis	0.89	0.64–1.24
Hexestrol	Mitosis	1.02	0.74–1.41
Diethylstilbestrol	Mitosis	1.08	0.78–1.49
Estradiol-3,17β	Epithelial thickness	0.99	0.68–1.45
Estriol	Epithelial thickness	0.69	0.45–1.05
Dienestrol	Epithelial thickness	0.57	0.38–0.86
Hexestrol	Epithelial thickness	0.68	0.47–0.98
Diethylstilbestrol	Epithelial thickness	1.12	0.75–1.38

[a] After Martin and Claringbold (1960).

The authors, however, chose to express results in terms of the ratio of the MED to that for estrone, giving this ratio fiducial limits of error as in Table VI. Even this necessarily rather imprecise measure has reasonable limits of error with only 8 animals per group, and it is clear that in the mitotic count assays as in intravaginal assays using cornification as the end point, estradiol stands out as being more potent than the other estrogens, which do not differ among themselves. In the epithelial thickness assay, however, estradiol was not found to be more potent than estrone, whereas dienestrol and hexestrol were significantly less potent. Repeat assays confirmed the greater potency of estradiol by the mitotic count technique.

The heterogeneity seen in these tests indicates the need for futher studies and for improvements in technique. The authors themselves suggest that it may arise from the practice of cutting all the sections for one dosage group from the same block, whereby chance variation in the thickness might affect group responses as a whole and give a greater variability than should otherwise occur.

C. VARIATIONS IN TECHNIQUE: SPECIFICITY

The effects of variation in the dose and route of administration of colchicine was found to be negligible within the range 0.5–50 μg intravaginally, but subcutaneous administration of 0.1 mg was preferred because of convenience. Total counts are somewhat greater by the intravaginal method, but not enough to matter.

The alternative vehicles of administration tried were 1% aqueous egg albumin, mentioned above, 25%, 50%, and 100% propylene glycol in water, and peanut oil. Peanut oil was found to be useless, in conformity with other intravaginal results (Emmens, 1939a), but egg albumin and 25% propylene glycol did not affect the assay. Higher percentages of propylene glycol reduced the slope of the dose-response line and 100% propylene glycol partially destroyed the epithelium, but caused about 100% of mitoses in the remaining cells.

In Allen-Doisy tests, inhibition of responses to estrogens is seen with high doses of androgens or progesterone (Courier and Cohen-Solal, 1937a,b; Courier, 1950), with cortisone and hydrocortisone (Szego and Roberts, 1953), with various newer steroids related to 19-nortestosterone (Edgren, 1957; Edgren and Calhoun, 1957; Emmens et al., 1960), and with various synthetic compounds related to diethylstilbestrol (Emmens and Cox, 1958; Emmens et al., 1959). These are effective in causing inhibition of vaginal cornification to varying degrees in both subcutaneous and intravaginal tests. Various tests were, therefore, made of their possible inhibitory effects in the present assay, but none except the synthetics had any effect. Up to 1 mg of progesterone, testosterone, or hydrocortisone either subcutaneously or intravaginally was tested, and up to 1 μg of 19-nortestosterone, 17-ethyl-19-nortestosterone, and 17-ethynyl-19-nortestosterone. No inhibition was seen in any test, but the higher doses of most compounds caused mitotic increases instead. This is a line with the finding that some of the 19-norsteroids are estrogenic in moderate doses, although they will inhibit at lower doses in the vaginal smear test (Emmens et al., 1960). Vitamin A was also found to be without effect. In Allen-Doisy tests, it suppresses vaginal cornification when administered locally (Kahn and Bern, 1950; Kahn, 1954a,b). It may be concluded, therefore, that the mitotic rate assay and the epithelial thickness assay are less subject to interference from likely contaminants, and less affected than Allen-Doisy tests by variation in technique.

These assay methods thus seem to possess considerable advantages over the conventional Allen-Doisy technique used intravaginally or subcutaneously. They are approached in sensitivity only by the intravaginal method, but are still ten times as sensitive and about four times as accurate, a saving of 40-fold in terms of material to be assayed, and 4-fold in terms of animals, except that the animals in vaginal smear tests are not killed. The high potency of estriol and the lack of influence of albumin solutions as the vehicle of administration in these tests indicate that differences in potency due to differential rates of loss of substance from the vagina are minimized. The lack of interference from any but the synthetic inhibitors has made these assays very useful tools for the analysis of antiestrogenic activity, in that they appear to be affected only by analog-type inhibitors of the natural and synthetic estrogens.

VIII. Vaginal Metabolic Activity

A. VAGINAL METABOLISM

Manometric studies in this laboratory indicated that vaginal respiration is elevated within 24 hours after estrogen treatment, although it was not possible to distinguish between an epithelial response and that of the whole vagina. Attempts at elaborating an assay method based on micromanometry were unsuccessful, and it was felt that a dyestuff undergoing color changes with reduction or oxidation might prove useful instead. In consequence, Martin (1960) studied the reduction of 2,3,5-triphenyltetrazolium chloride (tetrazolium) as a possible method of following changes in the metabolism of the vagina after estrogenic stimulation. Tetrazolium is a pale yellow, nontoxic, water-soluble

92   C. W. EMMENS

compound which interacts with a number of intracellular reductases as a hydrogen acceptor. It is reduced to a stable insoluble deep red pigment, a formazan, which is precipitated at the site of reaction. This formazan is soluble in a number of organic solvents and may be extracted from tissues and estimated colorimetrically. The method has been used in the localization of enzymes within the cell and the identification of actively growing tissues (see Martin, 1960, for summary).

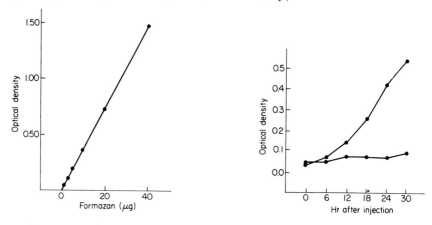

Fig. 13. (*Left*) Relationship between weight of formazan and optical density. (From Martin, 1960.)

Fig. 14. (*Right*) Increase in tetrazolium reduction by vaginal epithelium of mouse at various times after a single injection of estrone. Upper curve: 1×10^{-4} µg; lower curve 4×10^{-6} µg. (From Martin, 1960.)

Initial tests were made by introducing 0.5 mg of tetrazolium in 0.02 ml of distilled water into the vagina 30 minutes before killing the mouse and extracting the tetrazolium with an organic solvent. The best method was found to be to dissect out the vaginas, cut them open and wash away any excess of tetrazolium, dry on filter paper and place in 1 ml of 3:1 ethanol–tetrachloroethylene (cf. Jardetsky and Glick, 1956). The formazan was then estimated colorimetrically in a Uvispeck spectro-photometer at 500 mµ. The relationship between optical density and the weight of formazan in control solutions was found to be linear over the range 0–40 µg/ml (Fig. 13), hence direct readings have been used as an index of formazan formation and converted to logs for graphing and analysis.

These tests showed that formazan formation increased linearly after a single dose of intravaginal estrone for the next 30 hours at least (Fig. 14). The highly significant effect at 6 hours shows that biochemical changes occur very early and much precede mitosis and other gross morphological changes. The slope of the dose-response line increases steadily and is about maximal at 24 hours. A study of the effect of correcting for vaginal weight showed that this influences response, but only slightly, so that correcting for it is not worthwhile in ordinary circumstances. Frozen sections showed heavy deposition of formazan in the epithelium, but not in the tissues beneath; the basement membrane was quite clearly marked by formazan crystals. In sections of unstimulated vaginas, only scattered small crystals of formazan were seen.

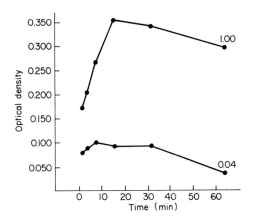

FIG. 15. Effect of time of injection of tetrazolium on tetrazolium reduction by vagina stimulated with 1.0 and 0.04 × 10⁻⁴ μg of estrone. (From Martin, 1960.)

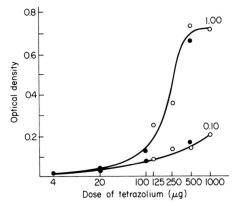

FIG. 16. Effect of dose of tetrazolium on reduction of tetrazolium after stimulation with 1.0 and 0.1 × 10⁻⁴ μg of estrone, ●, first experiment; ○, second experiment. (From Martin, 1960.)

94   C. W. EMMENS

Further tests showed that the rather arbitrary 0.5 mg of tetrazolium and a 30-minute period for reduction were in fact nearly optimal, and so they were retained. Tetrazolium reduction actually ceases after about 16 minutes, after which there is a gradual loss of formazan (Fig. 15), but 30 minutes is a more convenient period when work must be staggered to keep such an interval reasonably constant. Since a small proportion of the tetrazolium is reduced, it was somewhat surprising to find that, if less than 0.5 mg is used, a great reduction in formazan formation occurs (Fig. 16), and the author was clearly fortunate in his first guesses.

B. An Assay Technique

The dose-response line at 24 hours obtained by the methods described above is linear in the range 10–100 pg of estrone, and may extend above the upper limit. The linear segment for estradiol is similar if not identical, and no significant difference in slope has so far been detected. The slope for estrone in 10 repeated assays has proved both linear over the range quoted and homogeneous.

A quite extensive survey of the tetrazolium technique has been published by Martin (1964), showing that the volume of tetrazolium solution, dissection speed, and use of albumin solutions are without effect. Three randomly bred mouse strains were of comparable sensitivity, but an inbred strain (CBA) was so variable as to be unsatisfactory for use in assays. Estradiol-3,17β was 3–7 times as active as estrone, and estriol was about half as active, with additionally a lower slope than those for the other compounds. Diethylstilbestrol was slightly less active than estradiol and of equal slope. Some results are seen in Table VII.

Specificity might be expected to accompany that for the other assays depending on early responses, and it has so far been established that progesterone, testosterone, and hydrocortisone do not affect tetrazolium reduction in intravaginal doses up to 0.1 μg, and that the 19-norsteroids mentioned above do not inhibit the responses to estrone in similar doses. However, 17-ethynyl-19-nortestosterone and 19-nortestosterone increased reduction at the highest doses tested, as they do the mitotic count and epithelial thickness. Dimethylstilbestrol, the only synthetic of the potent series of inhibitors tested by Emmens, Cox, and Martin (1960) inhibits in the tetrazolium test. There is thus so far complete agreement between the methods of assay depending on early vaginal responses, as far as specificity and the actions of other steroids and inhibitors are concerned.

Schultze (1964) has investigated tetrazolium reduction in the rat uterus, using uterine segments from injected animals and incubating the segments with triphenyltetrazolium chloride for 1 hour before estimating

TABLE VII

RELATIVE POTENCY OF ESTRADIOL-3,17β, ESTRONE, AND ESTRIOL IN
SW MICE[a,b]

		0.625	1.25	2.50	5.00	10.0	20.0
Replicates 1–4	Estradiol-3,17β	—	0.306	0.381	0.381	—	—
	Estrone	—	0.121	0.230	0.306	—	—
	Estriol	—	0.122	0.166	0.191	—	—
Replicates 5–7	Estradiol-3,17β	—	0.399	0.475	0.648	—	—
	Estrone	—	0.170	0.250	0.475	—	—
	Estriol	—	0.171	0.206	0.302	—	—
Replicates 8–10	Estradiol-3,17β	0.168	0.273	0.432	0.586	—	—
	Estrone	—	0.146	0.191	0.316	0.402	—
	Estriol	—	—	0.148	0.205	0.229	0.310

SUMMARY OF ANALYSES OF VARIANCE

	Replicates 1–4		Replicates 5–7		Replicates 8–10	
Source of variation	DF	Mean square	DF	Mean square	DF	Mean square
Dose (D)						
Linear	1	16758[c]	1	19832[c]	1	48049[d]
Quadratic	1	1047[d]	1	52	1	23
Cubic	—	—	—	—	1	39
Estrogens (E)						
Estrone vs. estriol (A)	1	4236[c]	1	828[d]	1	368
Estrone/estriol vs. estradiol (B)	1	37679[c]	1	33712[c]	1	11044[c]
Replicates (R)	3	8348[c]	2	279	2	1454[d]
D × E						
Linear × EA	1	2531[c]				
Linear × EB	1	2509[e]				
Residual	2	124				
Residual interactions	24	227	16	226	22	479
Error	144	228	108	205	144	299
Estradiol	3.74 (2.26–6.17)[d]		3.81 (2.02–5.71)[d]		3.73 (2.81–4.94)[d]	
Estriol	0.58 (0.42–0.79)[d]		0.87 (0.67–1.11)[d]		0.42 (0.30–0.58)[d]	

[a] From Martin (1964).

[b] Results are expressed as mean optical densities, based on replicates of 5 animals per group. Each group of replicates was carried out with different batches of estrogens.

[c] $P < 0.001$.   [d] $0.01 < P < 0.05$.   [e] $0.001 < P < 0.01$.

formazan production. Homogenates were less successful than slices. To
relate the formazan production to estrogen dosage, female rats 70 days
of age were spayed and used 2 weeks later. Estradiol in olive oil was
injected subcutaneously daily for 2 days in doses of 0.125–1.0 μg, with
results as in Table VIII. As seen in Table VIII, the amount of formazan
produced was linearly related to log dose on either a wet or dry weight
basis. Differences were also shown in levels of tetrazolium reduction
during different phases of the estrous cycle.

TABLE VIII

DOSE-RESPONSE RELATIONSHIP BETWEEN ESTRADIOL AND
in Vitro TTC REDUCTION OF UTERINE TISSUE SEGMENTS[a]

Dosage (μg/day)	No. of animals	Micrograms of formazan produced per milligram of tissue	
		Wet weight basis	Dry matter basis
0	12	0.156 ± 0.055	1.02 ± 0.28
0.125	12	0.550 ± 0.050	3.03 ± 0.24
0.250	12	0.758 ± 0.068	4.21 ± 0.35
0.500	12	0.879 ± 0.080	4.86 ± 0.37
1.000	12	1.037 ± 0.065	5.59 ± 0.31

[a] From Schultze (1964).

IX. Uterine Weight

Little use of uterine weight assays, except when measuring the effects
of antiestrogens, has been seen in the last two decades, although studies
such as those of Huggins *et al.* (1954) of the so-called "impeded"
estrogens have used the uterus; these have not been aimed at bioassay.
They have confirmed, however, that the shape of the dose-response
lines for the natural estrogens are not identical, and that it may be no
more feasible to assay one estrogen in terms of another with uterine
weight tests than it is with many of the others. Another peculiarity of
uterine weight tests, at least in the rat, is the greater potency of both
estradiol and estriol compared with estrone, as seen below. When testing antiestrogens, the increase in uterine weight is quite reasonably
assumed to be caused by the estrogen also administered, but when the
method is used as an estrogen assay, care must be taken that the response is in fact an estrogenic one, and not due to progestational or other
metrotropic activity.

The account which follows therefore differs only in part from that of Emmens (1950a), where such tests were surveyed. The data there presented still seem worth repeating, as the assay methods, for particular purposes including studies of the actions of sex hormones on the uterus per se, are still worth consideration. The Dorfman and Dorfman (1954) work is, of course, new.

A. Four-Day Tests

Bülbring and Burn (1935) described a test in which young female rats were spayed at about 40 gm weight and injected 2 days later for 4 consecutive days with estrogen in olive oil. On the eighth day from operation, the uteri were excised, fixed, and weighed, after drying with filter paper. This and similar tests are cumbersome and take rather a long time to complete. Later investigators have successfully used immature intact rats, mice, or guinea pigs in shorter tests.

Using the immature, 22–23-day-old albino rat, weighing 34–39 gm, Lauson et al. (1939) developed a 4-day test. The animals were injected twice daily for 3 days with 0.5 ml of an aqueous solution of estrogen and killed on the fourth day (72–75 hours after the first injection). The uteri were separated from the vaginas by cutting through the cervix, the surrounding tissue was stripped off, and the uterotubal junction was severed. The uteri were then weighed fresh, after pressing out the intrauterine fluid on moistened blotting paper; a Roller-Smith torsion balance was used. Weights of uteri before expressing the intrauterine fluid were found to be valueless. Results with estradiol and estrone are shown in Table XI. Vaginal opening was also noted and is shown in the table. Estriol was also investigated, and was found to produce uteri with a maximal mean weight of about 50 mg, in contrast to the 90- to 100-mg levels found with the higher doses of estradiol and estrone. This confirms the finding of Dorfman et al. (1936), who used the difference as a means of distinguishing estriol from estrone. On the ascending portion of the curve, the approximate equivalents of 1 μg of estradiol are 6 μg of estriol and 20 μg of estrone. The greater potency of estriol as compared with estrone is a peculiarity of this type of assay.

The dose-response curves are of a type that lend themselves to an assay using uterine weight and log dose, with groups on the standard and unknown, but this method was not employed by the authors. Later, check assays with pure estrogens were made against the previously determined curves, with from 4 to 26 rats per dose. These gave a wide splay of errors, as would be expected from the conditions of testing, only 21 out of 25 assays of estrone and 25 out of 34 assays of estradiol coming within $\pm 50\%$ of the correct figure. From the data supplied by Lauson *et al.* (1939), it is, however, possible to calculate approximately the precision an assay of any given type would have. The standard deviations shown in Table IX, although rather higher on the average for estrone, are fairly constant for any one substance. An assay of estrone against estradiol would have an average unit variance of about 75, and

TABLE IX

Uterine and Vaginal Response to Estradiol and Estrone[a]

Substance	No. of rats	Total dose (μg)	Mean uterine weight (mg)	SD	No. of vaginas open
Estradiol	55	0	19.6	2.63	0
	13	0.025	27.5	3.20	0
	14	0.05	36.3	5.90	0
	14	0.10	50.0	5.80	0
	14	0.15	62.3	6.97	1
	14	0.20	67.4	5.43	9
	14	0.30	88.1	6.99	13
	14	0.40	92.8	8.57	14
	14	0.75	90.0	9.30	14
Estrone	15	1.0	41.1	9.06	0
	15	2.0	52.7	10.93	0
	15	3.0	60.3	8.43	2
	15	4.0	77.6	14.41	8
	15	6.0	91.6	9.58	12
	15	8.0	101.7	9.98	15
	15	10.0	105.4	10.40	15

[a] From Lauson *et al.* (1939).

slope of about 60 (uterine weight increase per 10-fold dose increase). If a total of 40 animals were used in a 4-point assay, the expected minimal limits of error are therefore approximately ($P = 0.95$) 81–124%, a reasonably low error. The fiducial limits of error, if not founded on a well-established slope from other similar assays, would be wider. It should be noted, however, that the marked dissimilarity in dose-response curves for estradiol and estriol would preclude the assay of one in terms of the other, and presumably of urine or other extracts in terms of a crystalline standard.

The use of oil solutions was also investigated, and it was found that rats receiving a daily injection in 0.2 ml of oil (type not stated) gave uterine weights similar, dose for dose, to those shown above. The authors also noted changes in sensitivity of the animals from time to time, a strong pointer, if any be necessary, to the need for the simultaneous assay of unknown against standard on each occasion.

The uterine reaction to gonadotropin in the mouse was studied by Hamburger and Pedersen-Bjergaard (1937) and by many others since, as it is a standard method for both clinical and research studies. The mouse is more sensitive than the rat, as in Allen-Doisy tests, and in gonadotropin assays it gives a more uniform response. Evans et al. (1941) therefore tried the mouse uterine assay for estrogens (the gonadotropin assay utilizes the production of estrogens by the stimulated gonads.) Their figures suggest that the mouse assay is more accurate than the assay using rats as described by Lauson et al. (1939), but this is an inference from the scatter of points about dose-response lines they present, made from tests with a similar injection and time schedule to that just described. Unfortunately, Evans et al. (1941) do not give sufficient details for a critical appraisal of their results, and no useful estimate can be made of the probable accuracy of tests.

The mouse uterine weight curves also seem to show differences in shape between the natural estrogens, but it is not certain, from the data presented, that this is not merely a reflection of differences in potency, as no flat maxima are shown for estriol and estrone. The order of activity, in contrast to the rat uterine tests, is estradiol, estrone, estriol (the weakest).

Uterine weight can be increased by androgens and progestogens, in considerably higher doses than are needed of the commonly encountered estrogens. These tests are therefore not completely specific, although the presence of sufficient androgenic or progestational material to augment the effects of estrogen seems unlikely, even in unfractionated urine extracts. Thus, Evans et al. (1941) found that the metrotropic activity of androsterone is less than one ten-thousandth that of estrone, and in tests in which androsterone and dehydroisoandrosterone were added to injections of estrone in ratios likely to be found in human urine, Evans and his colleagues found no significant effect.

Dorfman and Dorfman (1954) have used the immature rat uterus in the assay of estrogens, both by subcutaneous and oral administration. The rats were 22 or 23 days old at the start of tests and were injected once daily for 3 days with estrogen sulfates in 0.1 ml of oil, or fed once daily for 4 days by stomach tube with the same substance in 1 ml of water. The uteri were removed 24 hours after the last injection, blotted and weighed to 0.5 mg. Body weights were also determined, and the results were expressed as 100 times the uterine weight in milligrams per gram body weight.

C. W. EMMENS

Table X shows the results obtained with various preparations by the oral route, and Table XI a series of assays of sodium estrone sulfate against itself in 4-point or 6-point assays. These appear satisfactory—

TABLE X

RAT UTERINE RESPONSE TO ORALLY ADMINISTERED SODIUM
ESTROGEN SULFATES[a]

Preparation	Total dose (μg)	No. of rats	Mean uterine ratio $\pm$ SE
—	0	11	54 ± 3.7
—	0	13	56 ± 1.6
Sodium estrone sulfate	2.5	17	77 ± 5.7
	5.0	22	108 ± 9.4
	10.0	32	141 ± 7.8
	20.0	11	184 ± 12.3
Sodium equilin sulfate	4.0	10	75 ± 2.6
	8.0	17	108 ± 5.2
	16.0	10	144 ± 3.8
	32.0	9	188 ± 9.3
Reduced sodium equilin sulfate	2.0	9	151 ± 6.0
	4.0	17	191 ± 4.6
	8.0	9	196 ± 5.8
	16.0	7	216 ± 10.2

[a] After Dorfman and Dorfman (1954).

TABLE XI

ORAL ASSAY OF SODIUM ESTRONE SULFATE AGAINST ITSELF IN
FOUR-POINT ASSAYS WITH THE RAT UTERINE WEIGHT ASSAY[a]

No. per group	Dosse (μg)	Slope	λ	t	Percent potency $\pm$ SE
5	10; 20	106	0.352	2.84	67 ± 28
5	10; 20	179	0.191	0.68	127 ± 26
8	2.5; 5	105	0.117	0.96	104 ± 28
8	2.5; 10	120	0.103	0.33	99 ± 25
10	5; 10	86	0.397	1.14	127 ± 39
10	5; 10	102	0.428	0.25	75 ± 25
20	5; 10	100	0.369	0.54	96 ± 18

[a] After Dorfman and Dorfman (1954).

the potency should, of course, be 100%, but the authors stated that if fewer than 8 animals were used per group, unsatisfactory assays resulted that sometimes showed significant slope differences. The method gave a linear log dose-response relationship with subcutaneous estrone from 0.6 to 2.4 μg and with oral estrone from 2.5 to 20 μg. In a series of 10 runs in which estrone was assayed against itself by subcutaneous injection, using 8 rats per group (32 in all), the maximum standard error of the potency was 22%. Dorfman et al. (1961a,b) have also used essentially this test in investigations of antiestrogenic activity, giving a single dose of estrogen and various doses of antagonist.

Morgan has recently investigated the 4-day test giving 16 different estrogens subcutaneously or percutaneously in various vehicles. He reports that uterine weight is a better criterion than vaginal weight, and that the effectiveness of percutaneous administration is often very high, although the estrogen rank much the same. Table XII, from his paper, shows some of his comparisons.

Interest in oral dosage of estrogens for cattle and other livestock has recently led to various methods being evolved for feeding natural or synthetic estrogens to rats or mice, usually measuring uterine weight. Assays of essentially standard design have been used with such techniques by Stot et al. (1954), Turner (1956), Preston et al. (1956), and Umberger et al. (1958). Diethylstilbestrol and other synthetics are more effective by mouth than the natural estrogens, and so it is a reasonable way of approaching problems of bioassay of residual material in muscle, fat, etc.

A considerable use of the 4-day mouse or rat uterine weight method has been made by clinicians, who have given in some instances careful consideration to slopes and errors of various comparisons involving urine extracts and crystalline estrogens. Rosemberg (1965) has investigated in particular the validity of comparing estriol with estrone, finding that over a suitable range slopes are similar and comparisons valid. Table XIII shows this for the dosage range 12–36 μg of estriol as against 0.05–0.2 μg of estrone, with a relative potency estimate of 0.0074. Various extracts by Brown's method also gave valid assays, as shown in Table XIV.

B. Astwood's Six-Hour Test

Astwood (1938a) studied the early effects of estrogen on the uterus of the immature rat, and showed that a rapid increase in weight occurs during the first few hours after an injection. This increase is due almost entirely to the accumulation of water, as is shown in Fig. 17. The increase has been made the basis of a 6-hour test for estrogenic activity (Astwood, 1938b), at which time the early weight increase is at a maximum.

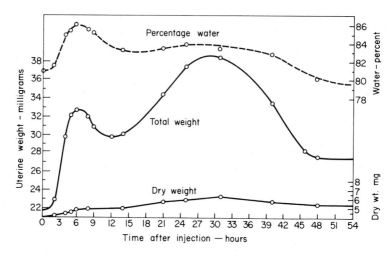

Fig. 17. Changes in percent water, total weight, and dry weight of immature rat uteri during 48 hours after a single subcutaneous injection of 0.1 μg of estradiol in oil. The curve represents mean figures from 370 rats. (From Astwood, 1938b.)

In Astwood's original work, all doses were given in a single injection of 0.1 ml sesame oil under the skin of the back. Female albino rats 21–23 days old were used, weighing 25–49 gm, mean 36 gm. After 6 hours, the animals were killed with chloroform, and the uteri were dissected out by cutting at the uterotubal junctions, stripping of the mesometria, and trimming the vagina from its attachment to the cervix. After blotting on absorbent paper, the uteri were quickly weighed on a damped analytical balance. Water determinations were made by desiccating the weighted uteri in an oven at 110°C. Astwood then "partially corrected" for variation in sizes of rats by expressing all uterine weights in terms of an animal of a standard body weight of 36 gm. He noted that the correction tended to overcorrect for animals at the extremes of the normal range. The crude data were then further treated in producing assay curves by using the percentage increase in uterine weight as a criterion of response, but as this was apparently done on the basis of a single group of controls, common to all assays, it would not be a source of time-to-time variation and would presumably leave the nature and accuracy of the dose-response line unaffected.

TABLE XII

RANKS OF ABSOLUTE POTENCY AND MEAN UTERINE WEIGHT VALUES FOR THREE TYPES OF ADMINISTRATION OF 16 ESTROGENS[a]

Hormones	Subcutaneous SO[b] Uterine wt. (mg/gm body wt.) (mean ± SE)	Comparison with control (=1.00)	Topical EOH[c] Uterine wt. (mg/gm body wt.) (mean ± SE)	Comparison with control (=1.00)	Topical PEG[d] Uterine wt. (mg/gm body wt.) (mean ± SE)	Comparison with control (=1.00)
DSB[e] dipropionate	1.983 ± 0.1664	14.37	1.503 ± 0.1306	10.91	1.144 ± 0.0999	8.29
Estradiol-17-cyclopentyl-propionate	1.531 ± 0.0587	11.09	1.033 ± 0.1038	7.48	0.623 ± 0.3071	4.51
Estradiol benzoate	1.483 ± 0.0906	10.75	1.269 ± 0.0463	9.20	0.333 ± 0.0208	2.41
Estradiol dipropionate	1.380 ± 0.0404	10.00	1.313 ± 0.1114	9.51	0.656 ± 0.0103	4.75
Ethynylestradiol	1.342 ± 0.1463	9.72	2.035 ± 0.0394	14.75	1.359 ± 0.0928	9.85
Benzestrol	1.280 ± 0.1143	9.28	0.771 ± 0.0493	5.59	0.232 ± 0.0260	1.68
DSB	1.209 ± 0.0733	8.76	1.583 ± 0.1172	11.47	1.073 ± 0.1709	7.76
Estrone	1.186 ± 0.1718	8.59	1.343 ± 0.0755	9.73	0.273 ± 0.0286	1.98
Estradiol-17β	1.107 ± 0.0987	8.02	1.882 ± 0.2090	13.64	0.866 ± 0.2125	6.28
Dienestrol	1.067 ± 0.0788	7.73	0.963 ± 0.0623	6.98	0.454 ± 0.0354	3.29
Promestrol dipropionate	0.943 ± 0.1416	6.83	0.718 ± 0.0598	5.20	0.406 ± 0.0341	2.94
DSB dipalmitate	0.911 ± 0.1059	6.60	1.037 ± 0.1413	7.51	0.800 ± 0.0965	5.78
Sodium estrone sulfate	0.552 ± 0.0203	4.00	0.814 ± 0.0789	5.90	0.201 ± 0.0114	1.46
Monomestrol	0.452 ± 0.0354	3.26	0.439 ± 0.0509	3.18	0.416 ± 0.0584	3.01
Hexestrol	0.342 ± 0.0354	2.48	0.166 ± 0.0112	1.20	0.181 ± 0.0067	1.31
Estriol	0.312 ± 0.0056	2.26	0.242 ± 0.0231	1.76	0.238 ± 0.0041	1.72
Control	0.138 ± 0.0065	1.00	0.138 ± 0.0065	1.00	0.138 ± 0.0065	1.00

[a] From Morgan (1963).
[b] In sesame oil.
[c] In ethyl alcohol.
[d] In polyethylene glycol 1500 (known commercially as Carbowax and used frequently as a face cream).
[e] DSB = diethylstilbestrol.

TABLE XIII

Bioassay of Estriol in Terms of Estrone—Composite Data[a]

Preparation	Dose (μg)	Standard estrone dose (μg)	No. of animals	Design	Significance of differences of slopes t (P)	Index of precision	Relative potency[b]	Confidence limits P: 0.95
Estriol	2, 4, 8	0.05, 0.1, 0.2	206	3 × 3	3.23 (< 0.01)	0.22	—	—
	12, 16, 36	0.05, 0.1, 0.2	197	3 × 3	1.14 (> 0.2 < 0.3)	0.19	0.0074	0.0065–0.0084
	2, 4, 8	0.05, 0.1, 0.2	271	6 × 3	4.68 (< 0.01)	0.30	—	—
	12, 16, 36							

[a] From Rosemberg (1965).
[b] Relative potency or units per microgram, 1 unit being the activity of 1 μg of estrone.

TABLE XIV

Bioassay of Urinary Unseparated Phenolic Extracts and Estrone Fractions[a]

Sample[b]	Doses of unknown (hours)	Doses of estrone (μg)	Design[c]	Number of animals	Significance of differences of slopes $t(P)$	Index of precision	Micrograms of estrone equivalent per 24°	Confidence limits $P: 0.95$
A Crude extract (A1)	0.125, 0.25	0.05, 0.1, 0.2	2 × 3	30	1.6 ($> 0.1 < 0.2$)	0.19	33.8	24.3–47.0
Estrone fraction (A2)	0.125, 0.25	0.05, 0.1, 0.2	2 × 3	30	0.40 (> 0.5)	0.22	22.5	15.5–32.5
B Crude extract (B1)	0.5, 1.0, 2.0	0.05, 0.1, 0.2	3 × 3	35	0.17 (> 0.5)	0.20	8.0	5.9–11.0
Estrone fraction (B2)	1.0, 2.0	0.05, 0.1, 0.2	2 × 3	30	0.62 (> 0.5)	0.28	7.5	4.6–12.2

[a] From Rosemberg (1965). Brown's Method: Standard, estrone.

[b] A: Pooled 48° urine sample divided into two aliquots A1 and A2 (24° each).
A1: 40 μg of crystalline estrone added. Processed to unseparated phenolic extract.
A2: 40 μg of crystalline estrone added. Processed to estrone-estradiol fraction.

B: Pooled 48° urine sample divided into two aliquots B1 and B2 (24° each).
B1: Processed to unseparated phenolic extract.
B2: Processed to estrone-estradiol fraction.

[c] Number of dose levels of unknown and standard.

Estradiol-17β and estrone were shown to have similar dose-response curves; that for estradiol-17β is shown in Fig. 18. This is a standard curve based on data accumulated over a period, with standard errors of the means shown graphically. Astwood does not give his data in such a form as to allow of calculations relating to the probable errors of assays, and one can only judge roughly from the figures and data given that the method is probably fairly accurate. No subsequent critical applications of the method seem to have been made.

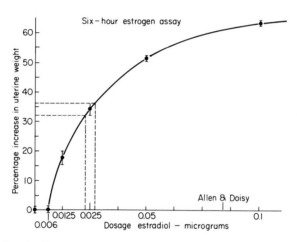

FIG. 18. Standardization curve from 300 rats in the Astwood 6-hour test. (From Astwood, 1938b.) R.U. = rat units.

In the hands of its author, the Astwood test covered a range of doses of from 0.006 to 0.1 μg of estradiol, and from about 0.07 to 1.2 μg of estrone, which has one-twelfth the potency of estradiol. Four assays of the potency of estrone in terms of estradiol, each on only 5–7 animals, made by reading from the standard curve, gave estimates of 12.7, 12.2, 11.4, and 13.6, mean 12.4 μg estrone = 1 μg estradiol. The wide dosage range over which estimates may be made is a recommendation, although a more orthodox method of conducting the assay is to be desired. It seems probably that a 4-point assay using crude uterine weight as the criterion of response, with covariance for body weight correction, instead of the arbitrary method described above, would give reasonably precise estimates of potency. It may be noted that, from Astwood's data, the log dose-response relationship is linear and adaptable to such an assay.

Hisaw (1959) has elaborated the Astwood test, but does not report assays of the type under discussion here. His results, discussed in some detail by Emmens and Martin (1964), show, however, that by observing uterine weights up to 72 hours quite different time-response curves are obtained with different estrogens, and cast doubt on the comparability of such substances in the test.

X. Vaginal Opening

Data such as those in Table IX are sometimes given, including observations of the incidence of vaginal opening, although not used by the authors for the estimation of relative potency. From the results of Lauson *et al.* (1939) it can nevertheless be seen that vaginal opening may be a

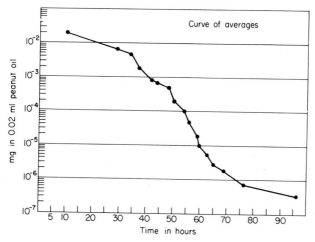

FIG. 19. Dose-response curve for the weanling guinea pig test using estradiol dipropionate in peanut oil. (From Hartman *et al.*, 1946.)

sensitive and accurate index of estrogenic activity. The slope of the probit-log dose line in this instance is approximately 7.8, steeper than an Allen-Doisy test, which is usually 5 to 6, and indicating that an assay based on vaginal opening might have greater accuracy than an Allen-Doisy assay. A further advantage of such a method of assay would be a saving of animals, which need not be killed at the end of the test.

Interest in such assays was aroused by the reports of Hartman and his colleagues that vaginal opening could be stimulated in immature rodents by the local injection of very small quantities of estrogen (Hartman and Littrell, 1945), or of 0.02 ml of finger blood from a woman. The estrogen or test material was injected around the region of the future vaginal opening in the 21-day-old female rat and then was followed in 4–5 days by premature vaginal opening. Recognizable changes were described within 1 day, the first being a crescent-shaped transverse dimpling at the future site of opening, followed by pin-point punctures with oozing of fluid. Large doses caused complete opening within 24 hours.

The same method was then explored in the guinea pig by Littrell *et al.* (1964a,b). One half of the total dose is injected with a short beveled needle on each side of the vulva. Five stages of response are described, four being short of complete opening. The assay may also be based on the time taken to a given level of response, that for full opening is shown in Fig. 19. It is based on only 1–3 observations per point and has a very gentle slope.

Lloyd *et al.* (1946) report poor results with the Hartman test in the rat, and it does not seem to have been used by others.

XI. *In Vitro* Assays

Estradiol-17β has been shown by Villee (1955) and Villee and Gordon (1955) to stimulate a reaction in human term placental extracts mediated by a nicotinamide-adenine dinucleotide (NAD)-dependent isocitric dehydrogenase. NAD is reduced to NADH and the product can be measured by absorption at 340 mμ in a spectrophotometer (Gordon and Villee, 1955), the rate of NAD reduction being a function of the concentration of estradiol in the medium. Estrone is as potent as estradiol in this system, but no other steroid tested (including estriol) stimulates NADH production. The authors, therefore, propose (Gordon and Villee, 1956) that the system can provide a sensitive *in vitro* method for assaying estradiol-17β and estrone. The dose-effect curve covers 0.1–0.5 μg over its steepest portion.

The placental extract is prepared by cutting human term placentas, obtained as soon as possible after delivery, into 3–5 cm pieces and washing in ice-cold physiological saline. The pieces are then sliced and dried, the gross connective tissue discarded, and the rest homogenized in cold 0.25 M sucrose. Cellular debris and residual connective tissue are separated by centrifuging at 2000 g for 10 minutes at 5°C. The supernatant is then centrifuged at 57,000 g for 60 minutes to remove mitochondria and microsomes. The clear, reddish fluid ($S_{57,000}$) is stored at 0°C until used; it retains maximum activity for at least 6–8 hours. Steroid suspensions or solutions must be in aqueous media, and suspensions are made by homogenization for 2–3 minutes with a Teflon pestle and are stored at 5°C.

In Gordon and Villee's (1956) estimations, the reduction of DPN was measured in a Beckman Model DU at 340 mμ. The reaction mixtures were incubated at room temperature in quartz cuvettes with a 1-cm light path, with a blank, control, and estrogen (3 cuvettes) used to make each

measurement. Each received 1.0 ml of 0.3 M tris(hydroxymethyl)-
aminomethane (Tris) buffer acidified to pH 7.4, 0.1 ml of 0.1 M CoCl$_2$
and 0.3 ml of 0.02 M isocitrate, but these were mixed before partitioning
between buffers as small changes in CoCl$_2$ concentration affect results.
The solution or suspension to be tested for estrogenic activity was added
(0.1–0.5 ml) to the estrogen cuvette; 1 ml of S$_{57,000}$ and water to give a
final volume of 3 ml was added to each cuvette, and 0.1 ml of the NAD

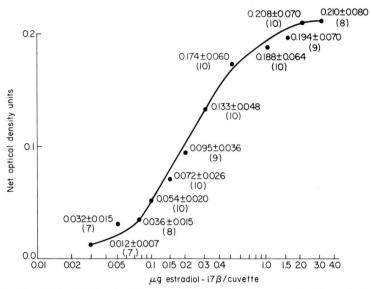

FIG. 20. NAD reduction by the placental S$_{57,000}$ fraction as a function of estradiol
concentration. Net optical density units (ordinate) is defined in the text. The numbers
are the means ± standard error of determinations with the number of different placental
preparations shown in parentheses. (From Gordon and Villee, 1956.)

solution (7.5 M NAD) was added to the control and estrogen cuvettes
to start the reaction. The cuvettes were inverted several times for mixing,
and the optical densities were recorded 1 minute and 20 minutes after
mixing.

A standard curve was made for each placental preparation with 5
concentrations of estradiol in the range 0.075–0.5 μg per cuvette. The
response is the optical density at 20 minutes minus that at 1 minute for
the estrogen (E) cuvette, minus the same figure (20 minutes − 1 minute)
for the control (C), or: E20 − C20 + Cl − El. It is not clear why a blank
was included, and it also seems likely that E20 − C20 would give a
better index.

Results from a number of placental preparations are given in Fig. 20;
the number of preparations used at each point is shown in parentheses

TABLE XV

EFFECT OF STEROIDS, SINGLY AND IN COMBINATION, ON NAD REDUCTION
BY THE PLACENTAL $S_{57,000}$ FRACTION[a]

Steroid	Micro-grams per cuvette	ΔOD at 340 mμ	Steroid pair	Micro-grams per cuvette	ΔOD at 340 mμ
Control	—	0.012	Control	—	0.014
Estradiol	0.3	0.224	Estradiol	0.3	0.190
Estrone	0.3	0.190			
Estriol	15.0	0.006	Estradiol and	0.3	0.160
17α-Ethynylestradiol	15.0	0.084	estriol	12.0	
Stilbestrol	15.0	0.016	Estradiol and	0.3	0.201
Estradiol-17β	15.0	−0.004	progesterone	12.0	
Progesterone	15.0	0.016			
Testosterone	15.0	0.167	Estradiol	0.3	0.212
Cortisone	15.0	0.006	and cortisol	12.0	
Corsitol	15.0	0.046			
Cholesterol	15.0	0.015	Estradiol and	0.3	0.273
			testosterone	15.0	

[a] From Gordon and Villee (1956).

TABLE XVI

COMPARISON OF ESTROGEN CONTENT OF URINE FRACTIONS BY A RAT VAGINAL
SMEAR ASSAY[a] AND THE *in Vitro* PLACENTAL EXTRACT TECHNIQUE[b]

		Microgram of hormone per milliliter	
Urine fraction	Hormone present	Placental extract technique	Rat vaginal smear assay
1	Estradiol	0.60	0.50–0.59
2	Estrone	3.87	4.0–5.2
3	Estriol	0.00	200–250
4	Estriol	0.00	200–250
5	Estradiol	4.70	3.35–4.50
6	Estradiol	1.12	0.67–0.78

[a] Smith and Smith (1952).
[b] From Gordon and Villee (1956).

under the mean response and its standard error. This is clearly not the standard error to be attached to the mean in a properly balanced assay, whether using one or more placental extracts, because an assay would (or should) be founded on *within-extract* comparisons. The authors state that an analysis of their data according to the method of Bliss (1944) showed an index of precision (λ) of 0.106 when the responses to 0.1, 0.15, 0.3, and 0.5 μg of estradiol were compared in alternate series of experiments using different placental extracts in each series. The meaning of this is not clear, but it would seem that a precise assay could be based on this method, although it is not very sensitive, and direct chemical methods can already rival it.

Results with other steroids are shown in Table XV. Estrone has a relative potency of about 0.9 compared with estradiol, while of the other compound tested, testosterone, cortisol and 17-ethynylestradiol had measurable stimulatory effects, but only in large amounts. Estriol, inactive alone, seemed to inhibit estradiol slightly. Assays of human urine extracts prepared by the method of Smith and Smith (1952) and compared with assay by the vaginal smear technique gave fair to good agreement for the estradiol and estrone fractions, but not of course for the estriol fraction (Table XVI).

TABLE XVII

CHICK OVIDUCT RESPONSES TO NATURALLY OCCURRING ESTROGENS
AND DERIVATIVES IN DIET[a]

Preparation	Dose (mg/kg)	No. of chicks	Oviduct ratio (mean ± SE)
—	0	32	16 ± 0.5
—	0	24	16 ± 0.5
—	0	32	14 ± 0.5
Sodium estrone sulfate (pure)	40	30	31 ± 4.0
	80	30	115 ± 11.0
	80	16	117 ± 17.0
	160	16	466 ± 90.0
Estrone	20	25	24 ± 2.0
	40	26	40 ± 3.0
	80	27	149 ± 24.0
	160	24	278 ± 21.0
Estradiol dipropionate	80	23	77 ± 6.0
	160	24	202 ± 38.0

[a] From Dorfman and Dorfman (1953).

XII. Oral Dosage to Chicks

Dorfman and Dorfman (1953) described an assay method using various estrogens and estrogen sulfates added to the diet, which gave surprisingly precise results. This method does not control individual dosage, hence some surprise at its accuracy.

TABLE XVIII

RELATIVE POTENCIES OF ORALLY ADMINISTERED ESTROGENS IN CHICKS[a]

Standard	Unknown	Doses (mg/kg)	No. of chicks	Potency	Limits of error P = 0.95 (%)
Stilbestrol		80:160	72		
	Sodium estrone sulfate	80:160	62	87	−12; +14
Stilbestrol		20:40	152		
	Ethynylestradiol	10:20	62	226	−9; +10
Stilbestrol		40:80	111		
	Estrone	80:160	51	74	−14; +17
Estrone		40:80:160	77		
	Estradiol dipropionate	80:160	47	64	−18; +22
Sodium estrone sulfate		80:160	62		
	MDDA[b]	80:160	39	100	−12; +13
Sodium estrone sulfate		40:80:160	60		
	Sodium estradiol sulfate	40:80:160	59	100	−16; +19

[a] From Dorfman and Dorfman (1953).
[b] Methoxybisdehydrodoisynolic acid.

Four-point assays with dose ratios of 2:1 or 4:1 were usually employed, with sex-linked pullets from a commerical hatchery. The end point was oviduct weight, expressed as a ratio to body weight. The chicks were placed on the diets containing estrogen for 13 days, commencing 2–3 days after hatching, and then killed.

Some results with natural estrogens are shown in Table XVII, and some relative potencies are shown in Table XVIII. It will be seen from these tables that the method is not suitable for small quantities of active material, but that it gives valid assays of various estrogens against each other, with reasonably narrow limits of error in view of the numbers of chicks used. It is not clear whether the method of expressing uterine weight in terms of body weight improved the results, or whether a technique such as covariance analysis would have improved them further.

XIII. Duration of Action

Diczfalusy *et al.* (1957) have described an assay based on the duration of vaginal cornification in mice when long-acting compounds are used. Adult females were spayed and used 2–4 weeks later without priming. After a single subcutaneous injection, smears were taken daily and the

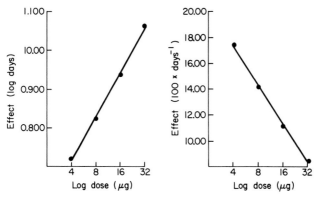

FIG. 21. Different transformations of the relationship between dose and response for ethynylestradiol in tests of duration of action. (From Diczfalusy *et al.*, 1957.)

duration of cornification was recorded for each mouse. A symmetrical 4-point assay was used, with up to 20 animals per dosage level.

A straight dose-response line was obtained for polyestradiol phosphate or ethynylestradiol when log time was plotted against log dose, or when the reciprocal of time was plotted against log dose, but in the latter instance the precision of assays was less. The two dose-response lines for ethynylestradiol are shown in Fig. 21. Valid assays seemed possible when different long-acting estrogens were compared with one another and if different vehicles were used. With 60–80 mice per assay, the fiducial limits of error ($P = 0.95$) were around 85–118%.

XIV. Estrogen Inhibition

Many of the assay methods outlined above may be used to measure the inhibition of estrogens. Examples are given in Chapter 1, from Claringbold *et al.* (1953), and by Emmens and Cox (1958) for the Allen-Doisy technique, worked out either by angles, or 0, 1, 2 scores. Examples using

C. W. EMMENS

vaginal mitosis, epithelial thickness or tetrazolium reduction are given by Emmens *et al.* (1959, 1960). The main point about inhibition assays is that it is not always very satisfactory to inhibit the effects of a single dose of estrogen, as the nature of the hormone-inhibitor relationship is not thereby elucidated. Instead, a factorial scheme should be employed, so that simultaneously a series of dose-response lines for the estrogen and for the inhibitor is established. Table XIX from Emmens and Cox (1958)

TABLE XIX

INHIBITION OF INTRAVAGINAL ESTRONE BY DIMETHYLSTILBESTROL (DMS) IN
ALLEN-DOISY TESTS[a]

(Scores are for groups of 10 mice by the 0, 1, 2 system)

Total dose DMS (μg.)	Total dose estrone in μg. $\times 10^{-4}$			
	6	12	24	48
0.0	12	12	17	19
0.02	4	10	13	19
0.20	0	2	7	14

ANALYSIS OF VARIANCE

Source of variation	DF	Sum of squares	Mean square	F
Estrone				
Linear	1	24.40	24.40	55.5***
Quadratic	1	0.41	0.41	0.9
Cubic	1	0.01	0.01	0.0
DMS	2	17.45	8.73	19.8***
Interaction	6	2.35	0.39	0.9
Residual (error)	108	47.65	0.44	—

[a] From Emmens and Cox (1958).
***$P < 0.001$.

shows the inhibition of estrone by dimethylstilbestrol, and the analysis of variance indicates that a series of parallel dose-response lines for the estrogen has been achieved, with no significant curvature or interaction. The action of the inhibitor may thus be assumed to be the same at all dose levels and at the two levels of inhibition. Figure 22 from Emmens *et al.* (1959) shows a similar set of responses in the mitotic index test, but this time there is significant curvature of the dose-response line for estrone, when inhibition is partial, and the situation is not simple. Over the greater part of the dose-range, however, parallel lines are in fact seen, and the curvature is due to the almost zero responses to the lowest dose of estrone and the highest dose of inhibitor.

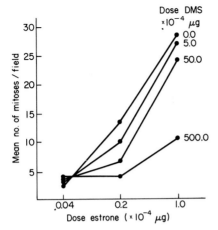

FIG. 22. Inhibition of estrone-stimulated mitosis in the mouse vagina by dimethyl-stilbestrol (DMS). (From Emmens et al., 1959.)

XV. Uterine and Vaginal Uridine Uptake

Miller and Emmens (1967) have recently shown that the uptake of uridine *in vivo* in the spayed mouse can be adapted to form a sensitive and very early assay of estrogens. The technique involves measurement of the uptake of tritiated uridine by the uterus or vagina 6 hours after estrogen administration and 2 hours after uridine-5-^{3}H administration,

TABLE XX

EFFECT OF ESTRADIOL DOSE ON URIDINE INCORPORATION INTO RNA[a,b]

Dose of estradiol ($\mu g \times 10^{-3}$)	Route of uridine administration					
	Uterus				Vagina	
	Intravenous		Subcutaneous		Intravenous	Subcutaneous
	muw	dpm	muw	dpm	dpm	dpm
0.00	20.5	644	20.6	509	561	466
2.67	18.9	563	18.2	435	605	403
4.00	19.3	705	20.5	612	562	525
6.00	20.1	1013	20.9	854	642	743
9.00	21.8	1604	20.5	1558	877	604
13.50	21.9	2664	25.5	2831	1153	1021
20.25	23.0	4721	31.0	3616	1527	1351
30.37	28.2	5702	28.5	4029	1794	1611

[a] From Miller and Emmens (1967).

[b] Results are expressed as mean uterine weights (muw) and mean disintegrations per minute (dpm), with five animals per group and two groups per treatment.

TABLE XXI

COMPARATIVE ACTIVITIES OF ESTRADIOL, *meso*-HEXESTROL, DIETHYLSTILBESTROL, ESTRIOL, ESTRONE, AND PROGESTERONE ON URIDINE INCORPORATION INTO RNA[a,b]

Substance	Dose $(\mu g \times 10^{-3})$	Uterus muw	Uterus dpm	Vagina dpm
Control	0	21.0	750	522
Estradiol	4	26.1	1021	595
	8+	24.8	1417	875
	16+	33.9	5693	1396
	32+	34.2	7165	2311
meso-Hexestrol	4	24.5	815	641
	8+	25.8	1002	491
	16+	25.2	2008	1038
	32+	28.2	3734	1432
Stilbestrol	4	27.0	1103	534
	8+	24.3	877	514
	16+	25.5	2058	1101
	32+	31.6	7710	1830
Estriol	4	28.8	1128	686
	8+	24.3	986	622
	16+	23.5	1473	1050
	32+	34.1	4178	1556
Estrone	8	26.7	960	595
	16	25.5	1061	660
	32+	27.6	1952	1018
	64+	30.6	4378	1656
	128+	28.5	6010	2088
Progesterone	32	24.6	945	596
	3200	21.5	736	548

ANALYSIS* OF VARIANCE

Source of variation	DF	Sum of squares	Mean square	F ratio
Compounds	4	3749	937	12.8[c]
Regression	1	14472	14472	198.4[c]
Parallelism	4	853	213	2.9
Deviations	5	458	92	1.3
Error	14	—	72.9	—

Estradiol	1.000		
meso-Hexestrol	$0.572(0.423–0.754)^d$	Estriol	$0.499(0.364–0.660)^d$
Stilbestrol	$0.668(0.498–0.878)^d$	Estrone	$0.262(0.191–0.333)^d$

[a] From Miller and Emmens (1967).

[b] Results are expressed as mean uterine weights (muw) and mean disintegrations per minute (dpm), with five animals per group and two groups per treatment.

[c] $P < 0.001$. [d] $P = 0.05$.

* The analysis was carried out on uterine uridine uptake values only, at the treatment levels indicated (+), after covariance correction for uterine weight.

which increases up to about 10-fold in the uterus and 5-fold in the vagina. The uterine response is clearly preferable, and refers to an organ in which a rapid and sensitive assay is most needed.

In preliminary tests, estradiol was injected subcutaneously in saline and 5 μCi of uridine-5-^{3}H, specific activity 20.5 mCi/mg, was injected by various routes, also in saline. The mice were killed by cervical dislocation, and the uteri and vaginas were dissected out, pooled into treatment groups, and then frozen and stored at $-23°$ until extraction. These tissues were pulverized in the frozen state and homogenized cold, and acid-insoluble material was precipitated with 1.0 N perchloric acid, shaking immediately and allowing to stand for 5 minutes. After centrifuging at $1600g$ for 15 minutes, the supernatant was discarded and the insoluble material washed three times in 5 ml of 0.2 N perchloric acid. Tests showed that more than 98% of the remaining radioactivity resided in the RNA fraction and thenceforth isolation of the uridine incorporated into RNA was considered unnecessary.

Usually, two pools each of five organs constituted a dosage group, from which an estimate of error was possible. The acid-insoluble residues were prepared for liquid scintillation counting by standard methods on a Nuclear Chicago Liquid Scintillation spectrometer. Results were expressed as mean disintegrations per minute per animal; the organs were usually weighed as well.

It was found that intravenous or subcutaneous injection gave similar dose-response lines (Table XX), the former being somewhat more satisfactory and adopted for routine assays, usually with uterine uptake of uridine as the endpoint. Table XXI shows some responses to various estrogens, in a typical assay. The analysis of variance and limits of error ($P = 0.05$) are appended to the table. Although covariance analysis for uterine weight was carried out in this particular assay, it has been found to be unnecessary if mice are selected at a uniform body weight.

This assay is sufficiently sensitive to be used as a measure of endogenous estrogen production in both mice and rats (Miller et al., 1968a, b). With its aid, it has been possible to examine the course of estrogen production in the estrous cycle and in early pregnancy or pseudopregnancy.

REFERENCES

Albrieux, A. S. (1941a). J. Clin. Endocrinol. 1, 889.
Albrieux, A. S. (1941b). J. Clin. Endocrinol. 1, 893.
Allan, H., Dickens, F., and Dodds, E. C. (1930). J. Physiol. (London) 68, 22.
Allen, E., and Doisy, E. A. (1923). J. Am. Med. Assoc. 81, 819.
Allen, E., Smith, G. M., and Gardner, W. U. (1937). Am. J. Anat. 61, 372.

118
C. W. EMMENS

Astwood, E. B. (1938a). *Anat. Record* **70**, Suppl. 3, 5.

Astwood, E. B. (1938b). *Endocrinology* **23**, 25.

Balmain, J. H., Biggers, J. D., and Claringbold, P. J. (1956a). *Australian J. Biol. Sci.* **9**, 139.

Balmain, J. H., Biggers, J. D., and Claringbold, P. J. (1956b). *Australian J. Biol. Sci.* **2**, 147.

Biggers, J. D. (1951). *J. Endocrinol.* **7**, 163.

Biggers, J. D. (1952). *Nature.* **170**, 895.

Biggers, J. D. (1953a). *J. Endocrinol.* **9**, 136.

Biggers, J. D. (1953b). *J. Anat.* **87**, 327.

Biggers, J. D., and Claringbold, P. J. (1953). *Australian J. Biol. Sci.* **6**, 305.

Biggers, J. D., and Claringbold, P. J. (1954a). *Australian J. Exptl. Biol.* **32**, 33.

Biggers, J. D., and Claringbold, P. J. (1954b). *Nature* **174**, 596.

Biggers, J. D., and Claringbold, P. J. (1954c). *J. Endocrinol.* **11**, 277.

Biggers, J. D., and Claringbold, P. J. (1955a). *J. Endocrinol.* **12**, 1.

Biggers, J. D., and Claringbold, P. J. (1955b). *J. Anat.* **89**, 124.

Biggers, J. D., Claringbold, P. J., and Emmens, C. W. (1954). *J. Endocrinol.* **11**, 26.

Bliss, C. I. (1944). *Science* **100**, 577.

Bülbring, E., and Burn, J. H. (1935). *J. Physiol. (London)* **85**, 320.

Burn, J. H., and Elphick, G. K. (1932). *Quart. J. Pharm. Pharmacol.* **5**, 192

Butenandt, A., and Störmer, I. (1932). *Z. Physiol Chem.* **208**, 129.

Chai, C. K. (1960). *Nature* **185**, 514.

Claringbold, P. J. (1953). *Australian J. Biol. Sci.* **6**, 657.

Claringbold, P. J. (1954). *J. Endocrinol.* **11**, 36.

Claringbold, P. J. (1955a). *J. Endocrinol.* **13**, 11.

Claringbold, P. J. (1955b). *Australian J. Biol. Sci.* **8**, 396.

Claringbold, P. J. (1956). *J. Roy. Statist. Soc.* **B18**, 133.

Claringbold, P. J., and Biggers, J. D. (1955). *Australian J. Biol. Sci.* **8**, 407.

Claringbold, P. J., Biggers, J. D., and Emmens, C. W. (1953). *Biometrics* **9**, 467.

Cohen, S. L., and Marrian, G. F. (1934). *Biochem. J.* **28**, 1603.

Courier, R. (1950). *Vitamins Hormones* **8**, 179.

Courier, R., and Cohen-Solal, G. (1937a). *Compt. Rend. Soc. Biol.* **118**, 683.

Courier, R., and Cohen-Solal, G. (1937b). *Compt. Rend. Soc. Biol.* **118**, 686.

Curtis, J. M., and Doisy, E. A. (1931). *J. Biol. Chem.* **91**, 647.

David, K., de Jongh, S. E., and Laqueur, E. (1935). *Arch. Intern. Pharmacodyn.* **51**, 137.

de Jongh, S. E., Laqueur, E., and De Fremery, P. (1932). *Biochem. Z.* **250**, 448.

Diczfalusy, E., Magnusson, A. M., Nilsson, O., and Westman, A. (1957). *Endocrinology* **60**, 581.

Dirscherl, W. (1936). *Z. Physiol. Chem.* **239**, 53.

Dodds, E. C., Golberg, L., Lawson, W., and Robinson, R. (1939). *Proc. Roy. Soc.* **B127**, 140.

Dorfman, R. I., and Dorfman, A. S. (1953). *Endocrinology* **53**, 301.

Dorfman, R. I., and Dorfman, A. S. (1954). *Endocrinology* **55**, 65.

Dorfman, R. I., Gallagher, T. F., and Koch, F. C. (1936). *Endocrinology* **19**, 33.

Dorfman, R. I., Kincl, F. A., and Ringold, H. J. (1961a). *Endocrinology* **68**, 17.

Dorfman, R. I., Kincl, F. A., and Ringold, H. J. (1961b). *Endocrinology* **68**, 43.

Edgren, R. A. (1957). *Acta Endocrinol.* **25**, 365.

Edgren, R. A., and Calhoun, D. W. (1957). *Proc. Soc. Exptl. Biol. Med.* **94**, 537.

Emmens, C. W. (1939a). *Med. Res. Council Spec. Rept. Ser.* **234**.

Emmens, C. W. (1939b). *J. Endocrinol.* **1**, 142.

Emmens, C. W. (1939c). *J. Endocrinol.* **1**, 373.

Emmens, C. W. (1941a). *J. Endocrinol.* **2**, 368.
Emmens, C. W. (1941b). *J. Endocrinol.* **2**, 444.
Emmens, C. W. (1942a). *J. Endocrinol.* **3**, 168.
Emmens, C. W. (1942b). *J. Endocrinol.* **3**, 174.
Emmens, C. W. (1943). *J. Endocrinol.* **3**, 316.
Emmens, C. W. (1947). *J. Endocrinol.* **5**, 170.
Emmens, C. W., ed. (1950a). *In* "Hormone Assay," Chapter XVI. Academic Press, New York.
Emmens, C. W. (1950b). *J. Endocrinol.* **6**, 302.
Emmens, C. W. (1957). *J. Endocrinol.* **16**, 148.
Emmens, C. W. (1959). *In* "Reproduction in Domestic Animals" (H. H. Cole and P. T. Cupps, eds.), Chapter 4. Academic Press, New York.
Emmens, C. W. (1965). *Acta. Endocrinol.* **49**, 83.
Emmens, C. W., and Bradshaw, T. E. T. (1939). *J. Endocrinol.* **1**, 378.
Emmens, C. W., and Cox, R. I. (1958). *J. Endocrinol.* **17**, 265.
Emmens, C. W., and Martin, L. (1964). *In* "Methods in Hormone Research" (R. I. Dorfman, ed.), 1st ed., Vol. III, p. 1. Academic Press, New York.
Emmens, C. W., Cox, R. I., and Martin, L. (1959). *J. Endocrinol.* **18**, 372.
Emmens, C. W., Cox, R. I., and Martin, L. (1960). *J. Endocrinol.* **20**, 198.
Emmens, C. W., Cox, R. I., and Martin, L. (1962). *Recent Progr. Hormone Res.* **18**, 415.
Evans, J., Varney, R., and Koch, F. C. (1941). *Endocrinology* **28**, 747.
Freud, J. (1939). *Acta Brevia Neerl. Physiol. Pharmacol. Microbiol.* **9**, 11.
Gordon, E. E., and Villee, C. A. (1955). *J. Biol. Chem.* **216**, 215.
Gordon, E. E., and Villee, C. A. (1956). *Endocrinology* **58**, 150.
Grundy, J. (1957). *Chem. Rev.* **57**, 281.
Hain, A. M., and Robson, J. M. (1936). *J. Pharmacol.* **57**, 337.
Hamburger, C., and Pedersen-Bjergaard, K. (1937). *Quart. J. Pharmacol.* **10**, 662.
Hartman, C. G., and Littrell, J. L. (1945). *Science* **102**, 175.
Hartman, C. G., Littrell, J. L., and Tom, J. (1946). *Endocrinology* **39**, 120.
Hisaw, F. L. (1959). *Endocrinology* **64**, 276.
Huggins, C., Jensen, E. V., and Cleveland, A. S. (1954). *J. Exptl. Med.* **100**, 225.
Jardetsky, C. D., and Glick, D. (1956). *J. Biol. Chem.* **218**, 283.
Jeener, R. (1947). *Nature* **159**, 579.
Jensen, E. V., and Jacobson, H. I. (1962). *Recent Progr. Hormone Res.* **18**, 387.
Kahn, R. H. (1954a). *Am. J. Anat.* **95**, 309.
Kahn, R. H. (1954b). *Nature* **174**, 317.
Kahn, R. H., and Bern, H. A. (1950). *Science* **111**, 516.
Krichesky, B., and Glass, S. J. (1947). *Endocrinology* **40**, 192.
Lauson, H. D., Heller, C. G., Golden, J. B., and Severinghaus, E. L. (1939). *Endocrinology* **24**, 35.
Layne, D. S., and Marrian, G. F. (1958). *Nature* **182**, 50.
Levin, L., and Tyndale, H. H. (1937). *Endocrinology* **21**, 619.
Littrell, J. L., Tom, J., and Hartman, C. G. (1964a). *Federation Proc.* **5**, 65.
Littrell, J. L., Tom, J., and Hartman, C. G. (1946b). *Anat. Record* **94**, 25.
Lloyd, C. W., Rogers, W. F., and Williams, R. H. (1946). *Endocrinology* **39**, 256.
Marrian, G. F. (1930). *Biochem. J.* **24**, 1021.
Marrian, G. F. (1948). *J. Endocrinol.* **5**, lxxi.
Marrian, G. F., and Parkes, A. S. (1929). *J. Physiol (London)* **67**, 27.
Martin, L. (1960). *J. Endocrinol.* **20**, 187.
Martin, L. (1964). *J. Endocrinol.* **30**, 21.

Martin, L., and Claringbold, P. J. (1958). *Nature* **181**, 620.

Martin, L., and Claringbold, P. J. (1960). *J. Endocrinol.* **20**, 173.

Meyer, R. K., Miller, L. C., and Cartland, G. F. (1936). *J. Biol. Chem.* **112**, 597.

Miller, B. G., and Emmens, C. W. (1967). *J. Endocrinol.* **39**, 473.

Miller, B. G., Owen, W. H., and Emmens, C. W. (1968a). *J. Endocrinol.* **41**, 189.

Miller, B. G., Owen, W. H., and Emmens, C. W. (1968b). *J. Endocrinol.* **42**, 351.

Morgan, C. F. (1963). *J. Endocrinol.* **26**, 317.

Mühlbock, O. (1940). *Acta Brevia Neerl. Physiol. Pharmacol. Microbiol.* **10**, 42.

Palmer, A. (1941). *Univ. Calif. Publ. Pharm.* **1**, 375.

Pedersen-Bjergaard, K. (1939). "Comparative Studies Concerning the Strengths of Oestrogenic Substances." Oxford Univ. Press, London and New York.

Pincus, G., and Werthessen, N. T. (1938). *Proc. Roy. Soc.* **B126**, 330.

Preston R. E., Cheng, C. D., Story, P. H., Pauls, J., and Burroughs, W. (1956). *J. Animal Sci.* **15**, 3.

Robson, J. M. (1936). *Proc. Soc. Exptl. Biol. Med.* **35**, 49.

Robson, J. M. (1937). *J. Physiol. (London)* **90**, 15(P).

Robson, J. M. (1938). *J. Physiol. (London)* **92**, 371.

Robson, J. M., and Adler, J. (1940). *Nature* **146**, 60.

Rosemberg, E. (1965). "Estrogen Assays in Clinical Medicine" (C. A. Paulson, ed.), p. 107. Univ. of Washington Press, Seattle, Washington.

Rowlands, I. W., and Callow, R. K. (1935). *Biochem. J.* **29**, 837.

Schoeller, W., Dohrn, M., and Hohlweg, W. (1935). *Med. Record N.Y.* **132**, 487.

Schultze, A. B. (1964). *Proc. Soc. Exptl. Biol. Med.* **116**, 653.

Smith, O. W., and Smith, G. V. (1952). *Recent Progr. Hormone Res.* **7**, 209.

Solmssen, U. V. (1945). *Chem. Rev.* **37**, 481.

Stockard, C. R., and Papanicolaou, G. N. (1917). *Am. J. Anat.* **22**, 225.

Stone, G. M. (1964). *Acta Endocrinol.* **47**, 433.

Stot, M., Andrews, F. N., and Zarrow, M. X. (1954). *Am. J. Vet. Res.* **15**, 319.

Sulman, F. G. (1952). *Endocrinology* **50**, 61.

Szego, C. M., and Roberts, S. (1953). *Recent Progr. Hormone Res.* **8**, 419.

Turner, C. W. (1956). *J. Animal Sci.* **15**, 13.

Umberger, E. J., Gass, G. H., and Curtis, J. M. (1958). *Endocrinology* **63**, 806.

Villee, C. A. (1955). *J. Biol. Chem.* **216**, 171.

Villee, C. A., and Gordon, E. E. (1955). *J. Biol. Chem.* **216**, 203.

Wade, N. J., and Doisy, E. A. (1935). *Proc. Soc. Exptl. Biol. Med.* **32**, 707.

Whitman, B., Winterstein, O., and Schwenk, E. (1937). *J. Biol. Chem.* **118**, 789.

Wilder-Smith, A. E., and Williams, P. C. (1947). *J. Endocrinol.* **5**, 152.

Chapter 3

Antiestrogens

RALPH I. DORFMAN

I. Introduction

Antiestrogens are defined as compounds that interfere with any action of an estrogen at a peripheral level. This type of activity has been shown for androgenic substances and related compounds (Robson, 1938; Emmens and Bradshaw, 1939; Velardo *et al.*, 1955; Edgren and Calhoun, 1957; Dorfman *et al.*, 1960a,b; Dorfman and Kincl, 1963), progestational substances (Robson, 1938; Astwood, 1940; Szego and Roberts, 1948; Courier, 1950; Mardones *et al.*, 1954; Huggins and Jensen, 1955b;

121

Edgren and Calhoun, 1957; Dorfman *et al.*, 1960a,b; Dorfman and Kincl, 1963), weak estrogens (De Fremery *et al.*, 1934; Allen and Meyer, 1935; Hisaw *et al.*, 1954), and corticoids (Robson, 1939; Szego and Roberts, 1948; Szego, 1952; Talalay *et al.*, 1952; Roberts and Szego, 1953; Beyler and Szego, 1954; Huggins and Jensen, 1955b; Velardo, 1955, 1956; Velardo and Sturgis, 1955, 1956; Velardo *et al.*, 1955). The relative effectiveness of corticoids has been summarized by Velardo

Dimethylstilbestrol (DMS)

Ethamoxytriphetol (MER-25)

Clomiphene (MRL-41)

U-11, 555 A

U-11, 100 A

CN-55, 945-27

(FIG. 1. For legend see opposite page.)

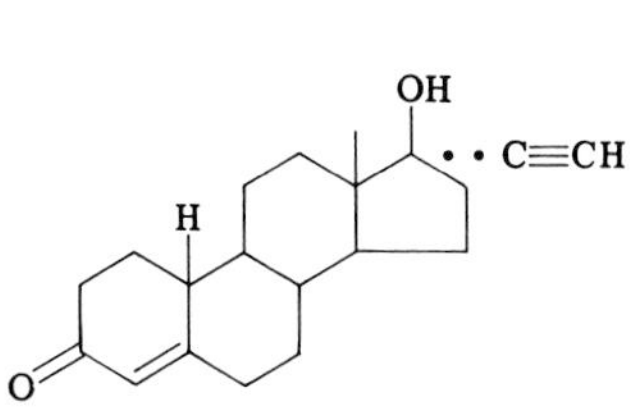

Norethinedrone

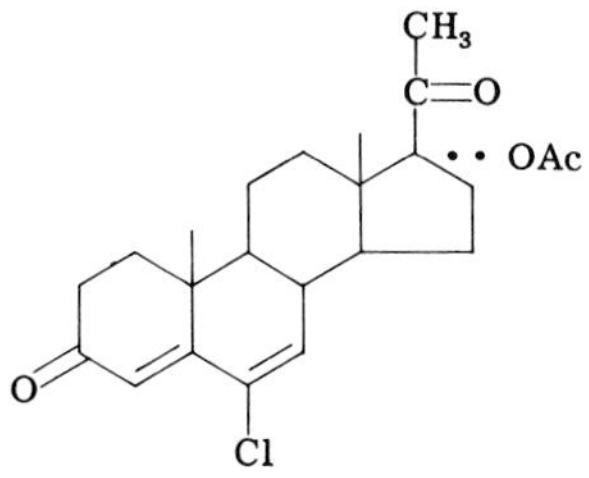

Chlormadinone acetate

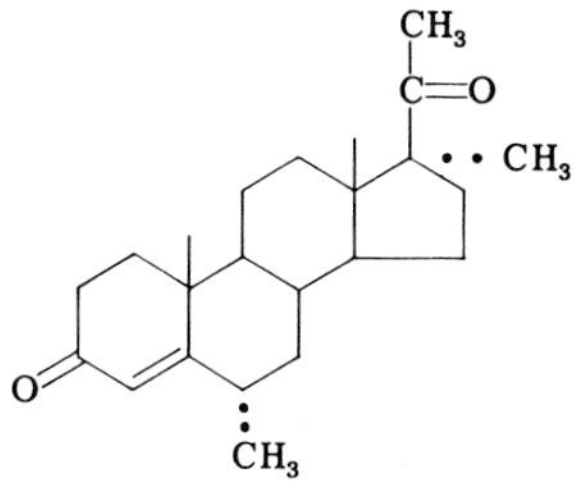

6α, 16α-Dimethyl-
progesterone

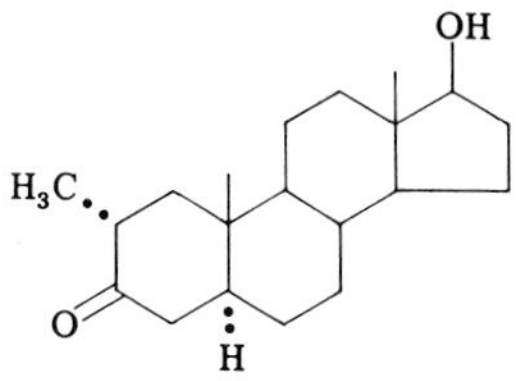

2α, 17α-Dimethyl-
17β-hydroxy-5α-
androstan-3-one

FIG. 1. Typical antiestrogens.

(1959) as 9α-fluoroprednisolone > 9α-fluorocortisol > cortisol > cortisone > prednisone > prednisolone > deoxycorticosterone. Neither the pituitary nor the adrenal were necessary for the reaction.

MER - 25 [1 - (p - 2 - diethylaminoethoxyphenyl) - 1 - phenyl - 2 - p - methoxyphenyl ethanol] (Fig. 1), a nonsteroidal antiestrogen, is unique since inhibition of estrogen action to the extent of 90–100% has been described (Lerner et al., 1958). The substance has a low uterotropic activity and antipituitary gonadotropin action. MER-25 is effective in intact and castrated rats, mice, monkeys, chicks, and rabbits. Lerner et al. (1958) have further demonstrated that the compound is effective against steroidal and nonsteroidal estrogens. Lerner (1964) has reviewed a good portion of the recent literature of antiestrogens and, particularly, additional properties of MER-25. A group of papers have appeared dealing with the antiestrogenic activity of certain synthetic steroids that show intense activity (Payne et al., 1956; Edgren and Calhoun, 1957; Sturtevant, 1957; Edgren, 1958; Edgren et al., 1959). Edgren et al. (1959) reported that certain 17α-alkyl derivatives are extremely active, that the nature of the alkyl group has an important effect on the potency, and that the dihydro-19-nortestosterone as well as the $\varDelta^{5(10)}$ isomers are much less active than the $\varDelta^4$ steroids. These studies, as with older studies, suffer from the fact that the stimulating and suppressing compounds were injected as a single solution at a single site. This technique may be faulty because the action of the inhibitor may be by way of interference with estrogen absorption. Certain synthetic compounds, such as (di-p-hydroxyphenyl)-butane: -pentane: -hexane: and -1,4-pentanedien-3-one, inhibit the proliferation and cornification in the vaginal epithelium of rats treated subcutaneously with estradiol benzoate (Banay et $al.$ 1955). Villee (1957) has shown that certain antiestrogenic activity may be detected with an in $vitro$ test employing the estrogen isocitric acid dehydrogenase reaction from human placental tissue.

A variety of nonsteroidal antiestrogens have been described, including compounds CN-55,945-27 (Callantine et $al.$, 1966), U-11,100A, U-11,555A, and MRL-41 (Roy et $al.$, 1964) (Fig. 1).

The assay of antiestrogens has been described and implied in various publications by in $vivo$ and in $vitro$ methods. The methods are not strictly quantitative, but rather qualitative tests suitable to establish an approximate rank order of relative potency. Some of these methods will be discussed and described in this chapter.

A rather wide range of compounds possessing this property has already been listed. In addition, it is known that folic acid is required for estrogen activity (Hertz and Sebrell, 1944; Hertz, 1945; Kline and Dorfman, 1951; Davis et $al.$, 1956; Davis, 1957). No obvious interrelationship between the folic acid antagonists and the known antiestrogens of the steroid type is apparent.

Emmens and his co-workers (Emmens and Cox, 1958; Emmens et $al.$, 1959) have indicated that substances such as testosterone and progesterone inhibit the action of estrogens with respect to their cornification action on the vaginal epithelium but fail to interfere with the mitosis caused by estrogens. On the other hand, three stilbestrol derivative products including dimethylstilbestrol, ethylstilbestrol, and n-propylstilbestrol, do interfere with the mitotic stimulation caused by estrogens when the agents are administered intravaginally.

Emmens and Martin (1964) reviewed the relative potencies of various types of antiestrogens.

Dimethylstilbestrol (DMS) and related compounds have been studied extensively by Emmens et $al.$ (1962).

On the mouse vagina these compounds appear to be competitive inhibitors of the classical estrogens at a common site of action. Dimethylstilbestrol lacks antiestrogenic activity in systemic test; this is explained

by Emmens *et al.* (1962) on the basis of possible metabolism of the
inhibitor to an estrogen or inert substance or to possible bad timing of
arrival of estrogen and DMS at the target site.

II. *In Vivo* Assays in Rodents

A. VAGINAL RESPONSE IN SPAYED RATS (INJECTION)

(LERNER *et al.*, 1958)

Spayed adult rats (Rolfmeyer Rat Company and Hamilton Laboratory Animals) are injected subcutaneously with estradiol-17β in olive oil
solution at time zero. The inhibitor is injected subcutaneously twice:
at zero and 8 hours. Vaginal smears are obtained at 56, 64, and 72 hours.
Positive smears are those containing nucleated or cornified epithelial
cells and not more than a few leukocytes.

TABLE I

INHIBITION OF ESTRADIOL-17β VAGINAL STIMULATION BY MER-25
IN THE SPAYED RAT (INJECTION)[a]

Total dose of MER-25 injected (mg)	Total dose of estradiol-17β injected (mg)	Number of rats	Positive vaginal response (%)
0	0	10	0
0	0.6	10	100
0.04	0	10	0
0.2	0	10	0
1.0	0	10	0
0.04	0.6	10	90
0.2	0.6	10	10
1.0	0.6	10	0

[a] Adapted from Lerner *et al.* (1958).

Typical results are illustrated in Table I. MER-25 administered alone
at doses from 0.04 to 1.0 mg showed no vaginal response, but a dose of
0.2 mg produced a highly significant inhibition of the peripheral action
of estradiol-17β.

B. VAGINAL RESPONSE IN SPAYED RATS (GAVAGE)

(LERNER *et al.*, 1958)

The method is the same as described in Section II, A except that the
test compound is administered in olive oil solution by gavage at zero and

8 hours. A dose of 0.4 mg of MER-25 was effective in inhibiting the estrogenic action of 0.6 μg of estradiol-17β. One milligram of this compound almost completely inhibited the same dose of estradiol-17β (Table II).

TABLE II

INHIBITION OF ESTRADIOL-17β VAGINAL STIMULATION BY MER-25
IN THE SPAYED RAT (GAVAGE)

Total dose of MER-25 by gavage (mg)	Total dose of estradiol-17β injected (μg)	Number of rats	Positive vaginal response (%)
0	0	10	0
0	0.6	10	100
0.4	0	10	0
1	0	10	0
2	0	10	0
0.4	0.6	10	70
1	0.6	10	10
2	0.6	10	0

C. UTERINE RESPONSE IN SPAYED RATS (INJECTION)

(VELARDO et al., 1956)

Virgin ovariectomized rats, 100 days of age, are injected subcutaneously once daily with 0.1 μg of estradiol-17β contained in 0.1 ml of sesame oil for 3 days starting 1 week after surgery. The test compounds are dissolved in 0.2 ml of sesame oil or aqueous media administered once daily for 3 days but at separate sites. Twenty-four hours after the last injection, the uteri are removed and weighed both wet and dry.

D. UTERINE RESPONSE IN HYPOPHYSECTOMIZED RATS (INJECTION)

(HUGGINS AND JENSEN, 1955a,b)

Female rats, 22 days of age, were placed on a synthetic diet consisting of casein 254 gm, dextrin 468 gm, corn oil 38 gm, Alphacel 50 gm, mixed vitamins 10 gm, salt mixture 40 gm, oleum percomorphum 3 drops, water 140 ml, and vitamin K 50 μg. The steroids were contained in a mixture of 10% ethanol in sesame oil. The stimulating estrogen and inhibitor were injected in a single solution.

The rats were hypophysectomized at 24 days of age, and the test compounds in 0.2 ml of vehicle were injected once daily for 7 days starting when the rats were 38 days of age. The uteri were removed at 45 days of age, 1 day after the last injection. Those animals which had a body weight of 75 gm or a spleen weight of 200 gm were discarded to avoid the possibility of using rats that were not completely hypophysectomized. In addition to the determination of wet uterine weight, the nitrogen content of uterus was determined.

Typical results are presented in Table III, which indicates that a variety of estrogens of low relative activity could inhibit the action of a

TABLE III

Inhibition of Estrone-Induced Uterine Growth by
Various Steroids[a]

		Inhibition of uterus (%)	
Steroid injected	Daily dose (μg)	Weight	Nitrogen content
Estriol	2.5	33	35
16-Epiestriol	2.5	40	37
17-Epiestriol	2.5	31	29
Estradiol-16α	5.0	37	38
Estradiol-16β	5.0	26	26
6-Ketoestrone	5.0	43	42
6-Ketoestradiol-17β	1.0	32	28

[a] Stimulating dose of estrone = 0.5 μg per day for 7 days. Six or more rats per group. Data from Huggins and Jensen (1955a).

highly active estrogen such as estrone. Huggins and Jensen (1955a) named these phenolic steroid inhibitors "impeded estrogens" since, in the words of the authors, "after a moderate increase of uterine weight (about one-third of maximal growth) has been induced by steroids in this class, a ten-fold increase in dosage causes little or no increment in growth."

E. Uterine Response in Immature Mice (Injection)
(Edgren and Calhoun, 1957)

Mice 23–25 days of age are injected once daily for 3 days with 0.1 ml of corn oil containing estrone alone or in combination with the test material. The total dose of estrone is 0.3 μg. In each experiment, groups of 8–10 mice were treated with estrone alone and estrone in combination with a series of doses of the test compound. One group of mice, receiving only corn oil, served as controls. At autopsy, 24 hours after the last injection, uterine weight was determined.

Figure 2 indicates some typical results obtained with the method of Edgren and Calhoun (1957) for testosterone propionate, progesterone,

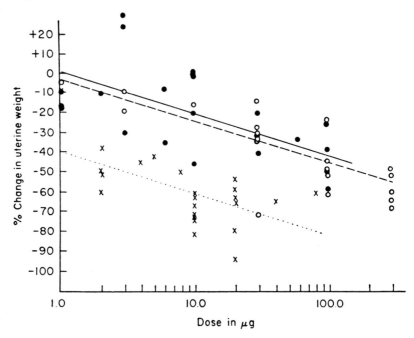

FIG. 2. Anti-uterotropic action of steroids. Effects of testosterone propionate (dots and solid line), progesterone (circles and dashed line), and 17-ethyl-19-nortestosterone (crosses and dotted line) on estrone-induced uterine growth of intact, immature mice. 0% change = response of uterus to 0.3 μg of estrone; −100% change = control uterine level. (From Edgren and Calhoun, 1957.)

and 17-ethyl-19-nortestosterone. Progesterone was judged to be 1.4 times as active as testosterone propionate, whereas the 19-nor compound was found to be about 70 times as potent.

F. UTERINE RESPONSE IN IMMATURE MICE (INJECTION)
(DORFMAN et al., 1960a)

Swiss albino mice 20–22 days old are injected subcutaneously once daily with estrone for 3 days. The total dose of 0.4 μg is contained in 0.3 ml of sesame oil, and 0.1 ml is injected daily. Control groups received

only the vehicle. The test substance is injected subcutaneously daily in
0.1 ml of an aqueous suspending medium at a different site from that used
for the estrone injection. The aqueous suspending fluid consists of sodium
chloride (0.9%), polysorbate 80 (0.4%), carboxymethyl celulose (0.5%),
and benzyl alcohol (0.9%). One day after the last injections the animals
are sacrificed and the uterine weights and body weights are determined.

The assays may be conveniently run in groups of 132 mice which are
divided into 14 groups. One group of 12 mice serve as sesame oil-injected
control animals. Another group of 12 mice receive a total dose of 0.4 µg

TABLE IV

RELATIVE ANTIESTROGENIC ACTIVITIES OF VARIOUS STEROIDS (INJECTION)[a]

Steroid	Total number of mice	Dosage range studied (µg)	Minimum dose to produce inhibition (µg)	Maximum inhibition (%)
2α,17α-Dimethyl-17β-hydroxyandrostan-3-one	81	2–4000	2	30
Norethisterone	180	1–4000	16	56
Testosterone	99	64–4000	500	36
Progesterone	129	10–4000	500	56
Deoxycorticosterone	245	2–4000	1000	21

[a] From Dorfman et al. (1960a).

of estrone. The remaining 12 groups of 9 mice each receive the test
compounds. Usually a single compound is studied at three or more
concentrations in any specific assay. To arrive at the relative activity of a
given compound, all the data for a specific compound at a specific dose
are combined. Compounds are compared on the basis of the minimum
weight necessary to produce a statistically significant inhibition ($P =
0.02$) and by the maximum intensity of the inhibition at any dose. Sample
relative potency data attainable with this method are presented in
Table IV.

G. UTERINE RESPONSE IN IMMATURE MICE (GAVAGE)
(DORFMAN et al., 1960b)

This method is practiced precisely the same as that described for the
injection method in immature mice by the same authors (Dorfman et al.,
1960a), except that the total dose of test compound is dispersed in

0.6 ml of aqueous medium and 0.2 ml is administered daily by gavage for 3 days. Representative data are presented in Table V.

TABLE V

RELATIVE ANTIESTROGENIC ACTIVITIES OF VARIOUS STEROIDS (GAVAGE)[a]

Steroids	Total number of mice	Dose range studied (μg)	Minimum dose to produce inhibition (μg)	Maximum inhibition (%)
Norethisterone	238	2–1000	32	40
17-Methyltestosterone	270	4–2000	250	36
Deoxycorticosterone	118	10–4000	2000	30
Ethisterone	103	50–4000	4000	20

[a] From Dorfman et al. (1960b).

H. MITOSIS METHOD IN SPAYED MICE (INTRAVAGINALLY)
(EMMENS et al., 1959)

The authors recommend a colony of ovariectomized randomly bred albino mice that are used one every 14 days. The intravaginal applications are made in 0.01 ml of 25% aqueous propylene glycol solutions. Two smears are taken at approximately 10 AM and 4 PM on the third day and are scored at 0, 1, or 2, according to whether a positive reaction occurred in no smear, in one, or both. For the study of mitotic counts, the ovariectomized mice are primed with 1 μg of estrone dissolved in peanut oil, and the test solutions are administered intravaginally in 0.005-ml doses. The stimulating dose of estrone and the inhibitor are administered intravaginally in a single solution. Colchicine (0.1 mg in 0.05 ml of water) is injected subcutaneously 7 hours before autopsy to arrest mitosis. The estrogen and inhibitor are administered 24 hours before autopsy, at which time the vagina is removed, fixed in Barr's fixative, and embedded in wax. Transverse sections, 6 μ thick, are stained in Heidenhain's hematoxylin and counterstained in van Gieson's picro-acid fuchsin.

Observations are made on the number of mitoses and the thickness of the epithelium. The final mitotic score of each animal is the sum of five fields. For the purpose of analysis, the authors employed the transformation $Y = \log_{10}(z + 2)$ (where z is the number of mitoses per field). The thickness of the epithelium is measured with an eyepiece micrometer and expressed in arbitrary units. The score for each mouse was the average of five observations.

TABLE VI

Inhibitory Effect of Dimethylstilbestrol on
Intravaginal Response to Estradiol-17β in
Ovariectomized Mice[a]

Dose of estradiol-17β (μg $\times$ 10^{-4})	Dose of dimethylstilbestrol	Total scores for 10 mice
6	0	8
	0.2	2
	0.4	0
12	0	16
	0.2	8
	0.4	1

[a] Data of Emmens et al. (1959).

Typical data for the inhibitory effect of dimethylstilbestrol on intra-vaginal response to estradiol-17β in ovariectomized mice are presented in Table VI. Figure 3 (see also Fig. 22 of Chapter 2) indicates the inhibitor of estrone-stimulated mitosis and epithelial growth.

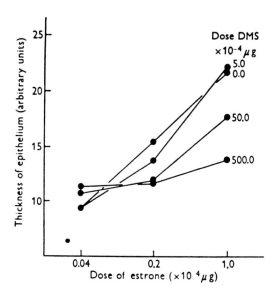

Fig. 3. Inhibition of estrone-stimulated growth by dimethylstilbestrol. (From Emmens et al., 1959).

I. ESTRADIOL-17β-^{14}C UPTAKE IN RAT UTERUS
(ROY et al., 1964)

In a typical study, immature female Sprague-Dawley rats weighing 56 ± 3.8 gm were divided into 5 groups, A, B, C, D, and E. Groups A and D served as control groups and received daily injections of 0.2 ml of corn oil for 6 days. Groups B and E received daily subcutaneous injections of 1 mg of clomiphene (as a model antiestrogen) dissolved in 0.2 ml corn oil for 6 days. Group C did not receive any injection until the final day of the experiment. On day 7, the animals were anesthetized with intraperitoneal injections of Nembutal (50 mg/kg), and 1 μCi (0.27 μg) of estradiol-6,7-^{14}C dissolved in 0.5 ml of 10% ethanol in normal saline was injected intravenously through the femoral vein. The rats in groups A and B were killed by decapitation 30 minutes later, and those in groups D and E were sacrificed 60 minutes after injection. The animals in group C received 2 mg of clomiphene dissolved in 0.2 ml of alcoholic saline intravenously only 10 minutes prior to estradiol injection and were killed 30 minutes after estradiol administration. After exsanguination the individual uteri were weighed and collected separately. The tissues were collected in containers, cooled in Dry-Ice, and stored in deep freeze until the time of biochemical processing.

The tissues were homogenized, with a Virtis homogenizer, in 10 ml of Krebs-Ringer phosphate buffer, and 50 μg of estradiol-17β in 0.2 ml of ethanol was added to each homogenate to serve as a carrier. The homogenate was extracted four times with 50-ml quantities of ether. The combined ether extract was washed twice with saturated sodium bicarbonate solution (5 ml) and once with water (5 ml) and then evaporated to dryness on a flash evaporator. The residue was taken up in 100 ml of toluene and transferred into a separatory funnel. The flask that contained the extract was washed with 1 N sodium hydroxide (25 ml), and the sodium hydroxide solution was also transferred to the separatory funnel. The toluene was then extracted with the sodium hydroxide, and the aqueous layer was separated. The flask and the toluene were washed 3 more times with 25-ml portions of sodium hydroxide. The combined sodium hydroxide solution was extracted once with 50 ml of hexane, and the pH of the extract was brought down to 8.0 by adding 12 N sulfuric acid drop by drop. The preparation was then extracted four times with 50-ml portions of ether. The ether extract was washed once with water (10 ml) and evaporated to dryness. A small aliquot of each extract was counted for tritium on a Tracerlab liquid scintillation counter for total radioactivity.

Each extract was then applied on the whole width of a Whatman 3MM chromatographic paper strip (22½ × 2 inches), and 25 μg quantities

of estradiol-17β were applied to four other strips of each batch to serve
as standards. The compounds were then run in a system consisting of
ligroin–benzene–methanol–water (67:33:80:20) for 3.5 hours after a
preliminary equilibration of 3 hours. The standards were stained with

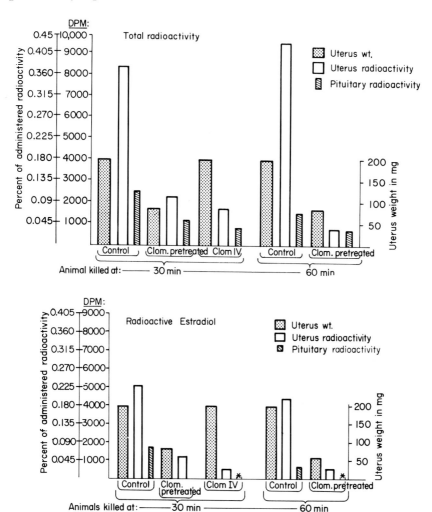

FIGS. 4 (*top*) and 5 (*bottom*). Diminished uterine and hypophyseal radioactivity uptake
of total radioactivity (Fig. 4) and estradiol (Fig. 5) in the clomiphene-treated rats. The
weight of the uterus was decreased in the animals that were pretreated with clomiphene
(subcutaneously) for 6 days while it remained unchanged in the animals that received
clomiphene intravenously 10 minutes prior to estradiol administration. (From Roy *et al.*,
1964.)

Folin and Ciocalteu reagent to locate the estradiol zone. The estradiol zone was eluted from paper using an ethyl acetate–methanol mixture (2:1) and evaporated to dryness. One aliquot of these fractions was counted for tritium while another aliquot was quantitated for estradiol-17β by means of fluorimetry on the Ittrich extraction product of Kober chromogens (Mahesh, 1964). Radiochemical purity was established by running aliquots on a Hyflo Supercel partition column (Preedy and Aitken, 1961); symmetrical Gaussian curves were obtained for radioactivity and sulfuric acid fluorescence. Good agreement was obtained also in the specific activity of estradiol before and after acetylation. The overall recoveries following the above procedure were 82.59%.

The mean values of total radioactivity and of the radioactivity of purified estradiol-17β in the uterus and pituitary gland in control as well as clomiphene-treated animals are presented in Figs. 4 and 5, respectively. The data on radioactivity are expressed as percentage of the respective controls.

It is noteworthy that the figures of total radioactivity are somewhat greater than those of purified estradiol radioactivity, and the differences in groups C and D are statistically significant ($P < 0.001$ and $P < 0.025$, respectively).

The mean values of total radioactivity in the uterus of animals pretreated with clomiphene (as a model antiestrogen) for 6 days and killed at 30 and 60 minutes after estradiol-17β administration were 27.2 and 9.5% of the controls, respectively. The corresponding values for the purified estradiol-17β radioactivity were 23.3 and 12.0%. In the animals which received clomiphene intravenously 10 minutes prior to estradiol-17β administration and were killed 30 minutes later, the total uterine radioactivity was 20.2% whereas the purified estradiol radioactivity was only 10% of the respective controls. There was no significant difference in the uterine radioactivity at 30 and 60 minutes in the control animals.

The uterine weight in the groups of animals pretreated with clomiphene for 6 days was significantly decreased ($P < 0.001$), whereas that in the animals which received clomiphene intravenously only 10 minutes prior to estradiol administration was not changed.

J. ESTRADIOL-17β-^{14}C UPTAKE IN RAT UTERUS
(CALLANTINE, 1967)

Antiestrogens such as CN-55,945-27 (Fig. 1) inhibit the estradiol-17β-^{14}C into the rat uterus. Oral administration of varying amounts of this antiestrogen once daily for 7 days significantly depresses the uptake of ^{14}C-labeled estradiol-17β. An example of this action is illustrated in Fig. 6.

K. UTERINE WEIGHT AND NUCLEIC ACID CONTENT

(CALLANTINE et al., 1966)

Twenty-eight-day-old rats, which were spayed at 21 days of age, were injected subcutaneously with 0.1 ml of peanut oil containing estradiol-17β (0.6 μg per kilogram body weight) once daily for 7 days. Aqueous vehicle and various doses of an antiestrogen, CN-55,945-27,

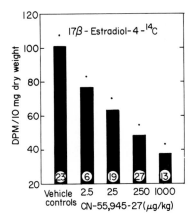

FIG. 6. Effect of nonsteroidal antagonist on estradiol uptake by uteri of ovariectomized rats. CN-55,945-27 given orally for 7 days; 17β-estradiol-4-^{14}C (0.38 μCi/animal) injected subcutaneously 4 hours prior to autopsy. Mean concentration of radioactivity (bar height) $\pm$ SEM (dots above bars) is shown. Number at bottom of each bar indicates number of animals employed. (From Callantine, 1967.)

were administered by gavage. Twenty-four hours after the last concomitant treatment with estradiol-17β and the test, the rats were sacrificed and their uteri were dissected free of surrounding tissue. The uterine horns were opened longitudinally and blotted on filter paper before being weighed. Similar studies are done with the test compound alone to determine its effect on uterine weight of immature ovariectomized rats. Uteri obtained from the experiment in which the test compound was administered concomitantly with estradiol-17β were frozen immediately after they were weighed. Subsequently their total nucleic acid content (RNA, DNA) was determined by the methods previously described by Callantine et al. (1965).

Typical results are presented in Table VII for a study in which estradiol-17β was the stimulating estrogen and CN-55,945-27 (Table VII and Fig. 7) was the estrogen antagonist. Both nucleic acid and uterine weight effects are illustrated in Table VII, but only uterine weight effects are plotted in Fig. 7.

TABLE VII

Antiestrogenic Effect of Orally Administered CN-55,945-27 on the Basis of Weight and Concentration of Nucleic Acids in the Rat Uterus[a]

Daily dose (μg/kg body wt)		Number of rats	Uterine weight (mg $\pm$ SE)	Total nucleic acids (μg/uterus $\pm$ SE)		
Estradiol-17β, subcutaneous injection	CN-55, 945-27			RNA	DNA	Ratio RNA:DNA
0	0	13	27.8 $\pm$ 1.9	214 $\pm$ 15	774 $\pm$ 33	0.28 $\pm$ 0.01
0.6	0	10	104.6 $\pm$ 2.9	834 $\pm$ 28	1518 $\pm$ 54	0.55 $\pm$ 0.01
0.6	5	10	95.4 $\pm$ 3.1	768 $\pm$ 31	1451 $\pm$ 54	0.53 $\pm$ 0.02
0.6	10	9	82.3 $\pm$ 3.2	727 $\pm$ 36	1415 $\pm$ 36	0.51 $\pm$ 0.01
0.6	25	10	64.4 $\pm$ 2.0	563 $\pm$ 16	1226 $\pm$ 33	0.46 $\pm$ 0.01
0.6	50	10	56.0 $\pm$ 1.6	427 $\pm$ 18	1096 $\pm$ 33	0.39 $\pm$ 0.01

[a] Data of Callantine *et al.* (1966).

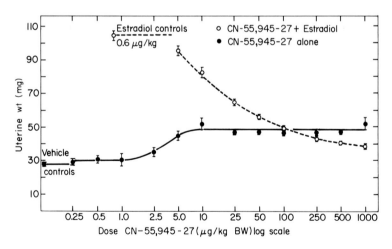

Fig. 7. Effect of CN-55,945-27 (orally) on uterine weight of ovariectomized immature rats when administered alone or with 17β-estradiol (subcutaneously). (From Callantine et al., 1966.)

L. ACTION ON ESTROGEN-STIMULATED MYOMETRIUM
(CALLANTINE, 1967)

Two antiestrogens have been investigated with regard to their effects on the activity of the myometrium. MER-25, when administered sub-cutaneously to ovariectomized rats treated with estradiol-17β decreased the ability of the uterus to contract *in vitro* (Cutler *et al.*, 1961). Likewise, CN-55,945-27 was observed to markedly inhibit uterine contractions when infused intravenously into unanesthetized rabbits post partum (Fig. 8). In the latter study, recordings of uterine contractions were made

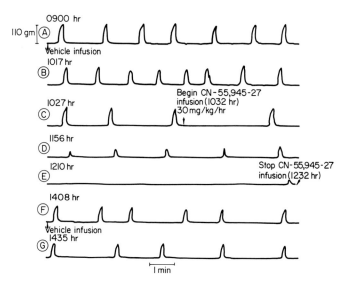

FIG. 8. Effect of intravenous infusion of nonsteroidal antagonist on uterine contrac-tions *in vivo* in unanesthetized rabbits post partum. gm = grams of tension. (From Callantine, 1967.)

under physiological conditions by means of small transducer units implanted on the uterine horns. The compound was infused into the animals via a permanent cannula placed in the jugular vein. *In vitro* studies showed that CN-55,945-27 will completely inhibit both spontane-ous and electrically induced contractions of uteri obtained from rats or rabbits immediately after coitus. The uterus, which at this time exhibits a high degree of tension and rhythmicity, apparently binds CN-55,945-27, since many washings are required to restore normal activity.

M. Various End Points in Rat Uterus
(Lerner, 1964)

Estradiol benzoate administration increased the total amount of
RNA and DNA in the uterus (Fig. 9). The concentration (micrograms of
nucleic acid per milligram wet weight) of RNA did not change whereas
the concentration of DNA decreased with increasing doses of the estrogen.

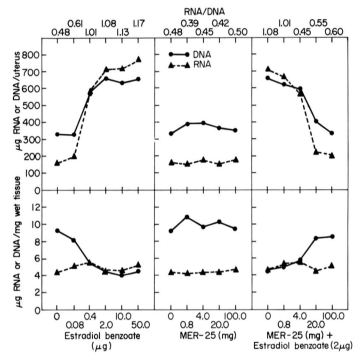

Fig. 9. Effect of estradiol benzoate and MER-25 upon the nucleic acids of the immature
rat uterus. RNA:DNA ratios are shown at the top. Total RNA or DNA is shown in the
upper graphs. Concentration of RNA or DNA is shown in lower graphs. (From Lerner,
1964.)

The resultant RNA:DNA ratios were elevated. MER-25 had no effect
on total nucleic acid or on nucleic acid concentration, but it effectively
reversed the nucleic acid response to estrogen.

Enzyme activities were expressed as micromoles of NADPH
generated per minute per 100 mg of tissue. Since the percentage of
nitrogen in the uterus remained unaltered regardless of treatment, the
specific enzyme activity, expressed per milligram of nitrogen, gave
identical results.

The effects of estradiol benzoate and MER-25 treatment on uterine enzyme activities are illustrated in Fig. 10. It is apparent that estradiol benzoate affects most profoundly the glucose-6-phosphate dehydrogenase system and to a lesser extent the malic dehydrogenase system. At lower, more physiological, doses of the estrogen, isocitric dehydrogenase activity appeared to be increased, but not at higher doses. MER-25 by itself did not affect any of these enzyme activities, but it did antagonize

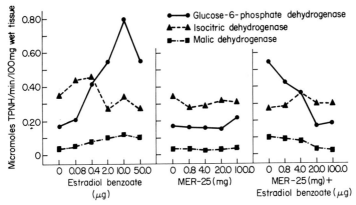

FIG. 10. Effect of estradiol benzoate, MER-25, and MER-25 + estradiol benzoate on the dehydrogenase enzyme activities of the immature rat uterus. (From Lerner, 1964.)

the effects of the estrogen. It would appear, therefore, that under the condition of chronic administration of estradiol benzoate, especially at pharmacological doses when maximal uterine growth is evoked, the primary NADPH-generating system utilized is the glucose-6-phosphate dehydrogenase. Malic dehydrogenase responds in a like manner, but to a smaller degree, and isocitric dehydrogenase appears to play a lesser role, if any. MER-25 clearly prevented the increase in the activity of these enzyme systems in response to estrogen (Fig. 10).

N. Vaginal Cornification Assay in Ovariectomized Mice (Injection) (Lee and Williams, 1964)

Lee and Williams (1964) devised an antiestrogen method using a constant estrogenic stimulation in ovariectomized mice stimulated with estrone or estradiol in the drinking water.

The end point was the percentage of the C57/B1 mice showing vaginal cornification. Over a 3-week period the mean percentage response ± SD for 15, 30, and 60 mg of estrone per milliliter was 31 ± 4, 30 ± 70, and 98 ± 3. Forty micrograms of estrone per milliliter in the drinking water was 88% ± 14, based on six consecutive observations ($N = 10$) of 96, 85,

67, 67, 94, and 70. This concentration, 40 mg/ml, was chosen for the antiestrogen studies.

A single subcutaneous injection of progesterone decreased the vaginal response maximally on day 3 or 4 after injection on day 1. The ED_{50} was about 75 μg, and in probit transformation a satisfactory straight-line log-dose response was found. By this method 17α-acetoxy-6-methyl-pregna-4,6-diene-3,20-dione was 37% more active than progesterone by the subcutaneous route.

III. *In Vivo* Assays in Chicks

A. CHICK OVIDUCT (INJECTION)
(LERNER et al., 1958)

Seven-day-old pullet chicks are injected subcutaneously twice daily with oil solutions of both estradiol-17β and the test compound for 6 days. The daily dose of each compound is contained in 0.1–0.2 ml of oil. One day after the last injections the animals are sacrificed and weights of the body and oviduct determined. The synthetic compound MER-25 produced inhibition of the estradiol-17β action on the oviduct when this method was used (Table VIII).

TABLE VIII

INHIBITORY ACTIVITY OF MER-25 ON THE OVIDUCT OF ESTRADIOL-17β-STIMULATED CHICKS[a]

Estradiol-17β injected (mg)	MER-25 injected (mg)	Number of chicks	Mean body weight (gm)	Mean oviduct weight (mg)
0	0	8	93	11
0	3	8	88	11
0.6	0	8	84	169
0.6	3	8	80	61

[a] From Lerner et al. (1958).

B. CHICK OVIDUCT (INJECTION)
(HERTZ et al., 1947; TULLNER AND HERTZ, 1956)

Female New Hampshire Red chicks are maintained on commercial starting mash and controlled lighting of 12 hours of light and 12 hours of darkness. Starting at 2 weeks of age the chicks are injected subcutaneously once daily for 8 days with 0.25 mg of stilbestrol in 0.1 ml of corn oil.

The test compounds as oil suspensions are injected subcutaneously at a different site once daily for 8 days. Twenty-four hours after the last injections the chicks are sacrificed and the weights of the body and oviduct are determined. Typical results with inhibitory steroids are indicated in Table IX.

TABLE IX

INHIBITORY EFFECT OF VARIOUS STEROIDS ON THE ACTION OF STILBESTROL
ON THE CHICK OVIDUCT[a]

Total dose of stilbestrol (mg)	Total dose of inhibitor Compound	Mg	Number of chicks	Body weight (gm ± SD)	Oviduct weight (mg ± SD)
0	0	0	NG[b]	NG	22
2	0	0	10	208 ± 17	1122 ± 199
2	Progesterone	1	11	209 ± 21	578 ± 86
2	Progesterone	5	5	189 ± 21	468 ± 35
2	11-Deoxycortisol	1	13	200 ± 23	825 ± 111
2	11-Deoxycortisol	5	9	216 ± 20	590 ± 115

[a] From Tullner and Hertz (1956).
[b] NG, not given.

IV. *In Vivo* Assays in Various Species

A. ORAL ANTIESTROGEN STUDIES IN WOMEN
(RUDEL et al., 1967)

Rudel et al. (1967) have suggested that antiestrogenic activity may be of great importance in continuous low dose progestagen type of contraceptive agents (Martinez-Manautou et al., 1966). A method for the evaluation of this biological activity has been developed.

Women of known fertility and with regular menstrual cycles were treated for one cycle with one of the following: chlormadinone acetate, 0.2, 0.3, 0.4, 0.5, 1.0, and 4.0 mg; norethindrone (estrogen free), 0.05, 0.1, 0.2, 0.25, 0.5, and 1.0 mg. Therapy was given in a single daily oral dose for 20 days, starting on day 5 of the menstrual cycle. A biopsy was taken from each patient between day 21 and day 27. The specimens were fixed in cold formalin (4°C), sectioned, and stained with hematoxylin and eosin. They were classified as proliferative, secretory, irregular secretory, irregular, and inactive endometria. The anatomical bases for these classifications are given in Table X. We have assumed that a normal

TABLE X

HISTOLOGICAL CLASSIFICATION OF ENDOMETRIUM[a]

Increasing antiestrogenic activity	Remarks
0 Secretory	Normal histological appearance
0 Proliferative	Normal histological appearance
1 Irregular secretory	Discrete to moderate tortuosity and secretion
2 Irregular	Discrete tortuosity and absence of secretion
3 Inactive	Absence of tortuosity and secretion

[a] From Rudel et al. (1967).

datable secretory endometrium or a proliferative endometrium following a 20-day cyclic course of progestagen treatment results when the progestagens fail to exert an effect on the endometrium (Rudel et al., 1965).

TABLE XI

ENDOMETRIAL GLANDULAR INHIBITION: NORETHINDRONE[a]

Dose (mg)	0 Secretory	0 Proliferative	1 Irregular secretory	2 Irregular	3 Inactive	Index of response
0.05	11	4	1	0	0	0.06
0.1	18	11	15	1	1	0.43
0.2	3	0	4	1	0	0.75
0.25	1	0	3	1	0	1.00
0.5	1	0	5	16	0	1.37
1.0	0	0	2	9	0	1.82

[a] From Rudel et al. (1967).

An arbitrary value of zero has been assigned to them. Irregular secretory, irregular, and inactive endometria are the consequence of increasing inhibitory effects of the progestagens, and in turn have been given values of 1, 2, and 3 plus, respectively. An index of response for each dose was calculated as a weighted average of the values.

The data are summarized in Tables XI and XII. The indices of response are graphically presented in Fig. 11. The results of the analysis indicate that norethindrone is three times as potent as chlormadinone.

A 95% confidence interval for the potency ratio is 2.3–4.0. The narrowness of the interval supports the precision of this assay.

TABLE XII

ENDOMETRIAL GLANDULAR INHIBITION: CHLORMADINONE

Dose (mg)	0 Secretory	0 Proliferative	1 Irregular secretory	2 Irregular	3 Inactive	Index of response
0.2	10	1	3	—	—	0.21
0.3	1	2	1	—	—	0.25
0.4	—	4	—	—	—	0
0.5	19	9	14	9	—	0.63
1.0	2	—	2	4	1	1.44
4.0	—	—	2	3	7	2.42

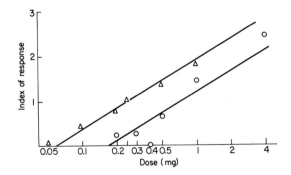

FIG. 11. Potency ratio in women = 3.0; 95% confidence interval = 2.3–4.0. △, Norethindrone; ○, chlormadinone acetate. (From Rudel et al., 1967.)

B. UPTAKE OF ESTRADIOL-17β-³H IN HUMAN TISSUE
(DESHPANDE et al., 1967)

The uptake of estradiol-17β-³H by normal and neoplastic breast tissue has been measured before and after treatment with dromostanolone propionate (2α-methyl-17β-hydroxy-5α-androstan-3-one-17-propionate). This treatment by the anti-mammary tumor compound (Segaloff, 1966) inhibits the uptake of estradiol-17β-³H by the tumor tissues (Fig. 12) but not by normal breast tumor (Fig. 13).

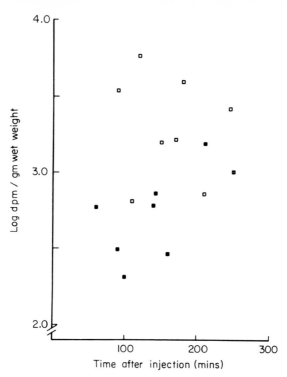

Fig. 12. The effect of pretreatment with dromostanolone propionate on the uptake of ³H-labeled estradiol-17β by tumor tissue. □ = Untreated patients; ■ = treated with dromostanolone propionate.

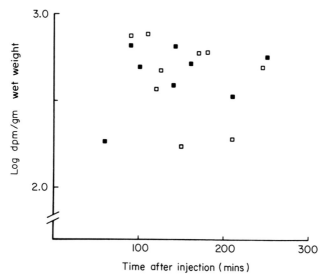

Fig. 13. The effect of pretreatment with dromostanolone propionate on the uptake of ³H-labeled estradiol-17β by normal breast tissue. □ = Untreated patients; ■ = treated with dromostanolone propionate.

C. INHIBITION OF SEXUAL RECEPTIVITY IN RHESUS MONKEYS
(MICHAEL et al., 1967)

This is not a quantitative method, but the study does demonstrate that progesterone, a steroid which by definition is an antiestrogen with respect to morphological aspects of female secondary sex characters, can function at the sex behavior level as well. This has been observed in the rhesus monkey although it must be remembered that progesterone does facilitate certain sexual receptivity behavior.

In the study of Michael et al. (1967), ovariectomized rhesus monkeys were treated daily with 5 μg of estradiol for 5 weeks, and then daily with 5 μg of the estrogen together with 10 or 25 mg of progesterone for 6 weeks. Treatment was started 197 and 218 days after ovariectomy. Observation and the scoring system have been described (Michael and Saayman, 1967). The behavioral end points included the number of sexual mounts made by the male upon the female per test and the number of active refusals per test made by the female when the male attempted to mount.

The results clearly show that progesterone seems to activate a refusal mechanism, and thus inhibits sexual receptivity in the female primate. This observation is in accord with the report of Michael (1965) that male mounting activity decreases in the early part of the luteal phase of the menstrual cycle.

V. *In Vitro* Assays

A. PLACENTAL ISOCITRIC DEHYDROGENASE
(VILLEE AND HAGERMAN, 1957)

Term human placentas are homogenized within 5 minutes of delivery, and a particle-free fraction is prepared by ultracentrifugation. Homogenates are prepared that contain 20% (weight per volume) of placenta in ice-cold 0.25 M sucrose. This is done by homogenization for 20 seconds in a smooth glass homogenizer fitted with a Teflon pestle, followed by centrifugation at 2000 g in an angle-head centrifuge in the cold room. The sediment and connective tissue is discarded and the particle-free supernatant ($S_{57,000}$), prepared in a Spinco model L preparative ultracentrifuge, is used for the incubations (Villee, 1955). The incubations are carried out in air at 37°C in 30-ml beakers shaken at 45 cycles per minute in a Dubnoff incubator. The beakers contain 1.0 ml of $S_{57,000}$ (particle-free supernatant), 1.0 ml of a buffer containing 30 μmoles of K^+, 10 μmoles of Mg^{++}, 20 μmoles of Cl^-, and 20 μmoles of phosphate buffered at pH 7.4; 3.0 μmoles of citrate, *cis*-aconitate, or *d*-isocitrate or 6.0 micromoles of *dl*-isocitrate; 0.75 μmoles of DPN, estrogen, and antiestrogens added as aqueous suspensions prepared by homogenization, and water to a total of 3 ml. After incubation for 1 hour, the following analyses are done: citric acid (Natelson *et al.*, 1498), α-keto acids (Friedemann and Haugen, 1943), and nitrogen by digestion and Nesslerization.

TABLE XIII

INFLUENCE OF ESTRIOL AND ESTRADIOL-17β ALONE
AND IN COMBINATION ON THE PLACENTAL ISOCITRIC
DEHYDROGENASE SYSTEM[a,b]

Concentration of estriol added (μg/ml)	Estradiol-17β added (μg/ml)		
	0	0.1	1.0
0	0.22	0.42	0.47
0.33	0.29	0.41	0.47
3.3	0.34	0.38	0.44
33.0	0.38	0.35	0.40

[a] From Villee and Hagerman (1957).

[b] Values are expressed as micromoles of α-ketoglutaric acid produced per 1 mg of N per hour (mean of 8 determinations).

The results obtained with the *in vitro* method are not necessarily correlated with the *in vivo* studies. Estriol is an example of an estrogen in the classic sense; that is, it causes stimulation of female sex structures, which in the intact animal can also suppress the action of a more active estrogen such as estradiol-17β. The *in vitro* enzyme studies show the same properties (Table XIII). However, other substances such as progesterone and cortisone, which are grossly classified as antiestrogens on the basis of the *in vivo* studies, neither stimulate the placental isocitric acid dehydrogenase system nor inhibit the action of the estradiol-17β.

B. ESTRADIOL-17β UPTAKE IN UTERUS *In Vitro*

(JENSEN *et al.*, 1966)

The interaction of estradiol-17β with uterine receptors has been demonstrated in an *in vitro* system using the rat uterus. Uteri but not diaphragms accumulate estradiol-17β and retain the estrogen during several hours of washing whereas under the same conditions estrone is not retained. The antiestrogen U-11,100 and metabolic inhibitors such as sodium cyanide and iodoacetamide inhibit the uptake.

VI. Conclusion

The assay methods developed for the detection and determination of antiestrogens of steroidal and nonsteroidal composition have not been developed to the point of desired precision, nor is there adequate information as to the meaning of the inhibition observed. Among the processes influenced, however, appears to be a blocking of estradiol-17β attachment to a critical binding site by the antiestrogen and thus preventing an initial necessary step in the mechanism of estrogen action. The number of substances that show antiestrogenic effects is great indeed, and their mechanisms of action are not necessarily similar. This is illustrated by a compound such as dimethylstilbestrol which has the ability to inhibit the action of estrogens on the cornification reaction of the vagina, on mitosis stimulation, and on the growth of epithelial layer of the vagina, but which is relatively inactive by other assays. Testosterone and progesterone can produce certain inhibitory actions but are unable to inhibit the mitosis produced by estrogens. Only future studies, most likely those involving the elucidation of the mechanism(s) of estrogen action, will lead to more definitive antiestrogen assays.

REFERENCES

Allen, W. M., and Meyer, R. K. (1935). *Anat. Record* **61**, 427.
Astwood, E. B. (1940). *Am. J. Physiol.* **129**, 302.
Banay, E., Morsing, P., Müller, W., Stallberg, G., and Stenhager, E. (1955). *Acta. Soc Med. Upsalien.* **60**, 69.
Beyler, A. L., and Szego, C. M. (1954). *Endocrinology* **54**, 334.
Boris, A. (1967). *Arch. Intern. Pharmacodyn.* **166**, 374.
Callantine. M. R. (1967). *Clin. Obstet. Gynecol.* **10**, 74.
Callantine. M. R., Humphrey, R. R., and Lee, S. L. (1965). *Endocrinology* **76**, 332.
Callantine, M. R., Humphrey, R. R., Lee, S. L., Windsor, B. L., Schottin, N. H., and O'Brien, O. P. (1966). *Endocrinology* **79**, 153.
Courier, R. (1950). *Vitamins Hormones* **8**, 179.
Cutler, A., Ober, W. B., Epstein, J. A., and Kupperman, H. S.,(1961). *Endocrinology* **69**, 473.
Davis, J. S. (1957). *Proc. Soc. Exptl. Biol. Med.* **95**, 247.
Davis, J. S., Meyer, R. K., and McShan, W. H. (1956). *Endocrinology* **59**, 505.
De Fremery, P., Kober, S., and Tausk, M. (1934). *Acta Brevia Neerl. Physiol. Pharmacol. Microbiol.* **4**, 119.
Deshpande, N., Jensen, E. V., and Bülbrook, R. D. (1967). *Steroids* **10**, 219.
Dorfman, R. I., and Kincl, F. A. (1963). *Steroids* **1**, 185.
Dorfman, R. I., Kincl, F. A., and Ringold, H. J. (1960a). *Endocrinology* **68**, 17.
Dorfman, R. I., Kincl, F. A., and Ringold, H. J. (1960b). *Endocrinology* **68**, 43.
Edgren, R. A. (1958). *Endocrinology* **62**, 689.
Edgren, R. A., and Calhoun, D. W. (1957). *Proc. Soc. Exptl. Biol. Med.* **94**, 537.
Edgren, R. A., Calhoun, D. W., Elton, R. I., and Colton, F. B. (1959). *Endocrinology*, **65** 265.

Emmens, C. W., and Bradshaw, T. E. T. (1939). *J. Endocrinol.* 1, 378.

Emmens, C. W., and Cox, R. I. (1958). *J. Endocrinol.* 17, 265.

Emmens, C. W., and Martin, L. (1964). *In* "Methods in Hormone Research" (R. I. Dorfman, ed.), Vol. III, Part A, p. 81. Academic Press, New York.

Emmens, C. W., Cox, R. I., and Martin, L. (1959). *J. Endocrinol.* 18, 372.

Emmens, C. W., Cox, R. I., and Martin, L. (1962). *Recent Progr. Hormone Res.* 18, 715.

Friedemann, T. E., and Haugen, G. E. (1943). *J. Biol. Chem.* 147, 415.

Hertz, R. (1945). *Endocrinology* 37, 1.

Hertz, R., and Sebrell, W. H. (1944). *Science* 100, 293.

Hertz, R., Larsen, C. D., and Tullner, W. W. (1947). *J. Natl. Cancer Inst.* 8, 123.

Hisaw, F. L., Velardo, J. T., and Goolsby, C. M. (1954). *J. Clin. Endocrinol. Metab.* 14, 1134.

Huggins, C., and Jensen, E. V. (1955a). *J. Exptl. Med.* 102, 335.

Huggins, C., and Jensen, E. V. (1955b). *J. Exptl. Med.* 102, 347.

Jensen, E. V., De Sombre, E. R., and Jungblut, P. W. (1966). *2nd Intern. Congr. Hormonal Steroids, Milan, Italy, Excerpta Med. Intern. Congr. Ser.* 111, 44.

Kline, I. T., and Dorfman, R. I. (1951). *Endocrinology* 48, 345.

Lee, A. E., and Williams, P. C. (1964). *J. Endocrinol.* 28, 199.

Lerner, L. J. (1964). *Recent Progr. Hormone Res.* 20, 435.

Lerner, L. J., Holthaus, F. J., Jr., and Thompson, C. R. (1958). *Endocrinology* 63, 295.

Mahesh, V. B. (1964). *Steroids* 3, 647.

Mardones, E., Inglesias, R., and Lipshutz, A. (1954). *Nature* 174, 839.

Martinez-Manautou, J., Cortez, V., Giner, J., Aznar, R., Casasola, J., and Rudel, H. W. (1966). *Fertility Sterility* 17, 49.

Michael, R. P. (1965). *Proc. Roy. Soc. Med.* 58, 595.

Michael, R. P. and Saayman, G. S. (1967). *Animal Behaviour* 15, 460.

Michael, R. P., Saayman, G. S., and Zumpe, D. (1967). *J. Endocrinol.* 39, 309.

Natelson, S., Pincus, J. B., and Lugovoy, J. K. (1948). *J. Biol. Chem.* 175, 745.

Payne, R. W., Helbaum, A. A., and Owens, J. N., Jr. (1956). *Endocrinology* 59, 306.

Preedy, J. R. K., and Aitken, E. H. (1961). *J. Biol. Chem.* 236, 1300.

Roberts, S., and Szego, C. M. (1953). *J. Biol. Chem.* 201, 21.

Robson, J. M. (1938). *J. Physiol. (London)* 92, 371.

Robson, J. M. (1939). *J. Physiol. (London)* 96, 21P.

Roy, S., Mahesh, V. B., and Greenblatt, R. B. (1964). *Acta Endocrinol.* 47, 669.

Rudel, H. W. (1964). *5th Ann. Meeting Mexican Endocrine Soc., Ixtapan de la Sol, Mexico.*

Rudel, H. W., Martinez-Manautou, J., and Maqueo-Topete, M. (1965). *Fertility Sterility*, 16, 158.

Rudel, H. W., Lebherz, T., Maqueo-Topete, M., Martinez-Manautou, M., and Bessler, S. (1967). *J. Reprod. Fertility* 13, 199.

Segaloff, A. (1966). *In* "Methods in Hormone Research" (R. I. Dorfman, ed.), 1st ed., p. 205. Academic Press, New York.

Sturtevant, F. M. (1957). *J. Pharmacol. Exptl. Therap.* 121, 369.

Szego, C. M. (1952). *Endocrinology* 50, 429.

Szego, C. M., and Roberts, S. (1948). *Am. J. Physiol.* 152, 131.

Talalay, P., Dobson, M. M., Ebersole, C. M., and Huggins, C. (1952). *Endocrinology* 50, 574.

Tullner, W. W., and Hertz, R. (1956). *Endocrinology* 58, 282.

Velardo, J. T. (1955). *Anat. Record* 122, 478.

Velardo, J. T. (1956). *Am. J. Physiol.* 186, 468.

Velardo, J. T. (1959). *Ann. N.Y. Acad. Sci.* 75, 385.

Velardo, J. T., and Sturgis, S. R. (1955). *Am. J. Physiol.* 183, 259.

Velardo, J. T., and Sturgis, S. R. (1956). *J. Clin. Endocrinol. Metab.* 16, 496.

Velardo, J. T., Hisaw, F. L., and Bever, A. T. (1955). *Anat. Record* **117**, 552.
Velardo, J. T., Hisaw, F. L., and Bever, A. T. (1956). *Endocrinology* **59**, 165.
Villee, C. A. (1955). *J. Biol. Chem.* **215**, 171.
Villee, C. A. (1957). *Cancer Res.* **17**, 507.
Villee, C. A., and Hagerman, D. D. (1957). *Endocrinology* **60**, 552.

Chapter 4

Androgens and Anabolic Agents

RALPH I. DORFMAN

I. Introduction

Androgens by definition are substances that possess characteristic biological activity affecting the secondary sex characters of various male animals. Traditionally, androgens have been assayed by the comb response in the fowl and on the seminal vesicles and prostate of the rodent. Many other parameters of activity are now known. It is the purpose of this section to deal with the multiple techniques employed, their sensitivity and their reproducibility.

Within the past few years there has been increased interest in the nitrogen-retaining activity of androgens and related steroids as therapeutic agents in certain debilitating diseases. The original demonstration that steroids can produce this effect in the castrated dog is credited to Kochakian (1937) and Kochakian and Murlin (1935, 1936); Kenyon *et al.* (1938, 1944) first observed this relationship in humans. The effect of various steroids on nitrogen retention in various species has been reviewed (Dorfman and Shipley, 1956). Eisenberg and Gordan (1950) suggested that the ability of a steroid to retain nitrogen was correlated with its ability to stimulate the levator ani muscle. The property of steroids to cause nitrogen retention and to stimulate the levator ani muscle, also called the anabolic action, is not necessarily correlated with the action of the compound on the mammalian androgen indicators, the seminal vesicle and prostate. Methods for the evaluation of this anabolic action are included in this chapter.

II. Surgical Procedures

Since some of the methods to be described deal with capons and castrated rats, the surgical procedures are described below.

A. Caponizing

White or Brown Leghorn cockerels are usually employed because of their relatively high sensitivity to androgens and because they are usually readily available. The cockerels are operated upon at approximately 6 weeks of age, but with care the operation can be conveniently done as early as 1–2 weeks of age. The 6-week-old animals are fasted for 24 hours before surgery, whereas 1- to 2-week-old cockerels need be fasted for only 6–8 hours.

After fasting, the animals are anesthetized with ether and placed on their sides. The incision is made between the last 2 ribs, the muscle layer is divided, and the incision is pulled apart with small retractors. The testis is found close to the midline of the posterior abdominal wall, alongside the vena cava. The capsule enclosing the testis is cut and the gonad is removed. It is imperative to remove the testis intact, as fragments left behind usually are vascularized and persist, giving rise to incompletely caponized animals. The incision is closed by sewing. The second testis is removed in a similar fashion on the other side.

Even if great care is taken to remove the testis, some animals will show comb growth subsequent to operation. These animals, called slips, are not suitable for assay purposes and must be discarded.

B. Castration in the Rat

Under ether anesthesia, an incision is made in the tip of the scrotum large enough to permit the removal of the testis. A single ligature is placed around the internal spermatic vessels, the deferential vessels, and the ductus deferens. The testis and epididymis are removed. The incision is closed by a suture or by a wound clip (Griffith and Farris, 1942).

III. Bird Methods

A. Capon Comb Growth

Most workers using the capon comb test have employed the White or Brown Leghorn capon. The English game bantam has been found to be a relatively reactive breed, but the heavier breeds are reported to be less reactive. The Plymouth Rock capon has been shown to be one-fifth as sensitive as the Brown Leghorn (Callow and Parkes, 1935). The relative sensitivity of various breeds will be discussed further under comments on the use of the chick's comb for androgen assay.

1. Injection

a. *Method of Gallagher and Koch (1935).* The method consists in determining the growth of the capon's comb after 5 daily intramuscular injections of the unknown and in comparing the comb response with that found for a standard preparation of crystalline material under the same experimental conditions.

The bioassay method may be employed in 1 or 12 different ways. The first consists essentially in using the original design of Gallagher and Koch (1935). In working with most urines the preferred standard is androsterone, since the greater part of the activity in human urines is due to this androgen. An exception to this is the urine from subjects with adrenal cortical tumors, where dehydroisoandrosterone makes up the bulk of the active androgens. In the original work of Gallagher and Koch (1935). the standard was a highly purified bull testis preparation, and a "characteristic curve" was determined. Testosterone or other suitable androgens could be used.

Another design consists in running two concentrations of unknown in parallel with two concentrations of the standard, according to the design of Bliss (1944).

At the beginning of an assay the sum of the length plus height $(L + H)$ of each individual comb is determined by measurement with a millimeter rule placed directly on the comb. It is often of value to record the exact barble used for the determination of the height. The capons are injected intramuscularly, daily, for 5 consecutive days. The daily dose is contained in 1 ml of olive or corn oil. Twenty-four hours after the last injection the combs are remeasured and the growth of the comb is expressed as the sum $(L + H)$ in millimeters. If the first method is used, the mean $L + H$ increment of 8 capons is referred to the standard curve and the unitage in international units (IU) or milligrams of the reference substance read directly from the dose-response curve. If the second method is used, the relative potency of unknown and standard is calculated according to the method of Bliss (1944). Factors that must be considered are as follows.

1. The initial comb size is of importance; for every millimeter of difference in the initial length (from 57 mm) of the comb, a correlation of 0.17 mm of comb growth may be used.

2. The body weight of capons has only an insignificant effect on growth of comb.

3. The unknown and standard should be run under identical light conditions.

4. Before a capon is used again for an assay, it is usually necessary to wait about 1 month to allow sufficient time for regression of the comb.

Gallagher and Koch (1935) found a mean error of 22.6% when the unknown was run in parallel with a standard, and groups of 16–25 capons were used for both the unknown and the standard.

b. Method of Greenwood et al. (1935). Greenwood et al. (1935) have employed the Brown Leghorn capon for the assay of androgens in a manner similar to that of Gallagher and Koch (1935). At the beginning of the experiment the length and height of the combs are measured with a millimeter rule. The hormone, in 0.2 ml of oil, is injected once daily

TABLE I

RESPONSE OF THE CAPON'S COMB TO ANDROSTERONE[a]

Type test (days)	Total dose (mg)	No. of capons	Mean comb growth, $L + H$ (mm $\pm$ SE)[a,b]
3	0.3	5	0.6 ± 0.59
	0.6	5	1.8 ± 0.20
	1.2	5	5.4 ± 0.75
	2.4	5	7.8 ± 1.15
	4.8	5	9.8 ± 0.73
5	0.5	5	2.8 ± 1.34
	1.0	5	6.2 ± 0.85
	2.0	5	10.6 ± 1.03
	4.0	5	15.4 ± 1.11
	8.0	5	17.4 ± 0.80

[a] Data of Greenwood et al. (1935).
[b] SE standard error of the mean.

into the pectoral muscle. At the end of 3 or 5 days, depending on the individual experiment, the combs are remeasured and the response is determined as the difference in length and height of the comb between the pre- and postinjection measurements.

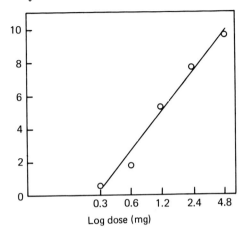

FIG. 1. Capon's comb response to androsterone injected daily for 3 days (Greenwood et al., 1935).

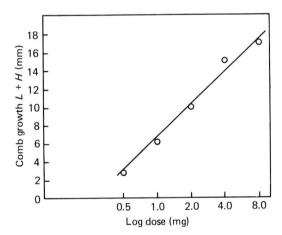

FIG. 2. Capon's comb response to androsterone injected daily for 5 days (Greenwood et al., 1935).

Table I and Figs. 1 and 2 illustrate the comb response after the 3- and 5-day injection periods, respectively. When the data of Greenwood et al. (1935) were plotted as the logarithm of the dose versus response, a linear function was realized for both the 3- and 5-day tests. This being the case, the slopes were calculated and the index of precision (λ) was determined. For the 3-day test the slope (b) was 8.09 and λ was equal to 0.189, while for the 5-day test $b = 12.72$, and $\lambda = 0.180$.

    c. Method of Emmens (1939). Emmens (1939) has studied the capon's comb growth response to androsterone in the Brown Leghorn. The method is similar to that of Gallagher and Koch (1935). Brown Leghorn cockerels are caponized at 6 weeks of age and used at 6–9 months of age. The hormone is administered daily in 0.1 ml of oil for 5 consecutive days. Comb measurements are done before treatment and 24 hours after the last injection by the method already described (see page 153).

TABLE II

RESPONSE OF THE CAPON'S COMB TO ANDROSTERONE
BY INJECTION[a] (THREE INJECTIONS)

Total dose (IU)	No. of capons	Mean comb growth, $L + H$ (mm $\pm$ SE)
0.75	10	1.70 ± 0.23
1.50	10	2.75 ± 0.23
3.00	8	3.25 ± 0.43
4.50	9	4.11 ± 0.41
6.00	9	5.11 ± 0.33
7.50	10	6.05 ± 0.57
9.00	9	7.33 ± 0.46

[a] Data of Emmens (1939).

TABLE III

RESPONSE OF THE CAPON'S COMB TO ANDROSTERONE
BY INJECTION[a] (FIVE INJECTIONS)

Total dose (IU)	No. of capons	Mean comb growth, $L + H$ (mm $\pm$ SE)
1.25	10	3.15 ± 0.32
2.50	10	4.50 ± 0.36
5.00	8	5.81 ± 0.43
7.50	9	7.77 ± 0.63
10.00	9	9.44 ± 0.47

[a] Data of Emmens (1939).

Tables II and III present the data of Emmens (1939) concerning the response of the comb to androsterone after 3 and 5 days of injections, respectively. The data at 3 or 5 days do not fit a linear relationship when the response is plotted against the logarithm of the dose (Fig. 3), but when

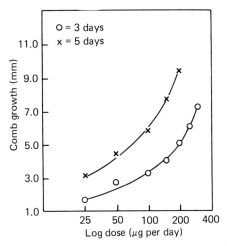

Fɪɢ. 3. Capon's comb response to androsterone injected daily for 3 and 5 days, respectively (Emmens, 1939).

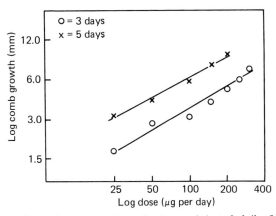

Fɪɢ. 4. Capon's comb response to androsterone injected daily for 3 and 5 days, respectively. Data plotted on basis of log dose–log response (Emmens, 1939).

the data are plotted as logarithm of dose versus logarithm of response, a linear relationship is found (Fig. 4). Making use of this latter relationship, the values of the slope have been calculated and the index of precision λ determined. In the 3-day test the slope was 0.568 and $\lambda = 0.197$, whereas in the 5-day test, the slope was 0.404 and $\lambda = 0.280$.

Table IV illustrates the estimated errors as calculated by Emmens (1939). Both the 3- and 5-day tests are considered.

d. Method of McCullagh and Cuyler (1939). The method is similar to that of Gallagher and Koch (1935). The pooled results are represented in Table V and Fig. 5. The total dose of androsterone ranges from 50 to

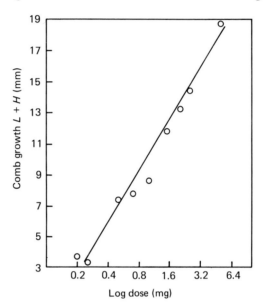

Fig. 5. Capon's comb response to androsterone injected daily for 5 days (McCullagh and Cuyler, 1939).

5000 µg administered over a 5-day period. Between 200 and 5000 µg, a linear relationship of the log dose to response was found. From these data a slope of 10.52 and $\lambda = 0.271$ was found.

2. Inunction

a. Method of Emmens (1939). White or Brown Leghorn capons may be used. The hormone dissolved in oil is applied daily for 3 days to the capon's comb; 0.1 ml of oil solution is used each day. Before treatment is started the combs are measured with a millimeter rule and again 24 hours after the last inunction (see page 153). The response length (L) plus height (H) is determined by the difference between the two measurements.

The data are those of Emmens, which have been calculated by the simplified design of Bliss (1944). Table VI and Fig. 6 present the response

TABLE IV

ESTIMATED ERRORS AT DIFFERENT COMB GROWTH LEVELS AND THE STANDARD
ERROR OF THE ESTIMATE OF THE DAILY DOSE OF A TEST PREPARATION
EXPRESSED AS A PERCENTAGE OF THE ESTIMATE, ASSUMING THE
DOSE-RESPONSE LINES TO BE ACCURATELY KNOWN[a]

Comb growth, $L + H$ (mm)	Average standard errors of response, approximate (pooled data from 3- and 5-day tests)			Standard error of estimate of daily dose (%)			
				3-Day		5-Day	
	(σ)	(σ'') 5 Birds	(σ'') 10 Birds	5 Birds	10 Birds	5 Birds	10 Birds
2	0.75	0.35	0.25	41.0	30	—	—
4	1.10	0.50	0.35	17.5	12	31	21
6	1.40	0.70	0.45	14.5	10	19	12.5
8	1.75	0.85	0.60	12.5	8.5	15.5	10.5
10	2.10	1.00	0.70	—	—	13.5	9.0

[a] From Emmens (1939).

TABLE V

RESPONSE OF THE CAPON'S COMB TO INJECTED
ANDROSTERONE BY METHOD OF GALLAGHER
AND KOCH[a,b]

Total dose (μg)	No. of birds	Mean comb growth $L + H$ (mm $\pm$ SE)
50	15	1.20 ± 0.37
100	15	1.53 ± 0.43
150	14	2.44 ± 0.46
200	15	3.75 ± 0.48
250	14	3.33 ± 0.48
300	16	5.08 ± 0.42
500	16	6.50 ± 0.59
500	14	7.67 ± 0.50
500	15	7.98 ± 0.74
700	16	7.80 ± 0.77
1000	16	8.66 ± 0.96
1500	16	11.91 ± 0.77
2000	16	13.41 ± 0.95
2500	15	14.51 ± 1.14
5000	14	18.83 ± 1.02

[a] Data of McCullagh and Cuyler (1939).
[b] Corrected for 57-mm comb size.

of the capon's comb to a total dose of 1.2–4.7 μg of androsterone. Table VII presents the results of 4 theoretical assays using a total of 20 animals, 10 on the standard and 10 on the unknown. Since the unknown and the standard are identical, the actual potency ratio is 100%. In the 4 tests

TABLE VI

Response of the Capon's Comb to
Androsterone Administered by Inunction
(Three Daily Inunctions)[a]

Total dose of androsterone (μg)	No. of capons	Mean comb growth $L + H$ (mm ± SE)
1.2	10	2.55 ± 0.60
2.4	10	5.30 ± 0.55
3.6	10	5.80 ± 0.78
4.8	10	7.05 ± 0.32

[a] Data of Emmens (1939).

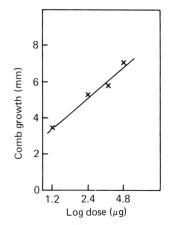

Fig. 6. Capon's comb response to androsterone inuncted daily for 3 days (Emmens, 1939).

the determined potency ratio varied from 92 ± 34 to 130 ± 16. In only one instance were the slopes of the unknown and standard significantly different. The index of precision varied from 0.108 to 0.360 with a mean of 0.184 ± 0.063.

b. *Method of McCullagh and Cuyler (1939).* This method is essentially the same as that of Gallagher and Koch (1935), described

TABLE VII

ASSAY OF ANDROSTERONE BY THE CAPON COMB INUNCTION
METHOD OF EMMENS (1939)[a]

$N = 5$
High dose of standard = High dose of unknown
Low dose of standard = Low dose of unknown
Standard = Unknown

Dosage level (μg)	b	λ	t	Potency ratio (% $\pm$ SE)
0.4, 0.8	9.33	0.108	1.215	130 $\pm$ 16
0.4, 1.2	6.88	0.360	0.684	92 $\pm$ 34
0.4, 1.6	7.50	0.186	0.875	97 $\pm$ 19
0.8, 1.6	5.83	0.079	2.610	119 $\pm$ 22

[a] Based on the data of Emmens (1939).

above, except for the application of the androgen solution directly to
the capon's comb. McCullagh and Cuyler (1939) have been able to demonstrate a log dose-response curve which is a straight line from a total dose
of 2–80 μg of androsterone.

The androgen is dissolved in sesame oil so that the total dose is
contained in 1 ml of solution. Each day for 5 consecutive days, 0.2 ml of
the androgen solution is applied evenly over the whole comb.

Table VIII presents the influence of androsterone by inunction on the
capon's comb. The total dose ranged from 2 to 100 μg. Between the

TABLE VIII

RESPONSE OF THE CAPON'S COMB TO
ANDROSTERONE ADMINISTERED BY INUNCTION[a]

Total dose of androsterone (μg)	No. of capons	Mean comb growth $L+H$ (mm $\pm$ SE)
2.0	15	1.0 $\pm$ 0.37
4.0	15	2.0 $\pm$ 0.43
7.0	15	2.53 $\pm$ 0.55
10.0	15	4.27 $\pm$ 0.52
20.0	15	7.93 $\pm$ 0.64
50.0	15	12.87 $\pm$ 0.67
100.0	15	14.33 $\pm$ 0.80

[a] Data of McCullagh and Cuyler (1939).

limits of 7 and 50 μg an excellent agreement was found for a linear relationship between the logarithm of the dose and the response (Fig. 7). The slope over this range was found to be 30.3 and $\lambda = 0.0763$.

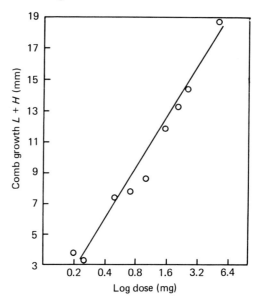

Fig. 7. Capon's comb response to androsterone inuncted daily for 5 days (McCullagh and Cuyler, 1939).

B. CHICK COMB GROWTH

1. General Remarks

The early studies of Ruzicka (1935), Burrows *et al.* (1936), Dorfman and Greulich (1937), and Frank and Klempner (1937) indicated the advisability of using the chick's comb as the test object for androgen assays. Ruzicka (1935) painted the chick's comb with a 0.5% solution of androsterone in oil each day for a period of several weeks and obtained large increases in comb area. He did not, however, study this reaction quantitatively. Frank and Klempner (1937) applied the androgens in oil solutions directly to the base of the comb of White Leghorn chicks. Applications were begun on day 6 after hatching and were repeated on 10 successive days. The animals were sacrificed and the comb weights were determined on the day following the last application. These workers were able to evoke a definite response with as little as 20 μg of androsterone. Burrows and his co-workers (1936) injected both androsterone and testosterone either into the base of the chick's comb or into the breast muscles and found that both of these androgens stimulated comb growth.

In all the studies mentioned the response is the weight of the comb, which perhaps represents an advantage over the less exact methods of measurement of the size of the capon's comb. However, the capon comb method has the advantage that each animal serves as its own control, since comb measurements are made before and after hormone administration.

2. Relative Reactivity of the Comb of Various Breeds of Chicks to Androgens (Dorfman, 1948b)

It has been known for some time that various breeds of fowl differ as to their practicability for use in androgen assays when the comb is used as the test organ. The reactivity of 3 breeds of chicks to testosterone propionate has been studied. The hormone was administered by direct application to the comb. This procedure should rule out variations in the metabolism or inactivation of the hormone in the body. In these experiments we are dealing only with the direct stimulation and the local inactivation of the hormone at the site of the comb.

The 3 breeds of chicks studied were the White Leghorn, the Rhode Island Red, and the Barred Rock. The animals were kept in a thermostatically controlled brooder and were fed chick starting mash and water exclusively. The chicks were 2–3 days of age at the beginning of the experiment. The total dose of testosterone propionate was contained in 0.35 ml of corn oil and administered once daily for 7 days. Five-hundredths of a milliliter of the hormone solution was dropped onto the comb from a 1-ml tuberculin syringe fitted with a No. 24 hypodermic needle. Twenty-four hours after the last hormone application the animals were killed, and body weight and comb weights were determined. The animals were autopsied at 9–10 days of age. The comb responses are expressed as the ratio of the comb weight in milligrams to the body weight in grams. Body weights did not vary significantly.

The dosage range of testosterone propionate investigated varied from 2 to 20,480 μg for the White Leghorn male and female chicks, and 40 to 20,480 μg for the Rhode Island Red and Barred Rock breeds (Table IX).

No significant difference was found in the comb ratios between male and female untreated chicks for any of the 3 breeds studied, but a significant difference in comb ratios was found between animals of different breeds. White Leghorn chicks showed the largest combs, the Barred Rocks the smallest, and the combs of the Rhode Island Reds were intermediate. This order of comb size of control chicks was true for both the males and females.

On the basis of the minimal quantity of testosterone propionate needed to produce a 20% increment in comb ratio, the male White Leghorns were 15 times as sensitive as the Rhode Island Reds and 20 times as sensitive as the Barred Rocks. Similarly, the female White Leghorn combs were 10 times as sensitive as those of the Rhode Island Reds, and 20 times those of the Barred Rocks.

The comparative sensitives of the combs of the 3 breeds were evaluated by selecting portions of the log 'dose-response curves where the

TABLE IX

RELATIVE REACTIVITY OF THE COMBS OF WHITE LEGHORN, RHODE ISLAND RED, AND BARRED ROCK CHICKS TO TESTOSTERONE PROPIONATE ADMINISTERED BY DIRECT APPLICATION TO THE COMB

Breed of chicks	Amount administered (μg)	No. of chicks M	No. of chicks F	Ratio $= \dfrac{\text{comb (mg)}}{\text{body weight (gm)}} \pm$ SE	
White Leghorn	0	62	56	0.38 ± 0.01	0.36 ± 0.01
	2	13	6	0.46 ± 0.04	0.43 ± 0.06
	5	28	34	0.55 ± 0.02	0.47 ± 0.02
	10	32	31	0.63 ± 0.03	0.52 ± 0.02
	20	18	45	0.65 ± 0.04	0.67 ± 0.02
	40	36	51	0.77 ± 0.05	0.69 ± 0.02
	80	46	38	1.03 ± 0.05	0.91 ± 0.05
	160	29	36	1.53 ± 0.01	1.54 ± 0.09
	2560	25	13	1.74 ± 0.07	1.74 ± 0.15
	5120	12	12	1.88 ± 0.15	1.98 ± 0.15
	20,480	8	13	1.89 ± 0.22	1.82 ± 0.16
Rhode Island Red	0	47	29	0.25 ± 0.01	0.23 ± 0.01
	40	14	11	0.33 ± 0.01	0.33 ± 0.02
	80	13	11	0.36 ± 0.03	0.40 ± 0.04
	160	9	14	0.48 ± 0.05	0.49 ± 0.05
	640	9	16	0.85 ± 0.10	0.82 ± 0.10
	1282	15	10	0.91 ± 0.07	0.87 ± 0.09
	2560	32	21	0.92 ± 0.05	1.03 ± 0.07
	5120	11	12	1.14 ± 0.07	1.03 ± 0.08
	20,480	—	19	—	1.10 ± 0.08
Barred Rock	0	26	37	0.21 ± 0.01	0.20 ± 0.01
	40	13	10	0.25 ± 0.02	0.22 ± 0.02
	80	12	13	0.23 ± 0.02	0.29 ± 0.02
	160	9	14	0.36 ± 0.04	0.32 ± 0.02
	640	12	17	0.54 ± 0.03	0.55 ± 0.03
	1280	11	15	0.61 ± 0.02	0.63 ± 0.04
	2560	24	31	0.85 ± 0.01	0.82 ± 0.04
	5120	9	15	0.97 ± 0.09	1.07 ± 0.08
	20,480	12	10	1.01 ± 0.11	1.02 ± 0.07

slopes of all 3 breeds were not significantly different, and by using the displacement of the curves as another measure of the relative sensitivity of the various breeds (Table X and Fig. 8). Under these conditions and expressing the sensitivity of the male White Leghorn chick comb as 100%, the sensitivity of the Rhode Island Red was found to be 10% and that of Barred Rock 1.8%. In the female chicks the relative comb sensitivities were similar: White Leghorn, 100%; Rhode Island Red, 8.9%; and Barred Rock 1.8% (Table XI).

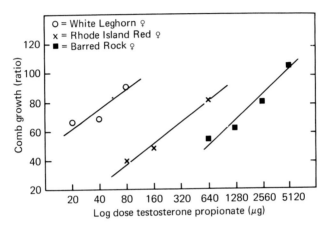

FIG. 8. Comb responses of three breeds of female chicks to testosterone propionate (Dorfman, 1948b).

TABLE X

MAXIMUM SLOPES OF COMB RESPONSE ATTAINABLE BY RHODE ISLAND RED
AND BARRED ROCK CHICKS
(LOGARITHM DOSE-RESPONSE)

Breed	Sex	Dosage levels of testosterone propionate (μg)	Total No. of animals	Slope ($b \pm$ SE)
White Leghorn[a]	M	20, 40, 80	100	0.677 ± 0.107
	F	10, 20, 40, 80	165	0.357 ± 0.023
Rhode Island Red	M	80, 160, 640	31	0.545 ± 0.026
	F	80, 160, 640	41	0.485 ± 0.110
Barred Rock	M	640, 1280, 2560	47	0.537 ± 0.101
	F	640, 1280, 2560, 5120	78	0.484 ± 0.110

[a] The White Leghorn comb response curve was taken where the slope was not significantly different from that of the other breeds.

A third criterion of sensitivity of the combs to androgen was the maximum slope attainable using a log dose-response relationship for at least 3 points. No significant difference in maximum slope was found for the Rhode Island Red and Barred Rock chick combs, but the White Leghorns showed a significantly greater slope (Table XII and Fig. 9).

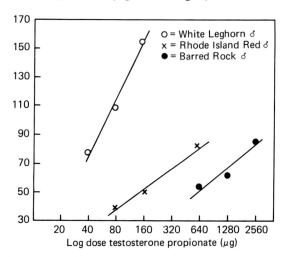

Fig. 9. Comb responses of three breeds of male chicks to testosterone propionate (Dorfman, 1948b).

TABLE XI

Relative Sensitivity of Various Breeds of Chicks to Testosterone Propionate as Measured by Amount of Hormone Necessary to Produce Similar Slopes

	Males		Females	
Breed	Sensitivity as percent of White Leghorn	Error range $(P = 0.95)$	Sensitivity as percent of White Leghorn	Error range $(P = 0.95)$
White Leghorn	100	0	100	—
Rhode Island Red	10.0	+32, −25	8.9	+48, −33
Barred Rock	1.8	+23, −19	2.0	+33, −25

An evaluation of the maximum percentage increase in comb size by androgen stimulation revealed that no significant difference could be demonstrated between the 3 breeds for either male or female chicks (Table XIII).

TABLE XII

COMPARISON OF MAXIMUM SLOPES ATTAINED BY REGRESSION OF
WHITE LEGHORN AND BARRED ROCK COMBS ON
TESTOSTERONE PROPIONATE[a]

Sex	Maximum White Leghorn (slope[b] ± SE)	Maximum Barred Rock (slope ± SE)	Total No. of chicks	t	P
M	1.215 ± 0.147	0.537 ± 0.101	158	3.027	0.01
F	1.361 ± 0.100	0.484 ± 0.110	223	8.240	0.01

[a] Rhode Island Red maximum slopes not significantly different from those of Barred Rock.

[b] Derived from 40-, 80-, and 160-μg doses of testosterone propionate.

TABLE XIII

COMPARATIVE MAXIMUM COMB RATIOS ATTAINED BY THREE BREEDS OF
CHICKS AFTER APPLICATION OF TESTOSTERONE PROPIONATE

Breed	Males		Females		Mean increase, male and female (%)
	Control ratio	Maximum increase (%)	Control ratio	Maximum increase (%)	
White Leghorn	0.38	395	0.36	415	405
Rhode Island Red	0.25	357	0.23	364	361
Barred Rock	0.21	344	0.20	426	385

3. Method of Frank et al. (1942)

The method was devised by Frank et al. (1942) and studied by Dorfman (1948a). Using it, Klempner et al. (1942) have shown that in 24 determinations of androsterone in the dosage range of 20–40 μg, the mean error was 13%, and in 39 determinations over the range of 10–50 μg, the mean error was 24.6%. In another study (Dorfman, 1948a) the results of Klempner et al. (1942) were confirmed. In the latter study, in the range of 20–40 μg, a mean error of 12% was found, and in the range of 10 to 40 μg, a mean error of 24% was found.

White Leghorn chicks should be used at 2–3 days of age. Mixed pullets and cockerels are used. The animals should be kept in a brooder with a thermostatic control. It is well to keep the temperature between 88° and 96°F.

The total dose of material to be administered to each chick is dissolved in 0.35 ml of sesame oil; 0.05 ml of oil is administered daily for 7 days, starting when the animals are 2–3 days of age. The material is dropped on the comb by means of a 1-ml tuberculin syringe fitted with a fine hypodermic needle. An attempt is made to apply the oil solution slowly so that spreading to the head feathers is minimized. Twenty-four hours after the last application of androgen solution, the chicks are autopsied (8–9 days of age).

Body weights are determined at the time of the first application of the androgens, and again at autopsy along with weight of comb and sex of of the animal. The combs are removed by two longitudinal incisions along the base of the comb at its juncture with the scalp. The incisions are extended vertically down to the skull. The comb is freed from the skull and the base is touched lightly on a towel to remove blood from the cut surface. The comb is weighed quickly, on a suitable torsion balance, to avoid drying.

Calculations:

Activity equivalent to 100 μg of androsterone per chick

$$= \frac{1.061(\sum W) - 0.043(\sum W^2) - 0.397(\sum B_i) - 0.267(\sum B_t) + 14.75 N_m + 18.54(N_f)}{100(N_m + N_f)}$$

where $\sum W$ = the sum of the comb weights, expressed in milligrams

$\sum W^2$ = the sum of the squared comb weights

$\sum B_i$ = the sum of the initial body weights, expressed in grams

$\sum B_t$ = the sum of the terminal body weights, expressed in grams

N_m = the number of male chicks used in the assay

N_f = the number of female chicks used in the assay

4. Method of Dorfman (1948a) (Inunction)

a. *Testosterone propionate.* The assay of testosterone propionate can be carried out by a chick comb method using the details of age of chicks, volume of oil, time of hormone application to comb, and determination of the comb weight as described on page 163. The experimental design and calculations are different.

The design of Bliss (1944) is employed, using 2 concentrations of the standard and 2 concentrations of the unknown. The total concentration of testosterone propionate used for each animal should be in the range of 20–160 μg. Within the range of 20–160 μg, using 32 animals on the standard and 32 animals on the unknown, errors in the determination of the potency ratio are lower than 38% at $P = 0.95$.

The response of the male and female White Leghorn chick comb to testosterone propionate is presented in Table XIV. In Table XV the data have been considered by the method of Bliss (1944). A linear relationship was found when the logarithm of the dose was plotted against the logarithm of the response, and the data are calculated on this basis. In

TABLE XIV

Response[a] of the Chick Comb to Testosterone Propionate

5 μg		10 μg		20 μg		40 μg		80 μg		160 μg	
S(M)[b]	U(M)	S(M)	U(M)	S(M)	U(M)	S(M)	U(M)	S(M)	U(M)	S(M)	U(M)
0.45	0.48	0.38	0.98	0.44	0.51	1.10	0.96	1.33	1.13	2.46	2.16
0.51	0.52	0.56	0.73	0.58	0.69	0.67	1.10	1.10	1.31	1.62	1.38
0.63	0.68	0.53	0.84	1.13	0.50	0.81	0.80	0.97	1.30	1.60	2.71
0.67	0.50	0.75	0.71	1.02	0.56	0.81	0.89	1.17	0.77	1.30	3.21
0.75	0.62	0.66	0.67	0.58	0.41	1.37	1.52	1.64	1.34	1.15	1.13
0.48	0.67	0.66	0.53	0.55	0.59	0.90	0.61	1.55	1.48	1.25	2.00
0.69	0.59	0.42	0.68	0.82	0.69	0.71	0.45	1.11	1.46	1.72	1.17
0.50	0.47	0.77	0.56	0.76	0.44	0.63	1.08	1.48	1.11	1.23	1.91
S(F)	U(F)	S(F)	U(F)	S(F)	U(F)	S(F)	U(F)	S(F)	U(F)	S(F)	U(F)
0.43	0.37	0.43	0.61	0.63	0.83	0.36	0.64	0.76	1.15	0.85	1.53
0.32	0.32	0.38	0.41	0.68	0.84	1.68	0.69	0.92	1.42	2.03	1.09
0.53	0.58	0.54	0.55	0.57	0.69	0.46	0.93	0.96	0.88	2.65	1.63
0.37	0.67	0.56	0.55	0.55	0.73	0.69	0.89	0.84	0.51	0.89	1.60
0.45	0.62	0.80	0.48	0.92	0.82	0.78	0.73	0.82	1.16	2.12	2.05
0.39	0.37	0.43	0.36	0.66	0.51	0.84	1.69	1.34	1.20	2.76	2.66
0.67	0.49	0.51	0.49	0.58	0.43	0.82	0.97	0.96	1.13	1.59	1.98
0.47	0.38	0.49	0.42	0.65	0.53	0.86	0.76	0.76	1.21	1.14	1.90

[a] Response expressed as ratio of comb weight in milligrams to body weight in grams.
[b] S = standard; U = unknown; M = male; F = female.

each instance, 2 dose levels of both the unknown and standard were considered. The number of animals in each group in 3 cases was 16 (8 males and 8 females), and 12 (6 males and 6 females) in the other comparisons.

At the level of 40–160 μg for groups of 16 (total number of animals, 64) an error range of −28 to +38% was found as compared to an error range of −31 to +46% for groups of 12 (total number of animals, 48).

In a second instance where groups of 16–12 were compared at the 20- and 80-μg levels, an error range of −7 to +38% was found for the groups of 16, while the groups of 12 showed an error range of −35 to +54% ($P = 0.95$).

The highest error range of the potency ratio was found at the levels of 20 and 40 μg, although 16 animals were used at each dose level. This error range was from −38 to +56%.

No significant difference was found in the slopes of the unknown and standard. The t values range from 0.318 to 1.835.

TABLE XV

Assay of Testosterone Propionate by Direct Comb Application

$$\frac{\text{High dose of standard}}{\text{Low dose of standard}} = \frac{\text{High dose of unknown}}{\text{Low dose of unknown}}$$

Standard = Unknown

(log dose = log response)

N (half M, half F)[a]	Dosage levels (μg)	b	λ	t	Potency ratio (% ± SE)	Error range $P = 0.95$ (%)
16	40, 160	0.5025	0.277	0.318	128 ± 21	−27, +38
12	40, 160	0.5000	0.322	1.835	129 ± 24	−31, +46
16	20, 80	0.4115	0.229	0.805	87 ± 14	−27, +38
12	20, 80	0.3729	0.329	0.785	95 ± 20	−35, +54
16	80, 160	0.5908	0.205	1.445	111 ± 13	−21, +26
16	20, 40	0.3848	0.369	0.694	102 ± 23	−38, +56

[a] Each group was composed of equal numbers of males and females.

TABLE XVI

Response of the Male Chick's Comb to Testosterone Administered by Application[a,b]

Total amount administered (μg)	No. of chicks	Comb ratio ± SE
0	62	38 ± 1
50	33	84 ± 4
100	32	112 ± 5
200	34	136 ± 7

[a] From Dorfman (1968).
[b] Seven days.

b. Testosterone. Testosterone was assayed by the same procedure used for testosterone propionate. A linear relationship was found between the logarithm of the dose and the response. The simplified design was employed (Bliss, 1944).

Table XVI and Fig. 10 illustrate the response of the male chick's comb to the direct application of testosterone. The assay is illustrated in Table XVII. The actual potency ratio was 1. The potency ratios varied from 0.92 to 1.29 in 5 different runs. No significant differences in the slopes of the unknown and standard were found.

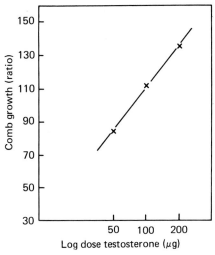

FIG. 10. Chick's comb response to inuncted testosterone (Dorfman, 1968).

TABLE XVII

Assay of Testosterone by Direct Comb Application[a]

$$\frac{\text{High dose of standard}}{\text{Low dose of standard}} = \frac{\text{High dose of unknown}}{\text{Low dose of unknown}}$$

Standard = Unknown

$N = 15$

Dosage levels (μg)	b	λ	t	Potency ratio $\pm$ SE
50, 100	105	0.238	0.145	92 $\pm$ 13
100, 200	87	0.415	1.510	124 $\pm$ 30
100, 200	137	0.251	1.840	94 $\pm$ 11
100, 200	102	0.360	1.160	102 $\pm$ 16
100, 200	86	0.408	0.684	129 $\pm$ 32

[a] Data of Dorfman (1968).

c. *Androsterone*. Valle *et al.* (1947) have studied the chick comb method by direct application of androsterone. Two-day-old White Leghorn male chicks are placed in brooders at a temperature of 32°–37°C. They are fed ad libitum bread and milk plus a dry food consisting of corn meal, 50%; rice bran, 15%; meat meal, 10%; and bone meal, 5%. Beginning with the third day of life and continuing for 7 consecutive days,

TABLE XVIII

RESPONSE OF THE MALE CHICK'S COMB TO ANDROSTERONE BY APPLICATION

Expt. No.	Dosage (μg)	No. of chicks	Mean comb weight (mg)	Variance	Slope	Sigma slope
A	15.0	20	46.7	267.95		
	22.4	20	53.1	272.77	42.264	11.54
	33.5	19	62.0	699.82		
	50.0	18	68.3	408.86		
B	15.0	18	41.9	247.32		
	22.4	14	49.0	218.30	41.685	10.56
	33.5	16	56.3	261.76		
	50.0	16	63.7	652.37		
C	15.0	14	55.2	305.41		
	22.4	16	60.9	389.34	41.516	11.42
	33.5	16	67.3	360.17		
	50.0	12	77.2	599.61		
D	15.0	17	42.5	204.34		
	22.4	20	48.9	253.78	55.975	10.04
	33.5	14	64.0	384.08		
	50.0	18	70.0	408.50		
E	50.0	17	78.8	606.74		
	75.0	16	91.8	797.63	115.114	16.14
	112.0	18	118.1	949.14		
	168.0	16	136.1	794.85		

0.05 ml of oil solution of the hormone is applied to the comb. Twenty-four hours after the last hormone application the animals are killed and the combs are removed by the method of Frank *et al.* (1942), described on page 163. Animals that gained less than 2 gm during the experimental period were discarded.

Table XVIII illustrates the results using androsterone by direct application. In experiments A through D low concentrations (15–50 μg)

of androsterone were applied. Under these conditions a mean slope of 44.1 ± 3.68 was found and a mean value of $\lambda = 0.424 \pm 0.033$ was calculated. Between 50 and 168 μg of androsterone, a steeper slope of 115.114 was found and a correspondingly more favorable value of 0.244 for λ.

5. *Method of Munson and Sheps (1958) (Inunction)*

This method is the most sensitive described for the chick's comb and has a useful range of 0.35–5.6 μg of androsterone total dose. This high sensitivity is due to the use of absolute alcohol as the vehicle, a small

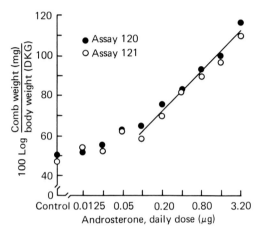

FIG. 11. Comb response to androsterone in two consecutive experiments (Munson and Sheps, 1958).

volume of vehicle, and, as in other chick comb methods, the use of a sensitive breed of chicks. One disadvantage is the fact that the total dose of any unknown material must be soluble in 0.07 ml of absolute ethanol. The mean index of precision (λ) was established as 0.34 with a standard deviation of 0.056. This means that with 40 chicks on the standard and 20 on the unknown the minimum standard error of a potency estimate is 24%.

For the assay single-comb White Leghorn cockerels were received on the day of hatching, and the following day were distributed randomly into groups of equal size. The cages and corresponding groups of chicks are numbered consecutively, and the treatments are assigned by formal randomization. The solutions are applied to the comb once daily for 7 days. For this a 0.01-ml micropipet fitted with bulbs made from rubber tubing is employed. Inunction is started either on the day of hatching or the following day.

To reduce the incidence of diarrhea the chicks are fed only cracked corn for the first 2 days. The diet is then changed to a mixture of equal amounts of corn and starting mash together with grit. Food is removed on the evening of day 7. The following morning the chicks are killed with ether, one group at a time. Combs are removed with a sharp No. 10 Bard-Parker scalpel, blotted on filter paper to remove blood, and weighed to the nearest 0.5 mg. For statistical calculations, the results are expressed as:

$$100 \times \log \frac{\text{comb weight in mg}}{\text{body weight in dg}}$$

Typical results obtained with the method of Munson and Sheps (1958) are illustrated in Fig. 11, which shows excellent agreement in the response to androsterone in two consecutive experiments.

6. Method of Dorfman (1948a) (Injection)

Testosterone propionate dissolved in corn oil is injected subcutaneously once daily for 5 consecutive days, starting 4 days after hatching. Male White Leghorn chicks are used. The daily dose is contained in 0.1 ml of oil. Twenty-four hours after the last injection the chicks are killed with chloroform, and the comb and body weights are determined. The combs are removed as described on page 163. The response is expressed as 100 times the ratio of the comb weight in milligrams to the body weight in grams. A linear relationship is found when the logarithm of dose is plotted against the response.

The results of three tests using the simplified design are shown in Table XIX. The actual potency ratio was 1. Potency ratios of 0.92 ± 0.20,

TABLE XIX

ASSAYS OF TESTOSTERONE PROPIONATE BY INJECTION[a]

$$\frac{\text{High dose of standard}}{\text{Low dose of standard}} = \frac{\text{High dose of unknown}}{\text{Low dose of unknown}}$$

Standard = Unknown

$N = 15$

Dosage level (mg)	b	λ	t	Potency ratio (% ± SE)
0.5, 1.0	47.5	0.374	1.278	92 ± 30
1.0, 2.0	83.9	0.276	0.106	120 ± 20
0.5, 2.0	66.2	0.275	1.865	102 ± 17

[a] Data of Dorfman (1968).

Compound	Dose/day (μg)	N	Comb ratio (Mean ± SE)
Vehicle controls	—	340	0.34 ± 0.013
Oxymetholone (17β-hydroxy-2-hydroxymethylene-17α-methyl-5α-androstan-3-one)	125	23	0.41 ± 0.017
	250	24	0.82 ± 0.026
	500	25	1.13 ± 0.057
Oxandrolone (17β-hydroxy-17α-methyl-2-oxa-5α-androstan-3-one)	125	25	0.41 ± 0.013
	250	24	0.68 ± 0.027
	500	24	0.73 ± 0.035
Methandrostenolone (17β-hydroxy-17α-methyl-androsta-1,4-dien-3-one)	500	25	0.40 ± 0.012
	750	20	0.49 ± 0.024
	1000	24	0.61 ± 0.027
Nandrolone phenpropionate (17β-hydroxyestr-4-en-3-one, 17-phenylpropionate)	31	24	0.47 ± 0.022
	62	25	0.69 ± 0.031
	125	23	0.87 ± 0.058
	250	24	1.35 ± 0.067
	500	24	1.62 ± 0.087
Norbolethone (±13β,17α-diethyl-17β-hydroxygon-4-en-3-one)	15	23	0.55 ± 0.039
	31	24	0.79 ± 0.058
	250	25	1.39 ± 0.080
	500	25	1.59 ± 0.080
Ethylestrenol (17α-ethyl-17β-hydroxyestr-4-ene)	15	22	0.42 ± 0.013
	31	25	0.60 ± 0.033
	250	25	1.21 ± 0.057
	500	25	1.39 ± 0.085
Bolasterone (7α,17α-dimethyl-17β-hydroxy-androst-4-en-3-one)	125	23	0.56 ± 0.028
	187	20	0.86 ± 0.043
	250	23	1.41 ± 0.089
Norethandrolone (17α-ethyl-17β-hydroxyestr-4-en-3-one)	62	25	0.60 ± 0.032
	125	24	0.89 ± 0.059
	250	25	1.23 ± 0.070
4-Hydroxy-17α-methyltestosterone (4,17β-dihydroxy-17α-methylandrost-4-en-3-one)	125	23	0.50 ± 0.023
	250	24	0.83 ± 0.036
	500	25	1.18 ± 0.059
	1000	25	1.43 ± 0.088
Methenolone acetate (17β-hydroxy-1-methyl-5α-androst-1-en-3-one, 17-acetate)	31	24	0.52 ± 0.032
	62	25	0.70 ± 0.052
	125	22	1.05 ± 0.043
	250	24	1.62 ± 0.081
4-Chlorotestosterone acetate (4-chloro-17β-hydroxyandrost-4-en-3-one, 17-acetate)	62	25	0.41 ± 0.013
	125	24	0.72 ± 0.024
	250	24	1.08 ± 0.045
Testosterone (17β-hydroxyandrost-4-en-3-one)	62	25	0.51 ± 0.017
	125	25	0.74 ± 0.039
	250	25	1.72 ± 0.107
Stanozolol (17β-hydroxy-17α-methyl-5α-androstano[3,2-c]pyrazole)	62	24	0.44 ± 0.019
	125	23	0.73 ± 0.029
	250	24	0.89 ± 0.050
	500	25	1.11 ± 0.036

[a] Data of Boris and Ng (1967).

1.20 ± 0.20, and 1.02 ± 0.17 were found. The slopes of the standards and unknowns did not differ significantly. The measure of precision, λ, was 0.374, 0.276, and 0.275.

7. Method of Boris and Ng (1967) (Subcutaneous Injection)

White Leghorn cockerels were 2 days old at the start of treatment and compounds were administered for seven consecutive days. Comb weights were determined on the day following the last treatment day. Results were expressed as the comb ratio (mg comb/gm body weight) (Table XX).

TABLE XXI

RELATIVE POTENCIES ON THE CHICK'S COMB OF CERTAIN STEROIDS
AS ESTIMATED GRAPHICALLY[a]

	Relative potency: testosterone = 1	
Steroid	Subcutaneous injection	Topical
Oxymetholone	0.5	0.05
Oxandrolone	0.3	0.09
Methandrostenolone	0.18	0.09
Nandrolone phenpropionate	1.5	0.03
Norbolethone	4.0	0.4
Ethylestrenol	2.5	0.09
Bolasterone	0.8	1.0
Norethandrolone	1.25	1.5
4-Hydroxy-17α-methyltestosterone	0.5	0.09
Methenolone acetate	1.5	0.3
4-Chlorotestosterone acetate	1.0	0.02
Stanozolol	0.8	0.09

[a] Data of Boris and Ng (1967).

Compounds were administered subcutaneously as suspensions in an aqueous vehicle that consisted of 0.9% NaCl, 0.9% benzyl alcohol, 0.5% carboxymethyl cellulose and 0.4% Tween 80 in distilled water. One injection per day was given in a volume of 0.1 ml/day. Control chicks were treated with vehicle alone. The relative potencies of subcutaneously administered anabolic agents are illustrated in Table XXI. The value of λ for this method was 0.150.

8. Method of Boris and Ng (1967) (Topical Application)

Compounds were administered topically in a vehicle consisting of $\lrcorner$% chloroform and 60% sesame oil (v/v). On each of the 7 treatment

TABLE XXII

Effects of Anabolic Steroids on Chick Comb Ratio:
Topical Administration[a]

Treatment	Dose/day (mg)	N	Comb ratio (mean ± SE)
Vehicle controls	0	531	0.39 ± 0.016
Oxymetholone	50	19	0.65 ± 0.031
	100	17	0.78 ± 0.032
	200	20	0.89 ± 0.037
	400	20	0.97 ± 0.040
Oxandrolone	20	18	0.61 ± 0.024
	40	19	0.70 ± 0.023
	50	20	0.99 ± 0.054
	100	20	1.10 ± 0.055
Methandrostenolone	50	20	0.87 ± 0.030
	100	20	1.02 ± 0.056
	200	20	1.09 ± 0.060
	400	20	1.27 ± 0.060
Nandrolone phenpropionate	50	20	0.55 ± 0.019
	100	20	0.68 ± 0.040
	200	20	0.77 ± 0.031
	400	20	1.01 ± 0.041
Norbolethone	5	20	0.67 ± 0.040
	10	20	0.85 ± 0.055
	20	18	1.18 ± 0.095
	40	18	1.25 ± 0.070
	50	20	1.46 ± 0.082
	100	20	1.75 ± 0.066
	200	20	1.93 ± 0.103
Ethylestrenol	20	18	0.57 ± 0.026
	40	20	0.70 ± 0.042
	50	20	0.99 ± 0.052
	100	20	1.14 ± 0.064
	200	20	1.57 ± 0.078
Bolasterone	5	18	0.98 ± 0.060
	10	20	1.22 ± 0.076
	20	19	1.43 ± 0.076
	50	19	1.96 ± 0.109
	100	20	2.25 ± 0.170
Norethandrolone	5	20	1.14 ± 0.066
	10	20	1.53 ± 0.079
	20	20	1.83 ± 0.090
	40	17	2.02 ± 0.111
4-Hydroxy-17α-methyl-testosterone	20	20	0.61 ± 0.032
	50	19	0.99 ± 0.047
	100	20	1.21 ± 0.060

(*Cont'd.*)

TABLE XXII (*Continued*)

Treatment	Dose/day (mg)	N	Comb ratio (mean ± SE)
Methenolone acetate	5	19	0.51 ± 0.031
	10	19	0.75 ± 0.036
	20	20	1.03 ± 0.059
	40	18	1.17 ± 0.067
4-Chlorotestosterone acetate	100	20	0.56 ± 0.019
	200	17	0.69 ± 0.048
	400	19	0.95 ± 0.070
Testosterone	5	20	0.97 ± 0.074
	10	20	1.24 ± 0.063
	20	19	1.64 ± 0.093
	40	20	1.89 ± 0.088
Stanozolol	20	17	0.56 ± 0.026
	50	20	0.86 ± 0.055
	100	19	1.03 ± 0.062

[a] From Boris and Ng (1967).

days, 0.05 ml was administered topically to the comb. Control chicks were treated with vehicle alone.

The effects of various anabolic steroids on the comb weight are illustrated in Table XXII and the relative potency, estimated graphically, is summarized in Table XXI.

9. *Method of Dorfman and Dorfman (1962) (Subcutaneous Administration)*

White Leghorn cockerels obtained from Hall Bros., Wallingford, Connecticut, were received in the laboratory 1 day after hatching and treatment started either on the same day or 1 day later. The chicks were injected once daily for 7 days. Corn oil or an aqueous Tween suspending medium was employed and, in either case, the daily injection volume was 0.1 ml. One day after the last injection the animals were sacrificed and body weights and comb weights were determined. The results were expressed as the ratio of milligrams of comb weight to grams of body weight, and statistical calculations were performed according to the methods of Fisher (1934) and Bülbring (1935).

The chick comb response to certain subcutaneously injected steroids in corn oil are presented in Table XXIII, and the calculated relative potencies compared to testosterone are presented in Table XXIV. The

TABLE XXIII

CHICK COMB RESPONSE TO VARIOUS STEROIDS INJECTED SUBCUTANEOUSLY
AND DISSOLVED IN CORN OIL[a]

Steroid	Total dose (μg)	No. of chicks	Comb ratio (mean $\pm$ SE)
0	0	59	0.36 ± 0.011
Testosterone	80	27	0.56 ± 0.023
	160	27	0.56 ± 0.025
	200	19	0.78 ± 0.044
	400	17	1.04 ± 0.043
	800	19	1.11 ± 0.069
Testosterone propionate	40	20	0.62 ± 0.030
	160	20	1.30 ± 0.06
Androst-4-ene-3,17-dione	200	18	0.54 ± 0.028
	400	20	0.64 ± 0.033
	800	19	0.78 ± 0.061
17β-Hydroxyandrostan-3-one	40	20	0.85 ± 0.03
	160	20	1.53 ± 0.08
Nortestosterone	80	26	0.44 ± 0.021
	160	28	0.50 ± 0.016
	320	27	0.52 ± 0.021
Adrenosterone	400	17	0.39 ± 0.019
	800	17	0.43 ± 0.022
	1600	19	0.46 ± 0.018

[a] From Dorfman (1962).

TABLE XXIV

RELATIVE POTENCY OF CERTAIN STEROIDS INJECTED SUBCUTANEOUSLY
IN CORN OIL[a]

Steroid	No. of chicks	Potency ratio: testosterone = 100	95% confidence limit
Androst-4-ene-3,17-dione	139	21	16–27
17β-Hydroxyandrostan-3-one	122	370	318–422
Testosterone propionate	122	395	339–451
Androst-4-ene-3α,17β-diol	147	101	70–138
Androst-4-ene-3β,17β-diol	160	99	76–126

[a] From Dorfman (1962).

TABLE XXV

Chick Comb Response to Various Steroids Injected Subcutaneously
and Suspended in Tween[a]

Steroid	Total dose (μg)	No. of chicks	Comb ratio (mean $\pm$ SE)
0	0	329	0.37 $\pm$ 0.005
Testosterone	20	59	0.39 $\pm$ 0.014
	40	86	0.42 $\pm$ 0.009
	80	84	0.46 $\pm$ 0.011
	160	67	0.61 $\pm$ 0.019
	200	29	0.61 $\pm$ 0.022
	400	28	0.88 $\pm$ 0.045
	800	29	1.17 $\pm$ 0.093
Androst-4-ene-3,17-dione	20	40	0.36 $\pm$ 0.011
	40	42	0.38 $\pm$ 0.013
	80	38	0.41 $\pm$ 0.012
	160	21	0.40 $\pm$ 0.014
	400	27	0.51 $\pm$ 0.022
	800	27	0.59 $\pm$ 0.023
	1600	28	0.66 $\pm$ 0.029
Nortestosterone	80	28	0.44 $\pm$ 0.011
	160	28	0.45 $\pm$ 0.013
	320	27	0.55 $\pm$ 0.018
Epiandrosterone	20	29	0.31 $\pm$ 0.014
	40	32	0.34 $\pm$ 0.015
	80	33	0.40 $\pm$ 0.015
	160	31	0.43 $\pm$ 0.018
	320	32	0.39 $\pm$ 0.014
Androst-5-ene-3β,17β-diol	20	32	0.38 $\pm$ 0.012
	40	34	0.46 $\pm$ 0.017
	80	34	0.46 $\pm$ 0.024
	160	33	0.50 $\pm$ 0.016
	320	31	0.66 $\pm$ 0.024
Dehydroepiandrosterone	20	33	0.42 $\pm$ 0.014
	40	33	0.43 $\pm$ 0.017
	80	32	0.38 $\pm$ 0.019
	160	29	0.46 $\pm$ 0.016
	320	33	0.52 $\pm$ 0.023
Adrenosterone	20	32	0.41 $\pm$ 0.015
	40	56	0.37 $\pm$ 0.009
	80	55	0.40 $\pm$ 0.015
	160	52	0.39 $\pm$ 0.011
	320	55	0.44 $\pm$ 0.014

[a] From Dorfman (1962).

4. ANDROGENS AND ANABOLIC AGENTS

corresponding data for steroids injected in a Tween suspension are presented in Tables XXV and XXVI.

The corn oil vehicle proved to be more efficient than the Tween suspending medium in expressing the activity of a given compound. Actually testosterone in Tween was only 38% as active than when dissolved in corn oil. Similarly, androst-4-ene-3,17-dione was only 31% as active as compared to the activity of the steroid in oil (Table XXVII).

TABLE XXVI

RELATIVE POTENCY OF CERTAIN STEROIDS INJECTED SUBCUTANEOUSLY
IN TWEEN SUSPENSION[a]

Steroid	No. of chicks	Relative potency: testosterone = 100	95% confidence limit
Androst-4-ene-3,17-dione	340	17	13.3–21.6
Androst-5-ene-3β,17β-diol	335	49	32–71
Dehydroepiandrosterone	331	65	51–83
19-Nortestosterone	293	35	30–40

[a]From Dorfman (1962).

By the injection route, androst-4-ene-3,17-dione was 21% as active as testosterone when injected in corn oil and 17% as active as the standard in a Tween suspending medium. This fact may indicate that the more highly active form of the steroid is the 17β-hydroxy derivative and that the rate of reduction to the 17β-form is indeed slow. The high activity of the 17β-hydroxy derivative is in keeping with the high activity of 17β-hydroxyandrostan-3-one which administered in corn oil was 370% of the activity of testosterone.

The activity of both androst-4-ene-3α,17β-diol and androst-4-ene-3β,17β-diol (Table XXIV) were precisely the same as that of testosterone, which argues for the rapid transformation of both these stereoisomers to testosterone.

The subcutaneous injection method does not have a high index of precision. When the Tween suspension vehicle was used, a mean of $\lambda = 0.483$ (range 0.383–0.636) was observed; this is not satisfactory for an assay procedure. This precision was far better with the oil medium since a mean λ of 0.212 (range 0.132–0.320) was calculated.

RALPH I. DORFMAN

TABLE XXVII

INFLUENCE OF THE VEHICLE IN A SUBCUTANEOUS CHICK COMB TEST[a]

Standard			Unknown			Potency ratio	Error range	
Steroid (vehicle)	Total dose (μg)	No. of chicks	Steroid (vehicle)	Total dose (μg)	No. of chicks		P = 0.95 +	% −
Testosterone (oil solution)	80, 160, 200, 400, 800	82	Testosterone (Tween solution)	80, 160, 200, 400, 800	237	35	35	26
Androst-4-ene-3,17-dione (oil solution)	200, 400, 800	57	Androst-4-ene-3,17-dione (Tween solution)	160, 400, 800, 1600	103	31	35	27

[a] Dorfman (1962).

10. Method of Dorfman and Dorfman (1963a) (Orally Administered)

White Leghorn cockerels 1 or 2 days old were placed on a chick starting mash containing the test compounds. Control chicks were fed the same diet without additions. After 7 days on the diet, the chicks were sacrificed with ether and comb and body weights were determined. Results are reported as the ratio of milligrams of comb weight to grams

TABLE XXVIII

CHICK COMB RESPONSE TO VARIOUS STEROIDS INCORPORATED
INTO THE DIET (TRIAL 1)[a]

Steroid	Dose (mg/kg)	No. of chicks	Comb ratio (mean ± SE)
0	0	491	0.382 ± 0.005
Testosterone	5	20	0.45 ± 0.025
	10	168	0.84 ± 0.020
	20	204	1.17 ± 0.020
	40	174	1.55 ± 0.011
	80	25	1.89 ± 0.106
Androst-4-ene-3,17-dione	10	111	0.735 ± 0.024
	20	141	1.07 ± 0.026
	40	133	1.33 ± 0.036
	80	62	1.73 ± 0.036
	160	41	2.01 ± 0.124
17α-Methyltestosterone	5	46	0.49 ± 0.019
	10	88	0.62 ± 0.023
	20	26	0.90 ± 0.030
	40	27	1.17 ± 0.042
19-Nortestosterone	10	55	0.76 ± 0.029
	20	55	0.96 ± 0.036
	40	55	1.42 ± 0.044
Dehydroepiandrosterone	10	13	0.53 ± 0.030
	40	19	0.42 ± 0.024
	80	18	0.47 ± 0.028
	160	20	0.58 ± 0.033
Androst-5-ene-3β,17β-diol	20	25	0.32 ± 0.014
	35	27	0.39 ± 0.017
	80	25	0.50 ± 0.021
11β-Hydroxy-androst-4-ene-3,17-dione	20	20	0.63 ± 0.036
	40	20	1.01 ± 0.076
	80	19	1.20 ± 0.073
Adrenosterone	40	40	0.89 ± 0.054
	80	41	1.20 ± 0.051
	160	22	1.43 ± 0.083

[a] From Dorfman and Dorfman (1963a).

of body weight, and statistical calculations were done as suggested by Bliss (1944).

The chick comb response to various steroids incorporated into the diet is presented in Tables XXVIII and XXIX. Table XXVIII indicates the data collected over a 10-month period, whereas the data in Table XXIX

TABLE XXIX

CHICK COMB RESPONSE TO VARIOUS STEROIDS INCORPORATED
INTO THE DIET (TRIAL 2)[a]

Steroid	Dose (mg/kg)	No. of chicks	Comb ratio (mean ± SE)
0	0	215	0.35 ± 0.008
Androst-4-ene-3,17-dione	10	98	0.71 ± 0.032
	20	95	0.95 ± 0.041
	40	88	1.18 ± 0.049
Dehydroepiandrosterone	10	23	0.43 ± 0.020
	20	22	0.46 ± 0.030
	40	64	0.44 ± 0.017
	80	63	0.54 ± 0.022
	160	42	0.69 ± 0.030
	320	19	1.24 ± 0.060
Epiandrosterone	20	20	0.37 ± 0.020
	40	40	0.40 ± 0.014
	80	38	0.51 ± 0.018
	160	29	0.60 ± 0.030
17α-Methyl-androst-5-ene-3β,17β-diol	20	20	0.35 ± 0.200
	40	23	0.47 ± 0.030
	80	44	0.50 ± 0.019
	160	42	0.79 ± 0.041
Androstane-3,17-dione	20	18	0.53 ± 0.030
	40	40	0.66 ± 0.026
	80	40	0.79 ± 0.026

[a] From Dorfman and Dorfman (1963a).

were collected over the following 6 months. Some overlap in compounds studied is indicated. Twenty-four trials were run; the experimental design of Bliss (1944) was used, with a total of 36–80 chicks. The mean potency ratio varied from 69 to 141% (mean 105) against a theoretical potency ratio of 100%. No statistically significant differences could be found for slopes, and λ varied from 0.13 to 0.40 with a mean of 0.248.

Table XXX illustrates typical results using three or four concentrations of the unknown and the standard.

The relative potency of 12 steroids is summarized in Table XXX. Testosterone, 19-nortestosterone, androst-4-ene-3,17-dione, and 17α-methyltestosterone have high relative potencies of 100, 76, 71, and 63% values, respectively. Particularly striking was the high value of 57% for 11α-hydroxyandrost-4-ene-3,17-dione, which seems to indicate that either the compound is active per se or may be converted to the 11-keto compound adrenosterone.

TABLE XXX

RELATIVE POTENCY OF STEROIDS INCORPORATED IN THE DIET[a]

Steroid	Total No. of chicks	Relative potency: testosterone = 100	95% confidence limit
19-Nortestosterone	756	76	68–85
Androst-4-ene-3,17-dione	1079	71	63–80
Methyltestosterone	778	63	55–72
11α-Hydroxyandrost-4-ene-3,17-dione	118	57	46–68
11β-Hydroxyandrost-4-ene-3,17-dione	650	39	34–45
Adrenosterone	694	32	28.5–35.8
Androstane-3,17-dione	91	21	15–29
	118	27	21–35
17β-Hydroxyandrostan-3-one	119	14	10.4–18.9
Dehydroepiandrosterone	675	7	6.3–7.7
Epiandrosterone	109	5	3.5–7.3
	99	7	5.6–8.7
17α-Methylandrost-5-ene-3β,17β-diol	170	5	4–6.2
Androst-4-ene-3β,17β-diol	152	124	123–151
Androst-4-ene-3α,17β-diol	129	97	73–129

[a] From Dorfman and Dorfman (1963a).

Compounds ordinarily considered to be relatively inactive by the oral route in mammals showed high activity when admixed with food. Four steroids, testosterone, androst-4-ene-3,17-dione, 17α-methyltestosterone, and 19-nortestosterone, all showed a high order of activity and were about equal in potency. Both Δ^5-3β-hydroxysteroids, dehydroepiandrosterone, and 17α-methylandrost-5-ene,3β,17β-diol, had a low order of activity, that is, less than 10% that of testosterone. This may be due either to a relative lack of absorption through the gut or low order of activity of the compounds per se, or a combination of both. The low order of activity of 17β-hydroxyandrostan-3-one (14% of testosterone), epiandrosterone (6% of testosterone), and androstane-3,17-dione (33% of androst-4-ene-3,17-dione) points up the relatively low activity of 5α-reduced steroids. This, too, may be due to poor absorption from the gastrointestinal tract.

Table XXX records the values obtained for the stereoisomers and rost-4-ene-3β,17β-diol and androst-4-ene-3α,17β-diol (and published previously by Dorfman and Dorfman, 1963a). The activity of these steroids were indistinguishable from that of testosterone.

The assay procedure has a reasonable precision, as indicated by a mean λ value of 0.248 (0.13–0.40).

11. Method of Dorfman and Dorfman (1963b) (Inunction of Corn Oil to Comb)

White Leghorn cockerels were received in the laboratory 1–2 days after hatching. The combs were inuncted once daily for 7 days with 0.05 ml of a corn oil or an absolute ethanol solution. Twenty-four hours after the last application, the animals were sacrificed with ether and the comb and body weights were determined. The responses are expressed as the ratio of the comb weight in milligrams to the body weight in grams. The statistical calculations were done by standard methods (Emmens, 1962).

Tables XXXI–XXXII list the relative response of various steroids when the compounds were inuncted to the comb in an oil solution. The data were collected over a four-year period. Table XXXI deals with data collected over the first two years, and Tables XXXII and XXXIII represent the data collected during the last two years, classified on the

TABLE XXXI

Chick's Comb Response to Various Steroids Inuncted in a
Corn Oil Solution (Trial 1)[a]

Steroid	Total dose (μg)	No. of chicks	Comb ratio (mean ± SE)
0	0	160	0.34 ± 0.007
Testosterone	30	33	0.58 ± 0.104
	40	50	0.58 ± 0.026
	60	33	0.75 ± 0.033
	160	11	1.38 ± 0.126
Δ4-Androstene-3,17-dione	15	22	0.52 ± 0.03
	30	23	0.96 ± 0.07
	45	21	0.88 ± 0.06
	60	22	1.26 ± 0.10
Δ1,4-Androstadiene-3,17-dione	50	9	0.82 ± 0.05
	100	10	1.20 ± 0.07
	200	10	1.29 ± 0.13
17β-Hydroxyandrostan-3-one	80	15	1.02 ± 0.08
	320	14	1.71 ± 0.16

TABLE XXXI (*Continued*)

Steroid	Total dose (μg)	No. of chicks	Comb ratio (mean ± SE)
19-Nortestosterone	50	17	0.58 ± 0.032
	60	33	0.79 ± 0.049
	80	39	0.76 ± 0.035
	100	42	0.94 ± 0.057
	120	31	1.08 ± 0.065
	200	46	1.17 ± 0.067
	400	32	1.57 ± 0.095
Dehydroepiandrosterone	400	21	0.43 ± 0.020
	80	19	0.50 ± 0.029
	160	18	0.72 ± 0.048
	200	10	1.44 ± 0.15
Epiandrosterone	100	51	0.54 ± 0.024
	200	49	0.69 ± 0.031
	400	23	0.95 ± 0.063
Androstane-3,17-dione	120	40	0.66 ± 0.029
	200	29	0.96 ± 0.042
	400	14	1.28 ± 0.113
11β-Hydroxy-$Δ^4$-androstene-3,17-dione	120	11	0.90 ± 0.06
	320	12	1.16 ± 0.10
11β-Hydroxytestosterone	30	10	0.33 ± 0.02
	60	21	0.46 ± 0.03
	120	20	0.46 ± 0.03
11-Ketotestosterone	30	10	0.32 ± 0.02
	60	21	0.44 ± 0.02
	120	20	0.51 ± 0.03
Androsterone	60	27	0.49 ± 0.03
	120	27	0.53 ± 0.02
	180	15	0.99 ± 0.08
$Δ^7$-Dehydrotestosterone	30	12	0.39 ± 0.02
	60	12	0.40 ± 0.03
	120	14	0.48 ± 0.04
	240	14	0.50 ± 0.03
Androsterone	15	97	0.59 ± 0.017
	20	97	0.65 ± 0.025
	30	63	0.89 ± 0.040
	40	121	0.83 ± 0.024
	45	13	0.76 ± 0.070
	60	60	1.18 ± 0.051
	120	25	1.76 ± 0.088
$Δ^{16}$-Dehydroprogesterone	100	30	0.45 ± 0.016
	200	28	0.60 ± 0.023
	800	30	0.82 ± 0.033

[a] From Dorfman and Dorfman (1963c).

188 RALPH I. DORFMAN

basis of the comb ratios of the control group. All data in Table XXXII and represented as Trial 2, were obtained when the vehicle control groups had a ratio of 0.37 or less, while the data of Table XXXII are those from experiments in which the vehicle controls had a mean comb ratio of 0.38 or greater.

TABLE XXXII

CHICK'S COMB RESPONSE TO STEROIDS ADMINISTERED BY INUNCTION IN CORN OIL (LOW CONTROL) (TRIAL 2)[a]

Steroid	Total dose (μg)	No. of chicks	Comb ratio (mean ± SE)
0	0	296	0.33 ± 0.004
Testosterone	40	70	0.65 ± 0.023
	80	82	0.75 ± 0.023
	160	83	0.94 ± 0.033
Δ^4-Androstene-3,17-dione	40	123	0.59 ± 0.014
	80	103	0.75 ± 0.023
	160	104	0.86 ± 0.028
Dehydroepiandrosterone	20	20	0.42 ± 0.025
	40	21	0.44 ± 0.020
	80	19	0.50 ± 0.029
Δ^1-(5α)-Androstene-3,17-dione	40	38	0.61 ± 0.027
	80	40	0.73 ± 0.030
	160	37	0.89 ± 0.046
11β-Hydroxy-Δ^4-androstene-	40	29	0.37 ± 0.014
	80	28	0.39 ± 0.014
	160	25	0.49 ± 0.023
9α-Fluoro-11β-hydroxy-Δ^4-androstene-3,17-dione	40	19	0.41 ± 0.012
	160	18	0.35 ± 0.020
	320	20	0.37 ± 0.018
11β-Hydroxy-Δ^1-17α-methyl-Δ^1-(5α)-androsten-3-one	20	16	0.52 ± 0.030
	40	16	0.67 ± 0.038
	80	15	0.80 ± 0.048
	160	15	0.91 ± 0.035
11α-Hydroxy-17α-methyltestosterone	40	14	0.35 ± 0.018
	160	14	0.41 ± 0.024
17β-Hydroxy-$\Delta^{1,4}$-androstadien-3-one	40	15	0.51 ± 0.018
	160	15	0.59 ± 0.028
6β-Hydroxy-Δ^4-androstene-3,17-dione	40	14	0.36 ± 0.014
	160	14	0.39 ± 0.013
6β-Hydroxy-Δ^4-androstene-3,11,17-trione	40	17	0.37 ± 0.017
	80	18	0.30 ± 0.058
	160	17	0.33 ± 0.068

[a] From Dorfman and Dorfman (1963c).

TABLE XXXIII

Chick's Comb Response to Steroids Administered by Inunction in Corn Oil (High Control) (Trial 3)[a]

Steroid	Total dose (μg)	No. of chicks	Comb ratio (mean ± SE)
0	0	372	0.43 ± 0.005
Testosterone	20	40	0.59 ± 0.025
	40	88	0.73 ± 0.023
	80	94	0.87 ± 0.031
	160	71	1.12 ± 0.048
	320	21	1.44 ± 0.080
Androsterone	20	83	0.64 ± 0.018
	40	73	0.73 ± 0.024
	80	79	0.85 ± 0.024
	160	17	1.08 ± 0.029
17α-Methyltestosterone	40	81	0.87 ± 0.028
	80	78	0.99 ± 0.035
	160	58	1.17 + 0.047
	320	21	1.13 ± 0.202
$\varDelta^4$-Androstene-3,17-dione	40	21	0.80 ± 0.035
	80	25	0.94 ± 0.090
$\varDelta^7$-Dehydrotestosterone	40	13	0.55 ± 0.030
	80	34	0.64 ± 0.021
	160	34	0.76 ± 0.027
	320	33	0.95 ± 0.039
	640	23	1.04 ± 0.040
17α-Methyl-$\varDelta^5$-androstene-$3\beta,17\beta$-diol	40	18	0.73 ± 0.038
	80	37	0.72 ± 0.033
	160	39	0.93 ± 0.039
	320	19	1.03 ± 0.070
11α-Hydroxy-17α-methyl-testosterone	40	22	0.42 ± 0.016
	80	21	0.40 ± 0.019
	160	20	0.45 ± 0.026
	320	21	0.45 ± 0.025
17α Ethynyl-19-nortestosterone	200	10	0.47 ± 0.025
	1000	10	0.46 ± 0.034
	2000	9	0.48 ± 0.027
11β-Hydroxy-17α-methyl-$\varDelta^1$-(5α)-androsten-3-one	40	22	0.74 ± 0.034
	80	21	0.87 ± 0.060
	160	21	1.32 ± 0.095
	320	21	1.53 ± 0.100
15-Hydroxytestosterone	20	16	0.34 ± 0.017
	80	18	0.36 ± 0.014
	320	18	0.38 ± 0.018
14α-Hydroxytestosterone	20	16	0.36 ± 0.018
	80	18	0.42 ± 0.022
	320	17	0.38 ± 0.022

[a] From Dorfman and Dorfman (1963c).

TABLE XXXIV

Chick's Comb Response to C-9 and C-11 Substituted Derivatives of
17α-Methyltestosterone Inuncted in Corn Oil

Expt. No.	Material administered	Total dose (μg)	No. of chicks	Comb ratio (mean ± SE)
1	0	0	23	0.39 ± 0.018
	17α-Methyltestosterone	20	15	0.71 ± 0.042
		40	14	0.72 ± 0.042
		80	14	1.11 ± 0.111
		160	15	1.12 ± 0.065
	11β-Hydroxy-17α-methyltestosterone	80	14	0.54 ± 0.032
		160	14	0.50 ± 0.031
		320	14	0.56 ± 0.029
	9α-Fluoro-11-hydroxy-17α-methyl-testosterone	80	13	0.46 ± 0.034
		160	14	0.48 ± 0.023
		320	14	0.49 ± 0.026
2	0	0	17	0.37 ± 0.025
	17α-Methyltestosterone	20	15	0.62 ± 0.041
		40	15	0.70 ± 0.054
		80	15	0.82 ± 0.068
		160	15	0.95 ± 0.059
	11β-Hydroxy-17α-methyltestosterone	80	14	0.43 ± 0.019
		160	14	0.51 ± 0.033
		320	13	0.52 ± 0.032
	9α-Fluoro-11β-hydroxy-17α-methyl-testosterone	80	14	0.39 ± 0.025
		160	14	0.37 ± 0.028
		320	14	0.45 ± 0.025
3	17α-Methyltestosterone	40	10	0.59 ± 0.042
		80	9	0.76 ± 0.066
	9α-Fluoro-11β-hydroxy-17α-methyl-testosterone	5	9	0.37 ± 0.024
		80	10	0.39 ± 0.084
		400	10	0.47 ± 0.029
	9α-Fluoro-11-keto-17α-methyltestosterone	5	10	0.38 ± 0.022
		80	10	0.45 ± 0.028
		400	10	0.59 ± 0.052
4	0	0	15	0.36 ± 0.015
	17α-Methyltestosterone	40	10	0.48 ± 0.027
		80	9	0.54 ± 0.026
		160	10	0.62 ± 0.032
	9α-Fluoro-11β-hydroxy-17α-methyl-testosterone	10	9	0.37 ± 0.021
		100	10	0.37 ± 0.019
	9α-Fluoro-11-keto-17α-methyltestosterone	10	9	0.39 ± 0.018
		100	9	0.46 ± 0.033

Table XXXIV lists the information obtained on various 9α-fluoro and 11-oxygenated derivatives of 17α-methyltestosterone when inuncted to the comb in oil.

Table XXXV summarizes the relative potencies of various steroids when applied to the comb in oil. Quite unlike the activity of androgens on a mammalian indicator such as the seminal vesicle, the 17 C=O compounds can be more active on the comb than the 17β-hydroxy compounds. This can be said since Δ^4-androstene-3,17-dione had 178% (121–234) the activity of testosterone. This was not true, however, in the androstane

TABLE XXXV

RELATIVE POTENCY OF VARIOUS STEROIDS BY A CHICK COMB INUNCTION TEST USING CORN OIL[a]

Steroid	Total No. of chicks	Relative potency: testosterone = 100%	95% confidence limits
Androsterone	643	198	182–204
	545	130	104–156
Δ^4-Androstene-3,17-dione	254	234	212–264
	335	121	99–145
Adrenosterone	235	22	24–42
17β-Hydroxyandrostan-3-one	195	194	159–247
$\Delta^{1,4}$-Androstadiene-3,17-dione	195	178	141–236
11β-Hydroxy-Δ^4-androstene-3,17-dione	189	59	36–95
	288	33	27–41
Dehydroepiandrosterone	234	44	33–58
	295	65	43–82
Androstane-3,17-dione	569	18	16–21
19-Nortestosterone	400	72	63–63
Epiandrosterone	289	23	18–30
Δ^{16}-Dehydroprogesterone	254	12	9–17
17α-Methyl-5-androstene-3β,17β-diol	406	65	53–78
Δ^7-Dehydrotestosterone	430	36	29–43
17α-Methyltestosterone	410	145	125–167
17α-Methyl-17β-hydroxy-Δ^1-5α-androsten-3-one	378	192	137–231
	158	123	93–140
Δ^1-(5α)-Androstene-3,17-dione	350	206	176–240
9α-Fluoro-11β-hydroxy-17α-methyltestosterone	88	5	3–7
	102	4	2–6
	50	2	1–3
11β-Hydroxy-17α-methyltestosterone	90	4	2–6
11-Keto-17α-methyltestosterone	50	6	4–8
Δ^4-Androstene-3β,17β-diol	103	117	99–141

[a] From Dorfman and Dorfman (1963c).

series, since 17β-hydroxyandrostan-3-one was 194% of testosterone, whereas androstane-3,17-dione was only 18% as active as the standard.

The introduction of the 17α-methyl group tended to increase significantly the androgenicity since 17α-methyltestosterone was 145% (range 125–167%) as active as testosterone (Table XXXV).

The introduction of an 11-oxygen function with or without a 9α-fluoro group caused severe decreases in biological activity. Adrenosterone was 22% as active as testosterone and 11β-hydroxy-Δ^4-androstene-3,71-dione was 46% (33 and 59% in two trials) as active. Similar decreases were observed in the methyltestosterone series. 11β-Hydroxy-17-methyltestosterone was 3% as active as 17α-methyltestosterone, 11-keto-17-methyltestosterone was similarly low at 4%. 9α-Fluoro-11β-hydroxy-17α-methyltestosterone was only 3% as active as methyltestosterone.

Reduction of the Δ^4 double bond to the 5α-reduced form increased the potency. Thus, 17β-hydroxyandrostan-3-one was almost twice as active as testosterone. This was not the case, however, for the reduction of Δ^4-androstene-3,17-dione. In this case the decrease in potency was of the order of 90%.

Perhaps the most remarkable finding in the series, represented in Table XXXV, is the androgenicity of Δ^{16}-dehydroprogesterone. It is of some interest in this case to ascertain whether the activity is due to the conversion to a C_{19} steroid or whether the C_{21} compound is active per se.

The chick comb inunction assay using the corn oil appeared to be significantly more accurate than the ethanol test. This was ascertained on the basis of the λ values, which varied from 0.195 to 0.320 with a mean of 0.257.

12. Method of Dorfman and Dorfman (1963c) (Inunction in Ethanol)

It is possible to increase the sensitivity of the assay by practicing the chick comb inunction technique using absolute ethanol. Typical responses to testosterone and other steroids are illustrated in Tables XXXVI and XXXVII. As little as 1 μg of testosterone (total dose in 0.35 ml) may be detected by this modification. Table XXXVI compares the response of the three steroids: testosterone, Δ^1-dehydro-17α-methyltestosterone, and 2-hydroxymethylene-17α-methyldihydrotestosterone. At the 3 μg total dose level, testosterone showed a highly significant increase in the comb size, and a reasonably linear log-dose-response relationship was found between 3 and 27 μg. Δ^1-Dehydro-17α-methyltestosterone produced a log-dose-response line parallel to that of testosterone. The steroid 2-hydroxymethylene-17α-methyldihydrotestosterone was inactive at the dose levels of 3, 9, and 27 μg and showed only a slight effect at a total dose of 81 μg.

Table XXXVII lists the chick comb response to absolute ethanol inuncted androgens which include androsterone, testosterone, dehydroepiandrosterone, androstane-3,17-dione, and Δ^7-dehydrotestosterone.

The values for λ for the chick androgen assay procedure using the absolute ethanol technique varied from 0.220 to 0.390 with a mean of about 0.305.

TABLE XXXVI

COMPARATIVE CHICK'S COMB RESPONSE TO TESTOSTERONE,
Δ^1-DEHYDRO-17α-METHYLTESTOSTERONE, AND
2-HYDROXYMETHYLENE-17α-METHYLDIHYDROTESTOSTERONE
(ETHANOL INUNCTION)[a]

Steroid	Total dose (μg)	No. of chicks	Comb ratio (mean ± SE)
0	0	18	0.34 ± 0.019
Testosterone	3	20	0.45 ± 0.020
	9	20	0.51 ± 0.025
	27	19	0.62 ± 0.028
	81	19	0.92 ± 0.047
Δ^1-Dehydro-17α-methyltestosterone	3	19	0.35 ± 0.015
	9	20	0.42 ± 0.020
	27	20	0.47 ± 0.022
	81	20	0.57 ± 0.037
2-Hydroxymethylene-17α-methyl-dihydrotestosterone[b]	3	20	0.37 ± 0.011
	9	20	0.36 ± 0.016
	27	19	0.35 ± 0.017
	81	19	0.41 ± 0.019

[a] From Dorfman and Dorfman (1963c).
[b] Dihydrotestosterone = 17β-hydroxyandrostan-3-one.

C. SPARROW'S BILL

Androgens cause blackening of the bill of the English sparrow. Thus, the male in the winter months has an ivory-colored bill, and as the testis function increases in the spring the bill blackens. This blackening is due to the increased concentration of androgen resulting from the increased testicular function, and it has been suggested for the assay of androgens but as yet has not been adapted to quantitative assay. Some of the results of Pfeiffer *et al.* (1944) are presented to illustrate the potentialities of the method.

English sparrows (*Passer domesticus*) were trapped as immature birds in summer. The males were castrated and females were used as intact

TABLE XXXVII

CHICK COMB RESPONSE TO VARIOUS STEROIDS INUNCTED IN
ABSOLUTE ALCOHOL[a]

Steroid	Total dose (μg)	No. of chicks	Comb ratio (mean $\pm$ SE)
0	0	411	0.36 $\pm$ 0.004
Androsterone	0.8	95	0.44 $\pm$ 0.010
	1.0	114	0.42 $\pm$ 0.009
	1.6	96	0.48 $\pm$ 0.012
	2.0	189	0.48 $\pm$ 0.009
	3.2	94	0.56 $\pm$ 0.014
	4.0	188	0.60 $\pm$ 0.014
	6.4	78	0.69 $\pm$ 0.021
	8.0	184	0.74 $\pm$ 0.017
	16.0	193	0.86 $\pm$ 0.022
Testosterone	0.8	58	0.45 $\pm$ 0.016
	1.6	56	0.51 $\pm$ 0.015
	2.0	15	0.45 $\pm$ 0.032
	3.2	56	0.54 $\pm$ 0.018
	4.0	15	0.56 $\pm$ 0.020
	6.4	42	0.69 $\pm$ 0.023
Dehydroepiandrosterone	0.8	31	0.41 $\pm$ 0.016
	1.6	30	0.46 $\pm$ 0.015
	2.0	14	0.48 $\pm$ 0.019
	3.2	29	0.49 $\pm$ 0.023
	4.0	15	0.59 $\pm$ 0.027
	6.4	15	0.53 $\pm$ 0.034
	8.0	37	0.56 $\pm$ 0.022
	16.0	37	0.64 $\pm$ 0.029
	32.0	23	0.72 $\pm$ 0.045
	64.0	21	0.78 $\pm$ 0.042
Androstane-3,17-dione	1.0	33	0.46 $\pm$ 0.020
	2.0	33	0.52 $\pm$ 0.023
	4.0	31	0.61 $\pm$ 0.031
	8.0	33	0.68 $\pm$ 0.026
	16.0	32	0.81 $\pm$ 0.041
Δ^7-Dehydrotestosterone	2.0	20	0.41 $\pm$ 0.023
	4.0	17	0.36 $\pm$ 0.018
	8.0	19	0.37 $\pm$ 0.058
	16.0	16	0.45 $\pm$ 0.031

[a] From Dorfman and Dorfman (1963c).

animals in the fall of the year. The animals were housed in wire cages measuring 3 × 3 × 4 feet. A dry mixture of finely cracked grain and poultry growing mash was fed along with an ample supply of fresh water. In the experiments presented in Tables XXXVIII–XL, some animals received the hormone by direct application to the breast; some animals

TABLE XXXVIII

RESPONSE OF THE SPARROW'S BILL TO TESTOSTERONE
PROPIONATE ADMINISTERED INTRAMUSCULARLY[a]

Daily dose (μg)	No. of birds and sex	No. of days	Animals responding (%)
2.5	4 F	10	0
5.0	4 F	10	0
10.0	4 F	10	100
2.5	3 M[b]	10	0
5.0	3 M	10	67
10.0	3 M	10	100

[a] Pfeiffer et al. (1944).
[b] M = castrate males.

TABLE XXXIX

RESPONSE OF THE SPARROW'S BILL TO TESTOSTERONE
PROPIONATE APPLIED TO THE SKIN OF THE BREAST[a]

Daily dose (μg)	No. of birds and sex	No. of days	Animals responding (%)
2.0	3 F	25	33
4.0	5 F	25	60
8.0	4 F	15	75

[a] Pfeiffer et al. (1944).

received the hormone subcutaneously; and still others received the hormone by direct application to the bill. The hormone was given intramuscularly in 0.05 ml of sesame oil per day, or was applied in absolute alcohol to the skin in the breast region. The local bill reaction was produced by placing one drop of an absolute alcohol solution on one side of the bill from a No. 22 hypodermic needle fitted to a 1-ml tuberculin syringe.

Table XXXVIII presents the response of the sparrow's bill to testosterone propionate administered intramuscularly. A total of 100 μg administered over 10 days produced 100% responses in both males and normal females. A total of 50 μg in the same period of time produced blackening in 2 of 3 castrated males. The application of the hormone to the skin in the breast area was not particularly effective (Table XXXIX).

TABLE XL

RESPONSE OF THE SPARROW'S BILL TO TESTOSTERONE AND
ANDROSTERONE APPLIED LOCALLY[a]

Androgen	Daily dose (μg)	No. of birds and sex	No. of days	Animals responding (%)
Testosterone	0.5	5 F	10	60
	1.0	2 F	10	100
	2.0	2 F	10	100
	0.063	6 M[b]	16	67
	0.125	3 M	10	100
	0.250	4 M	10	100
Androsterone	0.25	4 F	10	100
	0.50	4 F	10	100
	1.00	4 F	10	100
	3.30	4 F	10	100
	6.60	4 F	10	100
	13.30	3 F	10	100
	0.063	5 M	16	100
	0.125	5 M	10	60
	0.250	10 M	10	100

[a] Pfeiffer et al. (1944).
[b] M = castrate males.

However, direct application of androgens, either androsterone or testosterone, was the most sensitive test yet described. A total of 1 μg of testosterone administered in 16 divided doses produced positive responses in 4 of 6 castrated males, and a similar dose of androsterone produced 100% of positive responses in 5 castrated males (Table XL).

D. ADDITIONAL BIRD METHODS

In addition to the methods already described, reports on the use of the capon's comb by injection have been made by Ruzicka et al. (1934), Tschopp (1935), Butenandt and Tscherning (1934), and Dingemanse et al. (1931). Various methods using the direct comb application of androgens have been described by Dessau (1935, 1937), Voss (1937), Fussganger (1934), Oesting and Webster (1938), Mussio Fournier *et al.* (1940). Courier and Jost (1939) have published studies on the use of the chick comb method.

IV. Mammalian Assays

A. ANDROGEN METHOD OF MATHISON AND HAYS (1945)

The standard and unknown should be run simultaneously at each of two concentrations so that the ratio of the high dose to the low dose of both unknown and standard is equal to 4. For this purpose the high dose

TABLE XLI

ASSAY OF TESTOSTERONE PROPIONATE USING THE RESPONSE OF THE
SEMINAL VESICLES OF THE CASTRATED MALE RAT[a]

$$\frac{\text{High dose of unknown}}{\text{Low dose of unknown}} = \frac{\text{High dose of standard}}{\text{Low dose of standard}}$$

N	b	s	λ	t	Potency ratio ($\% \pm$ SE)	Theoretical potency ratio (%)
11	19.6	5.38	0.296	0.105	63 ± 13	80
11	20.7	5.26	0.255	1.078	80 ± 14	80
11	17.1	5.63	0.329	0.990	95 ± 22	100
11	21.4	4.68	0.218	0.679	109 ± 16	100
11	23.6	5.00	0.212	1.822	98 ± 14	120
11	18.7	4.75	0.254	0.493	133 ± 30	120

[a] Method of Mathison and Hays (1945).

will be taken as the material supplied, whereas the low dose will be prepared by diluting the material supplied in 1 part plus 3 parts of corn oil.

Rats weighing 40–75 gm are castrated between the ages of 26 and 29 days. The animals are used between 2 and 12 weeks after castration, at which time the animals are divided into 4 groups, each group containing 21 castrated animals.

Each castrated rat receives 0.2 ml of a solution containing either the unknown or the standard. The solutions are injected subcutaneously with a 1-ml tuberculin syringe fitted with a 24-gauge needle. Seventy-two hours after the administration of the test material the rats are killed and the body weights are determined. The ventral surface is opened to expose the male accessory organs and bladder. Two lateral incisions are made to permit easy access to the seminal vesicles. With a pair of forceps and curved iridectomy scissors, each vas deferens is cut and the seminal vesicles and prostate are removed by incision at a point near the base of the bladder. The tissue is dipped in physiological saline and placed on a cork board under a dissecting microscope. The coagulating glands are teased from the seminal vesicle, and the latter is incised at a point nearest the ejaculatory ducts. The seminal vesicles are again immersed in saline, dried on blotting paper for a few seconds, and weighed to the nearest 0.5 mg.

The results are listed in Table XLI. Previously, Mathison and Hays (1945) reported two assays using a solution of testosterone propionate containing 10 mg of the hormone ester per milliliter. They found 10.72 ± 1.83 and 9.26 ± 1.74, respectively.

B. METHOD OF CALLOW AND DEANESLY (1935)

The data of Callow and Deanesly (1935) are shown in Table XLII. Table XLII illustrates the response of the seminal vesicles and prostate to androsterone in prepubertally castrated rats treated daily for 10 days.

TABLE XLII

RESPONSE OF PREPUBERTALLY CASTRATED RAT ACCESSORY
GLANDS TO ANDROSTERONE [a,b]

Total dose of androsterone (mg)	Number of rats	Seminal vesicles (mg)	Prostate (mg)
3.5	5	9	44
6.0	6	14	64
10.0	5	32	112
15.0	5	17	129
20.0	5	26	129
28.0	5	46	394

[a] From Callow and Deanesly (1935).
[b] Ten-day treatment.

Table XLIII presents data on the seminal vesicle and prostate response of the postpubertally castrated rat to androsterone.

Postpubertal rats weighing 130–155 gm were castrated and injected with androsterone in arachis (peanut) oil for 14 consecutive days. Twenty-four hours after the last injection the animals were sacrificed.

The prepubertally castrated animals were operated at 35–70 gm body weight, usually between 40 and 50 gm. These castrates were treated once daily with the hormone dissolved in 0.1 ml of arachis oil for 10 consecutive days. Twenty-four hours after the last injection, the animals were sacrificed.

The entire reproductive tract was dissected free of fat, fixed in Bouin's fluid, and transferred to 70% alcohol. The prostates and seminal vesicles were dissected carefully, drained thoroughly, and weighed.

C. Androgen-Anabolic Assays

Eisenberg and Gordan (1950) suggested that the effect of steroids on the levator ani muscle of the castrated rat is a reasonable indicator of protein-anabolic activity. They pointed out that this myotropic effect is distinct from the androgenic effect and that, whereas the muscle is stimulated by pituitary growth hormone, the seminal vesicle does not respond to this treatment. A further argument in favor of this view has been the fact that the levator ani muscle of the castrated rat continues to grow in the absence of the gonads (Sakamoto *et al.*, 1951).

There is no universal agreement, however, that the levator ani muscle actually measures true anabolic activity of steroids. Some investigators feel rather that this muscle is just another tissue that has a relatively high sensitivity to androgens (Nimni and Geiger, 1957). These workers point out that androgens and anabolic steroids are able to stimulate the levator ani even on a protein-free diet that cannot support somatic growth. In spite of this argument, however, the relative potency of a compound on the levator ani has been shown to correlate, at least roughly, with the ability of the compound to retain nitrogen and promote growth in normal individuals and patients suffering from debilitating diseases. In this section levator ani anabolic tests will be presented.

1. Method of Eisenberg and Gordan (1950) (Modified by Saunders and Drill, 1957)

Male rats 23–25 days of age were castrated and 3 weeks later the test compounds, dissolved in corn oil, were intramuscularly injected once daily for 7 consecutive days. The volume of corn oil was 0.1 ml per day. One day after the last injection the animals were sacrificed and the seminal vesicles, ventral prostates, and levator ani muscles were removed and weighed. The evaluation of the relative anabolic or myotropic effect of a steroid was judged by its ability to stimulate the levator ani in relation to its ability to stimulate the "pure" androgen indicators, the seminal vesicles, and the prostate.

2. *Method of Hershberger et al. (1953)*

This method has an advantage over that of the Eisenberg and Gordan (1950) procedure in that the time is decreased from a period of 30 days to 7 days. Male rats 21 days of age were castrated and placed on a stock diet. Beginning on the day of surgery, the animals were injected sub-cutaneously once daily for 7 consecutive days with the test compounds dissolved in oil. One day after the last injection the animals were sacrificed

TABLE XLIII

INFLUENCE OF TESTOSTERONE AND RELATED STEROIDS ON THE
SEMINAL VESICLES, VENTRAL PROSTATE, AND LEVATOR ANI
OF THE CASTRATED RAT[a]

Compound administered	Total dose (mg)	No. of rats	Tissue weight (mg $\pm$ SE)		
			Seminal vesicle	Ventral prostate	Levator ani
0	0	25	9.7 ± 0.4	7.0 ± 0.3	12.2 ± 0.5
Testosterone	0.35	6	35.3 ± 1.8	14.7 ± 0.9	20.4 ± 2.3
	0.70	8	46.5 ± 4.6	17.8 ± 1.3	21.9 ± 2.0
	1.4	11	48.4 ± 2.3	27.4 ± 2.3	23.7 ± 1.0
	2.1	8	63.5 ± 4.5	38.2 ± 5.5	28.8 ± 0.9
19-Nortestosterone	0.7	5	19.7 ± 2.5	12.1 ± 1.7	21.6 ± 0.5
	1.4	11	20.7 ± 1.8	12.5 ± 0.6	24.5 ± 2.0
	2.1	5	27.5 ± 5.1	14.4 ± 1.1	28.1 ± 2.2
Androsterone	0.672	3	69.9 ± 8.9	7.6 ± 0.5	15.5 ± 0.5
	1.75	6	93.0 ± 3.7	11.2 ± 0.5	16.6 ± 1.3
	3.5	6	10.9 ± 4.1	13.8 ± 0.7	15.4 ± 2.0

[a] From Hershberger *et al.* (1953).

and the levator ani, ventral prostate, and seminal vesicles were dissected and weighed. In evaluating steroids for possible use as anabolic agents, Hershberger *et al.* (1953) suggested the use of the levator ani:ventral prostate ratio, which was defined as the ratio of the increase in levator ani weight divided by the increase in ventral prostate weight. Thus the larger the ratio of a given compound the more likely that the compound may be a therapeutically valuable agent. The authors did not calculate levator ani:seminal vesicle ratios because the seminal vesicles are less sensitive to small doses than the prostate and are believed to be affected more by nonandrogenic steroids.

Some typical data of Hershberger *et al.* (1953) are presented in Table XLIII. Differences in the levator ani:ventral prostate ratios for the different compounds are indicated in these data. Androsterone at the total dose of 1.75 mg had a ratio of 0.05 while 19-nortestosterone had a ratio of 1.1 at a dose level of 14 mg. Testosterone at a dose level of 14 mg had an intermediate ratio of 0.30.

3. Data of Dorfman (1968)

The method used in this study is based on that described on page 200, derived from the Hershberger *et al.* (1953) test, and consists in the use of 21-day-old, 40–55-gm rats, which were castrated on day 21 to day 24 of life. The test compounds were injected subcutaneously once daily for 10 consecutive days starting on the day of surgery. The vehicle is the

TABLE XLIV

RESPONSE OF THE CASTRATED RAT TO SUBCUTANEOUS INJECTION OF
TESTOSTERONE—10-DAY TEST[a]

Total dose of testosterone (mg)	Number of rats	Mean tissue weight (mg ± SE)		
		Seminal vesicle	Ventral prostate	Levator ani
0	42	11.5 ± 0.45	12.2 ± 0.58	29.0 ± 1.08
0.3	42	11.7 ± 0.58	18.8 ± 1.15	29.4 ± 0.84
0.6	46	21.8 ± 1.00	35.5 ± 1.49	34.2 ± 1.25
1.2	44	57.7 ± 3.69	71.9 ± 2.49	49.8 ± 1.60
2.4	39	101.0 ± 3.52	103.7 ± 3.30	62.2 ± 1.15

[a] From Dorfman (1968).

aqueous suspending medium (page 253), and the daily dose was contained in 0.5 ml of the solution. At autopsy, body, ventral prostate, seminal vesicle, and levator ani weights were determined to the nearest 0.5 mg.

Typical data are presented in Table XLIV for the seminal vesicle, ventral prostate, and levator ani responses to testosterone. This method has an overall λ value for the seminal vesicle, ventral prostate, and levator ani indicators in the range of 0.137, 0.162, and 0.171, respectively. Attempts to increase the precision of the assay by extending the number of treatment days was not particularly successful, although the time was extended up to 30 days (Dorfman, 1968).

The method may also be practiced by gavage, but the 10-day test period is inferior to a 20-day administration period. By using the latter conditions, a preliminary estimate of the index of precision (λ) was, for seminal vesicles 0.191 (0.137–0.272), for the ventral prostate 0.282 (0.192–0.417), and for the levator ani 0.218 (0.140–0.363).

D. Nitrogen Retention Methods—Anabolic Activity

1. Method of Stafford et al. (1954)

These workers have suggested a method involving the measurement of nitrogen excretion in the castrated rat fed a liquid diet and in nitrogen balance. The method was not recommended for strictly quantitative work, but by the use of three indices some estimate of the relative

TABLE XLV

Composition of Liquid Diet[a]

Component	Amount
Cell flour	180 gm
Salt mixture No. 2	120 gm
(Nutritional Biochemicals,	
Cleveland, Ohio)	
Brewers' yeast	300 gm
Casein	480 gm
Starch	600 gm
Dextrin	570 gm
Sucrose	600 gm
Water	3300 ml
Corn oil	570 ml
Cod liver oil	30 ml
Wheat germ oil	30 ml
Vitamin K, 0.5% in cottonseed oil	30 ml

[a] Stafford et al. (1954).

potencies of two compounds can be made. These indices include the "greatest daily retention" which is defined as the difference between the lowest daily N value after beginning of treatment and the preinjection mean. The second index "total N retention" is the sum of the differences between the preinjection excretion and the daily values during the retention period, and the third index is the "number of days in the retention period." This last index is the period between the last day on which N was equal to or higher than the preinjection average, and the last day before two consecutive values equal to or higher than the preinjection average were obtained.

The method of Stafford et al. (1954) consists in castration of 25-day-old rats which were kept untreated for 67 days (average weight of 300 gm). During the initial period the animals were kept on a stock diet, but at 67 days they were changed to a liquid diet-forced feeding regime (see Table XLV). At the start, the rats received 10 ml per day, and this was increased to 26 ml per day. Steroid treatment was started 24 days after the 26-ml per day level had been attained and continued for 30 days. The steroids were administered once daily. in 0.1 ml cottonseed oil. Twenty-four hour urine specimens were collected three times weekly and analyzed for total nitrogen. Results of a typical experiment are presented in Table XLVI.

TABLE XLVI

INFLUENCE OF TESTOSTERONE PROPIONATE (TP) AND NORTESTOSTERONE
CYCLOPENTYLPROPIONATE (NC) OR NITROGEN (N) EXCRETION IN THE
CASTRATED RAT[a]

Compound administered	Daily dose (mg)	No. of rats	Total N retained (mg)	No. of days in retention period	Greatest single retention (mg)
TP	0.25	5	398	16	44
	1.00	5	604	20	73
NC	0.5	4	507	16	54
	2.0	5	483	16	60

[a] From Stafford et al. (1954).

2. Nitrogen Retention in the Monkey (Stucki et al., 1960)

A method for the assay of anabolic steroids in the monkey (*Macaca mulatta*) had been suggested by Stucki et al. (1960). A linear dose-response curve was established over the range of 50–400 μg of fluoxymestrone (9α-fluoro-11β-methyltestosterone) per kilogram per day using the end point of nitrogen retention expressed as total N retained per day during the treatment period. A balanced twin cross-over assay was found to be satisfactory with an efficiency calculated to be 1.5–2.0. The authors pointed out that at least for one compound, fluoxymestrone, the effective dose found for the monkey on a kilogram basis was comparable to that previously established for humans for the same steroid.

3. Rat Nitrogen Retention Method of Lennon and Saunders (1964) (Modification of Saunders and Drill, 1958)

The effect of a test compound on nitrogen retention was studied in adult castrated male albino rats employing a method similar to that reported by Saunders and Drill (1958). Rats were castrated prior to sexual maturity and were maintained on a commercial laboratory diet fed ad libitum until they reached a body weight of about 325–350 gm. Then they were transferred to individual metabolism cages and fed 25 gm of a prepared liquid diet containing 350 mg of nitrogen daily.

The rats were allowed a 1-week period to become accustomed to the liquid diet, and urine was collected daily throughout a succeeding 5-day control period. Urine samples were assayed for total nitrogen (Koch and McMeekin, 1924).

TABLE XLVII

CHANGES IN URINARY NITROGEN (UN) EXCRETION AFTER ORAL ADMINISTRATION OF OXANDROLONE AND NORETHANDROLONE IN CASTRATED MALE RATS[a]

Compound	Dose (mg per rat per day)	No. of rats	Average UN (mg/rat/day)		
			Control period	Treatment period	Reduction
Control	—	32	205 (±4.6)[b]	196 (±4.8)	9 (±4.9)
Oxandrolone	5	10	206 (±2.5)	171 (±3.5)	35 (±6.0)
	2	15	189 (±12.5)	154 (±9.1)	35 (±5.0)
	1	15	180 (±13.8)	159 (±2.4)	21 (±12.3)
Norethandrolone	5	30	205 (±6.6)	159 (±5.4)	46 (±4.6)
	2	25	210 (±4.5)	165 (±4.5)	45 (±5.9)
	1	15	197 (±4.2)	161 (±7.1)	36 (±7.9)

[a] From Lennon and Saunders (1964).
[b] Values in parentheses are standard errors of the means.

Test compounds were dissolved in corn oil and added to the diet daily during a subsequent 5-day treatment period. Norethandrolone (Nilevar®), 17α-ethyl-17β-hydroxy-4-estren-3-one, was employed as the reference standard. Both norethandrolone and oxandrolone were tested in groups of 5 rats at each dose level. Control data were obtained from 32 groups (160 rats). The number of treatment groups varied from 2 groups (10 rats) to 6 groups (30 rats) per dose level.

Typical results are indicated in Table XVLII.

E. ADDITIONAL MAMMALIAN METHODS

1. Data of Gutman and Gutman (1939)

Data of Gutman and Gutman (1939) indicated that the prostate of the mature rhesus monkey contains high concentrations of an acid phosphatase, an enzyme which is lacking in the prepubertal monkey prostate.

These workers showed that testosterone propionate caused an important increase in acid phosphate. The data illustrated in Table XLVIII do not indicate a quantitative bioassay but rather a qualitative effect that may be developed into a possible precise bioassay. Some suggested details follow.

Experimental animals Nos. 7 and 8 (Table XLIX) were injected daily (except Sunday) with 12.5 mg of testosterone propionate and were

TABLE XLVIII

FACTORS FOR CONVERSION OF OBSERVED
ENZYME VALUES TO ACTIVITIES
EXHIBITED AT 25°C

°C	Factors
20	1.59
21	1.43
22	1.30
23	1.19
24	1.09
25	1.00
26	0.925
27	0.865
28	0.805
29	0.750
30	0.705

[a] From Kirk et al. (1962).

sacrificed after 18 and 13 days, respectively; No. 9 received 500 rat units of estradiol benzoate in oil daily for 12 days.

Tissue phosphatase activity at pH 9.0 was determined by the King and Armstrong method (1934) and, in optimal dilutions at pH 4.9 by the adaptation of that method previously outlined (Gutman and Gutman, 1938a). The results of tissue analyses are expressed in units, a unit being that degree of phosphatase activity which under the stated conditions of hydrolysis will liberate 1 mg of phenol in 1 hour from the specified buffer—monophenylphosphate substrate solution. Serum phosphatase activity was determined by the Bodansky method (1933).

A pH 4.9 marked phosphatase activity of prostate tissue of the *adult* rhesus monkey was found of the same order of magnitude as in man. Unlike man, adult monkey prostate tissue exhibits appreciable phosphatase activity at pH 9.0, as in the rat. In the *prepubertal* monkey, both "acid" and "alkaline" phosphatase activity of prostate tissue are

TABLE XLIX

PHOSPHATASE ACTIVITY OF PROSTATE TISSUE OF THE SEXUALLY MATURE AND IMMATURE RHESUS MONKEY; AND OF IMMATURE ANIMALS AFTER INJECTION OF TESTOSTERONE PROPIONATE OR OF ESTRADIOL BENZOATE[a]

Animal No.	Status	Weight (kg)	Treatment	Weight of both lobes prostate (gm)	Phosphatase activity[b]			
					at pH (units/gm fresh prostate tissue)		at pH (units/whole prostate gland)	
					4.9	9.0	4.9	9.0
1	Mature	10	Control	3.6	1,134	102	4080	367
2	Mature	9.4	Control	3.5	573	60	2001	210
3	Mature[c]	6.0	Control	3.2	356	22.5	1140	72
4	Immature	3.5	Control	0.7	1.2	2.1	0.8	0.8
5	Immature	3.5	Control	0.6	2.8	—	1.5	—
6	Immature	4.0	Control	0.3	4.8	0.4	1.4	0.1
7	Immature	4.0	Testosterone propionate (185 mg in 18 days)	2.0	975	30.5	1950	61
8	Immature	2.9	Testosterone propionate (150 mg in 13 days)	1.1	779	14.8	858	16.3
9	Immature	2.1	Estradiol benzoate (6000 rat units)	0.6	11.5	2.4	6.9	1.4

[a] From Gutman and Gutman (1939).

[b] pH 4.9: $M/200$ monophenylphosphate substrate; $M/10$ citrate buffer; 37°C; 1 hour.
pH 9.0: $M/200$ monophenylphosphate substrate; $M/20$ Na Veronal buffer; 37°C; 1 hour.

[c] Tuberculous animal.

negligible. After treatment with testosterone propionate, the phosphatase activity of immature monkey prostate gland increases strikingly at pH 4.9 and at pH 9.0, reaching adult levels at the former and possibly also at the latter pH. After treatment with estradiol benzoate an equivocal increase in phosphatase activity was noted which cannot be interpreted as significant without further study.

The serum phosphatase activity at pH 9.0 was found to vary between 20 and 30 Bodansky units per 100 ml in immature rhesus monkeys and was not significantly affected by injection of steroids; nor was the "acid" phosphatase activity of the serum (Gutman and Gutman, 1938b), which ranged between 2.5 and 3.6 units per 100 ml, affected thereby.

The phosphatase activity at pH 4.9 was found to be slight in the seminal vesicles (2.0–8.0 units per gram of fresh tissue), testis (4.0–5.6 units), and Cowper's glands (0.8 unit) of immature and mature rhesus monkeys, with no significant difference in steroid-treated animals. The values obtained at pH 9.0 (0.6–3.9 units, 2.3–2.8 units, and 0.3 unit, respectively) were also not different in the steroid-treated animals.

As in man, the prostate gland of the mature rhesus monkey contains high concentrations of an "acid" phosphatase, whereas the prepubertal monkey prostate is virtually devoid of this enzyme. It is shown that testosterone propionate causes a several hundredfold increase in "acid" phosphatase activity of the prepubertal monkey prostate gland to adult levels. It is inferred that in prepubertal man, so treated, an analogous increase occurs. In the monkey, "acid" prostate phosphatase is elaborated chiefly or solely in the caudal lobe.

2. Prostatic Acid Phosphatase Test for Evaluation of Androgen Activity in Man (Kirk et al., 1962)

The intact prostate of man responds to androgen stimulation with the production of acid phosphatase. Kirk et al. (1962) have used this parameter for evaluation of androgen stimulation by the following methods.

a. Collection of Prostatic Secretion. The prostatic secretion is obtained by gentle digital massage of the prostate, preferably by longitudinal strokes from the upper edge to the lower part of the gland, first of the lobes and then of the midline. The fluid is collected on a watch glass; if the prostatic secretion does not appear at the urethral opening immediately after the massage, it is advisable to wait for 45 seconds with the glass in position since it often takes some additional time for the viscous prostatic fluid to pass through the urethra. The sample may either be used immediately for enzyme activity determination or may be drawn into a glass capillary for storage. Glass capillaries with an internal diameter of 1.0 mm have proved convenient for such storage. After the sample has been drawn into the central part of the capillary, the openings of the tube are closed with petroleum jelly. If the prostatic secretion is stored undiluted at refrigerator temperature (4°C), the enzyme activity remains unchanged for at least 1 month; this stability of the phosphatase is a factor of great practical significance because reliable results are obtained even if the measurement of the enzyme activity is postponed.

In the case of young children, only one drop may appear at the urethral opening. Under such circumstances, the secretion is best collected by carefully applying the opening of a thin glass capillary directly to the drop. In order to obtain the most reliable results, it is usually advisable to make the collection of the prostatic fluid during the afternoon hours.

b. Reagents. Potassium acid phthalate buffer, 0.06 M, pH 5.0. The buffer is prepared by dissolving 1.225 gm of potassium acid phthalate (mol. wt. 204) in water. The pH of the solution is adjusted to 5.0 by addition of sodium hydroxide, after which the volume is made up to 100 ml.

Phenolphthalein diphosphoric acid. Of this compound, 0.72 mg is supplied (Sigma Chemical Co., St. Louis, Missouri) in lyophilized form in 15-ml vials for use in the test. The vials are stored in a desiccator jar placed in a refrigerator. Under such conditions, the compound was found to remain stable for at least 6 months. Storage of the vials at room temperature should be avoided because this releases some phenolphthalein from the substrate within a few days.

Instead of using lyophilized substrate in vials, a substrate solution containing 0.72 mg of phenolphthalein diphosphoric acid per milliliter of phthalate buffer may be employed. The substrate is weighed out from a stock supply (Sigma Chemical Co., St. Louis, Missouri) which has been maintained under desiccated and refrigerated conditions. The solution can be used for about 3 weeks if stored in a refrigerator.

Carbonate-bicarbonate buffer, 0.2 M, pH 10.4. This buffer is prepared by dissolving 1.630 gm of sodium carbonate and 0.386 gm of sodium bicarbonate in 100 ml of water.

c. Enzyme Test. i. Preparation of a 1:1000 dilution of the sample of prostatic secretion. A 1:1000 dilution of the prostatic secretion sample is made by measuring out 10 mm of the secretion by means of a Linderstrøm-Land constriction pipet and transferring the sample to 10 ml of potassium acid phthalate buffer contained in a separate test tube. In the analyses of samples with activities below 1500 Gutman units per milliliter, it is recommended that a 1:200 dilution of the sample be used instead of the regular 1:1000 dilution of the secretion.

ii. Preparation of reaction tube. The vial is removed from the refrigerator about 15 minutes before use or is heated briefly in tap water. One milliliter of potassium acid phthalate buffer is then added; the substrate goes into solution within a few seconds if the contents of the vial are swirled. If a substrate–buffer solution is used instead of the prepared vial, 1 ml of the solution if pipetted into an empty vial.

iii. Enzymatic reaction. Of the diluted prostatic secretion, 500 mm is pipetted into the vial. The contents are rapidly mixed, and the reaction is allowed to proceed for exactly 2 minutes at room temperature. A small thermometer is placed in the solution to record the temperature. At the end of the 2-minute period, 8.5 ml of carbonate-bicarbonate buffer is added to the sample. This stops the enzymatic reaction (pH after addition, 10.3), and if phenolphthalein has been released during the test, the sample becomes red.

In the analyses of samples with high phosphatase activity, a 1-minute reaction period may be used because the release of phenolphthalein during the first minute of the test constitutes 47–50% of the 2-minute value.

iv. Colorimetric determination. The phenolphthalein color remains constant for at least 15 minutes and decreases by only 1% during the first hour. The decrease during the subsequent 24 hours averages 4%.

d. Spectrophotometric Determination. The optical density of the sample is read in a Beckman spectrophotometer at 550 mμ with a cell having a 10-mm light path. If the color is very intense, it may be necessary to insert a Beckman No. 10536 silica spacer in the cell to obtain a light path of 1 mm. Instead of using spacing equipment, the sample may be diluted with an appropriate volume of carbonate-bicarbonate buffer to obtain an optical density suitable for reading in the conventional 10-mm cell.

If the determination of the color intensity is made at 10 mm light path and with a final volume of 10.0 ml, the Gutman units corresponding to the observed optical density can be read directly from Fig. 12 or, for samples exhibiting an optical density above 0.150, may be calculated from the following formula:

$$\text{Gutman units} = (\text{OD} - 0.150)\ 8683 + 1850$$

This calculation is valid for optical densities that do not exceed 2.160. The unit value is subsequently corrected for the temperature at which the test was conducted by multiplication with the factor listed in Table XLVIII.

Under the conditions of measurement (at pH 10.3), the molar extinction coefficient of phenolphthalein (mol. wt. 318.31) at 550 mμ

was found to be 31,200; this means that 1 μg of phenolphthalein per milliliter of solution (or 10 μg per 10 ml) will give an optical density of 0.098. The phenolphthalein values corresponding to the optical densities have been listed on the ordinate of Fig, 12.

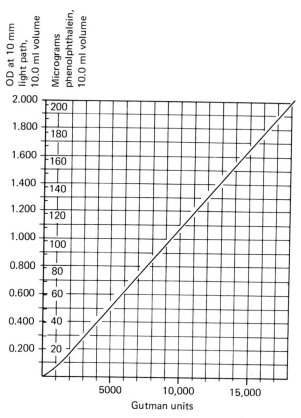

FIG. 12. Monogram for determining Gutman units of acid phosphatase (Kirk *et al.*, 1962).

e. Determination by Visual Comparison. In clinical practice, the color determination can be made by comparison of the sample with a set of permanent color standards or with a freshly prepared standard solution of phenolphthalein. A colorimeter with permanent color standards ranging from 1000 to 18,000 Gutman units has been made available for use in the present procedure (LaMotte Chemical Products Co., Chestertown, Maryland). A standard solution for comparison with the test sample in a Duboscq colorimeter may be prepared by diluting 1.0 ml of an alcoholic 0.5% phenolphthalein solution (Fischer Scientific Co., Pittsburgh, Pennsylvania) with a suitable volume of carbonate-bicarbonate buffer. The Gutman units corresponding to the visually measured phenolphthalein values can be read directly from Fig. 12; the calculation is valid for samples having a phenolphthalein content which does not exceed 200 μg/10 ml. The values must be corrected by multiplication with the appropriate factor listed in Table XLVIII.

f. Blank. A blank determination is performed by adding 1.5 ml of potassium acid phthalate buffer solution to a substrate-containing vial, followed by 8.5 ml of carbonate-bicarbonate buffer solution. The average optical density of the blank when read against distilled water at 550 mμ was 0.012.

g. Application of the acid phosphatase test. As mentioned in the introduction, the determination of the acid phosphatase concentration of the prostatic secretion can serve as a reliable measure of the androgen activity if the prostatic tissue is normal so that the gland is capable of responding to androgen stimulation with the secretion of the enzyme. Since the prostatic gland is the site of degenerative changes in some middle-aged and elderly men, the test is particularly applicable to adolescent boys and young men. It should be ascertained that the patients do not suffer from prostatitis because both the acute and chronic prostatitis affect the ability of the gland to produce phosphatase. However, in the majority of children and young men, there will be no limitations to the use of the test.

Seminal samples can also be used for acid phosphatase determination. Since the samples usually contain between 26 and 30% of prostatic secretion, the recorded phosphatase values should be multiplied by 3.5 to make them comparable with those found in analyses of expressed prostatic fluid. Because the prostatic secretion is contained mainly in the first fraction of the ejaculate, the seminal specimen must be thoroughly mixed before a sample is withdrawn for acid phosphatase activity measurement.

The acid phosphatase production by the prostatic gland is an early sign of beginning puberty. In normal children, the phosphatase usually makes its appearance at the age of 11 years and then increases gradually during the subsequent adolescent period. A study on 71 normal boys showed the following average values, expressed as Gutman units per milliliter: 11–12 years, 50; 12–13 years, 200; 13–14 years, 2800; 14–15 years, 7020; 15–16 years, 7380; 16–16½ years, 8700. At the age of 18–20 years the concentration generally reaches a value of 14,000 units or higher (Kirk *et al.*, 1962).

In adult subjects, the normal concentration of acid phosphatase in the prostatic secretion is 8000–14,000 Gutman units per milliliter or higher and values below 5000 units are classified as low values. A study by Kirk (quoted by Kirk *et al.*, 1962) on 200 subjects between the ages of 20 and 100 years has shown that the phosphatase activity tends to decrease with age. The phosphatase values observed in middle-aged and elderly men do not necessarily give an expression of the androgen activity, since a decrease in the phosphatase concentration may be the result of pathologic changes in the prostatic gland. However, it should be pointed out that an appreciable percentage of men over 40 years of age have normal phosphatase values and this fact is of practical importance to rule out the presence of hypoandrogenism. The simple and rapid procedure described in the present publication may assist in extending the use of the test both in clinical laboratories and by general practitioners.

3. *Method of Dorfman and Dorfman (1963b) (Subcutaneous Injection) (Castrated Rat)*

Male rats 21–23 days of age were castrated within 1 day of arrival, and injections usually started on the day of surgery. Subcutaneous injections were practiced once daily for 7–30 days. Usually the treatment period was 10 days.

The test compounds were suspended in an aqueous medium consisting of sodium chloride (0.9%), polysorbate 80 (0.4%), carboxymethyl cellulose (0.5%), and benzyl alcohol (0.9%); the daily dose was injected subcutaneously in 0.5 ml of this vehicle.

Twenty-four hours after the last injection, the animals were sacrificed with ether and body and blotted tissue weights were determined. Statistical analyses were made by conventional methods (Fisher, 1934; Bülbring, 1935; Emmens, 1962).

The typical response of the seminal vesicles, ventral prostate, and levator ani to testosterone administered over a 10-day period is represented in Table L. The data are pooled from four separate experiments.

Table LI lists the results of a series of bioassays where the number of injection days was increased from 10 days to 17, 20, 25, and 30 days, respectively. In one assay the rats were castrated at 31 days of age and 7 treatment days were employed, starting 10 days after surgery. This table lists the dose ranges employed, the slope, and the index of precision. These data are interpreted in Table LII, where a mean index of precision was calculated for the various assay conditions for each of the indicators: seminal vesicles, ventral prostate, and levator ani. Under the laboratory conditions encountered, no special value could be determined for the more lengthy injection schedule.

Table LII summarizes some relative potencies of various steroids administered by subcutaneous injection using the 10-day assay schedule. The accuracy of determination of relative potency was of the order indicated in Table LII. The mean λ value for this series of studies was as follows: seminal vesicles—mean 0.096 (range 0.080–0.152); ventral prostate—mean 0.128 (0.050–0.197); and levator ani—mean 0.248

TABLE L

RESPONSE OF THE CASTRATE RAT TO THE INJECTION OF
TESTOSTERONE (10-DAY ASSAY)[a]

Total dose testosterone (mg)	No. of rats	Mean tissue weight (mg ± SE)		
		Seminal vesicle	Ventral prostate	Levator ani
0	42	11.5 ± 0.45	12.2 ± 0.58	29.0 ± 1.08
0.3	42	11.7 ± 0.58	18.8 ± 1.15	29.4 ± 0.84
0.6	46	21.8 ± 1.00	35.5 ± 1.49	34.2 ± 1.25
1.2	44	57.7 ± 3.69	71.9 ± 2.49	49.8 ± 1.60
2.4	39	101.0 ± 3.52	103.7 ± 3.30	62.2 ± 1.15

[a] From Dorfman and Dorfman (1963b).

(0.122–0.432). These values are reasonably close to the λ values calculated from five assays chosen at random (Table LII). These mean λ values were as follows: seminal vesicles—0.137 (0.089–0.231); ventral prostate—0.162 (0.112–0.183); and levator ani—0.171 (0.097–0.232).

4. Method of Dorfman (1962) (Oral) (Castrated Rat)

On day 25 to day 28 of life these animals were castrated under ether anesthesia and randomized into various groups. Beginning with the day of surgery, the rats were treated once daily for 10–30 days with fluoxymestrone (9α-fluoro-11β-hydroxy-17α-methyltestosterone) suspended in 0.5 ml of an aqueous medium. The aqueous medium had the following composition: sodium chloride (0.9%), polysorbate 80 (0.4%), carboxymethyl cellulose (0.5%), and benzyl alcohol (0.9%).

Twenty-four hours after the last steroid administration the body, seminal vesicles, ventral prostate, and levator ani weights were determined. The dissection details have been described in full by Hershberger et al. (1953). Statistical calculations were performed as directed by Emmens (1962).

TABLE LI

ASSAY OF TESTOSTERONE BY INJECTION IN THE CASTRATED RAT UNDER DIFFERENT CONDITIONS[a,b]

Castration and start of injection (days)	No. of daily injections	Seminal vesicles				Ventral prostate				Levator ani			
		No. of rats	Dose levels (mg)	Slope b	Index of precision λ	No. of rats	Dose levels (mg)	Slope b	Index of precision λ	No. of rats	Dose levels (mg)	Slope b	Index of precision λ
29	17	44	0.1, 0.2, 0.4	5.325	0.134	44	0.1, 0.2, 0.4	2.104	0.136	44	0.1, 0.2, 0.4	0.630	0.243
28	17	25	0.4, 0.9, 1.6	1.886	0.153	25	0.4, 0.8, 1.6	1.124	0.176	25	0.4, 0.8, 1.6	0.343	0.224
27	20	48	0.5, 1.6, 4.5	3.479	0.126	48	0.5, 1.5, 4.5	1.643	0.149	48	0.5, 1.5, 4.5	0.682	0.154
26	20	64	0.5, 1.5, 4.5, 13.5	3.431	0.260	65	0.5, 1.5, 4.5, 13.5	1.270	0.335	45	0.5, 1.5, 4.5	0.774	0.238
27	20	34	0.4, 1.5	2.438	0.030	34	0.5, 1.5	1.305	0.066	34	0.5, 1.5	0.675	0.123
25	25	52	0.5, 1.5, 4.5	2.110	0.150	52	0.5, 1.5, 4.5	1.436	0.133	52	0.5, 1.5, 4.5	0.765	0.178
27	25	58	0.5, 1.5, 4.5	2.027	0.140	58	0.5, 1.5, 4.5	1.502	0.427	58	0.5, 1.5, 4.5	0.677	0.140
25	30	56	1, 2, 4	3.250	0.102	56	1, 2, 4	1.949	0.106	56	1, 2, 4	0.824	0.110
25	30	26	0.4, 0.8, 1.6, 3.2	3.561	0.084	25	0.4, 0.8, 1.6, 3.2	1.453	0.105	26	0.4, 0.8, 1.6, 3.2	0.448	0.183
26	30	35	1, 2, 4	2.981	0.116	35	1, 2, 4	1.923	0.074	35	1, 2, 4	0.689	0.109
28	30	38	0.8, 1.6, 3.2, 6.4	2.029	0.180	38	0.8, 1.6, 3.2, 6.4	0.811	0.210	37	1.6, 3.2, 6.4, 12.8	0.455	0.220

28	30	50	0.5, 1.0, 2.0, 4.0	2.981	0.103	50	0.5, 1.0, 2.0, 4.0	1.395	0.128	50	1, 2, 4	0.891	0.113
24	30	61	0.5, 1.0, 2.0, 4.0, 8.0	5.432	0.152	61	0.5, 1.0, 2.0, 4.0, 8.0	1.866	0.133	48	1, 2, 4	1.194	0.171
26	30	50	0.5, 1.0, 2.0, 4.0	4.306	0.110	50	0.5, 1.0, 2.0, 4.0	1.546	0.095	50	0.5, 1.0, 2.0, 4.0	0.651	0.143
26	30	48	0.5, 1.0, 2.0, 4.0	2.406	0.105	48	0.5, 1.0, 2.0, 4.0	1.572	0.140	48	0.5, 1.0, 2.0, 4.0	0.672	0.162
31[c]	7	25	0.2, 0.4, 0.8, 1.6	0.914	0.153	25	0.2, 0.4, 0.8, 1.6	0.509	0.354	25	0.2, 0.4, 0.8	0.365	0.192

[a] From Dorfman and Dorfman (1963b).
[b] Calculated on basis of ratio of tissue weight (mg) to body weight (gm).
[c] Injection started 10 days after operation.

TABLE LII

Analysis of the Androgen Myotrophic Assay (Injection)
(Variation in Index of Precision (λ) with
Number of Days of Treatment)[a]

Treatment[c]	No. of experiments	Mean index of precision[b] λ (range)		
		Seminal vesicles	Ventral prostate	Levator ani
10	5[d]	0.137	0.162	0.171
		(0.089–0.231)	(0.112–0.183)	(0.097–0.232)
17	2	0.144	0.156	0.234
		(0.134–0.153)	(0.136–0.176)	(0.224–0.243)
20	3	0.139	0.183	0.172
		(0.030–0.260)	(0.066–0.335)	(0.123–0.238)
25	2	0.153	0.222	0.143
		(0.102–0.217)	(0.106–0.427)	(0.110–0.178)
30	8	0.119	0.124	0.150
		(0.084–0.180)	(0.074–0.210)	(0.109–0.220)

[a] From Dorfman and Dorfman (1963b).

[b] Based on tissue ratios expressed as milligrams of tissue per gram of body weight.

[c] The analyses of these assays were based on the steepest portions of the dose-response curves and at times involved only 2 dose levels, whereas analyses of the other groups (17, 20, 25, and 30 injections) utilized 3 or 4 dose levels.

[d] Chosen at random.

Table LIII summarizes some typical experiences with the method. This table records the dose levels, the slope, and the index of precision for the end points seminal vesicles, ventral prostate, and levator ani. The doses were generally high in an effort to favor the slope of the curve for the levator ani. Considering all three end points, it was no particular advantage to administer the material over more than 10 days. Actually in one experiment involving a 25-day administration period, the index of precision rose to over 0.7 for the ventral prostate and over 0.4 for the levator ani. These unfavorable values were atypical for the series.

Although the method described in this paper does not compare in precision with the subcutaneous injection procedure, it is a reasonable technique. The index of precision, λ, by the subcutaneous route varied from 0.096 to 0.137 for the seminal vesicles, 0.128 to 0.162 for the ventral prostate, and 0.171 to 0.248 for the levator ani. This is to be compared with gavage values closer to 0.210 for the seminal vesicles, 0.190 for the ventral prostate, and 0.218 for the levator ani. Perhaps the single most important reason for the marginal precision values, that is, relatively high value, is the low value of the slope b. In the gavage studies b for the

TABLE LIII

ASSAY OF 9α-FLUORO-11β-HYDROXY-17α-METHYLTESTOSTERONE BY GAVAGE IN THE
CASTRATED RAT UNDER DIFFERENT CONDITIONS[a]

Age at castration	No. of single daily administrations	No. of rats	Dose levels (mg)	Seminal vesicles		Ventral prostate		Levator ani	
				Slope b	Index of precision	Slope b	Index of precision	Slope b	Index of precision
28	10	57	4, 8, 16	0.715	0.210	0.368	0.190	0.367	0.218
26	20	38	8, 16, 32	0.769	0.272	0.578	0.317	0.320	0.363
27	20	24	8, 16, 32	1.213	0.165	0.615	0.239	0.515	0.150
27	20	26	16, 32, 64	1.157	0.137	0.432	0.192	0.365	0.140
28	25	27	16, 32, 64	0.914	0.255	0.432	0.278	0.382	0.262
28	25	31	16, 32, 64	0.479	0.230	0.085	0.706	0.268	0.410
25	30	27	16, 32, 64	1.296	0.149	0.565	0.182	0.316	0.316
25	30	29	16, 32, 64	2.042	0.134	0.631	0.174	0.711	0.177

[a] From Dorfman (1962).

levator ani was usually about 0.320 to 0.711 with a mean in the region of 0.430, whereas in the subcutaneous injection studies the b values were from 0.343 to 1.194, with a mean of 0.670. The differences in slopes of the other end points was equal to or greater than that for the levator ani.

Perhaps the precision could be improved by increasing the number of doses per day and/or the vehicle.

Various investigators have reported on the use of the rodent for androgen assay. These include Tscherning (1936), Butenandt and Hanisch (1935), Morato Manoro (1940), Deanesly and Parkes (1936), Miescher *et al.* (1936, 1937), Korenchevsky *et al.* (1935), Ruzicka and Rosenberg (1936), Fischer (1938), Loewe and Voss (1931), Dirscherl *et äl.* (1936), Masson *et al.* (1942), Selye and Albert (1942), and Korenchevsky and Dennison (1936). These methods are not discussed here.

REFERENCES

Bliss, C. I. (1944). *J. Am. Statist. Assoc.* **39**, 479.

Bliss, C. I., and Cattell, Mc. K. (1943). *Ann. Rev. Physiol.* **5**, 479.

Bodansky, A. (1933). *J. Biol. Chem.* **101**, 93.

Boris, A., and Ng, C. (1967). *Steroids* **9**, 299.

Bülbring, E. (1935). *Quart. J. Exptl. Physiol.* **111**, 1.

Burrows, W. H., Byerly, T. C., and Evans, E. I. (1936). *Proc. Soc. Exptl. Biol. Med.* **35**, 60.

Butenandt, A., and Hanisch, G. (1935). *Z. Physiol. Chem.* **237**, 75.

Butenandt, A., and Tscherning, K. (1934). *Z. Physiol. Chem.* **229**, 167, 185.

Callow, R. K., and Deanesly, R. (1935). *Biochem. J.* **29**, 1424.

Callow, R. K., and Parkes, A. S. (1935). *Biochem. J.* **29**, 1414.

Courier, R., and Jost, A. (1939). *Compt. Rend. Soc. Biol.* **130**, 1515.

Deanesly, R., and Parkes, A. S. (1936). *Biochem. J.* **30**, 291.

Dessau, F. (1935). *Acta Brevia Neerl. Physiol. Pharmacol. Microbiol.* **5**, 94.

Dessau, F. (1937). *Acta Brevia Neerl. Physiol. Pharmacol. Microbiol.* **7**, 1.

Dingemanse, E., Freud, S., Kober, S., Laqueur, E., Luchs, A., and Munch, A. W. P. (1931). *Biochem. Z.* **231**, 1.

Dirscherl, W., Kraus, J., and Voss, H. E. (1936). *Z. Physiol. Chem.* **241**, 1.

Dorfman, R. I. (1948a). *Endocrinology* **42**, 1.

Dorfman, R. I. (1948b). *Endocrinology* **42**, 7.

Dorfman, R. I. (1962). *Acta Endocrinol.* **41**, 265.

Dorfman, R. I. (1968). Unpublished data.

Dorfman, R. I., and Dorfman, A. S. (1962). *Acta Endocrinol.* **41**, 101.

Dorfman, R. I., and Dorfman, A. S. (1963a). *Acta Endocrinol.* **42**, 240.

Dorfman, R. I., and Dorfman, A. S. (1963b). *Acta Endocrinol.* **42**, 245.

Dorfman, R. I., and Dorfman, A. S. (1963c). *Acta Endocrinol. Suppl.* **74**.

Dorfman, R. I., and Greulich, W. W. (1937). *Yale J. Biol. Med.* **10**, 79.

Dorfman, R. I., and Shipley, R. A. (1956). "Androgens, Biochemistry, Physiology, and Clinical Significance," 590 pp. Wiley, New York.

Eisenberg, E., and Gordan, G. S. (1950). *J. Pharmacol. Exptl. Therap.* **99**, 38.

Emmens, C. W. (1939). *Med. Res. Council Spec. Rept. Ser.* **234**, 1.
Emmens, C. W. (1962). *Methods Hormone Res.*, **2**, 59.
Fischer, A. (1938). *Rev. Franc. Endocrinol.* **16**, 1.
Fisher, R. A. (1934). "Statistical Methods for Research Workers." Oliver & Boyd, Edinburgh and London.
Frank, R. T., and Klempner, E. (1937). *Proc. Soc. Exptl. Biol. Med.* **36**, 763.
Frank, R. T., Klempner, E., Hollander, R., and Kriss, B. (1942). *Endocrinology* **31**, 63.
Fussganger, R. (1934). *Med. Chem. Abhandl. Med.-Chem. Forschungsstatten I.G. Farbenind. A.G.* **2**, 201.
Gallagher, T. F., and Koch, F. C. (1935). *J. Pharmacol. Exptl. Therap.* **55**, 97.
Greenwood, A. W., Blyth, J. S. S., and Callow, R. K. (1935). *Biochem. J.* **29**, 1400.
Griffith, J. Q., and Farris, E. J. (1942). "The Rat in Laboratory Investigation," p. 395. Lippincott, Philadelphia, Pennsylvania.
Gutman, A. B., and Gutman, E. B. (1938a). *J. Clin. Invest.* **17**, 473.
Gutman, A. B., and Gutman, E. B. (1938b). *Proc. Soc. Exptl. Biol. Med.* **38**, 470.
Gutman, A. B., and Gutman, E. B. (1939). *Proc. Soc. Exptl. Biol. Med.* **41**, 277.
Hershberger, L. G., Shipley, E. G., and Meyer, R. K. (1953). *Proc. Soc. Exptl. Biol. Med.* **83**, 175.
Irwin, J. O. (1937). *J. Roy. Statist. Soc.* **4**, 1.
Kenyon, A. T., Sandiford, I., Bryan, A. H., Knowlton, K., and Koch, F. C. (1938). *Endocrinology* **23**, 135.
Kenyon, A. T., Knowlton, K., and Sandiford, I. (1944). *Ann. Internal Med.* **20**, 632.
King, E. J., and Armstrong, A. R. (1934). *Can. Med. Assoc. J.* **31**, 376.
Kirk, J. E., Wang, J. C., and Schaus, R. (1962). *J. Lab. Clin. Med.* **59**, 705.
Klempner, E., Hollander, F., Frank, R. T., and Kriss, B. (1942). *Endocrinology* **31**, 71.
Koch, F. C., and McMeekin, T. L. (1924). *J. Am. Chem. Soc.* **46**, 2066.
Kochakian, C. D. (1937). *Endocrinology* **21**, 750.
Kochakian, C. D., and Murlin, J. R. (1935). *J. Nutrition* **10**, 437.
Kochakian, C. D., and Murlin, J. R. (1936). *Am. J. Physiol.* **177**, 642.
Korenchevsky, V., and Dennison, M. (1936). *Biochem. J.* **30**, 1514.
Korenchevsky, V., and Dennison, M., and Simpson, S. L. (1935). *Biochem. J.* **29**, 2131.
Lennon, H. D., and Saunders, F. J. (1964). *Steroids* **4**, 689.
Loewe, S., and Voss, H. E. (1931). *Med. Klin. (Munich)* **27**, 1719.
Masson, G., Borduas, A., and Selye, H. (1942). *Rev. Can. Biol.* **1**, 57.
Mathison, D. R., and Hays, H. W. (1945). *Endocrinology* **37**, 275.
McCullagh, D. F., and Cuyler, W. K. (1939). *J. Pharmacol. Exptl. Therap.* **66**, 379.
Miescher, K., Wettstein, A., and Tschopp, E. (1936). *Biochem. J.* **30**, 1970.
Miescher, K., Kagi, H., Scholz, C., and Wettstein, A. (1937). *Biochem. J.* **294**, 39.
Morato Manoro, J. (1940). *Arch. Clin. Inst. Endocrinol., Fac. Med. (Montevideo)* **1**, 343.
Munson, P. L., and Sheps, M. C. (1958). *Endocrinology* **62**, 173.
Mussio Fournier, J. C., Albrieux, A. S., and Prego, L. (1940). *Arch. Clin. Inst. Endocrinol., Fac. Med. (Montevideo)* **1**, 332.
Nimni, M. E., and Geiger, E. (1957). *Proc. Soc. Exptl. Biol. Med.* **94**, 606.
Oesting, R. B., and Webster, B. (1938). *Endocrinology* **22**, 307.
Pfeiffer, C. A., Hooker, C. W., and Kirschbaum, A. (1944). *Endocrinology* **34**, 389.
Ruzicka, L. (1935). *Bull. Soc. Chim. France*, **5**, 1497.
Ruzicka, L., and Rosenberg, H. P. (1936). *Helv. Chim. Acta* **19**, 357.
Ruzicka, L., Goldberg, M. W., and Meyer, J. (1934). *Helv. Chim. Acta* **18**, 210.
Sakamoto, W., Gordan, G. S., and Eisenberg, E. (1951). *Proc. Soc. Exptl. Biol. Med.* **76**, 406.

Saunders, F. J., and Drill, V. A. (1957). *Proc. Soc. Exptl. Biol. Med.* **76**, 406.
Saunders, F. J., and Drill, V. A. (1958). *Metabolism, Clin. Exptl.* **7**, 315.
Selye, H., and Albert, S. (1942). *Proc. Soc. Exptl. Biol. Med.* **49**, 361.
Stafford, R. O., Bowman, B. J., and Olson, K. J. (1954). *Proc. Soc. Exptl. Biol. Med.* **86**, 322.
Stucki, J. C., Forbes, A. D., Northam, J. I., and Clark, J. J. (1960). *Endocrinology* **66**, 585.
Tscherning, K. (1936). *Angew. Chem.* **49**, 11.
Tschopp, E. (1935). *Klin. Wochschr.* **14**, 1064.
Valle, J. R., Henriques, S. B., and Henriques, O. B. (1947). *Endocrinology* **41**, 335.
Voss, H. E. (1937). *Klin. Wochschr.* **16**, 769.

Chapter 5

Antiandrogens

RALPH I. DORFMAN

I. Introduction

Substances possessing antiandrogenic activity are of practical as well as theoretical interest. Systemically active compounds may be of enormous benefit for women suffering from certain types of hirsutism and men suffering from androgen-dependent prostatic tumors. Local use of antiandrogenic compounds could also be of use in women with hypertricosis, in prevention of certain types of male baldness, for the inhibition of facial hair growth in men, and for the treatment and/or prevention of acne in young men and women.

Studies on inhibition of androgens have been reviewed (Dorfman and Shipley, 1956). The following compounds have been reported to possess antiandrogenic activity: estrone, estradiol-17β, and progesterone (Mühlboch, 1938a,b; Hoskins and Koch, 1939); 3-p-methoxyphenyl-4-methyl-7-hydroxycoumarin (Gley et al., 1936); methylcholanthrene (Hertz and Tullner, 1947); 17-ethynyl-19-nortestosterone (Dorfman, 1959; Dorfman and Dorfman, 1960; Dorfman and Stevens, 1960); 2-acetyl-7-oxo-1,2,3,4,4a,5,6,7,9,10,10a-dodecahydrophenanthrene (Ro 2-7239) (Randall and Selitto, 1958; Dorfman, 1959; Dorfman and Stevens, 1960); 11α-hydroxyprogesterone (Byrnes et al., 1953); and A-norprogesterone (Lerner et al., 1960).

Two types of antiandrogen bioassays have been used—those involving the capon's or chick's comb and those involving mammalian androgen indicators, usually the seminal vesicles and prostate. A relatively large number of substances, particularly progestational agents, are antiandrogenic on the comb tests, whereas antiandrogenic substances are limited to a relatively few compounds. Ro 2-7239 and A-norprogesterone

are active in both the fowl and mammalian tests, and the latter compound
is unique in that it can produce 100% inhibition of the testosterone
stimulation of the comb. This chapter will discuss the various tests that
have been described and implied.

Testosterone propionate will not induce optimum growth of the
accessory sex organs if immature castrated rats are fed restricted diets
(Leatham, 1963). In earlier studies, Kline and Dorfman (1951) showed
that the same androgen is less effective in stimulating seminal vesicles of
rats deficient in folic acid than those of normal rats. Here too, however,
the effect could be explained on the basis of inunction. In the present
chapter, we presume that we are dealing with antiandrogenic factors
other than those attributable to inunction. This seems to be consistent
with the fact that the compounds considered in this chapter do not
influence body weight, appetite, or general well-being.

II. Chick Comb Methods

A. Inunction

Two bioassay methods have been described in this group: one consists
of the admixture of the androgen with the food while the test compound

TABLE I

INHIBITORY EFFECT OF PROGESTERONE AND
NORETHISTERONE INUNCTED ON THE COMBS OF
TESTOSTERONE-STIMULATED CHICKS[a,b]

Steroid inuncted	Total dose (mg)	No. of chicks	Comb ratio (mean ± SE)
0	0	396	1.75 ± 0.02
Progesterone	0.5	61	1.54 ± 0.05
	1.0	211	1.41 ± 0.03
	2.0	216	1.38 ± 0.03
	4.0	63	1.15 ± 0.04
Norethisterone	0.1	138	1.40 ± 0.03
	0.2	97	1.35 ± 0.03
	0.4	77	1.19 ± 0.04
	0.8	56	1.25 ± 0.06
	1.6	43	1.21 ± 0.04

[a] From Dorfman and Dorfman (1960).

[b] All chicks received testosterone incorporated in their
food, 80 mg per kilogram body weight.

is administered by direct inunction to the comb; and the other procedure consists of the single injection on day 1 of the assay of a long-acting androgen and the daily comb inunction of the test compound.

1. Method of Dorfman and Dorfman (1960)

This method employs 1- to 3-day-old male or female White Leghorn chicks which are housed in a heated brooder maintained at 80°F. Testosterone is incorporated into the finely ground chick starting mash at a concentration of 80 mg per kilogram of food. The chicks are placed

TABLE II

CHICK ANTIANDROGEN ASSAY: LOCAL APPLICATION[a]

Compound[b] RBG No.	Dose (mg/day)	Percent inhibition	
		Testosterone, 1 µg/day, local	Testosterone enanthate, 0.5 mg i.m. × 1
10	1	100	59
33	1	55	—
44	1	65	—
45	1	11	—
46	1	82	89
50	1	27	—
58	1	0	0
59	1	100	24
64	1	22	28
83	1	92	5
107	1	90	67

[a] From Segaloff and Gabbard (1964).
[b] For name of compound, see Table III.

on this diet on day 1. The test compound is dissolved in corn oil (or sesame oil) so that the total dose is contained on 0.35 ml of the vehicle. Each day for 7 days 0.05 ml of the oil solution is inuncted on the comb. Control chicks receive only the vehicle. Twenty to twenty-four hours after the last inunction the combs are removed; the cut edge is blotted, and the combs are weighed rapidly to the nearest 0.5 mg. Body weights are also determined. The results may be expressed in absolute comb weights or as the ratio of milligrams of comb per gram of body weight.

Typical results using progesterone and norethisterone (17α-ethyl-19-nortestosterone) are presented in Table I. Unstimulated combs in animals of this age usually have comb ratios of the order of 0.30–0.38.

TABLE III

CODE FOR COMPOUNDS LISTED IN TABLE II[a]

Code	Name of compound
RBG 10	17-Methyl-17β-hydroxyandrost-4-en-3-one
RBG 33	17,17-Dimethyl-18-norandrosta-4,13-dien-3β-ol
RBG 44	17-Methyl-4,17β-dihydroxyandrost-4-en-3-one
RBG 45	2α,17-Dimethyl-17β-hydroxy-5α-androstan-3-one
RBG 46	17-Methyl-17β-hydroxyestr-4-en-3-one
RBG 50	2α,17-Dimethyl-17β-hydroxyandrost-4-en-3-one
RBG 58	17-Methyl-17β-hydroxy-5α-androstan-3-one
RBG 59	17-Methyl-17β-hydroxy-5β-androstan-3-one
RBG 64	17-Methyl-5β-androstane-3α,17β-diol
RBG 83	17-Methyl-androst-5-ene-3β,17β-diol
RBG 107	17-Methyl-17β-hydroxy-A-norandrost-4-en-3-one

[a] From Segaloff and Gabbard (1964).

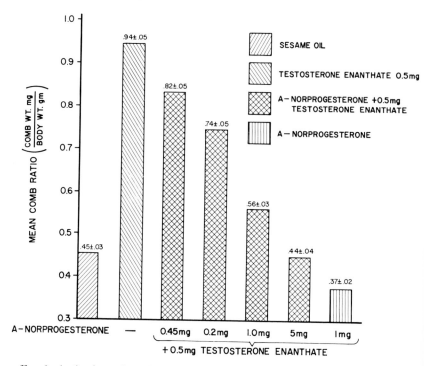

FIG. 1. Antiandrogenic activity of A-norprogesterone on testosterone-induced chick comb growth (Lerner *et al.*, 1960).

2. Method of Segaloff and Gabbard (1964)

Single-comb White Leghorn cockerels brought to the laboratory on
the day of hatching are started on study the next day. The steroids are
dissolved in mineral oil that is then diluted with 99 volumes of ethyl ether.
This solution of a suitable concentration is applied to the comb, using a
0.25 tuberculin syringe and a 27-gauge needle, in a volume of 0.05 ml
each day for 7 days. The chicks are sacrificed with ether 48 hours after

TABLE IV

INHIBITORY EFFECT OF NORETHISTERONE AND RO 2-7239
INUNCTED ON THE COMBS OF TESTOSTERONE ENANTHATE
(INJECTION) STIMULATED CHICKS[a,b]

Compound inuncted	Total dose (mg)	No. of chicks	Comb ratio (mean ± SE)
0	0	24	1.08 ± 0.07
Norethisterone	0.25	22	0.93 ± 0.04
	0.5	21	0.92 ± 0.04
	1.0	23	0.85 ± 0.04
Ro 2-7239[c]	0.1	17	0.97 ± 0.034
	0.2	17	0.92 ± 0.04
	0.4	17	0.73 ± 0.06
	1.6	13	0.74 ± 0.04

[a] From Dorfman (1959).
[b] All chicks received 0.5 mg of testosterone enanthate by injection on first day.
[c] Ro 2-7239 = 2-acetyl-7oxo-1,2,3,4,4a,5,6,7,9,10,10a-dodecahydrophenanthrene.

the last application. They are weighed and the combs are excised with
standard 6-inch, sharp and blunt operating scissors applied as closely
as possible to the skull. Results are listed in Table II. Compound code is
in Table III.

3. Androgen Injected—Test Compound Inuncted (Dorfman, 1959)

This method employs 1- to 3-day-old male or female White Leghorn
chicks which are housed in a heated brooder maintained at 80°F. A single
dose of 0.5 mg of testosterone enanthate contained in 0.5 ml of corn (or
sesame) oil is injected on the first day of the assay. The test compound
is dissolved in oil so that the total dose is contained in 0.35 ml of the
vehicle. Each day for 7 days 0.05 ml of the oil solution is inuncted on the
comb. Control groups receive only the vehicle. Twenty to twenty-four
hours after the last inunction the comb is removed; the cut edge is

blotted, and the comb is weighed rapidly to the nearest 0.5 mg. Body weight is also determined. The results may be expressed in absolute comb weight or as the ratio of milligrams of comb per gram of body weight.

Typical results using this method involving the injection of the androgen and inuncting the test compounds are illustrated in Table IV and Fig. 1.

4. Method of Lerner et al. (1960)

This assay method employs the chick comb end point in which both the androgen and antagonist are applied topically to the comb. Testosterone in sesame oil was applied daily in volume of 0.005 ml to one side of the comb, and the antagonist in a similar volume of oil was applied to the other side of the comb over a 7-day period. A-Norprogesterone inhibited the comb growth induced by testosterone. With this assay procedure, relatively small amounts of the antagonist were required for effectiveness. When A-norprogesterone was applied to the comb without exogenous androgen, a 38% reduction in the chick comb ratio resulted, thereby indicating the possible presence of endogenous androgenic substances in these young birds.

5. Method of Lerner et al. (1963)

Two-day-old White Leghorn cockerels were placed five per cage into a brooder maintained at temperatures of 88°–94°F. Beacon starter

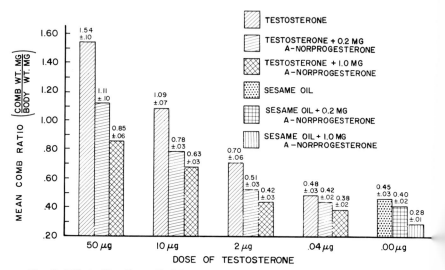

FIG. 2. Effect of locally applied A-norprogesterone and testosterone on the mean comb ratio (Lerner et al., 1963).

mash and water were provided ad libitum. Birds and cages were distributed in accordance with a random block design.

Testosterone and A-norprogesterone in several concentrations were dissolved in sesame oil for daily inunction volumes of 0.005 ml which were delivered to the chick comb by means of a Hamilton microsyringe

TABLE V

ANTAGONISM OF TESTOSTERONE-INDUCED CHICK COMB GROWTH BY
A-NORPROGESTERONE[a]

Treatment[b]	No. of chicks	Body weight (gm)		Comb weight (mg)
		Initial	Final	
Sesame oil	10	39.6 ± 1.44	76.2 ± 2.69	34.9 ± 3.40
T, 50 μg	15	39.7 ± 0.73	78.2 ± 2.09	120.8 ± 8.60
T, 10 μg	15	40.3 ± 0.93	83.5 ± 1.82	90.4 ± 5.85
T, 2 μg	15	39.1 ± 0.83	83.4 ± 1.89	58.5 ± 5.02
T, 0.4 μg	15	38.6 ± 0.68	80.5 ± 2.76	39.2 ± 2.37
A-NP, 0.2 mg, +T, 50 μg	13	39.1 ± 0.76	76.5 ± 1.77	80.7 ± 6.33
A-NP, 0.2 mg +T, 10 μg	15	38.8 ± 0.89	82.5 ± 2.63	64.7 ± 4.14
A-NP, 0.2 mg +T, 2 μg	15	38.5 ± 0.86	78.6 ± 2.59	40.7 ± 4.35
A-NP 0.2 mg +T, 0.4 μg	12	41.3 ± 1.04	78.8 ± 2.17	34.3 ± 2.04
A-NP, 1.0 mg +T, 50 μg	15	38.4 ± 0.79	79.2 ± 2.09	67.6 ± 5.66
A-NP, 1.0 mg +T, 10 μg	14	40.8 ± 1.01	82.4 ± 2.71	55.5 ± 2.22
A-NP, 1.0 mg +T, 2 μg	14	39.5 ± 0.87	80.9 ± 2.16	34.2 ± 2.77
A-NP, 1.0 mg +T, 0.4 μg	15	38.5 ± 0.90	81.1 ± 3.16	28.7 ± 1.64
A-NP 1.0 mg	15	39.4 ± 1.08	79.2 ± 2.04	21.9 ± 1.21
A-NP 0.2 mg	15	40.0 ± 1.00	80.3 ± 2.23	31.9 ± 2.11

[a] Lerner et al. (1963).
[b] Total dose was applied to comb over the 7 days of treatment. T = testosterone; A-NP = A-norprogesterone.

graduated in 0.001 ml divisions. The androgen was applied onto the left side of the comb and the A-norsteroid onto the right side once daily for 7 days. On day 8 the chicks were sacrificed. Body weights were recorded and the combs were excised with a single cut across the base of the comb. The combs were immediately weighed to the nearest 0.1 mg on a Roller-

Smith torsion balance. Mean comb ratio was calculated by dividing the body weight (grams) into the comb weight (milligrams).

Local application of testosterone, N-norprogesterone, or combinations of both compounds to the chick comb did not alter body weight gain (Table V). A 7-day treatment with total doses of 0.4, 2.0, 10.0, and 50.0 μg of testosterone produced mean comb ratios which were, respectively, 7, 56, 140, and 242% greater than those of the control chicks (Fig. 2). Inunction of a total dose of 1 mg of A-norprogesterone alone, without exogenous androgen, reduced the mean comb ratio by 38%.

A-norprogesterone at total doses of 0.2 mg in combination with total doses of 0.4, 2.0, 10.0, and 50.0 μg of testosterone reduced the androgen-stimulated comb growth (Table V). The antagonism of the testosterone-induced hypertrophy was 100, 76, 48, and 40%, respectively (Fig. 2). With similar doses of testosterone, total doses of 1.0 mg of A-norprogesterone inhibited the androgen-induced growth by 100, 100, 64, and 63%.

B. INJECTION

1. Androgen Fed—Test Compound Injected (Dorfman and Dorfman, 1960)

This method employs 1- to 3-day-old male or female White Leghorn chicks which are housed in a heated brooder maintained at 80°F. Testosterone is incorporated into the finely ground chick starting mash at a concentration of 80 mg per kilogram of food. The chicks are placed on this diet on day 1. The test compound is dissolved in corn (or sesame) oil so that the total dose is contained in 0.7 ml of the vehicle. Each day for 7 days 0.1 ml of the oil solution is injected subcutaneously. Control

TABLE VI

INHIBITORY EFFECT OF PROGESTERONE AND NORETHISTERONE (INJECTION ON THE COMBS OF TESTOSTERONE-STIMULATED CHICKS[a, b]

Steroid injected	Total dose (mg)	No. of chicks	Comb ratio (mean ± SE)
0	0	195	1.38 ± 0.03
Progesterone	0.5	101	1.31 ± 0.05
	1.0	123	1.37 ± 0.05
	2.0	119	1.13 ± 0.05
Norethisterone	4.0	9	0.92 ± 0.09

[a] Dorfman and Dorfman (1960).
[b] All chicks received testosterone in their food, 80 mg per kilogram of food.

chicks receive only the vehicle. At 20–24 hours after the last injection the combs are removed and, after blotting of the cut edge, weighed rapidly to the nearest 0.5 mg. Body weights are also determined. The results may be expressed in absolute comb weights or as milligrams of comb per gram of body weight.

A study using this method is presented in Table VI; it indicates that both progesterone and norethisterone are active by the injection route, but relatively less active than by the inunction method.

III. Mammalian Methods

A. Mouse

1. Method of Dorfman (1962)

Swiss albino mice were castrated at 21–23 days of age. On the day of operation and for a total of 7 consecutive days, the testosterone dissolved in 0.1 ml of sesame oil or an aqueous suspending medium (this medium consists of sodium chloride, 0.9%; polysorbate 80, 0.4%; carboxymethyl cellulose, 0.5%; and benzyl alcohol, 0.9%) was injected subcutaneously. The test material dissolved either in 0.2 ml of sesame oil or the aqueous suspending medium was injected once daily for 7 days, also starting on the day of operation. Twenty-four hours after the last injections the animals were autopsied and the body, prostate, and seminal vesicle weights were determined. The results are expressed as tissue ratios defined as milligrams of tissue per gram of body weight.

A total dose of 2 mg of testosterone injected in an oil solution was inhibited by 100-mg doses of 3 different compounds. The solvent-injected control groups had prostate and seminal vesicle ratios of 0.08 ± 0.006 and 0.08 ± 0.004, respectively. Testosterone at a total dose of 2 mg did not produce a significant difference in body weight, but did produce 4-fold increases in the prostate ratio and a 12-fold increase in the seminal vesicles ratio. One hundred milligrams of A-norprogesterone did not decrease the prostatic ratio significantly. However, the ratio of the seminal vesicles decreased from 1.10 ± 0.15 to 0.64 ± 0.11. Progesterone caused a similar but somewhat more intense response at the same dose level. Ro 2-7239 (2-acetyl-7-oxo-1,2,3,4,4a,5,6,7,9,10,10a-dodecahydrophenanthrene) at the total dose of 100 mg inhibited the action of testosterone on the prostate and seminal vesicle ratios.

Table VII deals with a series of experiments on the influence of progesterone on the action of testosterone when both compounds were administered in sesame oil solution. In these experiments 0.4 and 0.8

TABLE VII

Antiandrogenic Activity of Various Steroids in a Castrated Mouse Assay[a]

Expt.	Material injected	Total dose (mg)	Testosterone injected (mg)	No. of mice	Mean body weight (gm)	Tissue ratio ± SE Prostate	Tissue ratio ± SE Seminal vesicles
A	0	0	0	8	18	0.07 ± 0.008	0.13 ± 0.014
	0	0	0.4	10	19	0.21 ± 0.019	0.62 ± 0.057
	Progesterone	10	0.4	10	18	0.22 ± 0.025	0.70 ± 0.007
		20	0.4	10	14	0.30 ± 0.052	0.73 ± 0.069
		40	0.4	7	17	0.20 ± 0.018	0.46 ± 0.049
B	0	0	0	10	18	0.19 ± 0.032	0.24 ± 0.025
	0	0	0.4	7	17	0.33 ± 0.047	0.93 ± 0.122
	Progesterone	10	0.4	10	20	0.34 ± 0.027	0.77 ± 0.064
		20	0.4	8	17	0.38 ± 0.041	0.73 ± 0.066
		40	0.4	10	22	0.19 ± 0.018	0.37 ± 0.026
C	0	0	0	8	18	0.07 ± 0.008	0.13 ± 0.014
	0	0	0.8	8	17	0.23 ± 0.025	0.85 ± 0.068
	Progesterone	10	0.8	9	18	0.26 ± 0.017	0.81 ± 0.038
		20	0.8	9	17	0.24 ± 0.017	0.72 ± 0.035
		40	0.8	8	18	0.18 ± 0.012	0.47 ± 0.080
		40	0.8	8	18	0.18 ± 0.012	0.47 ± 0.080
D	0	0	0	10	18	0.19 ± 0.032	0.24 ± 0.025
	0	0	0.8	9	20	0.36 ± 0.047	0.90 ± 0.088
	Progesterone	10	0.8	5	19	0.34 ± 0.060	0.65 ± 0.092
		20	0.8	10	22	0.33 ± 0.038	0.71 ± 0.081
		40	0.8	10	19	0.26 ± 0.023	0.46 ± 0.047

mg of testosterone were injected and the dose of progesterone ranged from 10 to 40 mg. No significant antiandrogenic effect was elicited on the prostate at the 10-, 20-, or 40-mg dose levels of progesterone in experiment A. The 10- and 20-mg dose of progesterone was ineffective as an antiandrogen on the seminal vesicles, but the total dose of 40 mg produced a highly significant inhibition of seminal vesicle ratio from 0.62 ± 0.057 to 0.46 ± 0.049. In experiment B (Table VII) the 0.4 ml of testosterone injected over the 7-day period caused a significant increase in both prostate and seminal vesicle ratios. The prostate ratio was increased almost 100%, while the seminal vesicle ratio was increased something less than 4-fold. In this experiment as little as 10 mg per day total dose of progesterone significantly decreased the seminal vesicle ratio from 0.93 ± 0.122 to 0.77 ± 0.064, while the prostatic ratio remained unchanged. At the 20-mg total dose in experiment B, no change in prostate ratio was found, but again the seminal vesicle ratio was decreased. At 40 mg, however, a significant decrease in both prostatic and seminal ratios were observed. Experiment C was essentially similar to experiment A, and experiment D was similar to experiment B.

2. Method of Neumann and Elger (1966a)

NMRI mice were used as experimental animals with a starting weight of about 20 gm. The animals were grouped as follows: group 1—intact male mice; group 2—intact male mice treated with intramuscular doses of 1 mg of cyproterone acetate per animal every other day for 4 weeks; group 3—castrated male mice treated with intramuscular doses of 0.5 mg of testosterone propionate per animal every other day for 4 weeks; group 4—castrated male mice treated with intramuscular doses of 0.5 mg of testosterone propionate and 1 mg of cyproterone acetate per animal every other day for 4 weeks.

Six to eight animals were tested in each group. The duration of the test period was 4 weeks. After a test period of 14 days, a skin area of about 1 cm^2 on the lower back was plucked in order to study the effect of the antiandrogen on hair regeneration. After a test period of 4 weeks, the animals were sacrificed and the body weight as well as the weight of the seminal and preputial glands were determined.

For the histological study, an area of 1.5–2 cm by 0.5 cm of skin from the back was excised and fixed in 10% formalin. After these pieces were embedded in paraffin, sections 5 μ thick were prepared and stained with hematoxylin-eosin.

In each animal a skin section 1 cm in length and 5 μ thick was evaluated quantitatively. The number of alveoli in the sebaceous glands and the number of the glandular cells per alveolus were determined (the cells in a total of 20 alveoli were counted): the cell diameter of 40 glandular cells in various alveoli was determined for each section. By means of the cell diameter the relative cell volume was calculated according to the formula $4/3\pi r^3$, since we assumed the cells of the sebaceous glands to be almost spherical. The total volume of sebaceous tissue was calculated as follows: average relative cell volume times average number of counted glandular cells per alveolus times the number of alveoli in the skin areas of the evaluated length of skin (Tables VIII and IX).

TABLE VIII

SEMINAL VESICLE AND PREPUTIAL GLAND WEIGHTS OF MICE[a]

		Body weight		Organ weight (mg)	
Group[b]	No. of animals	Beginning weight	End weight	Seminal vesicle	Preputial glands
1. Intact male animals—controls (solvent only)	8	21 ± 0.4^c	26 ± 0.9	162 ± 18	61 ± 6.2
2. Intact male animals, after 4 weeks; animals received 1 mg AA+, i.m., every 2nd day	7	22 ± 0.4	18 ± 1.3	45 ± 8.6	34 ± 7.6
3. Castrated male animals, after 4 weeks; animals received 0.5 mg TP++, i.m., every 2nd day	8	23 ± 0.4	26 ± 1.0	361 ± 27	82 ± 14
4. Castrated male animals, after 4 weeks; animals received 0.5 mg TP++ and 1 mg AA+, i.m., every 2nd day	6	21 ± 0.5	22 ± 1.0	290 ± 32	54 ± 7.4

[a] From Neumann and Elger (1966a).
[b] AA+ = 6-chloro-17-hydroxy-1α, 2α-methylenepregna-4, 6-diene-3, 20-dione acetate (cyproterone acetate); TP++ = testosterone propionate.
[c] ± = Mean deviation.

B. RAT

1. Method of Randall and Selitto (1958)

Albino male rats weighing 70 gm were castrated under ether anesthesia. Starting 1 day after surgery, the rats were injected once daily with 0.15 mg of testosterone propionate in sesame oil (volume not specified). The test compound was also dissolved in sesame oil and injected subcutaneously daily for 7 days at a separate site. Twenty-four hours after the last injection the rats were sacrificed, at which time body, seminal vesicles, and levator ani weights were determined.

The antiandrogenic activity of Ro 2-7239 by this method is illustrated in Fig. 3. The stimulating total dose of testosterone of 1.05 mg caused

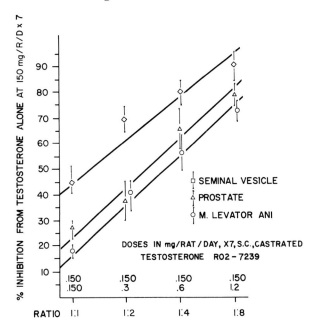

FIG. 3. Antiandrogenic activity of Ro 2-7239 in the castrated rat (Randall and Selitto, 1958).

weight increases of 565% in the seminal vesicles, 365% in the prostate, and 105% in the levator ani muscle. When the ratio of testosterone to Ro 2-7239 was 1:8, inhibitions of 70–90% were observed. Some typical data using this method are illustrated in Table X dealing with the anti-androgenic activity of A-norprogesterone.

2. Method of Dorfman and Stevens (1960)

Rats, 26–28 days of age, were castrated and, starting on the same day, were injected subcutaneously once daily with 0.5 ml of an aqueous suspension of testosterone (2 mg/3.5 ml) for 7 days. The test compound was also placed in aqueous suspension and the rats received 0.5 ml per day for 7 days, starting with the day of surgery. The aqueous suspending

TABLE IX

QUANTITATIVE EVALUATION OF SEBACEOUS GLANDS[a]

Group[b]	No. of animals	No. of sebaceous gland alveoli/cm of skin	No. of glandular alveoli	Cell diameter (μ)	Cell volume (μ^3)	Total volume sebaceous gland tissue (mm³/1 cm skin)	Total volume (% of controls)
1. Intact male animals—controls (solvent only)	8	19 ± 8[c] (1)[d]	6.9 ± 0.98 (5)	15.3 ± 0.4 (9)	1866 ± 113 (13)	0.000262 (17) ±0.000153	100
2. Intact male animals, after 4 weeks; animals received 1 mg AA+, i.m., every 2nd day	7	9 ± 5.8 (2)	5 ± 0.6 (6)	11.5 ± 1.9 (10)	862 ± 431 (14)	0.0000491 (19) ±0.00000447	18.8
3. Castrated male animals, after 4 weeks; animals received 0.5 mg TP++, i.m., every 2nd day	8	57 ± 17.4 (3)	8.8 ± 1.2 (7)	15.8 ± 0.35 (11)	2065 ± 140 (15)	0.00103 (19) ±0.000307	391
4. Castrated male animals, after 4 weeks; animals received 0.5 mg TP++ and 1 mg AA+, i.m., every 2nd day	6	25 ± 6.9 (4)	5.5 ± 0.83 (8)	13.8 ± 0.8 (12)	1390 ± 227 (16)	0.000196 (20) ±0.000071	75

[a] Neumann and Elger (1966a).

[b] AA+ = 6-chloro-17-hydroxy-1α,2α-methylenepregna-4,6-diene-3,20-dione acetate (cyproterone acetate); TP++ = testosterone propionate.

[c] ± = Mean deviation.

[d] Numbers in parentheses refer to Students t test; see tabulation below.

STUDENTS *t* TEST

Highly significant	Significant	Not significant
1:3 3:4 5:6 7:8 9:11 11:12 } $P < 0.001$ 13:14 13:15 13:16 15:16 19:20 5:7 17:18 } $0.001 > p < 0.005$	9:12 $0.01 > P < 0.025$	1:2 9:10 } $0.2 > P < 0.4$ 17:20 1:4 $p > 0.5$ 5:8 $0.05 > P < 0.1$

TABLE X

ANTIANDROGENIC ACTIVITY OF A-NORPROGESTERONE IN THE CASTRATED RAT[a,b]

Total dose of A-norprogesterone (mg)	Total dose of testosterone propionate (μg)	No. of rats	Mean tissue weight (mg $\pm$ SE)		
			Seminal vesicle plus coagulating gland	Ventral prostate	Levator ani
0	0	42	11.2 ± 0.3	11.3 ± 0.3	21.6 ± 0.7
0	175	42	52.7 ± 1.7	58.1 ± 1.8	31.2 ± 0.9
7	0	6	11.1 ± 0.7	11.6 ± 0.8	22.3 ± 2.3
35	0	4	8.6 ± 0.2	12.6 ± 1.5	18.9 ± 1.4
7	175	6	38.6 ± 3.6	36.2 ± 1.7	29.0 ± 2.0
35	175	4	24.6 ± 1.2	31.9 ± 1.7	20.3 ± 1.3
175	175	3	13.1 ± 0.5	13.1 ± 2.3	17.3 ± 1.6

[a] From Lerner et al. (1960).
[b] Seven-day assay.

medium consisted of sodium chloride (9.9%), polysorbate 80 (0.4%), carboxymethyl cellulose (0.5%), and benzyl alcohol (0.9%). One day after the last injection the rats were sacrificed and the weights of the body, seminal vesicles, prostate, and levator ani were determined. By using this method, it was possible to demonstrate a statistically significant interference with the peripheral action of testosterone (Table XI).

This method can be practiced precisely as described above for the injected castrate rat except that the test compound is administered by gavage instead of by subcutaneous injection. A typical experiment is

TABLE XI

INHIBITION OF THE ACTION OF TESTOSTERONE BY RO 2-7239[a]

Testosterone injected (mg)	Ro 2-7239 injected (mg)	No. of rats	Tissue ratio (mean ± SE)		
			Seminal vesicle	Prostate	Levator ani
0	0	7	0.05 ± 0.005	0.07 ± 0.007	0.24 ± 0.031
2	0	7	0.94 ± 0.058	0.96 ± 0.072	0.67 ± 0.045
2	50	7	0.68 ± 0.053	0.65 ± 0.031	0.57 ± 0.026

[a] From Dorfman and Stevens (1960).

presented in Table XII using a total dose of 2.4 mg of testosterone and
a total dose of 100 mg of Ro 2-7239. In this study, inhibition was found
only on the prostate end point.

TABLE XII

Inhibition of the Action of Testosterone by Ro 2-7239[a]

Testosterone injected (mg)	Ro 2-7239 by gavage (mg)	No. of rats	Tissue ratio (mean ± SE)		
			Seminal vesicle	Prostate	Levator ani
0	0	8	0.10 ± 0.007	0.16 ± 0.009	0.21 ± 0.013
2.4	0	9	1.03 ± 0.075	1.24 ± 0.082	0.40 ± 0.017
2.4	100	10	0.97 ± 0.087	0.98 ± 0.062	0.43 ± 0.017

[a] From Dorfman and Stevens (1960).

3. Method of Segaloff and Gabbard (1964)

The rat assay employs immature male rats of the homozygous Fischer
strain weighing 44–55 gm when they are castrated under ether anesthesia. On the day of castration they are started on the first of 7 daily

TABLE XIII

Chick Antiandrogen Assay; By Injection And Oral Administration

Compound,[b] RBG No.	Rat parenteral dose, inhibition		Rat oral, dose, inhibition	
	Dose (mg/day)	Testosterone, 1 μg/day, s.c.	Dose (mg/day)	Testosterone, 1 μg/day s.c.
10	10	70%	10	73%
33	10	0	10	67%
44	1	0	1	49%
45	10	0	10	74%
46	10	65%	10	43%
50	10	17%	10	29%
58	10	10%	10	86%
59	10	10%	10	24%
64	1	36%	1	6%
83	10	25%	10	75%
107	10	21%	10	61%

[a] Segaloff and Gabbard (1964).
[b] For name of compound, see Table III.

injections and are autopsied 24 hours after the last injection. The steroids are given subcutaneously in 0.1 ml of sesame oil. At sacrifice the ventral prostate, the right seminal vesicle, and the levator ani muscle are dissected out and weighed. In this assay 1 μg of testosterone per day was generally employed. We have had no compounds to date sufficiently antiandrogenic so that we felt warranted in the routine use of graded doses of testosterone. The testosterone is always given subcutaneously, and the antagonist is either injected at a separate site or given orally. Results are tabulated in Table XIII.

4. Method of Mahesh et al. (1966)

Male rats 21 or 32 days old were obtained from Sprague-Dawley, Inc., Madison, Wisconsin, and housed in an air-conditioned room (76–78°F). They were fed laboratory chow from Wayne Laboratories and tap water ad libitum. A suspension of 17α-methyl-B-nortestosterone at various dose levels in 0.2 ml of corn oil was injected subcutaneously for 10 days to experimental groups, whereas only corn oil was injected in control groups. Each experimental group consisted of 6 rats. In selected groups of animals 2 mg of testosterone per kilogram body weight was injected in corn oil.

a. Experiments with 32-Day-Old Rats. Three experiments were carried out with 32-day-old rats. In the first experiment 32-day-old intact rats were administered, per kilogram body weight, 60 mg, 100 mg, 150 mg, and 200 mg of a 17α-methyl-B-nortestosterone, and the weights of the testis, seminal vesicles, ventral prostate, and levator ani were recorded (Table XIV). The ventral prostate weight was significantly decreased at the 0.05 level with the 100 mg/kg body weight dose and at the 0.01 level with the 150 and 200 mg/kg dose. A highly significant decrease ($P < 0.01$) in the weight of the seminal vesicles occurred at the 60 mg/kg and higher dose levels. The body weight, testicular weight, and the weight of the levator ani were unaffected at all dose levels. The administration of testosterone (2 mg/kg body weight) brought about a significant decrease in testicular weight ($P < 0.01$) and an increase in the seminal vesicle, ventral prostate, and levator ani weights ($P < 0.01$). When rats were injected with 200 mg of 17α-methyl-B-nortestosterone per kilogram body weight along with testosterone at 2 mg/kg, there was no significant change in testicular and levator ani weights as compared to the group treated with testosterone alone, whereas the seminal vesicle and ventral prostate weights showed a highly significant decrease ($P < 0.01$).

b. Experiments with 21-Day-Old Rats. 17α-Methyl-B-nortestosterone was administered in doses of 30, 60, and 100 mg/kg body weight to 21-day-old intact male rats for 10 days; the results are shown in Table XV. The body weight, testicular weight and the weight of the levator ani

TABLE XIV

Effect of 17α-Methyl-B-nortestosterone on Intact 32-Day-Old Male Rats[a]

Treatment	Body weight, initial (gm)	Body weight, final (gm)	Relative organ weights (mg/100 gm body weight of the rat)			
			Testes	Ventral prostate	Seminal vesicles	Levator ani
Control	106 ± 2.1[b]	185 ± 1.3	1144 ± 24.5	59.1 ± 7.3	87.5 ± 5.8	40.0 ± 1.9
17α-Methyl-B-nortestosterone						
60 mg/kg	106 ± 0.5	178 ± 1.3	1203 ± 22.6	44.9 ± 4.5	52.7 ± 4.9[d]	41.0 ± 6.6
100 mg/kg	105 ± 0.4	190 ± 0.8	1161 ± 5.8	42.6 ± 1.8[c]	45.3 ± 0.8[d]	38.9 ± 0.5
150 mg/kg	109 ± 0.5	192 ± 1.8	1203 ± 44.6	39.6 ± 2.8[d]	45.8 ± 2.9[d]	40.6 ± 3.6
200 mg/kg	106 ± 0.7	190 ± 2.8	1152 ± 27.4	30.0 ± 4.4[d]	30.8 ± 3.5[d]	38.7 ± 3.7
Testosterone, 2 mg/kg	107 ± 0.5	191 ± 0.6	950 ± 17.4[d]	110.7 ± 2.7[d]	189.4 ± 4.1[d]	70.5 ± 3.2[d]
17α-methyl-B-nortestosterone, 200 mg/kg + testosterone, 2 mg/kg	105 ± 1.3	185 ± 2.4	851 ± 56.3[d]	64.8 ± 3.5[e]	138.7 ± 5.5[c]	63.5 ± 2.4

[a] Adapted from Mahesh et al. (1966).
[b] Mean ± standard error.
[c] Difference significant at the 0.05 level as compared to the control.
[d] Difference significant at the 0.01 level as compared to the control.
[e] Difference significant at the 0.01 level as compared to testosterone-treated group.

TABLE XV

EFFECT OF 17α-METHYL-B-NORTESTOSTERONE ON INTACT 21-DAY-OLD MALE RATS[a]

Treatment	Body weight, initial (gm)	Body weight, final (gm)	Relative organ weight (mg/100 gm body weight of the rat)			
			Testes	Ventral prostate	Seminal vesicles	Levator ani
Control	51 ± 2.5[b]	138 ± 4.0	510.3 ± 29.7	54.5 ± 4.5	35.9 ± 2.1	35.6 ± 0.9
17α-Methyl-B-nortestosterone, 30 mg/kg	48 ± 0.9	129 ± 3.6	488.5 ± 41.2	43.9 ± 3.1	28.6 ± 1.9	30.8 ± 2.2
17α-Methyl-B-nortestosterone, 60 mg/kg	48 ± 1.2	132 ± 3.0	461.4 ± 16.7	32.5 ± 3.6[d]	27.6 ± 3.9	40.6 ± 6.9
17α-Methyl-B-nortestosterone, 100 mg/kg	49 ± 1.8	134 ± 4.2	498.6 ± 29.8	41.6 ± 4.2[c]	23.5 ± 1.9[c]	30.3 ± 3.2
Control	53 ± 0.7	114 ± 0.8	554.2 ± 3.3	38.7 ± 1.1	22.0 ± 0.7	27.2 ± 14.3
Testosterone, 2 mg/kg	56 ± 0.6	121 ± 3.0	369.3 ± 6.3[d]	97.7 ± 3.1[d]	115.5 ± 1.5[d]	48.8 ± 1.9
17α-Methyl-B-nortestosterone, 200 mg/kg + testosterone, 2 mg/kg	53 ± 0.5	113 ± 1.5	294.4 ± 26.8[e]	57.3 ± 0.7[f]	57.6 ± 0.9[f]	39.8 ± 1.4[f]

[a] Adapted from Mahesh et al. (1966).
[b] Mean ± standard error.
[c] Difference significant at the 0.05 level as compared to control.
[d] Difference significant at the 0.01 level as compared to control.
[e] Difference significant at the 0.05 level as compared to testosterone-treated group.
[f] Difference significant at the 0.01 level as compared to testosterone-treated group.

were unaffected whereas the weights of the ventral prostate and seminal vesicles were significantly decreased ($P < 0.05$) at the higher dose level. In another experiment with the same type of animals, testosterone (2 mg/kg body weight) significantly reduced the testicular weight ($P < 0.01$) and increased the weight of the seminal vesicle and ventral prostate ($P < 0.01$). The effect of testosterone on the levator ani weight could not be evaluated in this group because of variability of the weights in the control group. When 17α-methyl-B-nortestosterone (200 mg/kg body weight) was administered along with testosterone (2 mg/kg), it potentiated the action of testosterone in the decrease of testicular weight ($P < 0.05$) and antagonized its action on seminal vesicles, ventral prostate, and the levator ani ($P < 0.01$).

5. Method of Neumann et al. (1965)

Male rats about 160 gm in weight received the test compound in oil solution daily for 21 days. At autopsy, weights of the testes and seminal vesicles were determined. Typical results of Neumann *et al.* (1965) are illustrated in Table XVI.

TABLE XVI

INFLUENCE OF CYPROTERONE ACTEATE ADMINISTERED DAILY FOR 3 WEEKS
(5 RATS PER GROUP)[a]

Subcutaneous dosage (mg)		Mean body weight (gm)	Organ weight (mg/100 gm) body weight	
Daily	Total		Testes	Seminal vesicles
0	0	177	1096	278
0.3	6.3	184	1238	121
1.0	21	175	1235	81
3.0	63	212	1140	95
10.0	210	184	1026	21

[a] Adapted from Neumann *et al.* (1965).

6. Method of Neumann and Kramer (1964)

It has been known for several years that after the administration of androgenically active steroid hormones during pregnancy the external genitalia of female newborn children may be masculinized. Animal experiments revealed that the fetuses of rats and mice react quite similarly. It can therefore be taken for granted that the fetal testes

already produce androgenic agents (such as testosterone) which transform the originally bisexual genitalia to male genitalia. At the time of
differentiation of the genitalia, steroids with androgenic properties exert
an effect in the female fetus similar to that of the androgenic agents of the
fetal testes in male fetuses. They cause a more or less pronounced counter-
sexual development. The uterus and the ovaries, however, always
remain unchanged.

As it is known that substances with antiandrogenic properties are
able to inhibit the effects of testosterone on the chicken comb or on the
accessory sexual glands of rats and mice, it was obvious that one could
examine the possibility of whether the masculinization of female fetuses
caused by androgenic agents could also be inhibited by antiandrogenic
compounds.

Female rats (Sprague-Dawley, fed with Latz pellets) were mated and
the beginning of pregnancy was determined by vaginal smears. From
day 16 to day 19 of pregnancy, the test substances were administered
subcutaneously in sesame oil or in a mixture of benzyl benzoate–castor
oil (1 : 20). Testosterone propionate was used as the androgenic agent,
and 6 - chloro - Δ^6 - 1,2α - methylene - 17α - hydroxyprogesterone acetate
was used as the antiandrogenic compound. Both steroids were injected
simultaneously in varying dose ranges but at different sites.

Table XVII shows the results of studies of the antagonism of
testosterone propionate and 6-chloro-Δ^6-1,2α-methylene-17α-hydroxy-
progesterone acetate on the degree of masculinization of female fetuses.
It will be noted that the addition of 6-chloro-Δ^6-1,2α-methylene-17α-
hydroxyprogesterone acetate to a constant dose of testosterone propionate causes a more or less dose-dependent reduction of the degree of
masculinization. As an example, 1 mg of testosterone propionate per
animal per day causes stage 4 of masculinization in 88% of the fetuses,
i.e., these animals do not possess a septum urethrovaginale (no vagina)
and the anogenital distance is already very considerably widened. The
urethra is masculine, S-shaped; the clitoris is enlarged like a penis.
However, after the additional administration of 10 mg of the antiandrogenic agent, 50% of the fetuses show no signs of masculinization.
Another 50% show a minor shortening of the septum urethrovaginale
only, and a moderate developmental inhibition in the posterior part of the
vagina. When the dose of the antiandrogenic agent is diminished, the
percentage of nonmasculinized and less-masculinized fetuses becomes
lower. With a dose relationship of 1 : 1, however, the antagonism between
both compounds is still distinct.

A dose of 10 mg of testosterone propionate leads to total masculinization (stage 5) in female newborn animals. The external genitalia of these

TABLE XVII

EFFECT OF TESTOSTERONE PROPIONATE AND 6-CHLORO-Δ^6-1,2α-METHYLENE-17α-HYDROXYPROGESTERONE ACETATE (ALONE OR COMBINED) ON THE DIFFERENTIATION OF GENITALIA OF FEMALE RAT FETUSES AFTER SUBCUTANEOUS ADMINISTRATION TO PREGNANT RATS ON DAYS 16–19[a]

	Dose (mg/animal/day)			Anogenital distance		Length of septum urethrovaginale measured under 47-fold magnification (cm)	Stages of masculinization (values in %)					
Group No.	Testosterone propionate	6-Chloro-Δ^6-1,2α-methylene-17α-hydroxyprogesterone acetate	No. of animals	Macroscopically (mm)	Microscopically measured under 47-fold magnification (cm)		0	1	2	3	4	5
A_1	1.0	0	8	1.7 ± 0.27	7.6 ± 1.24	−0.18[b]	—	—	—	12	88	—
A_2	1.0	1.0	15	1.3 ± 0.15	4.4 ± 0.57	+2.8 ± 1.3	13	60	27	—	—	—
A_3	1.0	3.0	10	1.2 ± 0.066	4.2 ± 0.41	+2.8 ± 0.91	20	70	10	—	—	—
A_4	1.0	10.0	8	1.2 ± 0.1	4.3 ± 0.37	+3.9 ± 0.92	50	50	—	—	—	—
B_1	3.0	0	9	2.2 ± 0.47	12.6 ± 2.52	None	—	—	—	22	78	—
B_2	3.0	1.0	11	1.3 ± 0.18	5.0 ± 1.01	+0.56 ± 1.37	—	10	36	27	27	—
B_3	3.0	3.0	10	1.2 ± 0.00	4.9 ± 0.48	+1.5 ± 1.61	—	40	30	30	—	—
C_1	10.0	0	4	2.8 ± 0.13	13.3 ± 0.64	None	—	—	—	—	—	100
C_2	10.0	3.0	8	1.4 ± 0.15	5.6 ± 0.52	−0.8 ± 0.85	—	—	13	62	25	—
	0	0	43	1.3 ± 0.13	4.3 ± 0.48	5.5 ± 1.16	91	9	—	—	—	—

[a] Adapted from Neumann and Kramer (1964).

[b] The standard deviation could not be calculated because only one animal possessed a "septum."

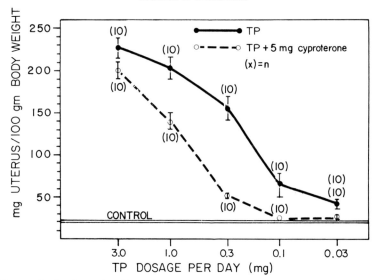

FIG. 4. Antiandrogenic effect of cyproterone on rat uterus. (From Neumann and Elger, 1966b.)

animals can no longer be distinguished from those of male fetuses. The clitoris has been transformed into a penis, the urethra opening at the tip of the organ. With simultaneous doses of 3 mg of the antiandrogenically active compound, i.e., with a dose relationship of 1:0.3, none of the animals is any longer entirely masculinized. Seventy-five percent of the

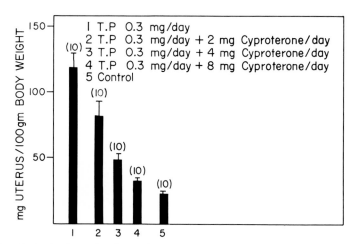

FIG. 5. Antiandrogenic effect of cyproterone in rats. (From Neumann and Elger, 1966b.)

fetuses again have a septum urethrovaginale, and thus a vagina. The administration of antiandrogenic agents alone to pregnant rats causes "feminization" of male fetuses.

7. Method of Neumann and Elger (1966b)

Sprague-Dawley female rats 40–45 gm in weight were ovariectomized. One week later the test compound and testosterone propionate were injected subcutaneously according to various dosage schedules. The treatment period was usually 12 days and the animals were autopsied on day 13, at which time the uteri and preputial glands were weighed.

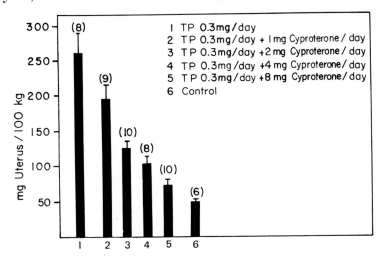

Fig. 6. Antiandrogenic effect of cyproterone on rat uterus. (From Neumann and Elger, 1966b.)

Testosterone propionate was administered in sesame oil solution and cyproterone was dissolved in a benzyl benzoate–castor oil mixture of 1:20. The daily dose was contained in 0.1 ml of solution. The results are indicated in Figs. 4–6 and Table XVIII.

8. Method of Chandra et al. (1967)

Chandra et al. (1967) have reversed this effect with the antiandrogen cyproterone. The details are presented as a possible antiandrogen assay.

RNA-polymerase activity of prostate nuclear aggregate preparations declines markedly within a few days of castration. They can be restored to normal by the administration of androgens.

Male castrated rats weighing about 200 gm were treated for 5 days with graduated doses of hormones, beginning 4 days after castration.

TABLE XVIII

INFLUENCE OF CYPROTERONE ON THE PREPUTIAL GLAND
OF CASTRATED IMMATURE RATS TREATED WITH
TESTOSTERONE PROPIONATE OVER A 12-DAY PERIOD[a]

Dosage (mg/day)		Number	Preputial gland
TP	Cyproterone	of rats	(mg $\pm$ SE)
0	0	10	55 ± 2.2
0.3	0	10	$163 (1)^b \pm 9.3$
0.3	8	10	$94 (2) \pm 6.5$
0.3	4	10	$116 (3) \pm 7.3$
0.3	2	10	$145 (4) \pm 5.4$
1	0	10	$205 (5) \pm 15.2$
1	5	10	$181 (6) \pm 14.9$
0.3	0	10	$165 (7) \pm 8.6$
0.3	5	10	$124 (8) \pm 10.1$
0.1	0	10	$116 (9) \pm 7.4$
0.1	5	10	$84 (10) \pm 6.21$

[a] Adapted from Neumann and Elger (1966b).
[b] Numbers in parentheses refer to Student's t test; see tabulation below.

Highly Significant	Significant	Not significant
1:2 ⎫		1:4 $0.1 > P < 0.2$
⎬ $P < 0.001$	2:3 $0.025 > P < 0.05$	1:4 $0.1 > P < 0.2$
2:4 ⎭		5:6 $0.2 > P < 0.4$
1:3 ⎫ $0.001 > P < 0.005$		
9:10 ⎭		
3:4 ⎫ $0.005 > P < 0.01$		
7:8 ⎭		

The animals were divided into 3 groups; one group received daily
0.3 mg of testosterone propionate per 100 gm body weight, the second
group received in addition 1 mg of cyproterone per 100 gm body weight,
and the third group received only oily injections. The prostate glands
from 25–40 animals were excised, the enzyme was prepared.

It follows from Table XIX that the weights of ventral prostates after
castration can be increased about 3-fold by the administration of testosterone. Simultaneous administration of cyproterone shows a marked
inhibition of the weight increments caused by testosterone.

The optimal conditions of the ribonucleotide incorporation into RNA
are shown in Table XX. It follows from the results that the polymerase

TABLE XIX

EFFECT OF CYPROTERONE ON THE VENTRAL PROSTATE WEIGHT OF RATS[a]

Group	Number of animals	Ventral prostate (mg/animal)
Castrated	40	78 ± 21.5
Castrated + testosterone	30	235 ± 42
Castrated + testosterone + cyproterone	40	126 ± 24

[a] From Chandra et al. (1967).

activity declines to 50% after castration. This decline of the polymerase activity can be restored to almost normal on treating the castrated rats with testosterone propionate. If, however, both the hormones are administered simultaneously then the polymerase activity decreases to a level exhibited by the castrated rats.

TABLE XX

EFFECT OF CYPROTERONE ON THE POLYMERASE ACTIVITY OF NUCLEAR
AGGREGATES OF RAT PROSTATES[a,b]

Group	System	Incorporation of AMP-^{3}H (nmole/gm prostate gland)	
Noncastrated	Complete	1.19	
	$-$UTP, CTP, GTP	0.19	
	$-$Mn^{++}	0.08	
	$-$Enzyme	0.06	
		Expt. I	Expt. II
Castrated		0.62	0.47
Castrated + testosterone		1.09	1.15
Castrated + testosterone + cyproterone		0.74	0.49

[a] Adapted from Chandra et al. (1967).

[b] The reaction mixture (0.05 ml) contained: 200 nmoles ATP-^{3}H (sp. act. 10.5 μCi/nmole); 300 nmoles each of GTP, CTP, and UTP; 33 nmoles Tris, pH 8.1; 33 μmoles KCl; 3.3 μmoles cysteine; 1.33 μmoles MnCl$_2$; and 0.1 ml of the washed aggregate polymerase. Incubations were made for 20 minutes at 37°C.

It is possible to correlate these findings with the effect of cyproterone at the ribosomal level, and it is suggested that the antagonistic action of cyproterone is due to a competition for the receptor molecule, responsible for the primary effect of testosterone in the target organ.

9. Possible Method of von Berswordt-Wallrabe and Neumann (1967)

The effects of the antiandrogen cyproterone (1,2α-methylene-6-chloropregna-4,6-dien-17α-ol-3,20-dione) on hypophyseal and serum FSH (and ICSH) content were studied in juvenile and in adult rats. FSH was determined in hypophysectomized juvenile rats. Parameter for FSH was the testicular weight increase of the recipients, expressed in milliunits (HMU) NIH-FSH S 1 (1 mg NIH-FSH S1 = 1000 MU FSH). Each juvenile donor rat was injected subcutaneously for 12 consecutive days with 10 mg, the adult donor rats for 21 consecutive days with 15 mg of cyproterone per day. Corresponding groups of intact and orchiectomized rats served as controls. Each recipient received the equivalent of one pituitary, or 18 ml of serum, per 6 days.

As a consequence of the orchiectomy, the FSH content of the pituitaries was considerably reduced, as compared with the intact donor rats (adults from 2500 to 780 MU of FSH; juveniles from 2300 to 480 MU of FSH). Under cyproterone, the hypophyseal FSH content was reduced from 2100 to 950 MU of FSH. Simultaneously, the serum FSH content exhibited the opposite trend: after orchiectomy there was an increase to 47 Mu of FSH in the adults and to 155 MU of FSH in the juvenile rats, as compared with 25 MU, no detectable amounts, and 35 MU of FSH in the untreated control rats. Under cyproterone a corresponding, although less pronounced, increase was significant.

Thus cyproterone, in analogy to orchiectomy, presumably enhances the FSH release into the circulation.

REFERENCES

Byrnes, W. W., Stafford, R. O., and Olson, K. J. (1953). *Proc. Soc. Exptl. Biol. Med.* **82**, 243.
Chandra, P., Orii, H., and Wacker, A. (1967). *Z. Physiol. Chem.* **348**, 1085.
Dorfman, R. I. (1959). *Endocrinology* **64**, 463.
Dorfman, R. I. (1960). *Science* **131**, 1096
Dorfman, R. I. (1962). *Proc. Soc. Exptl. Biol. Med.* **111**, 441–443.
Dorfman, R. I., and Dorfman, A. S. (1960). *Acta Endocrinol.* **33**, 308.
Dorfman, R. I., and Shipley, R. A. (1956). "Androgens, Biochemistry, Physiology and Clinical Significance," p. 133. Wiley, New York.
Dorfman, R. I., and Stevens, D. F. (1960). *Endocrinology* **67**, 394.
Gley, P., Mentzer, C., Delors, J. Molho, D., and Millon, J. (1946). *Compt. Rend. Soc. Biol.* **140**, 748.
Hertz, R., and Tullner, W. W. (1947). *J. Natl. Cancer Inst.* **8**, 121.
Hoskins, W. H., and Koch, F. C. (1939). *Endocrinology* **25**, 266.
Kline, I. T., and Dorfman, R. I. (1951). *Endocrinology* **48**, 34.

Leathem, J. H. (1963). *Natl. Cancer Inst. Monograph* **12**, 201.

Lerner, L. J., Bianchi, A., and Borman, A. (1960). *Proc. Soc. Exptl. Biol. Med.* **103**, 172.

Lerner, L. J., Bianchi, A., and Dzelzkalns, M. (1963) *Acta Endocrinol.* **44**, 398.

Mahesh, V. B., Zarate, A., Roper, B. K., and Greenblatt, R. B., (1966). *Steroids* **8**, 297.

Mühlboch, O. (1938a). *Acta Brevia Neerl. Physiol. Pharmacol. Microbiol.* **8**, 50.

Mühlboch, O. (1938b). *Acta Brevia Neerl. Physiol. Pharmacol. Microbiol.* **8**, 142.

Neumann, F., and Elger, W. (1966a). *J. Invest. Dermatol.* **46**, 561–572.

Neumann, F., and Elger, W. (1966b). *Acta Endocrinol.* **52**, 54.

Neumann, F., and Kramer, M. (1964). *Endocrinology* **75**, 428, 1964.

Neuman, F., Richter, R. D., and Gunzel, P. (1965). *Zentr. Veterinaermed.* **12**, 171.

Randall, L. O., and Selitto, J. J. (1958). *Endocrinology* **62**, 693.

Segaloff, A., and Gabbard, R. B. (1964). *Steroids* **4**, 433.

von Berswordt-Wallrabe, R., and Neumann, F. (1967). *Acta Endocrinol. Suppl.* **119**, 57.

Chapter 6

Standard Methods Adopted by Official Organizations

Cancer Chemotherapy National Service Center Program[1-3]

RALPH I. DORFMAN

An assay program involving certain selected tests of steroid hormone activity has been developed. Each assay, before adoption as an official test, either preliminary or quantitative, was modeled by at least two

[1] United States Public Health Service.

[2] The original assay program was developed by a subcommittee of the Endocrinology Panel of the Cancer Chemotherapy National Service Center composed of Drs. Ralph I. Dorfman (Chairman), M. X. Zarrow, Roland Meyer, Preston Perlman, James Leathem, Milton Eisler, Robert Stafford, Erwin Vollmer, Nathan Mantel, and Mr. Arthur G. Hilgar of the Cancer Chemotherapy National Service Center. (From 1st Edition, 1964.)

[3] Organizationally, credit goes to the Endocrine Evaluation Branch, General Laboratories and Clinics, N.C.I. Individuals involved: A. G. Hilgar worked over the specifications for years; Lois Trench helped him with the recent revision.

laboratories. The aim of the quantitative tests is to provide a method that would permit determination of activity of an unknown compared to a standard with an accuracy of $\pm 20\%$ at $P = 0.01$. The concentrations of test materials in the preliminary assays were so chosen as to indicate potency ratios of unknown to standard of 5% or better.

I. General Instructions for Hormone Assay Procedures[4]

A. MINIMUM STANDARD LABORATORY REQUIREMENTS

1. Animals

Obtain only from primary breeders.

2. Animal Rooms

Maintain at temperature between 70° and 80°F and provide adequate, draft-free ventilation preferably with air conditioning. Control of humidity between 40 and 50% is desirable.

3. Equipment and Facilities

Most types of metal cages are acceptable; solid-wall type preferred. Minimal cage area per mouse up to 60 days old will be 8 square inches; over 60 days old will be 10 square inches; and the maximal number of mice in any cage of any size will be 30. Adequate facilities for thorough cleaning of cages are necessary

4. Cleaning

To avoid *hormone contamination*, all equipment (cages, feeders, and water bottles) exposed to test animals must be cleaned throughly after completion of test by removing all debris, washing with an effective detergent, rinsing in hot water, and air-drying. During the course of an experiment, remove all waste, including unused food, regularly and frequently (preferably daily).

5. Animal Food

Use a commercial feed that does not deteriorate quickly and provides nutrition for adequate growth. Make food and water available for 24 hours each day, except when indicated otherwise in the specific instructions. Replace with fresh food and water at regular intervals (three

[4] Pertinent instruction taken from Cancer Chemotherapy Reports No. 1, January 1959, U.S. Department of Health, Education, and Welfare, Public Health Service pp. 67–69.

times weekly). Store food in rodent-proof rooms or containers to avoid contamination by wild rodents, etc.

Wherever possible, limit supply of food so that it will not be held longer than one month prior to use.

A sudden and marked change in ration can influence the animal's well-being. To avoid this undesirable effect, it is wise to provide the same ration as that used by the animal supplier.

B. ASSAY PROCEDURES

1. Vehicles for Administration

Use sesame oil as vehicle for administering estrogens and materials tested as estrogens. Administer all other compounds and test materials in Suspending Vehicle Special Formula No. 17874 (SV No. 17874), which consists of an aqueous solution of sodium chloride (0.9%), polysorbate 80 (0.4%), carboxymethyl cellulose (0.5%), and benzyl alcohol (0.9%).

2. Preparation of Materials in Aqueous Suspension

a. *Materials and Equipment.* Tenbroeck grinders for dispersing compounds into a suspension or equivalent. Manufacturer: Macalaster-Bicknell, Boston, Massachusetts, No. 2991, 7, 15, and 40 ml.

b. *Procedure.* Weigh compounds and transfer to a grinder of suitable size depending on the total volume to be used. Add to the Tenbroeck grinder a suitable amount of the total volume of suspending vehicle, usually about 10%, and reduce the material to a fine suspension with an additional 50% of the total final volume of fluid and transfer to a bottle or flask using a pipet. Wash the grinder with the remaining fluid, and transfer the fluid with a pipet.

3. Preparation of Animals

Before randomization, complete animal preparation which is common to all treatment groups in a given assay, i.e., castration, adrenalectomy, priming, conditioning, joining of parabionts.

4. Multiple Assays

When several assays, preliminary or quantitative, are performed simultaneously, modify the number of sets of controls as follows: For 1- or 2-test materials, use one set of controls as indicated in the specifications for each particular assay; for 3- to 6-test materials, use the equivalent of two sets of controls. However, this procedure does not apply to assays with a cross-over design.

5. *Randomization*

Use as an example assay J in Section II, which requires 116 adrenalectomized rats: 20 rats for solvent controls; 12 rats at each of two levels of standard; 6 rats at each of two levels of unknown for each of the 6 unknown compounds. These 116 rats are to be distributed among 15 treatment groups.

a. Mark 116 white index cards so that each represents a rat in a control group, some level of standard, or an unknown compound. Also mark 15 colored index cards so that each represents a treatment group. No prearranged order is necessary.

b. Using a table of random numbers, list a random, four-digit number on each card. Arrange the 116 white cards in numerical order. Arrange separately the 15 colored cards in numerical order. Resolve any ties that occur by tossing a coin.

c. As the rats (preliminary preparation already accomplished consists of adrenalectomy and insertion of cotton pellets) are picked out of their holding cages, assign them to the treatment listed on the card, i.e., first rat goes to treatment on first card, etc.

d. The order of the colored index cards corresponds to the order in which the groups are to be treated on each day and autopsied on the final day, i.e., the first treatment given on each of the 2 injection days is that shown on the first colored card. This will also be the first group autopsied the day after the last injection.

II. Specific Instructions for Hormone Assay Procedures

A. ANDROGENIC AND MYOGENIC ACTIVITY

Purpose: Determine the effect of the test compound compared with that of a reference androgen as measured by the change in weight of accessory sex organs.

Test Animal: Weanling (W) male (M) rat (R), Charles River (45) 21–24 days old, 50–65 gm

Surgery: Castration (0)

Standard Stimulator: Testosterone (T) for subcutaneous (2) and fluoxymestrone (H) for oral evaluation (3) administered in steroid suspending vehicle (0)

Dose Schedule:

Group code UNKNOWNS	Animals/group		Treatment	Total dose(s) (mg/animal/group)	
	1 or 2	3–6		S.c.	Oral
P					
R C	10	20	Vehicle	0.5 ml SSV	0.5 ml SSV
E S	5	10	Standard	0.6, 2.4	0.6, 9.6
L U	5	5	Unknown	0.6, 12.0	0.6, 12.0
I					
M					
Q					
U C	12	24	Vehicle	0.5 ml SSV	0.5 ml SSV
A S	12	24	Standard	0.3, 0.6, 1.2, 2.4	0.15, 0.6, 2.4, 9.6
N U	12	12	Unknown	×, 2×, 4×, 8×	×, 4×, 16×, 64×
T					

Procedure: Castrate, randomize, and weigh animals to the nearest gram. Start treatment the same day (day 1) once daily for 10 consecutive days. Sacrifice on day 11 and weigh to the nearest gram. Remove and weigh to the nearest 0.2 mg the ventral prostate (VP), seminal vesicle (SV) (without coagulating gland and devoid of fluid), and the levator ani (LA)

Test Objects: Ventral prostate (VP)—mg
Seminal vesicle (SV)—mg
Levator ani (LA)—mg

Compound Needs: Preliminary: subcutaneous—72 mg; oral—77 mg
Quantitative: subcutaneous—200×; oral—1400×

Analysis: Potency (P)

B. Uterotropic Activity

Purpose: Determine the effect of the test compound compared with that of reference estrogen as measured by the change in weight of the uterus.

Test Animal: Immature (I) female (F) mouse (M), Swiss albino (25) 21 days old, 8–11 gm

Surgery: None

Standard Stimulator: Estrone (E) for subcutaneous (2) and oral (3) evaluation administered in sesame oil (1)

Dose Schedule:

Group code UNKNOWNS		Animals/group		Treatment	Total dose(s) (µg/animal/group)	
		1 or 2	3–6		S.c.	Oral
P						
R	C	10	20	Vehicle	0.1 ml SO	0.2 ml SO
E	S	5	10	Standard	0.08, 0.32	0.8, 6.4
L	U	5	5	Unknown	0.08, 1.60	0.8, 16.0
I						
M						
Q						
U	C	12	24	Vehicle	0.1 ml SO	.20 ml SO
A	S	12	24	Standard	0.04, 0.08, 0.16, 0.32	0.8, 1.6, 3.2, 6.4
N	U	12	24	Unknown	×, 2×, 4×, 8×	×, 2×, 4×, 8×
T						

Procedure: Randomize and weigh animals to the nearest 0.5 gm. Start treatment the same day (day 1) once daily for 3 consecutive days. Sacrifice on day 4 and weigh to the nearest 0.5 gm. Remove and weigh the blotted, lightly compressed uteri (UT) to the nearest 0.2 gm.

Test Object: Uterus (UT)—mg

Compound Needs: Preliminary: subcutaneous—1 mg; oral—1 mg
Quantitative; subcutaneous and oral—200×

Analysis: Potency (P)

C. ANTIUTEROTROPIC ACTIVITY

Purpose: Determine the inhibitory effect of the test compound on the action of a reference estrogen as measured by change in weight of the uterus.

Test Animal: Immature (I) female (F) mouse (M), Swiss albino (25) 21 days old, 8–11 gm

Surgery: None

Standard
Stimulator: Estrone (E) administered subcutaneously (2) sesame oil (1)

Dose Schedule:

| Group code | UNKNOWNS | Animals/group | | Treatment | Total dose (per animal/group) | | |
		1 or 2	3–6		Standard (μg) S.c.	Unknown (mg) S.c.	Unknown (mg) Oral
P	C	10	8	Vehicle	0.1 ml SO		0.2 ml SSV
R	S	8	16	Standard	0.32	0.1 ml SSV	0.2 ml SSV
E	X	8	8	Standard and unknown			
L					0.32	0.01, 0.3, 9.0	0.05, 1.0, 10.0
I	U	8	8	Unknown	0.1 ml SO	9.0	10.0
M							

Procedure: Randomize and weigh animals to the nearest 0.5 gm. Start treatment the same day (day 1) once daily for 3 consecutive days. Each animal receives either 2 injections at different sites or 1 injection and on gavage each day. Sacrifice on day 4 and weigh to the nearest 0.5 gm. Remove and weigh the blotted, lightly compressed uteri (UT) to the nearest 0.2 mg.

Test Object: Uterus (UT)—mg

Compound Needs: Subcutaneous—200 mg; oral—220 mg

Analysis: Group   Formula
                    X   S-X/S (0)
                    U   U-C/S-C (1)

D. Progestational Activity

Purpose: Determine the effect of the test compound compared with that of a standard progestin on the stimulation of endometrial proliferation.

Test Animal: Immature (I) female (F) rabbit (B), New Zealand White (70), 1000–1400 gm

Surgery: None

Standard
Primer: 17β-Estradiol benzoate (B) administered in sesame oil (1) subcutaneously (2)

Stimulator: Progesterone (P) for subcutaneous (2) and 17-ethynyl-19-nortestosterone for oral (3) evaluation administered in steroid suspending vehicle (0).

Dose Schedule:

Group code	UNKNOWNS	Animals/group 1 or 2	Animals/group 3–5	Treatment	Total dose (mg/animal/group) S.c.	Total dose (mg/animal/group) Oral
P	C	3	6	Primer and vehicle	0.5 ml SSV	2.0 ml SSV
R						
E	S	3	6	Primer and standard	0.4, 1.6	0.2, 1.6
L						
I	U	3	3	Primer and unknown	0.4, 8.0	0.2, 4.0
M						
Q	C	5	10	Primer and vehicle	0.5 ml SSV	2.0 ml SSV
U						
A	S	5	10	Primer and standard	0.2, 0.4, 0.8, 1.6	0.2, 0.4, 0.8, 1.6
N						
T	U	5	10	Primer and unknown	×, 2×, 4×, 8×	×, 2×, 4×, 8×

Procedure

Preliminary: Randomize and weigh animals to the nearest 0.5 gm. Start to prime all animals the same day (day 1) once daily for 6 consecutive days by subcutaneous injection of 5.0 μg of 17β-estradiol benzoate suspended in 0.2 ml of sesame oil. On day 7 start progestin and test treatment once daily for 5 consecutive days. Sacrifice on day 12 and weigh to the nearest gram. Remove and weigh the blotted ovary (OV) and uterus (UT) to the nearest 0.2 mg. Remove a slice from the midsection of each horn and fix in Bouin's fluid; section and stain with hematoxylin and eosin. Determine histologically the degree of endometrial response (ER), using a rating of 0 through 4 to the nearest 0.5.

Quantitative: Same as preliminary, and longitudinally section the remainder of the uterus, rinse with cold saline and remove and weigh the endometrial tissue. Homogenate the tissue in a 10-fold dilution of cold distilled water and refrigerate overnight. Measure the volume of CO_2 evolved following the reaction of 0.2 ml of the supernatant in a buffered peptone solution with 1 ml of 0.1 M sodium bicarbonate. Convert the volume of evolved CO_2 to enzyme units by titrating a suitable purified preparation of carbonic anhydrase (CA).

Test Objects:
Ovary (OV)—mg
Uterus (UT)—mg
Endometrial response (ER)—0–4
Carbonic anhydrase (CA)—enzymes units/gram tissue (quantitative only)

Compound Needs:
Preliminary: subcutaneous—40 mg; oral—20 mg
Quantitative: subcutaneous and oral—50×

Analysis: Subjective comparison with standard, ie., no computation (9)

E. ANTIPROGESTATIONAL ACTIVITY

Purpose: Determine the effect of the test compound compared with that of a standard inhibitor of endometrial proliferation.

Test Animal: Immature (I) female (F) rabbit (B), New Zealand White, 1000–1400 gm

Surgery: None

Standard

Primer: 17β-estradiol benzoate (B) administered in sesame oil (1) subcutaneously (2)

Stimulator: Progesterone (P) administered in steroid suspending vehicle (0) subcutaneously (2)

Inhibitor: 2-Naphthalenepropionic acid, β-ethyl-6-hydroxy-α,α-dimethyl (K) for subcutaneous (2) and oral (3) evaluation administered in steroid suspending vehicle (0)

Dose Schedule:

Group code		Animals/group		Treatment	Total dose (mg/animal/group)	
	UNKNOWNS	1 or 2	3 to 5		S.c.	Oral
P R	C	3	6	Primer, stimulator, and vehicle	0.5 ml SSV	2.0 ml SSV
E L	Y	3	6	Primer, stimulator, and inhibitor	0.5, 2.0	0.5, 2.0
I M	X	3	3	Primer, stimulator, and unknown	1.0, 20.0	1.0, 20.0
Q U	C	5	10	Primer, stimulator, and vehicle	0.5 ml SSV	2.0 ml SSV
A N	Y	5	10	Primer, stimulator, and inhibitor	0.25, 0.5, 1.0, 0.2	0.5, 1.0, 2.0, 4.0
T	X	5	5	Primer, stimulator, and unknown	×, 2×, 4×, 8×	c, 2×, 4×, 8×

Procedure: Randomize and weigh the animals to the nearest gram. Start to prime all animals the same day (day 1) once daily for 6 consecutive days by subcutaneous injection of 5.0 μg of 17β-estradiol benzoate suspended in 0.2 ml of sesame oil. On day 7 administer 0.16 mg of progesterone once daily for 5 consecutive days (total dose 0.8 mg). Also start treatment on day 7 and administer once daily for 5 consecutive days. Sacrifice on day 12 and weigh to the nearest gram. Remove, blot, and weigh the ovary (XO) and uterus (XU) to the nearest 0.2 mg. Determine the endometrial response (ER) histologically and the carbonic anhydrase (CA) activity biochemically, employing the procedure outlined in Assay D.

Test Objects: Ovary (XO)
Uterus (XU)
Endometrial response (ER) 0–4
Carbonic anhydrase (CA) enzyme units/gram tissue

Compound Needs: Preliminary: subcutaneous and oral—80 mg
Quantitative: subcutaneous and oral—80×

Analysis: Subjective evaluation with standards; i.e., no computation (9)

F. GLUCOCORTICOID ACTIVITY (GLYCOGEN DEPOSITION)

Purpose: Determine the effect of the test compound compared with that of a standard corticoid as measured by glycogen deposition in the liver.

Test Animal: Young adult (Y) male (M) or female (F) rat (R), Charles River (45) 140 to 160 gm

Surgery: Adrenalectomy (1)

Standard Stimulator: Cortisol for subcutaneous (2) and oral (3) evaluation administered in steroid suspending vehicle (0)

Dose Schedule:

Group code UNKNOWNS	Animals/group		Treatment	Total dose(s) (mg/animal/group)	
	1 or 2	3–6		S.c.	Oral
P R E L I M C	5	10	Vehicle	0.5 ml SSV	0.5 ml SSV
S	5	10	Standard	0.4, 0.8, 1.6	0.8, 3.2, 12.8
U	5	5	Unknown	0.8, 4.0, 16.0	1.6, 8.0, 32.0
Q U A N T C	10	20	Vehicle	0.5 ml SSV	0.5 ml SSV
S	8	16	Standard	0.4, 0.8, 1.6, 3.2	0.2, 0.8, 3.2, 12.8
U	8	8	Unknown	×, 2×, 4×, 8×	×, 4×, 16×, 64×

Procedure: Bilaterally adrenalectomize, randomize, and weigh the animals to the nearest gram. Maintain on a stock diet and isotonic saline drink through the afternoon of postoperative day 4, at which time food is removed. Administer treatment the morning of postoperative day 5. Seven hours after treatment anesthetize the animals by i.p. injection of Nembutal. Remove the whole liver from the living animal, trim, blot and weigh to the nearest 10 mg. Digest immediately in 10 ml of preheated 30% potassium hydroxide solution for 1 hour at 80°–90°C. Dilute the alkaline digests with distilled water to a final volume of 100 ml and refrigerate overnight. The next morning mix 0.1 ml of the digest with 4.9 ml of distilled water and 10 ml of anthrone reagent, allow to equilibrate to room temperature, and read at 620 mμ. Run suitable reagent blanks and three levels of glucose standards (20, 50, and 100 μg) simultaneously with unknown digest. Results are expressed as percentage of glycogen in liver to the nearest 0.01% .

Test Objects: Liver (XL)—gm
Glycogen (GL)—% in liver

Compound Needs: Preliminary: subcutaneous—160 mg; oral—310 mg
Quantitative: subcutaneous—125×; oral—750×

Analysis: Potency (P)

G. Thymolytic and Anti-inflammatory Activity

Purpose: Determine the effect of the test compound compared with that of a standard corticoid as measured by the change in weight of the thymus and induced granuloma.

Test Animal: Immature (I) male (M) or female (F) rat (R), Charles River (45), 23–26 days old, 60–80 gm

Surgery: Adrenalectomize and implant cotton pellets subcutaneously (2)

Standard Stimulator: Cortisol for subcutaneous (2) and oral (3) evaluation administered in steroid suspending vehicle (0).

Dose Schedule:

	Group code UNKNOWNS	Animals/group		Treatment	Total dose(s) in mg/animal/group	
		1 or 2	3–6		S.c.	Oral
P	C	10	20	Vehicle	0.1 ml SSV	0.5 ml SSV
R	S	6	12	Standard	1.2, 4.8	2.0, 16.0
E	U	6	6	Unknown	1.2, 24.0	4.0, 80.0
L						
I						
M						
Q	C	15	15	Vehicle	0.1 ml SSV	0.5 ml SSV
U	S	15	15	Standard	0.6, 1.2, 2.4, 4.8	2.0, 4.0, 8.0, 16.0
A	U	15	15	Unknown	×, 2×, 4×, 8×	×, 2×, 4×, 8×
N						
T						

Procedure: Bilaterally adrenalectomize and implant two 5 mg (±1 mg) cotton pellets subcutaneously in the animals. Randomize and weigh to the nearest gram. Start treatment the same day (day 1) once daily for 3 consecutive days. Sacrifice on day 4 and weigh to the nearest gram. Remove, blot, and weigh the thymus (TH) to the nearest 0.2 mg. Remove and dry the cotton pellet granulomas (GR) for 24 hours at 100°C and weigh to the nearest 0.2 mg and then subtract the weight of the original cotton pellet.

Test Objects: Thymus (TH)—mg
Granuloma (GR)—dry weight in mg

Compound Needs: Preliminary: subcutaneous—220 mg; oral—620 mg
Quantitative: subcutaneous and oral—250×

Analysis: Potency (P)—Thymus (TH)
C-U/C (2)—Granuloma (GR)

H. ANTI-ACTH ACTIVITY

Purpose: To compare the effect of test compounds with that of a reference corticoid on the inhibition of ACTH production and/or release measured indirectly by weight changes in the thymus and adrenal glands.

Test Animal: Immature (I) male (M) or female (F), consistent within an assay, rat (R), Charles River (45), 24–27 days old, 65–75 gm

Surgery: None

Standard
Stimulator: Cortisol for subcutaneous (2) and oral (3) evaluation administered in steroid suspending vehicle (0)

Dose Schedule:

| Group code UNKNOWNS | Animals/group | | Treatment | Total dose (mg/animal/group) | |
	1 to 2	3–6		S.c.	Oral
C	10	20	Vehicle	0.2 ml SSV	0.5 ml SSV
S	5	10	Standard	2.0, 8.0	6.0, 24.0
U	5	5	Unknown	1.0, 20.0	6.0, 120.0

Procedure: Randomize and weigh to nearest 0.5 gm. Start treatment on same day (day 1) once daily for 10 consecutive days. Sacrifice on day 11 and weigh to nearest 0.5 gm. Weigh the adrenals (AD) (sum of both) and thymus (TH) glands to the nearest 0.2 mg.

Test Objects: Adrenals (AD)—weight in mg
Thymus (TH)—weight in mg

Compound Needs: Preliminary: subcutaneous—130 mg.; oral—770 mg

Analysis: C-U/C (2)

I. Mineralocorticosteroid Activity

Purpose: To compare the effect of test compounds with that of a reference corticoid upon sodium retention and potassium excretion.

Test Animal: Young adult (Y) male (M) rat (R), Charles River (45), 135–145 gm

Surgery: Adrenalectomy (1)

Standard

Deoxycorticosterone (Q) administered subcutaneously (2) in steroid suspending vehicle (0)

Stimulator: Deoxycorticosterone acetate (C) administered orally (3) in steroid suspending vehicle (0)

Dose Schedule:

Group Code		Animals/group	Treatment	Total dose(s)/animal/group	
				S.c. (µg)	Oral (mg)
P R E L I M	C	10	Vehicle	0.2 ml SSV	0.5 ml SSV
	S	10	Standard	3, 6, 12	1, 4
	U	10	Unknown	1, 300, 3000	1, 20
Q U A N T	C	10	Vehicle	0.2 ml SSV	0.5 ml SSV
	S	10	Standard	3, 6, 12, 24	0.5, 1, 2, 4
	U	10	Vehicle	To be assigned	

(continued)

I. MINERALOCORTICOSTEROID ACTIVITY (*continued*)

Procedure: Randomize and weigh to nearest gram. Maintain on a stock diet and 0.85% NaCl drink for 3–5 days. At 24 hours before administration of treatment, replace saline drink with tap water. Remove food but leave water on day of treatment. Give half the total dose followed immediately by a subcutaneous injection of 2.5 ml of 0.85% saline solution. Three hours after the first treatment administer the remaining half dose. At 4 hours the animals are slightly etherized, the bladder urine is expressed, and the urethra is ligated. At 6 hours the animals are sacrificed and weighed to the nearest gram. The bladder is exposed by abdominal incision, and the urine is aspirated from the bladder with a syringe and 18-gauge needle by first introducing 2 ml of distilled water. The volume is adjusted to 5 ml with distilled water and a clear supernatant is obtained by centrifugation. The supernatant is refrigerated overnight. The next morning 1 ml of supernatant plus an internal lithium standard is diluted to 100 ml with distilled water. Sodium (NA) and potassium (KX) are determined with a flame photometer, and suitable reagent blanks and standards containing sodium and potassium are run simultaneously.

Test Objectives: Sodium (NA)—total mg
Potassium (KX)—total mg
Potassium/sodium ratio (KN)

Compound Needs: Subcutaneous—55 mg; oral 25 mg

Analysis: Subjective comparison with standard; i.e., no computation (9)

J. INHIBITION OF ANDROGENIC AND MYOGENIC ACTIVITY

Purpose: To measure the inhibitory effect of test compounds on exogenous androgen stimulation of secondary sex structures and muscle.

Test Animal: Weanling (W) male (M) rat (R), 21–24 days old, 50–65 gm

Surgery: Castration (0)

Standard Stimulator: Testosterone (T) given subcutaneously (2) in steroid suspending vehicle (0)

Dose Schedule:

Group code	Animals/group	Treatment	Standard S.c.	Unknown S.c.	Unknown Oral
				Total dose(s) (mg/animal/group)	
C	10	Vehicle	0.5 ml SSV	0.5 ml SSV	1.0 ml SSV
S	5	Standard	0.6	0.5 ml. SSV	1.0 ml SSV
X	5	Standard and unknown	0.6	6, 60	6, 60
U	5	Unknown	0.5 ml SSV	10.0	10.0

(continued)

J. Inhibition of Androgens and Myogenic Activity (*continued*)

Procedure: Randomize and weigh animals to the nearest 0.5 gm. Start treatment the same day (day 1) once daily for 7 consecutive days. Each animal receives either 2 injections at different sites or 1 injection and 1 gavage each day. Sacrifice on day 8 and weigh to the nearest 0.5 gm. Weigh to the nearest 0.2 mg the ventral prostate (VP), seminal vesicle (SV) without coagulating gland and devoid of fluid, and the levator ani (LA).

Test Objects: Ventral prostate (VP)—mg
Seminal vesicle (SV)—mg
Levator ani (LA)—mg

Compound Needs: Subcutaneous and oral—480 mg

Analysis:

Group	Formula
X	S-X/S-C (0)
U	U-C/S-C (1)

K. Inhibition of Androgenic Activity

Purpose:

To determine the inhibitory effect of test compounds on the endogenous or exogenous androgen stimulation of prostatic secretion and on the character of the prostatic fluid.

Test Animal:

Mature (M) male (M) dog (D)

Surgery:

Prostatic resection (5) with castration (6)

Standard
 Stimulator:

Pilocarpine hydrochloride (NSC-5746)

Dose Schedule:

Two dose levels as determined by biological activity in other test systems.

Procedure:

The study is comprised of three periods: control period (day 1 through 9); test period (day 10 through 19); and recovery period (day 20 through 27). Castrate animals are maintained on 5.0 mg of testosterone daily at all times. Start treatment on day 10 once daily for 10 consecutive days. Prostatic fluid is collected for 1 hour on each of the following days: 1, 4, 7 (control period); 11, 14, 17 (test period); 21, 24, 27 (recovery period). Secretion is induced by subcutaneous injection of a predetermined dose of pilocarpine. Record the total fluid volume (PS) to the nearest 0.1 ml and the acid phosphatase (AP) in milligrams of PO_4 per milliliter of fluid.

Test Objects:

Prostatic fluid (PS)—ml
Acid phosphatase (AP)—mg PO_4/ml

Compound Needs:

Variable, determined by prior assay data

Analysis:

Subjective evaluation with standard; i.e., no computation (9)

L. Chronic Anti-adrenal Activity in Dogs

Purpose: To determine the effect of test compounds on the secretion of 17α-hydroxycorticosteroids from the adrenal cortex of dogs.

Test Animal: Adult (0) male (M) or female (F) dog (D) 12–15 kg

Surgery: Cannulation of the right lumboadrenal vein (A) (after treatment)

Standard   ACTH (1) given intravenously (5) in 1 ml of aqueous
 Stimulator: vehicle (4) (commercial preparation)

Dose Schedule: Daily dose of 50.0% mg/kg (lower or higher depending on toxicity)

Procedure: Compound is given intravenously in 15.0 ml of SSV per injection or gavage or orally in capsules once daily for 7 days. On day 8 anesthetize the fasted dog with Nembutal and cannulate the right lumboadrenal vein. Collect a 10-minute sample of blood. Clamp off all adrenal veins but the cannulated vein during blood collection. Infuse a peripheral vein with 10 units of ACTH in 2–3 minutes and take a 10-minute sample of adrenal venous blood. Sacrifice after the last blood collection and excise, weigh, section, and examine histologically both adrenals. Perform Porter-Silber determinations for the 17α-hydrocorticosteroids on all blood samples.

Test Objects: Blood 17α-hydroxycorticosteroids—μg/10 minutes Adrenal histology

Compound Needs: Approximately 7 gm

Analysis: Subjective evaluation with Standard Reference Inhibitor NSC-38721—o, p-DDD 25.0, 50.0, or 100 mg/kg given orally in capsules; i.e., no computation (9)

M. ACUTE ANTI-ADRENAL ACTIVITY IN DOGS

Purpose:

To determine the immediate effect of test compounds on the secretion of 17α-hydroxycorticosteroids in dogs

Test Animal:

Adult (0) male (M) or female (F) dog (D) 12–15 kg

Surgery:

Cannulation of the right lumboadrenal vein (A) (before treatment)

Standard
  Stimulator:

ACTH (1) given intravenously (5) in 1 ml of aqueous vehicle (4) (commercial preparation)

Dose Schedule:

Single dose of 50.0 mg/kg lower or higher depending on toxicity

Procedure:

Anesthetize a fasted dog with Nembutal and cannulate the lumboadrenal vein. Collect a 10-minute blood sample with all adrenal veins except the cannulated vein clamped off. Using a peripheral vein in one of the limbs administer test compound intravenously in 15 ml of SSV with saline and 5% glucose as a single injection over a 5-minute period and collect a 10-minute sample of blood after a 30-minute rest interval. Infuse with 10 units of ACTH over a period of 5 minutes, and 3 minutes later collect a final 10-minute sample of blood. Sacrifice after the last blood collection and excise, weigh, section, and examine histologically both adrenal glands. Perform Porter-Silber determinations for the 17α-hydroxycorticosteroids on all samples of blood.

Test Objects:

Blood 17α-hydroxycorticosteroids—μg/10 minutes
Adrenal histology

Compound Needs:

Approximately 1 gm

Analysis:

Subjective evaluation with Standard Reference Inhibitor NSC-44410—Amphenone B 25 mg/kg in 15 ml SSV; i.e., no computation (9)

N. General Screen

Purpose: To compare the effects of test compounds with those of selected reference steroids on a broad spectrum of test objects.

Test Animals: Assay 24—Immature (I) male (M) rat (R) 21 days old, 40–55 gm
Assay 30—Immature (I) female (F) rat (R) 27 days old, 60–80 gm

Surgery: None

Standard: None

Dose Schedule:

Group code	Animals/group	Treatment	Total dose(s) (mg/animal/group)	
			S.c.	Oral
C	10	Vehicle	0.2 ml SSV	0.5 ml SSV
U	10	Unknown	2.0, 20.0	2.0, 20.0

Procedure:

Randomize and weigh animals to the nearest 0.5 gm [and measure the body and tail lengths to the nearest 0.1 cm]*. Start treatment the same day (day 1) once daily for 14 consecutive days. Sacrifice on day 15 and weigh to the nearest 0.5 gm [and measure the body (BL) and tail (TL) length to the nearest 0.1 cm]. Weigh the spleen (SP), liver (LI), and left kidney (KI) to the nearest 0.01 gm. Weigh the adrenals (AD), thymus (TH), lymph nodes (LN), and pituitary (PI) to nearest 0.1 mg. If male, weigh the ventral prostate (VP), seminal vesicle (SV) without coagulating gland and devoid of fluid, and the levator ani (LA) to the nearest 0.1 mg and testes (TE) to the nearest 0.01 gm. If female, weigh the ovaries (OV) and uterus (UT) to the nearest 0.1 mg; [determine the ovarian response (OR)]. Do a complete blood count, i.e., hemoglobin, hematocrit, white blood count, red blood count, differential, and report on summary sheet.

Test Objects on print-outs:

Assay 24—VP, SV, LA, AD, TH, LN, PI—mg
        SP, KI, TE, LI—gm
Assay 30—OV, UT, AD, TH, LN, PI—mg
        SP, KI, LI—gm

Compound Needs: Subcutaneous and oral—300 mg

Analysis: C
             S U/C (5)

* Items in brackets are optional and done only at the request of the Center.

III. Interpretation of Biological Assay Data

A. Purpose

The assay program is designed to screen compounds for specific effects, in order to obtain profiles of their biological properties. This testing involves obtaining potency estimates for each compound by comparing its biological effects with those of standard reference compounds, or, as in the inhibition type assays, to measure the inhibiting effect of test materials on biological reactions brought about by standard compounds or occurring spontaneously.

B. Titration of Standard

A standard reference compound for each type of biological assay is first tritrated to obtain the sensitive working range (Graph I). On the basis of this working range, two types of assays are designed: preliminary and quantitative assays for estimating potency, and assays for measuring inhibition of effects.

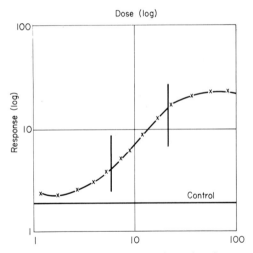

GRAPH I. Standard compound (×) titration.

C. Assays for Estimating Potency

1. Preliminary Assay

   a. Objective. To screen test materials for estimates of a minimal relative potency of 5%, with an error usually not exceeding 50% (95% confidence limits).

b. Design. For standard reference compound, use two doses as far apart as possible but still within the sensitive working range. Usually give two doses of the test material. Give one dose at the same level as the low dose of the standard to detect potencies equivalent to or greater than the standard. Gear the higher dose of the test material to the lowest potency (5%) to be detected, hence 20 times the low dose of the standard.

c. Illustrative Interpretation (Graph II). Test material No. 1 shows less than 5% potency, and testing of compound for this particular activity is considered complete. Test material No. 2 shows greater than 5% potency; quantitative assay will be performed. Test material No. 3

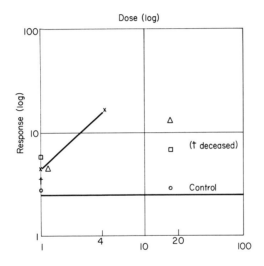

GRAPH II. Preliminary assay. *Key*: × = standard compound; ○ = test material No. 1; △ = test material No. 2; □ = test material No. 3; † = test material No. 4.

shows greater than 5% potency but without parallelism of effect; quantitative assay will be performed. Test material No. 4 indicates probable toxicity at high dose level; preliminary assay will be repeated at new dose levels.

2. Quantitative Assay

a. Objective. To obtain more precise estimates of relative potency with an error usually not exceeding 20% (95% confidence limits) on test materials that show minimal activity in the preliminary assay.

b. Design. Typically, four doses of the standard which represent the sensitive range are compared with four levels of the test material chosen on basis of preliminary estimates of potency.

c. *Illustrative Interpretation (Graph III).* Test material No. 2: slopes judged parallel indicate similar activity; test compound appears less active than preliminary assay indicated. Test material No. 3: non-parallel slopes indicate possible different activity since both materials appear to have been tested in the sensitive range.

Estimates of relative potencies will be given as percentages without reference to differences in slopes of the dose-response curves except when these differences are believed to indicate dissimilar biological activity.

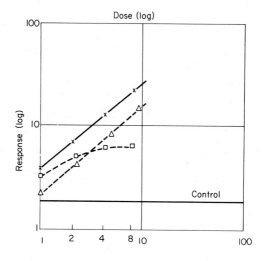

GRAPH III. Quantitative assay. *Key:* × = standard compound; △ = test material No. 2; □ = test material No. 3.

An assay in which technical errors are evident is repeated unless it gives some indication of potency that could be used as an aid to getting more precise data.

In general, the assays may not yield relative potencies, but rather pseudo relative potencies, since there is no guarantee that the physiological function tested is the same for the unknown as for the standard.

D. ASSAYS FOR MEASURING INHIBITION OF EFFECTS

Although inhibition-type assays generally refer to assays in which the effect of a standard compound is inhibited, they may also be used to measure the inhibition of a spontaneous process. In neither case is there an attempt to ascertain relative potency.

Inhibition of Effects of Standard Compounds

a. Objective. To determine whether a compound can inhibit the biological effect produced by the standard compound.

b. Design. For the standard reference compound level, use a dose which produces a near maximum response in the sensitive range of the titration curve. For the test material, use three doses covering a very wide range.

c. Illustrative Interpretation (Graph IV). Test material No. 1 produces 25% reduction in effect at low dose, no reduction at middle dose, and no reduction at high dose. Test material No. 2 produces 10% reduction at low dose, 25% reduction at middle dose, and 45% reduction at high dose.

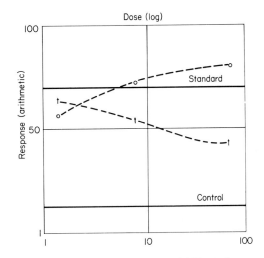

GRAPH IV. Inhibition assay. *Key:* ○ = test material No. 1; † = test material No. 4.

PART III

Protein Hormones and Related Hormones and Substances

Chapter 7

Adrenaline and Noradrenaline: Quantitation and Functional Evaluation

NORMAN KIRSHNER

I. Introduction

Since the discovery of adrenaline (Oliver and Schafer, 1895) biological assays have been used for the quantitation of adrenaline (epinephrine) and noradrenaline (norepinephrine), and until about ten years ago offered the only reliable method for measuring these compounds in submicrogram quantities. With the development of rapid and sensitive fluorimetric methods, the use of biological assays has greatly declined. However, some workers still prefer biological assays, and in some instances, because of their high sensitivity and because plasma and blood can be assayed without purification, they are the preferred methods (Vane, 1964). In addition, because of the optical specificity of the biological indicators, they have been valuable in determining the amounts of D- and L-adrenaline and noradrenaline in mixtures of the optical isomers.

287

Biological methods are chiefly important today not as quantitative assays of adrenaline and noradrenaline, but rather as methods for studying the functional aspects of the sympathetic nervous system. The wide variety of animal and tissue preparations provide powerful tools for investigating the physiological mechanisms of storage and release of neurotransmitters, for assessing relative potencies of new sympathomimetic drugs and blocking agents, for studies of drug-receptor interactions, for metabolic studies, and for other studies that will eventually describe in intimate detail the mechanisms by which the nervous impulse liberates the neurotransmitters and how these transmitters interact with the receptor site to produce a physiological response.

Very few new developments in methods of biological assay have occurred since this subject was last reviewed in the previous edition of this volume (Elmadjian, 1962) and by Gaddum (1959). This chapter will discuss the various methods of assay currently used and the applicability of the assay preparations as well as other tissue preparations for studying functional aspects of the sympathetic nervous systems. Details of the procedures may be obtained from the original articles or from the textbook by Burn (1952). Vane (1966) has recently reviewed various aspects of biological assays. Brown and Lands (1964), Green and Boura (1964), and Boura and Green (1964) have presented excellent and extensive discussions of the pharmacological evaluation of drugs that affect the sympathetic nervous system.

II. Parallel Assays

Adrenaline and noradrenaline in equimolar doses generally have the same qualitative effect but different quantitative effects on the various biological preparations. Thus one cannot differentially estimate the amounts of adrenaline and noradrenaline in mixtures using a single biological assay. However, if two tissues are selected that have different sensitivities to adrenaline and noradrenaline, then it is possible to estimate the amounts of each of these compounds in a mixture by comparing the ratio of the responses of the two different tissues to their responses to standard solutions of adrenaline and noradrenaline. Von Euler (1948) has used a combination of the cat's blood pressure and hen's rectal cecum; Gaddum and Lembeck (1949) used the rat colon and rat uterus, and Bülbring and Burn (1949) simultaneously measured the effects on the blood pressure and nictitating membrane of the spinal cat; Gaddum et al. (1949) have studied a number of preparations and combinations suitable for biological assay (Table I).

TABLE I

COMPARATIVE SENSITIVITY OF BIOASSAY METHODS[a]

Methods of assay (biological)	Amount (ng)[b] required for each test[c]	
	Adrenaline	Noradrenaline
Cat's blood pressure	200	100
Rat's blood pressure (C_6)	50	3
Rat's blood pressure (pithed)	7	5
Rat's uterus (2-ml bath)	0.1	15
Rabbit's ear (perfused)	0.5	1
Rabbit's ear (Armin and Grant, 1955)	0.002	—
Rabbit's gut (10-ml bath)	40	40
Fowl rectal cecum (2-ml bath)	2	50

[a] From Gaddum and Holzbauer (1957).

[b] 1 ng = nanogram = 10^{-6} mg.

[c] The amount required for an accurate bioassay would be 5–10 times the amounts given in this table.

III. Specificity of Biological Assays

The ability to distinguish adrenaline from noradrenaline by the use of parallel assays was crucial to the development of our current concepts of adrenergic function. It enabled Cannon and Rosenblueth (1933, 1937) to show that the substance liberated from the hepatic nerves of the cat was not adrenaline; von Euler (1948a) used the cat's blood pressure and hen rectal cecum to identify the principal active substance in extracts of adrenergic nerves as noradrenaline; Bacq and Fisher (1947) identified noradrenaline in sympathetic nerves and extracts of the spleen, using the cat's uterus and nictitating membrane; and Peart (1949) used several tissues of the rat and cat to obtain evidence that the substance liberated upon stimulation of the spleen was noradrenaline.

Many substances, both synthetic and naturally occurring, may interfere with the measurement of adrenaline and noradrenaline (Gaddum, 1959). Some of the compounds, such as tyramine, dopamine, and many synthetic sympathomimetic amines, may have responses qualitatively similar to that of adrenaline and noradrenaline, and their presence can be detected in parallel assays by the failure to obtain reasonable matching responses on two different tissues. Other substances such as serotonin (Armitage and Vane, 1964) may potentiate the response of the tissue to adrenaline and noradrenaline and give erroneously high values. Histamine and acetylcholine generally have effects opposite to that of adrenaline and noradrenaline and when present in extracts will decrease the response of the tissue. Other substances, such as α and β adrenergic blocking agents, which may be present in tissue extracts, urine, and blood of drug-treated animals, or such as naturally occurring substances, may prevent the response of the tissues to adrenaline and noradrenaline. It is frequently possible to prevent the interferences of acetylcholine, histamine, and serotonin by administering their specific antagonists to whole-animal preparations or by including them in the bathing medium of isolated tissue. The most effective and most commonly used procedure of avoiding interference is to purify tissue extracts or body fluids by some simple method.

IV. Purification of Tissue Extracts and Body Fluids

Whole blood or plasma of venous effluents from spleen or adrenal glands, as well as alcoholic, trichloroacetic, or perchloric acid extracts of adrenal glands, have such high concentration of catecholamines and so little of any interfering compounds that, under normal circumstances, they may be assayed without further purification. However, urine, blood, and extracts of other tissues generally require purification and concentration, and this can most readily be accomplished by adsorption on alumina. Methods of purification were discussed in Volume I of this edition (Kirshner, 1968). Adrenaline and noradrenaline are not separated from other catecholamines on alumina but may be estimated after separation by ion-exchange chromatography (Kirshner, 1968) or by filter paper chromatography (Gaddum, 1959; Vogt, 1959). It has been the author's experience that ion-exchange chromatography, though more time consuming, is generally better for the separation and quantitative estimation of adrenaline and noradrenaline. When only very small quantities of adrenaline and noradrenaline are present, filter paper chromatography is useful.

V. Methods of Biological Assay

Although many tissues and whole-animal preparations are suitable for the estimation of adrenaline and noradrenaline in mixtures, the methods and preparations most commonly used are the pressor response of anesthetized or spinal cat (Burn, 1952); the relaxation of the chicken rectal cecum (Barsoum and Gaddum, 1935; von Euler, 1949); the blood pressure of the pithed rat (Shipley and Tilden, 1947; Brown and Gillespie, 1957), the uterus of the rat or rabbit (de Jalon et al., 1945; Gaddum et al. 1949; Harvey and Pennefeather, 1962a,b), rat or rabbit intestinal preparations (Gaddum *et al.* 1949), the cat nictitating membrane (Cannon and Rosenblueth, 1937; Burn, 1952), rabbit atrial strips (Furchgott and Bhadrakom, 1953; Furchgott, 1960), and the rat stomach fundus (Armitage and Vane, 1964).

VI. Cardiovascular Responses and Cardiovascular Tissues

The pressor response to adrenaline and noradrenaline has been widely used to measure the total catecholamine content of mixtures of adrenaline and noradrenaline and as one of the two biological indicators in a parallel assay. The pithed rat (Shipley and Tilden, 1947; Brown and Gillespie, 1957), treated with atropine, is very sensitive and can respond to as little as 0.5 nanograms (ng) of noradrenaline. The spinal cat (Burn, 1952) and the anesthetized cat are frequently used and are sensitive to 0.05–0.10 μg of noradrenaline. The anesthetized cat is treated with atropine, ergotamine, an antihistamine, and cocaine to prevent reflex cholinergic effects, to stabilize the blood pressure, to prevent interference by histamine which may be present in the extract and to increase the sensitivity of the preparation (von Euler, 1948; Karki, 1956). Because of the ease of monitoring blood pressure it is one of the most frequently used assays for the quantitation of catecholamines and for the qualitative and quantitative evaluation of new drugs.

The responses of heart rate, contractile force, arterial and ventricular pressures, and cardiac output *in situ* or in isolated perfused hearts are frequently measured to assay and evaluate sympathomimetic drugs and sympatholytic agents.

The development of miniature strain gauges has greatly facilitated the measurement of the ventricular contractile force in dogs. Boniface *et al.* (1953) and Cotten and Bay (1956) have described strain gauge arches suitable for this purpose. The experiments can be carried out in open chest dogs, or, after attaching the strain gauge arch to the ventricle, the animal may be sutured and experiments conducted after recovery from anesthesia. This technique has been widely used (Gaffney *et al.*, 1962; Cotten and Cooper, 1962; Harrison *et al.*, 1963; Harakal *et al.*, 1964).

The isolated heart-lung preparation (Patterson and Starling, 1914; Krayer, 1931) has yielded much useful physiological and pharmacological information (Krayer and Mendez, 1942). The method is still used (Alper and Schmier, 1962; Fawaz and Simaan, 1963) for the evaluation of drugs and studies of physiological mechanisms.

The isolated perfused heart (Langendorf, 1895; Burn, 1952) for studies of the inotropic and chronotropic effects is one of the simplest and most widely used preparations. West (1943) used the isolated perfused frog heart for the assay of adrenaline. McEwen (1956) describes a preparation of the isolated rabbit heart with intract nerves that will respond for 6–9 hours. James and Nadeau (1963, 1964) have studied the chronotropic effect of tyramine on normal and reserpinized dogs by direct perfusion of the sinus node.

Isolated atria (Burn, 1952) containing the sinus node have been used for measuring chronotropic and inotropic responses to sympathomimetic amines and for evaluating the effects of drugs on these parameters (Muskus, 1962; Thier et al., 1962; Stafford, 1963). Hukovic (1959) has described a preparation of the isolated rabbit atria with intact sympathetic nerves. In this preparation cocaine and phenoxybenzamine increased the response to stimulation. Atria from reserpine-treated animals were inhibited by stimulation, and this inhibition was increased by reserpine and abolished by atropine. These data are consistent with Burn's hypothesis (1960) that noradrenaline release is mediated by acetylcholine.

In the absence of the sino-auricular node, whole atria and atrial and ventricular strips (Rosen and Farah, 1955) must be electrically driven and are good preparations for measuring inotropic effects. Furchgott and Gubareff (1958), using the electrically stimulated guinea pig atria, found that under various experimental conditions which alter contractile strength no significant changes occurred in the high energy phosphate content of the tissue. Bhagat and Shideman (1963), Angelakos and Torchiana (1963), and Kirpekar and Furchgott (1964) have used similar preparations of rat and rabbit atria.

Spiral-cut strips of rabbit aorta or carotid artery (Furchgott and Bhadrakom, 1953; Furchgott, 1960) are very sensitive to adrenaline and noradrenaline and can be used in a parallel assay to differentiate between these two substances. Aortic strips can also be used where it is not necessary to discriminate between the two, such as in venous outflow from spleen or in the clinical evaluation of pheochromocytomas (Helmer and Sanders, 1957; Ewer et al., 1959). This tissue preparation is very useful for the quantitative comparison of various drugs which cause contraction, for studying reversible and irreversible competition and for evaluation of blocking agents (Furchgott, 1960; Maxwell et al., 1962; Yates and Gillis, 1963). Bevan (1962) devised a rabbit pulmonary artery preparation with intact sympathetic nerves to study postganglionic transmission to vascular smooth muscle. Both direct and indirect stimulation produced contractions which were measured isometrically. The indirect response was potentiated by cocaine. Pretreatment of the rabbit with reserpine prevented the indirect response but not the direct response.

VII. Rat Uterus

The rat uterus is one of the most sensitive and best preparations for distinguishing between adrenaline and noradrenaline. In the method originally described by de Jalon *et al.* (1945) the spontaneous contractions of the isolated uterus were abolished by reducing the Ca^{++} concentration of the medium and lowering the bath temperature to 25°. Controlled contractions were produced by adding acetylcholine and were inhibited by adding epinephrine to the bath 1 minute before the acetylcholine. The degree of inhibition was proportional to the amount of added adrenaline. Gaddum *et al.* (1949) improved the procedure by using uteri from stilbestrol-treated rats and substituting carbachol for acetylcholine. In these preparations the uterus is 75–300 times more sensitive to adrenaline than it is to noradrenaline and will respond to less than 0.1 ng of adrenaline. Harvey and Pennefeather (1962a,b) have increased the sensitivity of the method 20-fold by eliciting contraction by electrical stimulation of the uterus in an alternating current field of 4–8 V, 50 cycles per second for 10–12 seconds. Adrenaline was 10^4–10^6 times more potent than noradrenaline in inhibiting the electrically induced contractions.

In addition to its use for the quantitative estimation of adrenaline and noradrenaline, the isolated rat uterus is an excellent preparation for evaluating new α- and β-adrenergic blocking agents and sympathomimetic drugs. In recent studies, Levy and Tozzi (1963) have found only β-receptors in the uteri of pregnant, nonpregnant, and diethylstilbestrol-treated rats. The response of the uterus to adrenaline, isoproterenol, or phenylephrine was not affected by α-adrenergic blocking agents but was inhibited by a variety of β-blockers. The adrenergic receptors of the cat uterus appear to be different from that of the rat. Tsai and Fleming (1964) studied the relative effects of adrenaline, noradrenaline and isoproterenol as well as the blocking effect of dichloroisoproterenol and phenoxybenzamine on the uteri of virgin and pregnant cats. Their evidence indicates that both α- and β-receptors are present in the cat uterus and that the hormonal state of the animal determines which of the two types of receptors produce the dominant response. In the virgin cat, uterine relaxation was elicited and this response was inhibited by β-adrenergic blocking agents whereas in the pregnant cat, uterine contraction was evoked and was inhibited by α-adrenergic blockers. In other studies, Rudzik and Miller (1962) demonstrated that the uterine inhibitory action of relaxin-containing ovarian extracts (Sawyer *et al.*, 1953) was mediated through the release of adrenaline and noradrenaline. The change in the adrenaline content of the uterus throughout estrus (Rudzik and Miller, 1962a) indicates an important role for adrenaline in the physiology of the uterus.

VIII. Intestinal Muscle

Various animal preparations of intestinal smooth muscles have been used by many investigators. Stewart and Rogoff (1919) used the inhibitory effect of adrenaline on the rabbit intestine in studies of the release of neurotransmitter substances. Burn (1952) gives details of the procedure. Gaddum *et al.* (1949) used the ascending colon of the rat or guinea pig in a manner similar to that of the uterus. Barsoum and Gaddum (1935) found that the hen's rectal cecum was relaxed by low concentrations of adrenaline. Von Euler (1948a) subsequently observed that the rectal cecum was much more sensitive to adrenaline than noradrenaline, and he used this and the pressor response of anesthetized cats in parallel assays.

IX. Nictitating Membrane

The nictitating membrane of the spinal cat (Cannon and Rosenblueth, 1937; Burn, 1952) has been used not only for the quantitation of adrenaline and noradrenaline, but in many studies delving into the physiology and pharmacology of adrenergic transmission. The nictitating membrane has been so widely used that it is not possible to give here even a cursory description of its many applications. The few references that follow were selected to illustrate its application to current physiological and pharmacological investigations: Burn *et al.* (1963), Trendelenberg and Weiner (1962), Trendelenberg *et al.* (1962a,b), Haefely *et al.* (1963), Smith (1963), Day and Rand (1963a,b, 1964). Mirkin and Cervoni (1962) have used pressure transducers under semi-isometric conditions to record the response of the nictitating membrane in investigations of neurohormonal transmission in that tissue.

X. Eye Measurements

Beaver and Riker (1962) used the isolated rat or mouse eye to measure the mydriatic effect of adrenaline, noradrenaline, and isoproterenol after contraction of the pupillary diameter by standard doses of acetylcholine. The eye was most sensitive to adrenaline; the relative order being adrenaline, noradrenaline, isoproterenol. Adrenaline and noradrenaline were detectable in the bath at concentrations of 10^{-5} to 10^{-6} M. Anden *et al.* (1964) used the protrusion of the eyeball of the rat in response to supramaximal stimulation of the preganglionic sympathetic nerve as a test for sympathetic nerve function after administration of reserpine. They observed a correlation between the ability of the nerve to take up and store tritiated norephinephrine and the recovery of nerve activity.

XI. Rat Stomach

Armitage and Vane (1964) have developed a new sensitive assay for adrenaline and noradrenaline. A strip of fundus from the rat stomach suspended in Krebs solution containing 5-hydroxytryptamine is relaxed upon addition of isoprenaline, adrenaline, or noradrenaline. The degree of relaxation is proportional to the concentration of added amine. The sensitivity of the fundus to catecholamines is greatly increased in the presence of 10 μg of 5-hydroxytryptophan per liter in the bathing solution. The preparation was most sensitive to isoprenaline and least sensitive to noradrenaline. When used in a parallel assay with the hen's rectal cecum, adrenaline and noradrenaline can be differentially estimated. Vane (1964) describes a procedure for the assay of adrenaline and noradrenaline in circulating blood by superfusing the rat fundus and hen's rectal cecum and returning the blood to the circulation. With suitable detectors, the method can also be used for the assay of other biologically active substances.

XII. Perfused Rabbit Ear

Both adrenaline and noradrenaline constrict the blood vessels of the rabbit's ear, which, under a constant pressure head, results in a decreased perfusion rate (Schlossman, 1927). After a small cannula is tied into the central artery, the ear is removed and perfused with Tyrode's or Ringer's solution in a constant temperature bath. The rate of outflow is measured by allowing the perfusate to collect in a funnel and counting the drops. Alternatively the two marginal veins can be cannulated, connected to a T-tube, and the outflow recorded by counting drops. The rabbit ear is very sensitive to adrenaline and noradrenaline and can respond to 1–2 ng in 0.1 ml of solution (Savini, 1956). Page and Green (1948) and Burn (1952) describe methods of preparing the rabbit's ear for perfusion. By directly observing the blood vessels microscopically in the intact rabbit's ears, Armin and Grant (1955) were able to detect adrenaline and noradrenaline in amounts of 0.003–0.005 ng.

The perfused rabbit ear is not now generally used for quantitative measurement of adrenaline and noradrenaline, but it is employed for evaluating symphatomimetic agents, adrenergic neuron-blocking agents and antagonists of adrenaline and noradrenaline (Boura and Green, 1959, 1963; Green and Robson, 1964; Walaszek and Chapman, 1962). Other tissue preparations may be used in a manner similar to that for the rabbit ear. Gaddum et al. (1949) have used the hind limbs of the rat, rabbit, and mouse, rabbit kidney, and frog lungs.

XIII. Spleen

Contraction of the spleen due to adrenaline and noradrenaline may be used to assay for these substances. The spleen of the spinal or anesthetized cat is brought through the abdominal wall and enclosed in a plethysmograph (Burn, 1952). Changes in spleen volume are measured with a pressure recorder. Peart (1949) and Brown and Gillespie (1957) collected the venous effluent from the spleen and showed that only noradrenaline was released upon stimulation of the splenic nerve. Thoenen *et al.* (1963) have described a procedure for isolating the spleen with the nerve supply intact and perfusing it in a plethysmograph. The output of noradrenaline and changes in volume and vascular resistance can be recorded simultaneously. The spleen is not generally used for quantitating adrenaline and noradrenaline in mixtures, but it is widely used in investigations of adrenergic-neuron blocking agents (Doda *et al.*, 1963; Green and Robson, 1964), receptor blocking agents (Kirpekar and Cervoni, 1963; Ahlquist, 1962), and sympathomimetic amines (Stone *et al.*, 1963; Day and Rand, 1963b) and in many other physiological and pharmacological investigations.

XIV. Isolated Preparations with Intact Nerve Supply

Several other preparations of isolated smooth muscle with intact nerve supplies have been useful in physiological and pharmacological investigations. Chang and Rand (1960) found that transmission in sympathetic nerves was blocked by hemicholinium in the guinea pig vas deferens–hypogastric nerve preparation (Hukovic, 1961), rabbit isolated uterus–hypogastric nerve (Varagic, 1956), rabbit isolated colon (Finkleman, 1930), perfused rabbit ear (Burn, 1952), cat isolated atria (Hukovic, 1959), and piloerector muscles in the cat tail. These observations support the hypothesis put forth by Burn (1960) that noradrenaline release from adrenergic fibers is mediated through the release of acetylcholine from accompanying cholinergic fibers. Day and Rand (1961) obtained further evidence to support this hypothesis by demonstrating the presence of cholinergic fibers in the sympathetic nerves of the isolated rabbit ileum.

The preparations of isolated smooth muscle with intact nerve supply have been used in studies of ganglion-blocking and postganglionic sympatholytic drugs (Bentley and Sabine, 1963) and in studies of adrenergic neuronal and receptor blocking agents (Day and Rand, 1961; Hukovic, 1959; Varagic, 1956).

XV. Electrophysiology

The development of techniques for the electrophoretic injection of chemicals into individual nerve cells and for the recording of electrical activity from these cells (Curtis and Eccles, 1958) has provided a direct method for investigating the role of catecholamines in central neural transmission. Curtis and Davis (1962) studied the effects of various drugs upon the nerves of the lateral geniculate nucleus. Krnjevic and Phillis (1963) tested derivatives of tryptamine, phenylethylamine, and other amines on the cerebral cortex of cats. Baumgarten *et al.* (1963) and Bloom *et al.* (1963) measured the effects of injections of acetylcholine, noradrenaline, and 5-hydroxytryptamine into single neurons of the olfactory bulb and hypothalamus. In all these studies a variable fraction of the total number of injected neurons responded. These studies provide strong evidence for the participation of catecholamines in central neural transmissions. Although it is difficult at present to obtain quantitative comparative evaluation of different chemicals (Krnjevic *et al.*, 1963), the technique offers an elegant approach for investigating the effects of catecholamines on central neural transmission.

REFERENCES

Ahlquist, R. T. (1962). *Arch. Intern. Pharmacodyn.* **139**, 38.
Alper, M. H., and Schmier, J. (1962). *J. Pharmacol.* **137**, 235.
Anden, N.-E., Magnusson, T., and Waldeck, B. (1964). *Life Sci.* **3**, 19.
Angelakos, E. T., and Torchiana, N. L. (1963). *Acta Physiol. Scand.* **59**, 161.
Armin, J., and Grant, R. T. (1955). *J. Physiol. (London)* **128**, 511.
Armitage, A. K., and Vane, J. R. (1964). *Brit. J. Pharmacol.* **22**, 204.
Bacq, Z. M., and Fisher, P. (1947). *Arch. Intern. Physiol.* **55**, 73.
Barsoum, G. S., and Gaddum, J. H. (1935). *J. Physiol. (London)* **85**, 1.
Baumgarten, R. v., Bloom, F. E., Oliver, A. P., and Salmoiraghi, G. C. (1963). *Arch. Exptl. Pathol. Pharmakol.* **277**, 125.
Beaver, W. T., and Riker, W. F. (1962). *J. Pharmacol.* **138**, 48.
Bentley, G. A., and Sabine, J. R. (1963). *Brit. J. Pharmacol.* **21**, 190.
Bevan, J. A. (1962). *J. Pharmacol.* **137**, 213.
Bhagat, B., and Shideman, N. E. (1963). *Brit. J. Pharmacol.* **20**, 56.
Bloom, F. E., Oliver, A. P., and Salmoiraghi, G. C. (1963). *Intern. J. Neuropharmacol.* **2**, 181.
Boniface, K. J., Brodie, O. J., and Walton, R. T. (1953). *Proc. Soc. Exptl. Biol.* **84**, 263.
Boura, A. L. A., and Green, A. F. (1959). *Brit. J. Pharmacol.* **14**, 536.
Boura, A. L. A., and Green, A. F. (1963). *Brit. J. Pharmacol.* **20**, 36.
Boura, A. L. A., and Green, A. F. (1964). *In* "Evaluation of Drug Activities; Pharmaco-metrics" (D. R. Laurence and A. L. Bacharach, eds.), Vol. 1, Part II, pp. 431–456. Academic Press, New York.
Brown, G. L., and Gillespie, J. S. (1957). *J. Physiol. (London)* **138**, 81.
Brown, T. G., and Lands, A. M. (1964). *In* "Evaluation of Drug Activities; Pharmaco-metrics" (D. R. Laurence and A. L. Bacharach, eds.), Vol. I, Part II, pp. 353–368. Academic Press, New York.

Büllbring, E., and Burn, J. H. (1949). *Brit. J. Pharmacol.* **4**, 202.

Burn, J. H. (1952). "Practical Pharmacology." Blackwell, Oxford.

Burn J. H. (1960). *In* "Adrenergic Mechanisms" (J. R. Vane, G. E. W. Wolstenholme, and M. O'Connor, eds.), p. 502. Churchill, London.

Burn, J. H., Dromey, J. J., and Lange, D. J. (1963). *Brit. J. Pharmacol.* **21**, 97.

Cannon, W. B., and Rosenblueth, A. (1933). *Am. J. Physiol.* **104**, 557.

Cannon, W. B., and Rosenblueth, A. (1937). "Autonomic Neuro-effector Systems." Macmillan, New York.

Chang, V., and Rand, M. J. (1960). *Brit. J. Pharmacol.* **15**, 588.

Cotten, M. de V., and Bay, E. (1956). *Am. J. Physiol.* **187**, 122.

Cotten, M. de V., and Cooper, T. (1962). *J. Pharmacol.* **136**, 97.

Curtis, D. R., and Davis, R. (1962). *Brit. J. Pharmacol.* **18**, 217.

Curtis, D. R., and Eccles, R. M. (1958). *J. Physiol. (London)* **141**, 435.

Day, M. D., and Rand, M. J. (1961). *Brit. J. Pharmacol.* **17**, 245.

Day, M. D., and Rand, M. J. (1963a). *Brit. J. Pharmacol.* **20**, 17.

Day, M. D., and Rand, M. J. (1963b). *Brit. J. Pharmacol.* **21**, 84.

Day, M. D., and Rand, M. J. (1964). *Brit. J. Pharmacol.* **22**, 72.

de Jalon, T. G., Bayo, J. B., and de Jalon, N. G. (1945). *Farmacoterap. Actual (Madrid)* **2**, 213.

Doda, N., Feher, O., Gyorgy, L., and Nador, K. (1963). *Brit. J. Pharmacol.* **21**, 10.

Elmadjian, F. (1962). *In* "Methods in Hormone Research" (R. I. Dorfman, ed.), Vol. II, p. 371. Academic Press, New York.

Ewer, R. W., Aikens, J. A., Hefferman, B. T., and Lennon, E. J. (1959). *J. Clin. Endocrinol. Metab.* **19**, 1037.

Fawaz, G., and Simaan, J. (1963). *Brit. J. Pharmacol.* **20**, 569.

Finkleman, B. (1930). *J. Physiol. (London)* **70**, 145.

Furchgott, R. F. (1960). *In* "Methods in Medical Research" (H. D. Bruner, ed.), Vol. 8, p. 177. Year Book Publ., Chicago, Illinois.

Furchgott, R. F., and Bhadrakom, S. (1953). *J. Pharmacol.* **108**, 129.

Furchgott, R. F., and Gubareff, Toisija, de (1958). *J. Pharmacol.* **124**, 203.

Gaddum, J. H. (1959). *Pharmacol. Rev.* **11**, 241.

Gaddum, J. H., and Holzbauer, M. (1957). *Vitamins Hormones* **15**, 151.

Gaddum, J. H., and Lembeck, F. (1949). *Brit. J. Pharmacol.* **4**, 401.

Gaddum, J. H., Peart, W. S., and Vogt, M. (1949). *J. Physiol. (London)* **108**, 467.

Gaffney, T. E., Morrow, D. H., and Chidsey, C. A. (1962). *J. Pharmacol.* **137**, 301.

Green, A. F., and Boura, A. L. A. (1964). *In* "Evaluation of Drug Activities; Pharmacometrics" (D. R. Laurence and A. L. Bacharach, eds.), Vol. 1, Part II, pp. 369–430. Academic Press, New York.

Green, A. F., and Robson, R. D. (1964). *Brit. J. Pharmacol.* **22**, 349.

Haefley, W., Hurlimann, A., and Thoenen, H. (1963). *Brit. J. Pharmacol.* **21**, 27.

Harakal, C., Sevy, R. W., and Russe, B. F. (1964). *J. Pharmacol.* **144**, 89.

Harrison, D. C., Chidsey, C. A., and Braunwald, W. (1963). *J. Pharmacol.* **141**, 22.

Harvey, J. A., and Pennefeather, J. N. (1962a). *J. Physiol. (London)* **160**, 14P.

Harvey, J. A., and Pennefeather, J. N. (1962b). *Brit. J. Pharmacol.* **18**, 183.

Helmer, O. M., and Sanders, R. M. (1957). *J. Lab. Clin. Med.* **50**, 737.

Hukovic, S. (1959). *Brit. J. Pharmacol.* **14**, 372.

Hukovic, S. (1961). *Brit. J. Pharmacol.* **16**, 188.

James, T. N., and Nadeau, R. A. (1963). *Am. J. Physiol.* **204**, 9.

James, T. N., and Nadeau, R. A. (1964). *J. Pharmacol.* **144**, 83.

Karki, N. T. (1956). *Acta Physiol. Scand.* **39**, Suppl. 132.

Kirpekar, S. M., and Cervoni, T. (1963). *J. Pharmacol.* **142**, 59.

Kirpekar, S. M., and Furchgott, R. N. (1964). *J. Pharmacol.* **143**, 64.

Kirshner, N. (1968). *In* "Methods in Hormone Research" (R. I. Dorfman, ed.), 2nd ed., Vol. I, pp. 383–410. Academic Press, New York.

Krayer, O. (1931). *Arch. Exptl. Pathol. Pharmakol.* **162**, 1.

Krayer, O., and Mendez, R. (1942). *J. Pharmacol.* **74**, 350.

Krnjevic, K. and Phillis, J. W. (1963). *Brit. J. Pharmacol.* **20**, 471.

Krnjevic, K., Laverty, R., and Sharman, D. F. (1963). *Brit. J. Pharmacol.* **20**, 491.

Langendorff, O. (1895). *Arch. Ges. Physiol.* **61**, 291.

Levy, D., and Tozzi, S. (1963). *J. Pharmacol.* **142**, 178.

McEwen, L. M. (1956). *J. Physiol. (London)* **131**, 678.

Maxwell, R. A., Daniel, A. I., Sheppard, H., and Zimmerman, J. H. (1962). *J. Pharmacol.* **137**, 31.

Mirkin, B. L., and Cervoni, P. (1962). *J. Pharmacol.* **138**, 301.

Muskus, A. J. (1962). *J. Pharmacol.* **138**, 296.

Oliver, G., and Schafer, E. A. (1895). *J. Physiol. (London)* **18**, 230.

Page, I. H., and Green, A. F. (1948). *In* "Methods in Medical Research" (Van R. Potter, ed.), Vol. I, p. 123. Year Book Publ., Chicago, Illinois.

Patterson, S. W., and Starling, E. H. (1914). *J. Physiol. (London)* **48**, 357.

Peart, W. S. (1949). *J. Physiol. (London)* **108**, 491.

Rosen, H., and Farah, A. (1955). *Am. J. Physiol.* **180**, 75.

Rudzik, A. D., and Miller, J. W. (1962). *J. Pharmacol.* **138**, 82.

Rudzik, A. D., and Miller, J. W. (1962a). *J. Pharmacol.* **138**, 88.

Savini, E. C. (1956). *Brit. J. Pharmacol.* **11**, 313.

Sawyer, W. H., Frieden, E. H., and Martin, A. C. (1953). *Am. J. Physiol.* **172**, 547.

Schlossmann, H. (1927). *Arch. Exptl. Pathol. Pharmakol.* **121**, 160.

Shipley, R. E., and Tilden, J. H. (1947). *Proc. Soc. Exptl. Biol.*, **64**, 453.

Smith, C. B. (1963). *J. Pharmacol.* **142**, 163.

Stafford, A. (1963). *Brit. J. Pharmacol.* **121**, 261.

Stewart, G. N., and Rogoff, J. M. (1919). *J. Pharmacol.* **13**, 195.

Stone, C. A., Stevoski, J. M., Ledden, C. T., Wagner, H. C., Ross, C. A., Totaro, J. A., and Porter, C. C. (1963). *J. Pharmacol.* **142**, 147.

Thier, D. M., Gravenstein, J. S., and Hoffman, R. G. (1962). *J. Pharmacol.* **136**, 133.

Thoenen, H., Hurlimann, A., and Haefley, W. (1963). *Helv. Physiol. Acta* **21**, 17.

Trendelenburg, U., and Weiner, N. (1962). *J. Pharmacol.* **136**, 152.

Trendelenburg, U., Muskus, A. J., Fleming, W. W., and Gomez, B. Alonso de la Sierra (1962a.) *J. Pharmacol.* **138**, 170.

Trendelenburg, U., Muskus. A. J., Fleming. W. W., and Gomez. B. Alonso de la Sierra (1962b). *J. Pharmacol.* **138**, 181.

Tsai, T. H., and Fleming, W. W. (1964). *J. Pharmacol.* **143**, 268.

Vane, J. R. (1964). *Brit. J. Pharmacol.* **23**, 360.

Vane, J. R. (1966). *Pharmacol. Rev.* **18**, 317.

Varagic, V. (1956). *J. Physiol (London)* **132**, 92.

von Euler, U. S. (1948). *Arch. Intern. Pharmacodyn.* **77**, 477.

von Euler, U. S. (1948a). *Acta Physiol. Scand.* **16**, 63.

von Euler, U. S. (1949). *Acta Physiol. Scand.* **19**, 207.

Vogt, M. (1959). *Pharmacol. Rev.* **11**, 249.

Walaszek, E. J., and Chapman, J. E. (1962). *J. Pharmacol.* **137**, 285.

West, G. B. (1943). *J. Physiol. (London)* **102**, 367.

Yates, C. M., and Gillis, C. N. (1963). *J. Pharmacol.* **140**, 52.

Chapter 8

Thyroidal Substances

C. W. Turner

I. Introduction

Great progress has been made in our knowledge of thyroidal substances since the first edition of this volume appeared. This progress has been due in large part to the increased use of radioactive iodine (^{131}I) in following steps in synthesis and metabolism of thyroidal preparations. The binding of thyroxine and triiodothyronine by blood proteins has been studied intensely. It has been suggested that only the "free" hormone in the blood may be taken up by the tissues.

The biological activity of L-thyroxine and L-triiodothyronine and their analogs continues to be studied. In the study of the oral effectiveness of thyroidal substances, increased understanding of the role of the so-called "antithyrotoxic" substances has been gained.

While many of the biological effects of thyroidal substances have been known for a long time, knowledge of their role in protein synthesis, erythropoiesis, fat and cholesterol metabolism, and certain tissue enzymes, such as α-glycerophosphate dehydrogenase, have been increased.

Finally, the development of methods of determining thyroid hormone secretion rate (TSR) have contributed greatly to our knowledge of the factors influencing secretion rate.

II. Thyroidal Substances

A. Chemistry of Thyroxine, Derivatives, and Isomers

The two biologically active hormones of the thyroid gland are L-thyroxine (L-T$_4$) and L-triiodothyronine (L-T$_3$). The free acid of L-thyroxine can be converted into a mono- and di (Na or K) salt. The monosodium salt is obtained with 0.1 N sodium carbonate, in which it is soluble, and then precipitation by chilling the solution to 0°C. This salt contains 63.46% iodine.

The disodium salt is formed by dissolving thyroxine in NaOH. It is readily soluble, and more so in 50% alcohol. By raising the alcohol to 80%, the disodium salt precipitates out as colorless glistening leaflets. This salt contains 61.69% iodine.

D-Thyroxine is not a naturally occurring substance. It is produced in solution of L-thyroxine by a process of racemization in which equal amounts of D- and L-thyroxine come into equilibrium in an alkaline solution, as in its extraction from hydrolyzates of thyroglobulin or thyroprotein.

The thyroxine available earlier was DL-thyroxine, whether extracted from the thyroid gland or synthesized. More recently synthetic L-thyroxine became available, and is now the usual standard of reference.

In addition to L-thyroxine, the presence of 3,5,3'-triiodo-L-thyronine has been demonstrated in the thyroid glands and blood of many species.

It will be noted that triiodothyronine is the first step in the metabolism of thyroxine by deiodination, a process which probably is carried on stepwise: diiodo, iodo, and finally to thyronine. The biological activity of these compounds will be considered later.

The oxidative deamination of the alanine side chain of thyroxine and related compounds to the acetic acid analogs has been demonstrated *in vivo*. In addition, the propionic and butyric acid analogs have been prepared. The biological activity of some of these preparations will be reported.

B. SYNTHESIS

In the synthesis of the thyroid hormones, it has been suggested that the first step is the iodination of monoiodotyrosine (MIT) in the thyroglobulin molecule, followed by the addition of a second iodine to form diiodotyrosine (DIT). When one MIT becomes oxidatively coupled with one DIT molecule, triiodothyronine (L-T_3) is formed. When two DIT molecules are joined thyroxine (L-T_4) is formed. Pitt-Rivers (1962) reported that MIT increased rapidly shortly after ^{131}I administration in the rat but decreased as DIT increased. The final concentration of ^{131}I was MIT 15%, DIT 45%, L-T_4 15%, and L-T_3 3%.

In iodine-deficient animals it has been shown that the MIT content of the gland is very high with MIT/DIT ratios of 2 or more being found (Lachiver and Leloup, 1955; Leloup and Lachiver, 1955; Querido *et al.*, 1957; and Bois and Larsson, 1958). In these glands abnormally high values for L-T_3 were observed.

C. Extrathyroidal Thyroxine Formation

Purves and Griesbach (1946) and Hum *et al.* (1951) reported that high levels of iodide partially prevented the degranulation of pituitary acidophils which occurs after thyroidectomy.

Evans *et al.* (1960) injected from 1–5 mg of iodide (KI) to young male rats when growth ceased after thyroidectomy. An immediate resumption of growth occurred, especially on the higher levels. There were a few more acidophils and basophilic gonadotrophs. No L-T_4-^{131}I or L-T_3 could be detected in the plasma, however.

Evans *et al.* (1966) compared the efficacy of iodide and of L-T_4 in treating the deficiences caused by thyroidectomy in rats. It was reported that growth, basal metabolic rate (BMR), heart rate, pituitary, adrenal, and reproductive function were identical with large quantities of iodide or daily injection of 0.25–0.5 μg L-T_4. Propylthiouracil abolished most of the responses to iodide while not interfering with L-T_4.

Taurog and Evans (1967) claim that by an improved technique they have been able to detect L-T_4-^{131}I in the plasma of thyroidectomized rats given large doses of ^{131}I.

It is interesting to note that Hegsted (1967) reported that thyroparathyroidectomized rats failed to grow within a few weeks when given a purified diet but grew at nearly normal rates when given Purina laboratory chow.

D. Thyroid, USP

Thyroid, USP, is defined as the thyroid glands of domesticated animals that are used for food by man; it is free from connective tissue and fat, dried, and powdered. It contains not less than 0.17% nor more than 0.23% iodine in the thyroid combination and is free from iodine in inorganic or any form of combination other than that peculiar to the thyroid gland. A desiccated thyroid of a higher iodine content may be brought to this standard by admixture with a desiccated thyroid of a lower iodine content or with lactose, NaCl, starch, or sucrose.

The Pharmacopoeia Internationalis requires that thyroid glands contain not less than 0.2% organically combined iodine and not less than 0.045% and not more than 0.055% of thyroxine iodine. Standard methods for determining organically combined iodine and thyroxine iodine are described.

Methods of extraction and purification of thyroglobulin from the thyroid glands of domestic animals have been reported.

That the iodine content of thyroid, USP, is not a satisfactory index of biological activity was suggested by observation of Stasilli and Kroc

(1956), who reported, on the basis of either the USP total combined iodine or the "Blau thyroxine-iodine" that cattle thyroid was much less active than swine thyroid in both goiter prevention and calorigenic assays in the adult rat. Johnson and Smith (1961) and Webb (1961) reported a lack of agreement between British thyroid "thyroxine-iodine" values and physiological activity in preparations of swine, cattle, and sheep thyroid.

Similarly, Wiberg et al. (1962) reported samples of cattle and sheep thyroid were less potent than swine thyroid in biological assays when the doses were administered either on the basis of British "thyroxine-iodine" or USP total combined iodine. The explanation of this discrepancy was shown to reside in the relation of L-T_4 to L-T_3 in the thyroid preparations.

Danowski and Moses (1965) reported that 3 grains of purified desiccated thyroid, Proloid, in which the proportion of L-T_4 to L-T_3 was 2.5:1, which duplicates that in fresh pork thyroid, yielded euthyroid levels of serum PBI, the binding of L-T_3 to red cells, and normal serum levels of total and α- and β-lipoprotein, and cholesterol in hypothyroid and myxedema patients.

E. HORMONE SECRETION BY FETAL THYROID GLAND

French and Van Wyk (1964) reported that the human fetal thyroid can take up iodine early in pregnancy, and Hodges et al. (1955) reported ^{131}I uptake by the third month.

Beierwaltes (1967) gave ^{131}I to 17 pregnant beagle dogs after surgical thyroidectomy. After 3 days fetal serum was studied. It contained ^{131}I in the L-T_4 area of the chromatograph at 42 days or more of gestation.

Shepard (1967) studied the uptake of ^{125}I in human fetal thyroids ranging in crown-rump length from 22–142 mm with estimated age of 45–112 days. In 7 fetuses of less than 68 mm no organic iodine or tissue-bound ^{125}I was found. At the 68-mm stage (74 days) and at all later stages MIT, DIT, L-T_4, and occasionally L-T_3 were found.

F. RELEASE OF "NEW'" AND "OLD" THYROGLOBULIN

It has been suggested that newly iodinated thyroglobulin mixes ramdomly in all the thyroidal thyroglobulin. Thus iodide newly transported into the gland equilibrates rapidly with existing stores to produce a functional homogeneity of the major portion of the thyroglobulin.

Rosenberg et al. (1966) presented evidence which they have interpreted as showing that this is not true but thyroidal iodine is turned over in a heterogeneous manner.

Loewenstein and Wollman (1967) studied autoradiographs of thyroidal organic ^{125}I made 1 hour and later. Most follicular lumens were homogeneously labeled, but some images were in the shape of a ring. The ring was high after 1 hour but fell to a low level after 1 day. In a few the ring persisted for 16 days and even 99 days. It is suggested that a period of rapid diffusion is followed by slow diffusion within some follicles.

G. Circadian Rhythm in Thyroid Gland

Woods et al. (1966) studied the daily fluctuations in thyroidal ^{131}I in 31 cycles of 10 cats. Peak radioactivity occurred at 7 A.M. with a minimum at about 7 P.M. In 2 monkeys the cycles were longer. The cyles persisted after transplantation and after division of the spinal cord in the lower cervical region. In 2 decerebrated cats no cycles were observed.

H. L-T_4 and L-T_3 as Standards

The availability of L-T_4 in a highly purified form serves as an excellent standard in all biological assays. Since this is the form in which thyroxine is secreted by the thyroid gland and, further, is the form present in thyroprotein, the administration of L-thyroxine gives the biological equivalent of normal thyroidal hormone secretion. The iodine content is 65.5%.

L-T_3 is now also available in a highly purified form, and comparisons of these two biologically active hormones of the thyroid gland are reported. The iodine content is 58.5%.

I. Synthetic Thyroprotein (Thyroactive Iodinated Casein)

The synthesis of thyroactive material by the iodination of casein and subsequent treatment to produce oxidative coupling of diiodo-tyrosine molecules in the protein has made available a relatively inexpensive source of thyroxine-like material (Reineke and Turner, 1942, 1945, 1946). The thyroxine content of thyroprotein has been a subject of study since its synthesis. On the basis of early work using the n-butanol-soluble iodine as an index, it was estimated that about 3% thyroxine was present (Reineke et al., 1945). It was later shown by Friedberg and Reineke (1952) that hydrolyzed thyroprotein contained at least 10 iodinated compounds including mono- and diiodotyrosine, diiodo- and triiodothyronine, as well as thyroxine. It was then shown by Reineke (1954), by a radioactive isotope dilution technique in a group of 7 preparations, that thyroprotein which showed an estimated 3.24% thyroxine in the butanol-soluble fraction contained 1.04% true thyroxine.

The earlier studies using the higher estimated thyroxine content of thyroprotein indicated very low oral absorption. However, in using the value of 1.0% true thyroxine, the oral effectiveness of thyroprotein, thyroglobulin, and L-thyroxine in ruminant animals is comparable.

In the literature its commercial name, Protamone, is frequently used. This preparation is standardized by the manufacturer to contain 1% L-T_4.

J. LIST OF THYROXINE AND ITS ANALOGS

3, 5, 3′, 5′-Tetraiodo-L-thyronine (L-T_4) (L-thyroxine)

3, 5, 3′, 5′-Tetraiodo-D-thyronine (D-T_4) (D-thyroxine)

3, 5, 3′, 5′-Tetraiodothyroacetic acid (Tetrac)

3, 5, 3′, 5′-Tetraiodothyroformic acid (T_4F)

3, 5, 3′-Triiodo-L-thyronine (L-T_3) (L-triiodothyronine)

3, 5, 3′-Triiodo-D-thyronine (D-T_3) (D-triiodothyronine)

3, 5, 3′-Triiodothyroacetic acid (Triac)

3, 5, 3′-Triiodothyroformic acid (T_3F)

3, 5-Diiodo-L-thyronine (L-T_2)

3, 5-Diiodo-D-thyronine (D-T_2)

3, 5-Diiodothyroacetic acid (Diac)

3, 5-Diiodothyroformic acid (T_2F)

3′-Choloro-3,5 diiodo-L-thyronine

3′,5′-Dichloro-3,5-diiodo-L-thyronine

3′-Ethyldiiodothyronine

3′-Methyldiiodothyronine

3′-Isopropyldiiodothyroacetic acid

2′,3′-Dimethyldiiodothyroacetic acid

3,5,3′5,′-Tetraiodothyropropionic acid (ToP)

3,3′,5-Triiodopropionic acid (T_3P)

III. Biological Activity of Thyroidal Substances

A. COMPARISON OF BIOLOGICAL POTENCY OF L-, D-, AND DL-THYROXINE

For comparisons of these compounds in studies prior to 1960, the reader is referred to the previous report (Turner and Premachandra, 1962).

Pipes and Dale (1963) compared the biological activity of L-T_4, D-T_4, and L-T_3 by the TSR method in female rats. L-T_4 was found to be 10 times as potent as D-T_4, whereas L-T_3 was 2.17 times as potent as L-T_4.

1. Clinical Use of D-T$_4$

Starr (1961) reported that D-T$_4$ at levels of 4–12 mg orally to athyreotoxic patients maintained the BMR and serum cholesterol at a normal level. This level is about 10 times that required of L-T$_4$.

2. Growth of Rats on L- and D-T$_4$

Lew et al. (1963) thyroidectomized rats by giving 100 μCi of ^{131}I intraperitoneally at 2, 4, and 6 weeks of age. Beginning at 7 weeks of age, either 2.0 mg Na L-T$_4$ or 20 mg of Na D-T$_4$ per kilogram of diet was fed to week 17. (It was estimated that the rats ate 3 μg and 30 μg per 100 gm body weight.) It was reported that both males and females on these levels of D- and L-T$_4$ were normal.

B. COMPARISON OF BIOLOGICAL POTENCY OF L-T$_4$ AND L-T$_3$

For the earlier comparisons of these compounds in various species up to 1960, the reader is referred to the previous review (Turner and Premachandra, 1962).

1. Rat

Hirvonen and Lang (1962) observed a close parallelism between heart rate and oxygen consumption in rats treated with L-T$_4$ and L-T$_3$. Duration of effects were practically equal. The beat rate of isolated atria of L-T$_3$-treated rats were very close to that recorded in intact animals. The mean heart rate of 20 control animals ranged from 272–281 beats per minute and of thyroidectomized (with ^{131}I) between 258– and 281. However, the rate of hypothyroid atria was less than 60% of the control preparations.

Pipes and Dale (1963) reported that L-T$_3$ by the TSR method was 2.2 times as potent as L-T$_4$ on an equal molar basis in female rats. In male rats, Bauman and Turner (1965) found L-T$_3$ to be 2.64 times as active biologically by the TSR method.

Evans et al. (1964) thyroidectomized Long-Evans rats at 28 days of age. Injections of 0.01, 0.05, 0.1, and 0.2 μg of L-T$_4$ and L-T$_3$ were given for 98 days. Some growth was stimulated with 0.05 μg and the response was graded with increasing levels, but L-T$_3$ was no more effective than L-T$_4$. Pituitary acidophils increased suddenly to 50% of normal at the 0.2-μg dosage. Erythropoiesis was not stimulated by these levels of either hormone. The adrenal cortices showed graded responses at all levels and the ovaries were essentially normal at the 0.2-μg dose.

Meyer and Evans (1964) thyroidectomized rats. After 49 days, growth ceased. The rats were then injected with 1 mg of cortisol acetate for 14 days. The acidophils increased from 0–60%. The GH content was estimated to be 8 times increased over controls but 8 times less than in normal animals.

Bray and Goodman (1965) studied the time required for physiological response to L-T_3 and L-T_4 in thyroidectomized rats. The heart rate and the lipolytic effect of epinephrine on adipose tissue were increased 3 hours after giving 45 μg of L-T_3 intravenously and at 6 hours after giving 15 or 45 μg subcutaneously. Five micrograms of L-T_3 and 60 μg of L-T_4 produced significant effects on heart rate and on adipose tissue at 12 hours. Body temperature was sometimes increased by 12 hours.

2. Raccoon

Bauman et al. (1965a) compared the biological value of L-T_3 and L-T_4 in the raccoon. When L-T_3 was substituted for L-T_4 in the estimation of TSR, it was found to be 1.92 times as active as L-T_4 in adult males but only 1.06 times in the juveniles.

3. Opossum

Bauman and Turner (1966a) substituted L-T_3 in the TSR procedure for L-T_4. It was 1.1 times as effective as L-T_4.

4. Fowls

In earlier studies with fowls, it was claimed that L-T_3 was no more potent biologically than L-T_4. Srivastava and Turner (1967) determined the relative effectiveness of L-T_3 and L-T_4 by the TSR method. In 2 strains of male "docile" and "flighty" birds L-T_3 was shown to be 2.16 and 2.13 times as effective as L-T_4.

In 4-year-old New Hampshire fowls, Srivastava and Turner (1967) compared L-T_3 and L-T_4 by injection. In the male birds L-T_3 was 2.2 times as active, whereas in females it was 1.5 times as active by the TSR method. In male birds, it appears that L-T_3 is more than 2 times as active as L-T_4 by the TSR method, which involves the suppression of TSH secretion.

C. Biological Half-Life $(t_{1/2})$ of L-T_3 and L-T_4

1. Man

The $t_{1/2}$ of L-T_3 and L-T_4 in man has been reported by several workers (Table I).

Walfish et al. (1961) followed the diurnal rate of disappearance of L-T_4-^{131}I in 11 patients. Based on daily observations, the rate was 12% per 24 hours or 0.5% per hour. However, from 8 AM to 2 AM the rate was about 1% per hour, or 24% per day. From 2 AM to 8 AM the plasma radioactivity would have to increase 12%. It is suggested that this may be due to a change in plasma volume, a reduction in the rate of disappearance, or a return of radioactivity to the serum.

Oddie *et al.* (1964) described a technique for the study of the metabolism of L-T_4-^{131}I by whole-body counting in man. Later, Fisher and Oddie (1964) presented a similar study using L-T_3-^{131}I.

Blomstedt and Einhorn (1965) reported that the slope of the L-T_4-^{131}I disappearance curve for blood was reduced during the administration of large doses of cortisone.

TABLE I

COMPARATIVE HALF-LIFE ($t_{1/2}$) OF L-T_4 AND L-T_3

Species	Thyroxine (days)	Triiodothyronine (days)	Reference
Man	6.7	2.7	Sterling *et al.* (1954)
Man	7.4	1.3	Kuhl *et al.* (1961)
Man	—	1.3	Wiswell and Coronbo (1962)
Man, normal	7.4	—	Inada *et al.* (1964)
Man, Hypothyroid	7.2	—	Inada *et al.* (1964)
Man, Hyperthyroid	4.1	—	Inada *et al.* (1964)

Oddie *et al.* (1966) summarized data in 30 published reports on 726 subjects on the effect of sex, age, pubertal status, weight, height, and clinical state for the extrathyroidal L-T_4 distribution space (V, ml), the fractional degradation rate (b, days^{-1}), and the L-T_4 turnover rate (H_4, μg/liter per day). Sex and pubertal state showed no significant effect. The space V was found dependent only on weight, independent of height and age, and not influenced by clinical states except hepatitis and obesity. The degradation rate b was dependent on age, independent of weight and height, and altered significantly in certain clinical states.

Gregerman and Solomon (1967) noted the $t_{1/2}$ of L-T_4 during bacterial pulmonary infection and fever. In 18 male subjects the normal $t_{1/2}$ was 10.5 ± 2.74 days compared to 2.38 ± 0.93 days during fever. In 8 females the corresponding data were 11.3 ± 5.2 and 2.22 ± 0.7 days. It is suggested that fever accelerated L-T_4 secretion. The $t_{1/2}$ of L-T_3 in six patients was 8.8 hours compared to a normal of 33.7 hours.

Rabinowitz and Myerson (1967) reported that the $t_{1/2}$ of L-T_3 of obese patients was only 1.6 days compared to that of individuals of 2.9 days. After L-T_3 therapy the $t_{1/2}$ increased toward normal.

Surks *et al.* (1967) studied L-T$_4$ metabolism of 5 young males first at 5280 feet and then for 8 days at 14,100 feet (Pikes Peak, Colorado). L-T$_4$ degradation was increased during the first 3 days, then remained slightly elevated. Plasma total and free L-T$_4$ were not changed during the first 2 days but then increased continually for the rest of the period.

2. *Rat*

Feldman (1960) compared the $t_{1/2}$ of L-T$_4$ and L-T$_3$ in controls and rats on an iodine-deficient diet. Iodine deficiency had no effect on the $t_{1/2}$ of L-T$_4$, but L-T$_3$ had a significantly shorter $t_{1/2}$ (Table II).

TABLE II

HALF-LIFE $(t_{1/2})$ IN THE RAT

Species	No. of animals	L-T$_4$ (hours)	L-T$_3$ (hours)	Remarks	Reference
Male	7	18.2	11.0	Normal	Feldman (1960)
Female	7	18.6	10.3	Iodine deficient	Feldman (1960)
Thyroidectomized + 1.5 μg L-T$_4$/100 gm bw	38	16.6			Pittman *et al.* (1964)
Controls	10	19.5	—	—	Grossie *et al.* (1965)
Thyroidectomized	19	23.7	—	—	Grossie *et al.* (1965)
Thyroidectomized + 1.0 μg L-T$_4$/100 gm bw	23	17.8	—	—	Grossie *et al.* (1965)
Methimazole, 30 days (400 μg/100 gm bw/day)	10	18.5	—	—	Grossie *et al.* (1965)
Female, normal	14	21.8 (blood)	—	—	Anderson *et al.* (1968)
		24.8 (whole body)	—	—	Anderson *et al.* (1968)
Female methimazole	14	20.3 (blood)	—	—	Anderson *et al.* (1968)
		21.2 (whole body)	—	—	Anderson *et al.* (1968)
Female, hypo- physectomized	22	20.7 (blood)	—	—	Anderson *et al.* (1968)
		47.1 (whole body)	—	—	Anderson *et al.* (1968)

Pittman *et al.* (1964) studied the effect of thyroxine analogs on the $t_{1/2}$ of L-T$_4$ in thyroidectomized rats maintained in a euthyroid state with L-T$_4$. D-T$_4$, DL-T$_3$, 3,3′,5′-triiodothyropropionic acid, and 3,5-diiodothyroacetic acid lengthened the $t_{1/2}$ of L-T$_4$-^{131}I, increased the recovery in the feces, and decreased the amount in the urine. They suggested that the way these analogs antagonize the calorigenic action of L-T_4 is related to competition for mechanisms by which L-T_4 is degraded.

Grossie *et al.* (1965) observed a mean $t_{1/2}$ of control rats of 19.5 hours, whereas 7 days after thyroidectomy the $t_{1/2}$ increased to 23.7 hours. When L-T_4 at a level of 1.0 μg/100 gm body weight was injected, the $t_{1/2}$ was 17.8 hours. The daily injection of 400 μg methimazole/100 gm body weight for 30 days had no effect on the $t_{1/2}$.

Anderson *et al.* (1968) compared the $t_{1/2}$ of L-T_4 by blood sampling and by whole body count of female rats. Normal rats had a $t_{1/2}$ of 21.8 hours by blood count and 24.8 hours by whole-body count. When methimazole was given, the $t_{1/2}$ was 20.3 and 21.2 hours, respectively. In hypophysectomized rats the $t_{1/2}$ was 20.7 and 47.1 hours, respectively.

3. Guinea Pig

Premachandra *et al.* (1962) and Ray and Premachandra (1964) have determined the $t_{1/2}$ of L-T_3 and L-T_4 in the guinea pig (Table III).

TABLE III

HALF-LIFE ($t_{1/2}$) OF L-T_4 AND L-T_3 IN GUINEA PIG

Species	No. of animals	L-T_4 hours	No. of animals	L-T_3 (hours)	Reference
Guinea pig					
Control	7	30.4 (24–37)	6	33.0 (22–39)	Premachandra *et al.* (1962)
Adjuvant treated	3	29.4 (25–32)	2	27.3	Premachandra *et al.* (1962)
Thyroglubulin and adjuvant, 5 weeks	6	37.3 (29–38)	3	26.4 (23–28)	Premachandra *et al.* (1962)
Thyroglobulin and adjuvant, 12 weeks	5	71.6 (69–125)	3	61.5 (49–72)	Premachandra *et al.* (1962)
Normal	14	31.3 + 5.3	14	30.2 + 4.8	Ray and Premachandra (1964)
Methimazole	12	29.3 + 4.6	12	32.4 + 6.2	Ray and Premachandra (1964)

It will be noted that the difference in the $t_{1/2}$ of L-T_4 and L-T_3 was not significant. The addition of methimzaole to prevent recycling of the ^{131}I did not influence the $t_{1/2}$.

Brown-Grant (1963) estimated the $t_{1/2}$ of L-T_4 and L-T_3 from the urinary and fecal excretion of [131]I. By this technique the $t_{1/2}$ of L-T_4 was 31 hours and of L-T_3 17 hours.

4. Raccoons

Bauman *et al.* (1965a) determined the $t_{1/2}$ of L-T$_4$ in the raccoon. In adult male raccoon the $t_{1/2}$ was 0.91 with a range from 0.84–0.97 days. In the juveniles, the mean $t_{1/2}$ was 0.82 days with a range from 0.76–0.92.

5. Cattle

Premachandra *et al.* (1960) reported that the mean $t_{1/2}$ of L-T$_4$ was 2.54 days at a mean temperature of 47°F and of 2.65 days at a temperature of 71°F. L-T$_3$ had a $t_{1/2}$ of 1.99 days.

Lundgren and Johnson (1964) reported that 6 lactating Holstein cows held at a temperature of 65°F, the $t_{1/2}$ was 2.9 days whereas at 88°F the $t_{1/2}$ was 4 days.

Premachandra and Turner (1961) determined the $t_{1/2}$ of 8 normal cows as 2.32 days. When maintained in a hyperthryoid state 50% above their estimated daily TSR by exogenous L-T$_4$, the $t_{1/2}$ was reduced to 1.05 days, a reduction of 54.3%.

Hendrich and Turner (1964) determined the $t_{1/2}$ of 7 calves 7–10 months of age in the late fall. The mean $t_{1/2}$ was 1.85 days.

Bauman *et al.* (1968) determined the $t_{1/2}$ of 6 dry cows at 2.67 days. When injected with L-T$_4$ at levels of 25 and 50% above their normal TSR, the $t_{1/2}$ was reduced to 2.11 and 1.62 days, respectively.

6. Horses

Irvine (1967) determined the $t_{1/2}$ of L-T$_4$ in various groups of horses as follows: untrained at 11.1°C, 2.31 days; untrained at 2.8°C, 2.11 days; partly trained, 1.44 days; fully trained, 0.88 days; during cold adaption at 2.8°C, 1.55 days; and during pregnancy, 2.09 days.

7. Fowls

Shellabarger and Tata (1961) determined the $t_{1/2}$ of L-T$_4$ and L-T$_3$ by whole-body counting (Table IV).

TABLE IV

HALF-LIFE ($t_{1/2}$) IN FOWLS[a]

White Leghorn cockerels	$t_{1/2}$ 0–24 hours	$t_{1/2}$, 24–54 hours
L-T$_4$	9.4	24.0
L-T$_4$	11.0	16.0
L-T$_3$	9.5	19.0
L-T$_3$	8.6	27.0

[a] Data from Shellabarger and Tata (1961).

When human TBG was mixed with L-T_4 and L-T_3 at the time of injection, the $t_{1/2}$ of L-T_4 was increased to 14.2 hours but the L-T_3 $t_{1/2}$ was not influenced.

When the TBG was injected either 15 minutes or 1 day after the hormone, the $t_{1/2}$ was not altered for the first 24 hours or for the longer period.

Heninger and Newcomer (1964) determined the $t_{1/2}$ of L-T_4 and L-T_3 in 6-week-old White Leghorn cockerels. From 1–24 hours, the $t_{1/2}$ of L-T_4 was 8.3 hours and of L-T_3 7.2 hours; and from 1–4 days, 16.5 and 16.3 hours, respectively.

Hendrich and Turner (1967) observed that hens maintained in an environment of 12.8°C during the winter months had a $t_{1/2}$ of 7.6 hours and during the summer of 11.4 hours. Placing them in a constant 4.4°C

TABLE V

HALF-LIFE ($t_{1/2}$) IN FROGS AND TOADS[a]

Species	L-T_4	L-T_3
Frog *Rana pipiens* Toad	3.4 days	NS[b]
Bufo marinus	4.8 days	NS
Bufo americanus	3.2 days	NS

[a] Data from Dowling *et al.* (1964).
[b] NS = difference not significant.

chamber for 1, 7, or 21 days had no effect upon the $t_{1/2}$. After long-term exposure to cold the $t_{1/2}$ increased to 11.3 hours, which was not significantly different due to great variability.

Hendrich and Turner (unpublished) determined the $t_{1/2}$ of Cornish cross-bred chickens at 4 and 7 months of age which had been thyroidectomized with ^{131}I and received graded replacement therapy. Hypo- and hyperthyroid levels of L-T_4 failed to cause significant differences compared to control values of 10.3 hours during the fall and 7.1 hours during the winter. Without L-T_4 the $t_{1/2}$ was 33.3 hours.

8. Frogs and Toads

Dowling *et al.* (1964) reported that the $t_{1/2}$ of thyroxine and triiodothyronine in frogs and toads was similar but temperature dependent. It was suggested that thyroxine-binding activity in amphibian plasma is low (Table V).

D. Metabolism of l-T$_3$ and l-T$_4$

The metabolism of l-T$_4$ has been studied in man with iodide appearing as the only labeled product in serum. Research with *in vitro* deiodinating systems has demonstrated a dissimilarity in the metabolism of iodine in the $3':5'$-position of l-T$_4$ from that in the $3:5$-position, the former producing only iodide while the latter gave several compounds including $3:5$-diiodotyrosine.

Flock *et al.* (1958) reported that conjugation with glucuronic acid constitutes an important metabolic pathway for thyroxine (l-T$_4$).

Similarly, Roche *et al.* (1954) and Flock *et al.* (1957) reported a similar pathway for l-T$_3$. The glucosiduronic acids of these hormones normally are excreted in the bile, and small amounts appear in the urine.

Brown-Grant and Gibson (1955) reported in the rabbit 52% of l-T$_4$ appeared in the feces after an intravenous tracer dose. Forty-seven percent appeared in the urine as iodide. About 8% or less was accumulated by the thyroid gland. A large dose of l-T$_4$ disappeared more rapidly from the blood, and a higher proportion was deiodinated.

Conjugation of l-T$_3$ with sulfuric acid has been demonstrated in the rat, man, and dog. Flock *et al.* (1960) also reported $3,3'$-T$_2$ sulfate. Flock *et al.* (1961) reported that l-T$_4$ administered to the dehepatized dog appeared as $3,3',5'$-T$_3$ glucuronide as well as $3,3'$-T$_2$ sulfate.

Butyl hydroxydiiodobenzoate (BHDB) was fed to rats a few hours prior to the injection of l-T$_4$, l-T$_3$, and other analogs labeled with ^{131}I in the $3'$ or $5'$ position. BHDB greatly stimulated conjugation of these substances and their metabolites and increased the excretion into the bile. It also inhibited deiodination of the hormones from the $3'$ or $5'$ position and thus decreased excretion of ^{131}I in the urine.

Flock *et al.* (1963b) administered l-T$_3$ or l-T$_2$ labeled with ^{131}I in the $3'$ or $5'$ position to normal dogs and with biliary fistulas and to dogs after total hepatectomy and to rats with fistulas. In dogs, stepwise deiodination led to the formation of $3,3'$-T$_2$ and $3'$-monoiodothyronine (T$_1$) from l-T$_3$ and of $3'$-T$_1$ from $3,3'$-T$_2$. The metabolites were found chiefly in conjugated form in bile or, after hepatectomy, in urine.

Deiodination from the beta ring of these compounds was fairly rapid in the rat, and a large amount of ^{131}I iodide was excreted in the urine.

Dunn and Werner (1964) gave patients l-T$_4$-^{131}I. Only l-T$_4$ and small amounts of iodide could be identified in the serum samples. It was concluded that the α-phenyl ring of l-T$_4$ was deiodinated to iodide with no detectable intermediates.

Ford and Rhines (1964) reported that following the injection of l-T$_3$-^{131}I, mono- and diiodotyrosine and l-T$_3$ appeared in urine collected from the bladders of rats at 0.5 hour but was high to hour 7.

Galton (1965) studied deiodination in rats *in vivo* by measuring urinary excretion of L-T_4-^{131}I when thyroid function was blocked with potassium perchlorate. About 50% of the daily dose was excreted in the urine. Excretion was increased following epinephrine and was decreased by reserpine.

Pittman and Shimizu (1966) studied the metabolism of L-T_4 with ^{131}I and ^{14}C in 4 positions. They believe that the diphenyl ether moiety of L-T_4 is metabolized independently of deiodination. There are two pathways in the rat. L-T_4 is conjugated in the liver and excreted into the bile mainly as L-T_4 glucuronide, which is hydrolyzed in the intestine or acted upon by the intestinal bacteria. Some free L-T_4 is reabsorbed, and the remainder passes out in the feces.

The main excretory pathway of degraded L-T_4 appears to be through the kidneys. Because all 3 ^{14}C-L-T_4 have given rise to similar metabolites, it is believed that the bulk of circulating L-T_4 is degraded without rupture of the diphenyl ether linkage.

1. Deiodination of L-T_4-^{131}I and Calorigenic Action

Anbar *et al.* (1965) measured the *in vivo* rate of deiodination of L-T_4 in normal and thyroidectomized rats. Small doses of actinomycin D given with L-T_4 almost completely abolished the increase in BMR but slightly elevated the rate of deiodination.

In thyroidectomized rats a single injection of L-T_3 stimulated an increase in BMR before the increase in deiodination. It is suggested that deiodination is not an integral part of the mechanism that initiates the calorigenic action.

2. Effect of 5- and 6-Propylthiouracil of Metabolism of L-T_4 in Man

Hershman (1964) gave 10 normal patients 5- and 6-propylthiouracil, then L-T_4-^{131}I was given intravenously. Potassium perchlorate was given to block recycling. 5-PTU reduced urinary [131]I 30–44%, and increased fecal ^{131}I in all patients. 6-PTU reduced urinary ^{131}I only 0–11% and increased fecal ^{131}I in only 1 patient.

3. Effect of Vitamin Deficiencies on L-T_4 Metabolism

Galton and Ingbar (1965) assessed the deiodinating activity in both *in vivo* and *in vitro* studies of rats deficient in various vitamins. No effect was observed in animals deficient in vitamins A, B_6, niacin, D, or K. Activity was greatly decreased in homogenates or slices of liver from riboflavin-deficient animals. Normal activity was restored by normal diet in 6 days. Deiodinating activity was greatly increased in preparations of liver and muscle from E-deficient rats.

4. Bile

Blomstedt and Neujahr (1964b) reported that when L-T_3-^{131}I was injected into rats and humans, the L-T_3 occurring in the bile was mainly conjugated with glucuronic acid, but some was found in diiodotyrosine.

After injection of diiodotyrosine-^{131}I in rats only ^{131}I was detected in bile, while in man most was ^{131}I but a small part of diiodotyrosine.

5. L-T_4 and L-T_3 in Human Feces

Blomstedt and Neujahr (1964a) described a method for the extraction and purification of ^{131}I amino acids from human feces sufficient to provide an estimate of the L-T_4, L-T_3, and diiodotyrosine.

Blomstedt and Neujahr (1964b) injected L-T_4-^{131}I intravenously. The excretion of ^{131}I in the feces during 12 days ranged from 7.8 to 32.1% with a mean of 16%. The ^{131}I in the feces was derived from free L-T_4-^{131}I. When L-T_3-^{131}I was injected, the radioactivity was derived from free L-T_3.

6. ^{131}I in Urine

Blomstedt (1965) determined ^{131}I in the urine of euthyroid patients given L-T_4-^{131}I during a period of 12 days. It ranged from 42.8–60.0% of the dose (mean, 49.8%) of which 90% was ^{131}I and 5% L-T_4 in the free form. Diiodotyrosine and L-T_3 accounted for a small fraction. The mean 24-hour excretion of L-T_4 was 3 μg, only 2–3% of the amount catabolized.

7. Metabolism of D-T_4

Flock et al. (1963a) have reviewed the literature concerning differences between L- and D-T_4.

Differences in the metabolism in the dog and rat were reported. In the dog deiodination of D-T_4 from the 3 or 5 position of the alpha ring was more rapid than of L-T_4. Deiodination from the beta ring of D-T_4 like that of L-T_4 was greatly diminished after total hepatectomy and little iodide-^{131}I was excreted in the urine.

In the rat, D-T_4 was metabolized more rapidly than L-T_4. Metabolites excreted in the bile were similar after injection of D-T_4, and L-T_4.

8. Deiodination of Diiodotyrosine (DIT)

Maayan and Rosenberg (1963) reported that the injection of TSH into normal rats increased the thyroidal deiodination of L-DIT in as short a time as 3 hours. Maayan (1964) observed that this process was markedly decreased in hypophysectomized rats. When TSH was administered for 10 days (but not 5 days) the deiodination was increased. In a continuation of this research, Maayan (1966) gave TSH, GH, and TSH + GH to hypophysectomized rats for 21 days. The deiodination of L-DIT-^{131}I was measured in homogenates of thyroid and liver. It was greatly increased by TSH after 7 days. Significant titers of anti-TSH antibodies began to appear after 10 days and were significant after 21 days. GH for more than 7 days increased and GH + TSH induced greater responses in deiodination. GH stimulated the hepatic deiodination of L-DIT.

IV. Iodinated Compounds in the Thyroid Gland

1. Method of Digestion of Thyroid Gland

Tong et al. (1963) reported on the value of various enzymes for the hydrolysis of thyroid proteins in the determination of L-T_4.

In the estimation of the L-T_3 and L-T_4 content of thyroid glands, proteolytic digestion of the gland is followed by their separation. Pronase and pancreatin have been used. In a recent study Inoue and Taurog (1967) reported that losses that have been observed previously were almost completely eliminated when the digestion was performed with pronase under anaerobic conditions in the presence of 0.05 M methyl-mercaptoimidazole for 18 hours.

2. Human

Brasch et al. (1955) reported that normal thyroid gland tissue contained L-T_4, 35%; L-T_3, 8%, DIT, 25%; and MIT 17%. Similar relations were observed in exophthalmic goiters and after the administration of Lugol's solution.

Lissitzky et al. (1967) reported the thyroid gland of a 12-year-old boy with congenital goiter and hypothyroidism was practically free of thyroglobulin and was replaced by iodinated albumin-like proteins, one of which was identified as serum albumin by amino acid composition, molecular weight, and immunoelectrophoresis. L-T_3 was the major circulating hormone (80%), and free iodotyrosines were found in blood and urine.

3. Domestic Animals

Wiberg et al. (1962) chemically analyzed cattle, sheep, and swine thyroid preparations for L-T_4 and L-T_3. It was reported that the molar ratio of L-T_4 to L-T_3 was approximated 2:1 in swine and 3:1 in cattle and sheep.

Devlin and Stephenson (1962) determined the L-T_4 and L-T_3 content of 5 samples of swine thyroids. Assuming a molecular weight of 650,000 for thyroglobulin, it is suggested that there is 1 mole of L-T_3 and 2 moles of L-T_4.

Wiberg *et al.* (1964) compared porcine and bovine thyroid glands by the goiter prevention assay using various goitrogens. Assays employing thiouracil, thiourea, aminotriazole, or perchlorate produced equivalent potency estimates indicating that porcine thyroid was significantly more active than the bovine on basis of iodine content. On the basis of the L-T_3 content, the potency of the two types of thyroid were equivalent.

Pileggi *et al.* (1965) reported the L-T_3 and L-T_4 content of commercial thyroid preparations. A range of 9.3–15.8% for L-T_4 and 3.5–5.4% for L-T_3. The molar ratio of the two was approximately 200.

Kologlù *et al.* (1966) studied the effectiveness of a number of proteolytic enzymes on the hydrolysis of bovine and porcine desiccated thyroid glands. Protease (Sigma) incubated for 24 hours was found to be most effective. The L-T_4 and L-T_3 contents, as a percentage of total iodine were: porcine, L-T_4, 26.7%; L-T_3, 6.6%; and bovine 21.3% L-T_4; 4.3% L-T_3. The molar ratios, L-T_4/L-T_3, were porcine thyroid 2.96 and bovine thyroid 3.71.

4. Rat

Pitt-Rivers and Rall (1961) determined the percentage content of iodinated compounds in the rat thyroid glands as follows: iodide, 13%; monoiodotyrosine, 20%; diiodotyrosine, 46%; L-T_4, 18%; and L-T_3, 3%. In the blood, L-T_4 constituted 94.5 and 92.2%; and L-T_3, 4.2 and 4.4%.

Stolc (1962) reported 10.69% L-T_4 and 5.28% L-T_3 on a molecular basis in thyroids of rats and 20.02 of L-T_4 and 7.51% in thyroids of guinea pigs.

Rosenberg and La Roche (1964) compared several methods for the determination of thyroidal iodoamino acids and the effect of the time interval after ^{131}I injection. After 1 day the percentage distribution of the compounds was I, 1.8%; MIT, 22.1%; DIT, 48.8%; L-T_4, 20.1%; and L-T_3, 2.6% in a typical run.

Shimoda (1964) reported that propylthiouracil (PTU) in the rat inhibited the formation of L-T_3 and L-T_4 most easily and MIT next. In contrast, the formation of MIT and DIT was depressed in hypophysectomized animals. In animals given PTU and thyroxine, inhibition was similar.

Matsuda and Greer (1965) reported the percentage of iodinated compounds in rat thyroids as follows: I, 4–5%; MIT, 45–50%; DIT, 25–30%; L-T_3, 3–4%; and L-T_4, 15–18%.

Pitt-Rivers (1966) determined the ^{131}I uptake and distribution of [31]I in the iodoamino acids of the thyroid glands of rats fed a low iodine diet and small amounts of goitrogenic chemical. After 4 and 16 hours, the labeled MIT was inversely proportional, and the DIT and L-T$_4$ content directly proportional to the ^{131}I uptake.

Heninger and Albright (1966) compared the ^{131}I compounds in normal and iodine-deficient rats under steady-state conditions. In the control rats 20.1% of the total radioactivity was MIT; DIT, 37.1%; L-T$_4$, 26.6%; L-T$_3$, 3.3%. In the iodine-deficient animals 22.5% was MIT, 26.8% DIT, 14.9% was L-T$_4$ and L-T$_3$ was 8.9%. These data indicate that in the iodine-deficient animals the L-T$_3$ increases.

Nagataki et al. (1966) noted a progressive increase of organic iodine in the rat thyroid when fed graded chronic doses of iodide up to 405 μg/20 gm but declined with larger doses.

Emrich et al. (1966) observed that both exogenous TSH and that stimulated by sodium perchlorate caused a change in the L-T$_4$/L-T$_3$ ratio in favour of L-T$_3$ in rats and rabbits.

Cowan and Margossian (1966) reported that severe protein depletion caused a marked reduction in thyroid growth accompanied by a suppression of thyroidal activity. No impairment of L-T$_4$ synthesis was noted, as indicated by the distribution of the iodinated amino acids of thyroid digests.

V. Thyrocalcitonin

In addition to the iodinated hormones of the thyroid gland, it is now suggested that a second type of hormone is secreted by the parafollicular or "C" cells. It is called thyrocalcitonin and has been extracted from the thyroid glands of man, monkey, domestic animals, dog, and rat. This hormone causes a reduction in Ca blood level and is believed to act in conjunction with the parathyroid hormone in maintaining a normal Ca level.

VI. Iodinated Compounds in Thyroid Venous Blood

In a study of sheep, Taurog et al. (1956) reported that ^{131}I compounds secreted by the thyroid gland were more readily identifiable in thyroid venous blood than in the peripheral circulation. Thus L-T$_3$, which could not be identified in the peripheral circulation was detected in thyroid venous blood. It was observed that ^{131}I-labeled iodotyrosines were not detectable in thyroid venous blood even at a time when MIT-^{131}I and DIT-^{131}I comprised the largest fraction of the thyroid-^{131}I.

It has been suggested by Pitt-Rivers and Rall (1961) that all the L-T$_3$ in the blood is derived from the T^3 in the thyroid and that L-T$_3$ is secreted from the thyroid in the same ratio to L-T$_4$ as they occur in the blood. In rat blood it was observed that if L-T$_4$ is considered 1, the proportion of T$_3$ was 0.048.

Taurog et al. (1964) collected thyroid venous blood from rabbits, cats, and dogs before and after the injection of TSH. L-T_4-^{131}I was always the major constituent with L-T_3-^{131}I in much lower concentration. Other compounds were not detectable.

When TSH was administered, after a latent period of 15–30 minutes, the L-T_4 level increased 3- to 10-fold within 1–2 hours. Iodide-^{131}I increased. L-T_3 usually showed an increase but the other iodothyronines were not detectable even at the peak of the TSH effect.

Pileggi et al. (1964) reported that column chromatographic fractionation of human serum and plasma failed to reveal detectable amounts of MIT or DIT.

Falconer and Hetzel (1964) described a method of exteriorization of the sheep thyroid allowing venous blood to be obtained. Rise in PBI[131] were noted 15–30 minutes after insertion of a cannula. Noise and barking dogs also caused increase up to 2 hours. Injection of TSH induced similar but larger increases in [131]PBI.

West et al. (1965) described a method for measuring L-T_4 in serum. The average serum L-T_4 level was 5.24 ± 1.06 $\mu g/100$ ml in 117 euthyroid subjects, 1.1 μg in 51 hypothyroid patients, and 12.9 μg in 64 hyperthyroid patients.

Matsuda and Greer (1965) determined the iodinated substances in the rat venous blood after ^{131}I injection 24 hours previously. Only iodide, L-T_4 and an inconstant amount of L-T_3 was present. Intravenous injection of 1–5 U of TSH caused a prompt rise in the quantity of iodinated compounds. DIT and occasionally MIT were detected. TSH increased L-T_3, iodide, and L-T_4 in this order.

Shimaoka and Jasani (1965) determined the ratio of L-T_3 to L-T_4 in the blood of 6 thyrotoxic and 12 thyroid cancer patients. The ratio was found to be 0.046 ± 0.004. No significant difference was found between the 2 groups of patients. When the binding properties of these hormones are considered, the contribution of L-T_3 to the metabolic effect was estimated to be one-half that of L-T_4.

A few patients have been observed where L-T_3 was the only thyroid hormone, or at least the major one (Maclagan et al., 1957; Mack et al., 1961; Rupp et al., 1959; Rupp and Paschkis, 1961; Werner et al., 1960). Shimaoka (1963) reported such a case.

Inoue et al. (1967) developed a method for perfusing the rat thyroid gland in situ and analyzing the effluent from the thyroid vein thus avoiding contamination from recirculating radioactive materials. Labeling with ^{125}I at 24 hours before, and ^{131}I at 10 minutes before, was employed. TSH added to the perfusing blood at a level of 12.5 mU/ml markedly increased the secretion of idothyronines and of iodide. The

L-T_3/L-T_4 ratio of both ^{125}I and ^{131}I were always slightly higher than the ratio of these materials found in the thyroid gland. TSH did not cause any dramatic shift in the L-T_3/L-T_4 ratio either in the thyroid gland or in the effluent.

1. Determination of L-T_4 in Blood

Murphy and Pattee (1964) described a method for the determination of serum L-T_4. The mean level was 10.1 μg/100 ml and a range from 6.1–13.8 μg. In a further study of the method, Murphy et al. (1966) reported mean values of 6.36 μg/100 ml in euthyroid men and 6.60 μg in euthyroid women. A comparison of L-T_4 and PBI values showed a correlation of $r = 0.823$. It was observed that L-T_4 decreased with Dilantin and L-T_3.therapy and increased with D-T_4 or estrogen.

West et al. (1966) described a new method for the determination of serum L-T_4. In 124 euthyroid patients the average level was 4.7 μg/100 ml, in 27 hypothyroid patients all were less than 3.1 μg while they were greater than 7.3 μg in 29 hyperthryoid patients.

Nakajima et al. (1966) described a method of determining L-T_4 in serum. Their values for hypothyroidism were 2.3 $\pm$ 0.7 μg/100 ml, euthyroid 5.7 $\pm$ 1.08, hyperthyroidism 10.9 $\pm$ 2.3 μg and in pregnancy 7.0 $\pm$ 1.31 μg.

Favino et al. (1967) described a method for the quantitative determination of L-T_3 and L-T_4 in human plasma by thin-layer chromatography after ^{131}I administration.

2. Exchange of L-T_3 and L-T_4 between Blood and Tissue

The study of factors determining cellular uptake and release of L-T_4 has resulted in the concept that binding of L-T_4 is reversible in both plasma and tissues, that only free L-T_4 crosses the cell membrane, that free and bound L-T_4 are in equilibrium in the plasma, and that the cellular uptake of L-T_4 is in inverse proportion to the number of available extracellular L-T_4 binding sites.

Gorman et al. (1966) reported that rat liver which had taken up L-T_4 from the blood in vivo 1–20 hours previously can, after isolation and perfusion, release L-T_4 to the blood, which accounted for more than 80% of the activity in the liver before perfusion, was rapidly released to the blood, and in less than 60 minutes an equilibrium was established. Concurrently with the release of unchanged L-T_4 to the blood, the liver conjugated L-T_4 with glucuronide and excreted this in the bile and deiodinated some L-T_4 and added the iodide to the blood.

Livers from rats given L-T_3-^{131}I released only a small amount of L-T_3 to the blood, but deiodination and conjugation were greater compared to L-T_4.

VII. Transport of Thyroid Hormones

The transport of thyroid hormones from the sites of production in the thyroid gland to those of their utilization by the tissues will be described. The exact mechanism by which L-T_4 and L-T_3 pass from the thyroid tissue into the blood is not known. The serum protein-bound iodine (PBI) determination indicates that almost all the circulating hormone is bound to serum proteins.

Gordon et al. (1952) first described the migration of thyroxine in human serum during electrophoresis in a zone between the α_1- and α_2-globulins. This fraction has been called the thyroxine (L-T_4)-binding globulin (TBG). Ingbar (1958) noted that L-T_4 also migrated with a prealbumin fraction. This fraction has been called L-T_4-binding prealbumin (TBPA). Both proteins bind L-T_4 avidly. Human serum albumin (HSA) also binds L-T_4.

Hollander et al. (1962) reported that human serum was bound about 46% by TBG, TBPA 30%, and albumin 20% of L-T_4-[131]I.

Oppenheimer et al. (1963) reported that when a small quantity of L-T_4-^{131}I is added to normal human serum in glycine-acetate buffer, approximately 60% is bound to TBG, 30% to TBPA, and 10% to albumin. The total binding capacities of these proteins at saturation concentrations of L-T_4 are in reverse order. The maximum binding capacity of TBG was about 25 μg/100 ml of serum, and that of TBPA 250–300 μg/100 ml. Ross and Tapley (1966) studied the ability of a number of analogs of L-T_4 to inhibit the binding of L-T_4 to TBG and TBPA. A high concentration of L-T_4-[131]I (250 μg/100 ml) was used. For optimal binding to TBG, the alanine side chain appears to be essential, and the amino group appears to be the essential constituent. The substituted diphenyl ether structure, with a free or methylated phenolic hydroxyl, is necessary for normal binding. For optimal binding to TBPA, the alanine side chain appears not to be essential; the amino group in the side chain may, in fact, inhibit binding. The diiodo-substituted phenolic ring with the hydroxyl group in the 4'-position appears to be necessary for optimal binding. The diphenyl ether structure is not essential.

Mitchell et al. (1964) studied factors affecting the transport of L-T_3-^{131}I by serum proteins. It was shown that the uptake of L-T_3 by TBG was reduced significantly in hyperthyroidism and increased in myxedema and in pregnancy. In hyperthyroidism, after treatment with ^{131}I or goitrogens, the low TBG-T_3-^{131}I values gradually increased, whereas in myxedema thyroid therapy caused the elevated TBG-T_3-^{131}I values to decline.

Tata (1963a) suggested that the main physiological implications of thyroxine-binding by serum proteins are that (a) it represents a mechanism of transport of the hormones to tissue cells since only the free fraction of hormones is available for diffusion into tissues; (b) a change in the level of TBG, or total number of thyroxir ?-binding sites, will affect the disappearance rates of thyroid hormones and their circulating level via the pituitary feedback system; (c) relative potencies or speeds of action, of analogs of thyroxine, will be influenced by the speed with which they enter into tissues and, hence, the relative intensities of binding to serum proteins.

It has been suggested the binding of the thyroid hormones and serum protein is a reversible process most probably governed by electrostatic forces. TBG binds L-T_4 with such a high affinity that only 1/1000 of the hormone is free. Its binding capacity is very limited, however, because TBG is present only as a trace protein. There is a high degree of specificity in the binding of the analogs by TBG, TBPA, and albumin.

Hershman (1963) reported that salicylates, dinitrophenol, estradiol as well as a number of thyroxine analogs inhibit the binding of L-T_4 to serum protein in the rat (see also Christensen, 1960).

Cuaron and Fucugauchi (1964) described the binding of L-T_3-^{131}I by serum protein involving Sephadex column chromatography, and the separation of free iodide, free L-T_3 and protein-bound L-T_3 makes possible the estimation of the binding of L-T_3 to serum. A high degree of accuracy in the diagnosis of thyroid function was demonstrated.

Nicoloff et al. (1964) reported that 6 members of a family showed the near absence of TBG. The defect appeared to be transmitted as a Mendelian autosomal dominant.

Nikolai and Seal (1966) observed absent or reduced TBG in 3 generations of a family. Ten male members had no detectable TBG and 8 females, heterogeneous for the trait, varied from very low to normal. It was suggested that the mode of transmission was a sex-linked or X-chromosome-linked dominant inheritance.

Thorson et al. (1966) presented evidence that TBG is composed of two parts, TBG-1 and TBG-2, of different molecular size and with different L-T_3 and L-T_4 binding affinities.

Lightfoot and Christian (1966) studied the binding of L-T_4 and diphenylhydantoin to human serum proteins. Both compounds were bound to albumin and 2α-globulin arcs. L-T_4 alone was bound to prealbumin. They suggest that at least 4 serum components bind L-T_4.

Oppenheimer and Werner (1966) administered high doses of prednisone to 5 patients. It caused a progressive increase in the maximal binding capacity of TBPA and a decline in the binding capacity of TBG.

No change in the net binding of L-T_4 to plasma proteins was observed.

Nikolai and Seal (1966) reported that 8 male members of a 3-generation family had no detectable TBG binding activity for either L-T_4 or L-T_3. The 13 heterozygous females had binding activity varying from low to normal but always present. The L-T_4 $t_{1/2}$ was 3.8 days compared to normal of 6–8 days. Estrogen treatment had no effect on the males, but the females responded. It is believed that the trait is transmitted by X-chromosome-linked dominant inheritance.

Jones and Seal (1967) reported that 2 males and 7 females of a family had elevated TBG, PBI, and serum L-T_4 content. The resin L-T_4 uptake was decreased. The free L-T_4 was normal. Estrogen further increased the TBG. It was suggested that transmission of the trait was X-chromosome-linked codominant inheritance.

It has been reported that estrogen tends to increase the L-T_4-binding capacity of TBG while androgens tend to decrease the binding capacity. Braverman et al. (1967) reported serum from females had a higher L-T_4 binding capacity of TBG and a lower capacity for TBPA than in males. The resin-sponge uptake of L-T_3 was slightly but significantly lower in serum from females than from males.

Braverman and Ingbar (1967) reported that doses of 40–50 mg/day of norethandrolone decreased the L-T_4 binding of TBG and increased the binding capacity of TBPA; however, the total daily L-T_4 disposal was not significantly changed.

Goldsmith et al. (1967) reported that maximal L-T_4 binding capacity for TBG fell with increasing maturation in male adolescents, while TBPA capacity rose in both sexes. The slight change in serum PBI with sexual maturity correlated directly with the slight change in TBG binding capacity. No correlation between PBI and TBPA binding was observed as maturity progressed.

Imarisio and Greco (1964) observed that pure γ-globulin bound L-T_3 at two levels of tenacity, weak and strong. Albumin had only a strong binding capacity. It was suggested that the weak binding capacity was the source of the "free" hormone fraction.

1. Free L-T_4 Content of Serum

Since it has been suggested that only the free form of L-T_4 is available to the tissues, methods of estimating the free L-T_4 have been reported.

Sterling and Hegedus (1962) estimated that 0.11% of L-T_4 was free, whereas Ingbar et al. (1965) lowered the estimate to 0.050, Sterling and Brenner (1966) to 0.046, and Oppenheimer and Surks (1964) to 0.024%. Schussler and Plager (1967) reported removing a contaminant and observed that free L-T_4 of 21 normal patients was $0.026 \pm 0.004\%$ of serum protein-bound L-T_4.

These methods have been reviewed by Lee *et al.* (1964) and a new method for estimating free L-T_4 is described. Oppenheimer and Surks (1964) reported that the free thyroxine is, in large measure, independent of the dilution of the serum.

Surks and Oppenheimer (1964) reported that the free thyroxine increased a mean of 63% after surgery (range 37–125%). The maximum was reached on postoperative days 2 to 5 and returned to normal by the postoperative days 8–28.

Clark and Horn (1965) suggested that the free thyroxine could be estimated by multiplying the PBI by the resin uptake of L-T_3-^{131}I. The free thyroxine index is suggested to indicate the true thyroid status.

Marks (1965) suggested that free L-T_4 is elevated in 3- to 5-day-old infants.

Liewendahl and Lamberg (1965) described a method of estimating free thyroxine by dialysis and Sephadex G 25 filtration.

Osorio and Myant (1965) described experiments on monkeys in which the injection of L-T_4 and salicylate on the binding and on its excretion in bile was studied. The results were consistent with the hypothesis that only free L-T_4 in the plasma is extracted by the liver.

De Nayer *et al.* (1966) determined that the amount of free L-T_4 in maternal and cord blood was the same. Malvaux *et al.* (1966) reported free L-T_4 concentration decreases in adolescents as compared to adults and especially in the late stage of sexual maturity. TBPA maximal binding capacity and blood concentration are reduced at the beginning of puberty.

Shambaugh and Beisel (1967) reported a rise in free L-T_4 within 24 hours during acute infection in man. In the tularemia group the elevation persisted for 3 days, then fell to a level below normal. The PBI fell within 24 hours and persisted below normal.

Haibach and McKenzie (1967) measured the ratio of free to protein-bound L-T_4 and the concentration of the free hormone in the serum of rats before and after a standard operative stress. Both indices were increased postoperatively. The ratio was elevated maximally after 40–42 hours.

Inada and Sterling (1967) studied L-T_4 transport in 16 cases of active acromegaly. All patients showed elevated plasma HGH. The sera of 5 patients had significantly elevated TBPA and diminished free L-T_4 values. In 6 others diminished TBG was noted with normal free L-T_4. Because of low PBI values, the free L-T_4 iodine was diminished in 5 of 6 and low normal in the sixth. Hollander *et al.* (1967a) presented evidence indicating that an elevation of long-chain fatty acids was associated with an increase in free L-T$_3$ and L-T$_4$.

Volpert *et al.* (1967) reported that commercial L-T$_4$-^{131}I contained 3.7% of 3,5,3'-L-T$_3$ and 5.4% of 3,3',5'-L-T$_3$ thus contributing to the error of measuring free L-T$_4$. L-T$_4$-^{125}I was found to contain much smaller amounts of contaminants.

2. Thyroglobulin in Human Serum

It has been assumed that thyroglobulin does not leave the thyroid gland. It has been shown recently that the lymphatics draining the thyroid gland contain thyroglobulin (Daniel *et al.*, 1966, 1967).

Evidence for the presence of a "thyroglobulin-like" substance in some normal human serum has been reported. Roitt and Torrigiani (1967) reported positive evidence of undegraded thyrogobulin in 60% of normal sera, while the serum of athyreotic cretins gave negative results.

3. Iodinated Compounds in Lymph Fluid

Eichoff and Herberhold (1965) describe a method for obtaining lymph fluid from men. By paper chromatography, it was possible to demonstrate the presence of MIT, L-T$_3$, and L-T$_4$, thus indicating that lymph is a pathway for the transport of thyroid hormones.

4. Thyroxine-Binding Protein in Other Species

Farer *et al.* (1962) reported that the baboon and chimpanzee had thyroxine-binding patterns very similar to man. The rhesus monkey exhibited a variation in its prealbumin fraction.

Ungulates (cattle, sheep, swine, goat, horse, and mule) showed a sharp peak in α-globulin (TBG) and very little in albumin (TBPA). In cattle and swine no TBPA was detected.

Tata and Shellabarger (1959) reported that chicken and duck blood lacks the specific thyroxine-binding protein (TBG). Further, the serum albumin fraction of chicken and duck blood bind L-T$_4$ and L-T$_3$ with almost identical intensities.

Balfour and Tunnicliffe (1960) reported that a prealbumin component binds L-T$_4$ in the duck.

Heninger and Newcomer (1964), however, reported in the fowl that L-T$_4$ is bound more extensively and firmly than L-T$_3$.

Hutchins (1965) reported that *in vitro* erythrocyte L-T$_3$-^{131}I uptake was not useful for the measurement of thyroid function in fowls.

5. Thyroid Function Test Using Red Cells or Resin

As a by-product of the study of the protein-binding of L-T$_3$ and L-T$_4$ and the concept of the importance of the free forms of these hormones, a series of studies have been reported concerning the absorption of L-T_3-^{131}I by red cells or by resin.

Hamolsky *et al.* (1957) presented a method of incorporating L-T_3-^{131}I in human 'erythrocytes when added to whole blood and incubated; the radioactivity was measured in separated washed red cells as a percentage of whole blood radioactivity corrected to a hematocrit reading of 100. In euthyroid subjects the uptake ranged from 10.3–17.0%, average 13.9%. Hyperthyroid patients ranged from 16.4–34.2%, average 21.9%. Hypothyroid, 5–11%, average 9.3%.

Adams *et al.* (1960) suggested an improved hematocrit correction, and Barrett *et al.* (1960) studied the effect of various erythrocyte abnormalities.

Saxena *et al.* (1964) adapted this method for evaluation of thyroid function in rats.

Carter *et al.* (1964) observed that the RBC ^{131}I-L-T_3 binding coefficient was increased in rabbits after administration of phenylhydrazine. The induced reticulocytosis (immature red cells) is suggested as the cause.

Szabo and Mixner (1964) studied variables influencing the uptake of L-T_3-^{131}I from plasma by RBC of dairy cattle. The uptake was increased when incubation was carried out in tubes flushed with CO_2.

Mitchell (1958) and Mitchell and O'Rourke (1959) demonstrated distinct differences in the resin absorption of T_4-^{131}I from the serum of pregnant women and in patients with hyperthyroidism and myxedema. Later an improved resin sponge was used (Mitchell *et al.*, 1960). In the use of L-T_3-^{131}I, with hyperthyroid patients, the sponge uptake ranged from 35–57% with a mean of 44.2%. Normal patients ranged from 25–35 with a mean uptake of 30.1%. Hypothyroid patients ranged from 20–27 with a mean of 25%, and pregnant women ranged from 18–25 with a mean of 21.6%.

It is suggested that the observations indicate the competition between the resin and the binding sites of the serum proteins.

A modification of the method was suggested by Sterling and Tabachnick (1961). By their method the mean percentage uptake in hypothyroidism was 27%, normal 35%, and hyperthyroidism 53%.

Woldring *et al.* (1961) compared the use of red blood cells and resin in the uptake of L-T_4 and L-T_3 by plasma of patients. In hypothyroid patients the percentage uptake by L-T_4 was 5.1%; by L-T_3, 10.7%; in normal patients, 14.9% by L-T_4 and 20.5% by L-T_3; and in hyperthyroid patients, 22.1% by L-T_4 and 32.7% by L-T_3.

Slight modifications and standardization of conditions have been suggested by Nava and De Groot (1962) and Godden and Garnett (1964).

Levy *et al.* (1964) reported that L-T$_4$ raised the PBI while L-T$_3$ lowered it. The resin sponge uptake showed a significant uptake with L-T$_4$ therapy, but L-T$_3$ was ineffective. This difference was confirmed by an *in vitro* study.

Lemarchand-Beraud *et al.* (1964) reported that of 6 hypothyroid patients, the L-T$_3$-^{131}I uptake by the erythrocytes was low and the TBP-binding capacity was higher than normal. In 6 hyperthyroid patients, free L-T$_4$ was elevated and TBP-binding was low.

Szabo and Mixner (1964) studied some factors influencing the uptake of L-T$_3$-^{131}I from the plasma by RBC of dairy cattle. The *in vitro* uptake was increased when incubation was carried out in tubes flushed with CO_2. Antibiotic treatment of blood during storage delayed but did not prevent the decline in uptake. Storage up to 2 days had no effect.

Malkasian and Tauxe (1965) followed the uptake of L-T$_3$-^{131}I by erythrocytes during pregnancy in 201 women. By the third lunar month, the mean uptake was decreased, and by the sixth lunar month it was more than 2 standard deviations below the nonpregnant range.

Farran and Evans (1965) described a simplified method in which filter paper impregnated with resin was used as the absorbing medium.

Goolden *et al.* (1965) compared the uptake of L-T$_3$-^{131}I by the red cells and by the resin sponge test. It was shown that the two tests are comparable in their ability to distinguish between the various types of patients.

Clark and Horn (1965) compared the diagnostic accuracy of PBI, resin uptake of L-T$_3$-^{131}I and the "free thyroxine" index. PBI and resin uptake tests were highly satisfactory in the diagnosis of thyroid dysfunction but may be invalid when variations of the thyroxine-binding proteins of plasma occur.

Bois-Svensson *et al.* (1966) studied the effect of large doses of inorganic and organic iodine in 38 euthyroid patients. The resin sponge uptake was unaffected but it depressed thyroidal uptake and PBI.

Goolden *et al.* (1967) reported that the addition of methylthiouracil increased the uptake of L-T$_3$-^{131}I by the red cells in 100 thyrotoxic patients but not in 50 euthyroid patients. They have suggested that this modification of the test improves its diagnostic value in thyrotoxicosis.

Cuaron (1966) observed a normal range for the uptake of L-T$_3$ by RBC in 180 individuals to be 16–25% (mean 20.8%). Values below 16% are indicative of hypothyroidism, and values higher than 25% are indicative of thyrotoxicosis. The normal range for the binding of labeled L-T$_3$ to serum proteins was 80–91% (mean 85.5%). Values below 80 are indicative of thyrotoxicosis, and values higher than 91% are indicative of hypothyroidism. Among 400 subjects the uptake of L-T_3 by RBC was in agreement with clinical diagnosis in 359 or 89.8% while the binding of L-T_3 to serum protein agreed with the diagnosis in 383 or 95.8%.

Clark and Horn (1966) reported a significant negative correlation between PBI and resin uptake in euthyroid and pregnant subjects and a significant positive correlation in thyrotoxicosis.

Clark and Crispell (1967) pointed out that the resin uptake of L-T_3-^{131}I was considerably less from heparinized plasma than from serum.

Starr and Nicoloff (1967) reported the mean PBI of 437 Negro school children was 6.4 ± 0.06 μg/100 ml while 614 Caucasian children had a mean of 5.6 ± 0.07. Comparison of L-T_3-^{131}I red cell uptake values demonstrated a significant depression in the Negro children. TBG saturation capacities of Caucasian children were 24.7 ± 0.6 for ages 6–11 years and 21.3 ± 1.1 for ages 12–19, which were not different from adult values (22.9 ± 0.8). In Negros these values were 28.9 ± 0.7, and 25.4 ± 1.9, which were significantly higher. TBPA values were significantly depressed in adolescent children below the adult value, but no racial difference was observed.

Blomstedt and Einhorn (1967) gave euthyroid patients large doses of cortisone. The mean serum volume increased 21%. The PBI in a given volume decreased but the PBI in the total volume of serum was unchanged. The resin sponge uptake decreased, but the decrease was lower than expected from the volume change. Within 3 days after withdrawal the initial values returned.

Schatz et al. (1967) fasted 11 obese patients for 21–27 days. Weight loss was 0.98 lb/day. No significant change in PBI or total serum L-T_4 was observed. There was an increase in L-T_3 resin uptake, a decrease in TBG and TBPA in 8/11 patients and a rise in free L-T_4.

Siegel and Sachs (1964) reported that the leukocyte concentrates much greater amounts of ^{131}I, L-T_3, and L-T_4 as compared to the erythrocyte.

6. TBG in Early Neonatal Period

Hunter and Chow (1962) studied the *in vitro* uptake of L-T_3-^{131}I by erythrocytes in newborn infants; in 14 infants 6–72 hours old the range was 15.2–31.2% with most values over 20%.

Slebodzinski (1965a,b) studied the interaction between L-T_3-^{131}I and TBG in pigs from 12 hours to 11 days, and up to 6 months. There was a sharp decline in uptake shortly after birth, and at the end of a week uptake was similar to that in pigs 1–6 months old. A similar relation was found in lambs. These observations indicate a high level of free thyroxine in very young pigs.

Florsheim *et al.* (1966) reported that ^{131}I uptake showed a marked peak immediately after birth in the rat. Hormone stores dropped to stable levels by day 4. An increase in hepatic GPD suggested increased hormone secretion about the time of birth. MIT declined just before birth but recovered by day 3.

Geloso and Bernard (1967) concluded that the thyroid gland of the fetal rat (21 days) is the main source of hormone in fetal blood. Thyroidectomy of the mother did not alter the BEI level of the fetuses. The ablation of the fetal thyroid markedly decreased fetal BEI both in intact and thyroidectomized mothers. Some maternal hormone passes through the placenta into the fetus but is too limited to compensate for the absence of the fetal gland.

VIII. Placental Transfer of L-T$_4$ and L-T$_3$

1. Rabbits

Hall and Myant (1956) and Myant (1958) reported that thyroid hormones are transferred and that L-T$_3$ passed more readily than L-T$_4$ in all stages of pregnancy.

2. Guinea Pigs

Peterson and Young (1952) presented evidence for transfer of L-T$_4$ whereas Hirvonen and Lybeck (1956) presented evidence to the contrary. London *et al.* (1963) reported that L-T$_3$ did not pass from maternal to fetal circulation whereas L-T$_4$ appeared to pass in small amounts.

D'Angelo (1966) reported that propylthiouracil administered to guinea pigs during the last weeks of pregnancy induced pituitary and thyroid enlargement of the offspring.

3. Rat

Knobil and Josimovich (1959) gave indirect evidence of greater placental permeability to L-T$_4$ than L-T$_3$ based on the greater suppressive action of L-T$_4$ on fetal goiter. Nataf *et al.* (1956) reported L-T$_3$ radioactivity in fetal plasma to be one-half that of the mother within 1 hour and near equilibrium within 2 hours.

Roy and Kobayashi (1962) injected L-T$_4$-^{131}I into rats on day 20 of pregnancy, and maternal and fetal blood was examined 24 hours later. L-T$_3$ of mother and fetus was similar, but L-T$_4$ was only one-half that of mother. Both hormones were concentrated by the placenta, but L-T$_3$ was 15-fold more than L-T$_4$.

Fisher *et al.* (1964) in a study of placental transport of L-T$_4$ concluded that maternal-fetal placental transport of L-T$_4$ in human term gestation is limited by the increased concentration of maternal TBG as well as by an inherent placental impermeability to L-T$_4$.

The reader is referred to a panel discussion of hyperthyroidism in pregnant women and the neonate with Werner (1967) as moderator.

IX. Biological Responses to L-T$_4$ and L-T$_3$

The physiological effects of thyroid hormones may be observed by thyroidectomy and graded replacement therapy. Because of variation in the TSR of normal animals, many animals respond in various ways to the injection of L-T$_4$ and L-T$_3$.

In addition to the recognized effects upon body growth, mammary gland growth and lactation, blood composition, metabolism, reproductive physiology, and pituitary function, other effects have been observed recently which will be reviewed.

A. Effect of L-T$_4$ on Endochondral Osteogenesis

Fell and Mellanby (1955) observed a stimulatory effect of L-T$_4$ on the *in vitro* culture of chick long-bone rudiments showing that L-T$_4$ acts directly on the skeletal rudiments.

Riekstniece and Asling (1966) studied the possibility that thyroxine is required to support the chondrogenetic effects of growth hormone in endochondral osteogenesis. It was observed that L-T$_4$ in doses of 0.25 and 0.5 μg/day in rats (a) restored vigorous endochondral osteogenesis in thyroidectomized rats, (b) increased their pituitary GH content to normal, and (c) in hypophysectomized-thyroidectomized rats augmented the effect of a dose of GH to equal that when the GH dose was given alone to hypophysectomized rats.

It is generally accepted that L-T$_4$ increases the rate of bone formation and resorption and raises the levels of plasma and urinary calcium. Thus the action of L-T$_4$ and parathyroid hormone on Ca metabolism are qualitatively similar. Gabbiani *et al.* (1967) reported that pretreatment with L-T$_4$ in the rat inhibits the calcification of the kidney, heart, and aorta produced by parathyroid extract over dosage. In animals receiving parathyroid extract, thyroxine decreases calcemia and increases phosphatemia and phosphaturia without affecting the urinary excretion of Ca and the plasma clearance of both electrolytes.

B. L-T₄ AND THYROCALCITONIN

Gittes and Irvin (1966) reported that parathyroidectomized rats counteracted the hypercalcemia induced by intraperitoneal injection of Ca more rapidly than thyro-parathyroidectomized rats whether L-T$_4$ treated or not. It suggests that the thyroid alone, in the absence of all parathyroid secretion, effects a Ca-lowering response in hypercalcemia, presumably by the release of thyrocalcitonin.

C. EFFECT OF L-T₄ AND ANALOGS ON PROTEIN SYNTHESIS

Dutoit (1952) reported that the incorporation of radioactive alanine in protein by liver slices was depressed after thyroidectomy and stimulated after the administration of large doses of thyroxine.

Sokoloff and Kaufman (1959, 1961) demonstrated that L-T$_4$ either administered *in vivo* or added directly to the incubation mixtures *in vitro* stimulated the rate of amino acid incorporation into protein in cell-free liver preparations from normal rats. Thyroidectomy resulted in a reduction in the rate of amino acid incorporation into protein.

Studies of the mechanism have localized the stimulation to the step in protein synthesis involving the transfer of soluble-RNA-bound amino acid to microsomal protein. It does not appear to be secondary to an effect on the generation of GTP, ATP, or GSH, known or suspect co-factors in this step.

Stein and Gross (1962) reported that the microsomal system derived from the livers of thyroidectomized rats showed a marked reduced ability to incorporate L-leucine-^{14}C into protein. This effect was corrected by pretreatment of thyroidectomized rats with L-T$_3$ but not with growth hormone.

Michels *et al.* (1963) treated rats with L-T$_4$ and increased the incorporation *in vivo* of radioactive amino acids into the protein of liver, kidney, and heart but not spleen, testis, or brain. The effects among the organs was the same as that observed in L-T$_4$ stimulation of oxidative metabolism.

Blockade of protein synthesis and, therefore, also the L-T$_4$ effect on protein biosynthesis by puromycin acutely restores the increased metabolic rate of thyroxine-treated rats to the euthyroid level (Weiss and Sokoloff, 1963) or prevents the stimulation of O_2 consumption in hypothyroid rats by L-T$_3$ (Tata, 1963b).

Campbell *et al.* (1964) reported that D-T$_4$ administered *in vivo* was without effect but when added to the reaction mixture it was as effective as L-T$_4$. L-T$_3$ and tetraiodothyroacetic acid stimulated amino acid incorporation after both *in vivo* and *in vitro* administration. *In vivo* both are as active as L-T$_4$, but *in vitro* L-T$_3$ has only a fractional part of the activity of L-T$_4$, and tetraiodothyroacetic acid is effective at one-fourth the level of L-T$_4$. The analogs have the following order of effectiveness L-T$_4$, L-T$_3$, L-T$_2$. Thyronine is without effect. The acetic and propionic acid side chains are about equal.

Brown (1966) noted that L-T$_4$ stimulated amino acid incorporation into protein of muscle cells associated with an increase in oxygen consumption. The effect as it applies to microsomes is dependent upon the presence of mitochondria and an oxidizable substrate.

Buchanan and Tapley (1966) showed that rat liver mitochondria free of soluble RNA and ribosomes incorporated amino acids into acid precipitable material when incubated with K, Mg, inorganic phosphate, and an oxidizable substrate. L-T$_4$ and a number of its analogs, added *in vitro* markedly stimulated this incorporation. This effect is depressed by low concentrations of chloramphenicol, puromycin, and tetracycline. High concentrations of ribonuclease and deoxyribonuclease were not inhibitory.

D. Effect of L-T$_4$ on Fowl Growth and Egg Production

Hendrich and Turner (1966) destroyed the thyroid glands with ^{131}I in day-old Cornish-cross chicks of both sexes. L-T$_4$ was then injected in increasing levels from 0.25–3.0 μg/100 gm daily for 8 months. The mean TSR of the control males was 1.03 μg, and for the females 0.86 μg at both 8 and 12 weeks of age. The control females at 18 weeks of age weighed 2758 gm whereas the birds without replacement weighed 1703 gm. The control males weighed 3658 gm and without replacement 1850 gm. The groups that received 1 μg of L-T$_4$/100 gm/day were most similar to the control birds. At autopsy, weights of the various glands and organs were determined. At the highest level of L-T$_4$, the males appeared to be more sensitive than the females.

Miller *et al.* (1962) destroyed the thyroid glands of cross-bred chicks. At 2 weeks of age 1 and 3 μg/100 gm were injected on alternate days until 24 weeks of age. Starting at this time egg production was measured. At these levels of L-T$_4$, little effect on body weight or egg production was observed compared to controls. Cessation of injection caused the birds to go out of production within 4 weeks. When high levels of hormone were given, it caused pullets to stop laying and start a rapid molt. A mortality of 47% resulted.

E. Effect of L-T₄ on Growth of Fish

Earlier reports on the effectiveness of L-T$_4$ in stimulating growth of fish were negative; however, Barrington *et al.* (1961) reported that the immersion of yearling rainbow trout in L-T$_4$ solution or the feeding of thyroid powder had a markedly stimulatory effect upon growth in weight and length.

F. Effect of L-T₄ on the Pituitary

MacLeod (1965) reported that a goitrogen decreased the rate of growth of a pituitary tumor. No growth occurred after thyroidectomy but implantation of thyroid glands or L-T$_4$ caused a prompt restoration of growth. Thyroidectomy of rats bearing large pituitary tumors caused an immediate cessation of further growth.

Tonoue and Yamamoto (1967a) reported that the uptake of the unmetabolizable α-aminoisobutyric acid was stimulated by thyroidectomy in the rat and this uptake was eliminated by L-T$_4$ treatment. In a further study (1967b) it was shown that thyroidectomy, orchiectomy, or adrenalectomy all enhanced alanine-^{14}C incorporation into pituitary proteins. In thyroidectomized rats, L-T$_4$ suppressed increased incorporation within 3 hours.

The pituitary differs from other tissues such as the liver, kidney, heart, skeletal muscles and intestine in which thyroidectomy decreases and L-T$_4$ increases incorporation of amino acids.

G. Effect of L-T₄ on Pituitary Lactogenic Hormone

Grosvenor (1961) determined the lactogenic hormone level in the AP of normal and ovariectomized rats. Injection of tapazole for 2 weeks caused a large reduction of hormone. When L-T$_4$ at 1.5 μg/100 gm per day was given there was an increase in lactogen considerably above the normal level. When 2.5 μg was given no change in lactogen level was observed. Similar results were obtained in ovariectomized rats.

H. Metabolic Rate

Thyroxine normally stimulates an increase in basal metabolic rate. In pigeons suffering from a thiamine deficiency this effect is absent (Rubino and Pennetti, 1957). Adrenalectomized mice also showed no response (Ganju and Lockett, 1958). Thiamine-deficient mice and adrenalectomized mice injected with thiamine were also unresponsive (Bhagat and Lockett, 1961).

Bray and Hildreth (1967) compared the calorigenic response to L-T_4 and L-T_3 in hypothyroid rats treated with either propylthiouracil or methimazole. Propylthiouracil reduced the calorigenic response to L-T_4, but methimazole did not. Neither diminished the calorigenic response to L-T_3.

I. EFFECT OF L-T_4 ON SERUM TYROSINE

Levine et al. (1962) noted the elevation of plasma tyrosine in thyrotoxic patients.

Rivlin and Levine (1963) reported that plasma tyrosine level in rats increased from 14.1 μg/ml to 17.1 μg when treated with L-T_4, and decreased to 11.5 μg after radiothyroidectomy. The same treatment increased hepatic tyrosine-α-ketoglutarate transaminase from 89.7 μmoles of p-hydroxyphenylpyruvic acid formed per gram dry weight per hour to 126 whereas thyroidectomy decreased enzyme activity to 44 μmoles. L-T_4 increased plasma tyrosine levels in 1–3 days, but hepatic enzyme activity was unchanged.

Melmon et al. (1964) observed elevated plasma tyrosine in 8 thyrotoxic patients. The same condition was produced in normal patients by the administration of L-T_3 which would revert to normal after withdrawal for 2 or 3 days.

Rivlin and Kaufman (1965) reported that hepatic phenylalanine hydroxylase activity remained unchanged in rats after L-T_4 administration but was reduced 27% by thyroidectomy. They suggest that the elevated level of plasma tyrosine induced by L-T_4 is not derived from an increased conversion from phenylalanine.

Malamos et al. (1966) determined the serum tyrosine level in 22 normal patients, 17 with nontoxic goiter, 10 with hypothyroidism, 37 with thyrotoxicosis, and 8 old patients. Low values were obtained in hypothyroidism and high values in thyrotoxicosis, with little overlap with euthyroid subjects. Vitamin C reduced the high values of tyrosine to normal levels.

J. EFFECT OF L-T_4 ON ERYTHROPOIESIS

Earlier workers suggested that the role of the thyroid hormones in the process of erythropoiesis was related to the increase in the metabolic rate and oxygen need (Meineke and Crafts, 1959). However, Donati et al. (1964) reported that comparable increased erythrocyte-^{59}Fe was observed with both L-T_3 and D-T_3. Since D-T_3 causes little increased oxygen utilization, it was suggested that the stimulation of erythropoiesis was not dependent upon increased oxygen need.

In a recent study Meineke and Crafts (1964) altered their previous position. They reported that thyroxine has an effect on erythropoiesis, as judged by ^{59}Fe uptake, which is greater than would be expected from its influence upon oxygen consumption.

Donati et al. (1966) extended their study of L-T$_3$ and D-T$_3$ and observed similar increases in RBC-^{59}Fe incorporation in polycythemic rats at levels of 25, 100, or 250 μg. The ^{59}Fe was minimally increased at 24 hours and continued to increase 48 and 72 hours after a single dose of either. They suggested that increased erythropoietin production is not the mechanism involved.

Shalet et al. (1966) questioned this suggestion and concluded that it is improbable that the erythropoietic effect of L-T$_3$ is exerted by an intermediate other than erythropoietin.

Hollander et al. (1967b) induced hypothyroidism in dogs with ^{131}I. The depressed BMR was restored to normal or above with L-T$_4$ and dinitrophenol. The total red cell volume returned to normal with L-T$_4$ but was unaffected by DNP, iron, copper, cobalt, pyridoxine, folic acid, and vitamin B$_{12}$ therapy. It is suggested that there is a dissociation between BMR and erythropoiesis and that L-T$_4$ may act by some pathway other than by increasing O$_2$ consumption.

K. Effect of L-T$_4$ on Fat Metabolism

Ellefson and Mason (1962) reported that hypothyroid rats on a sterol-free diet containing 10% fat exhibited hypercholesterolemia but maintained normal levels of liver cholesterol. On the same diet hyperthyroid rats maintained subnormal concentrations of nonesterified cholesterol in plasma and greater than normal concentrations in liver. Hepatic levels of lipid phosphorus and total fatty acids were higher than those in normal rats.

Ellefson and Mason (1964) reported that L-T$_4$·administered to intact rats promoted increases in the hepatic concentration of all fatty acids with increases of palmitate and oleate especially great. In plasma, the proportion of stearate and arachidonate increased while the proportion of oleate and linoleate decreased. In hypophysectomized rats, L-T$_4$ had the same effect on hepatic concentration of stearate and arachidonate, but oleate and linoleate decreased. Thyroidectomized rats had greater than normal concentrations of fatty acids of intermediate molecular weight in liver, but the hepatic concentration of total fatty acids were normal.

L. EFFECT OF L-T_4 ON CHOLESTEROL SYNTHESIS

Rosenman *et al.* (1952) noted that thyroid hormone led to an increase in the amount of cholesterol excreted in the bile of rats. Fletcher and Myant (1958) showed that cholesterol synthesis was increased by liver slices *in vitro* in rats when treated with L-T_4 before the liver was removed. In later work Fletcher and Myant (1962) reported also a decrease in fatty acid synthesis in liver slices, a marked decline in glycogen, and a moderate fall in ATP. It is suggested that glycogen plays an essential role in the synthesis of lipids, supplying the energy for the regeneration of ATP.

It has been recognized that thyroxine analogs have an effect on the heart rate and on serum cholesterol. The discovery of analogs which would have a maximum effect in lowering serum cholesterol and a minimal effect on heart rate would be desirable. Boyd and Oliver (1960b) reported that this is true of some iodothyronines. In human subjects D-T_4 was found to be worthy of further clinical assessment (Boyd and Oliver, 1960a). Study of thyroxine analogs in relation to serum cholesterol in rats has been reported by Cuthbertson *et al.*, 1960 (see also McClure *et al.*, 1961; Starr *et al.*, 1960).

Ruegamer and Silverman (1961) reported that a dietary concentration of 5 μg % of 3,5-diiodothyroacetic acid (Dioc) was optimal for the prevention of elevated liver cholesterol and lipid concentration in rats fed a high fat diet containing 1% cholesterol.

Kritchevsky *et al.* (1961) reported that 3,5,3′-triiodothyropropionic acid (Triprop), D-T_3, and L-T_4 lowered the serum and liver cholesterol levels of the rat.

Nichols (1962) reported that triiodothyropropionic acid (T_3P) lowered serum cholesterol without evident calorigenic effect.

Strand (1962) determined the effect of L-T_3, D-T_3, and propylthiouracil on the excretion of bile acids in male and female rats. It was shown that D-T_3 with minimal calorigenic effect gave the same picture as observed in hyperthyroid rats. The goitrogen treatment reduced bile acids to one-fifth normal.

Jablonski *et al.* (1962) reported that D- and L-T_4 and L-T_3 uniformly produced a fall in total serum cholesterol due to a decrease in the β-lipoprotein cholesterol fraction. No significant changes in total content or lipoprotein partition of the phospholipids or triglycerides were observed.

Thyropropionic acid (ToP) had no perceptible calorigenic or goiter prevention effect in rats at 400 mg/100 gm in the diet of rats, but it caused a 51% inhibition of acetate-1-^{14}C incorporation into liver cholesterol (Eades and Stasilli, 1963).

3,3′,5-Triiodothyropropionic acid (T_3P) in diets as low as 0.2 mg/100 gm feed elevated O_2 consumption only slightly, but produced a

27.2% lowering of serum cholesterol and inhibited acetate-1-^{14}C incorporation into liver cholesterol 36.6%. It had "thyroxine-like" activity at doses only slightly higher than L-T$_3$.

Feldman and Carter (1963) reported that D-T$_4$ in moderate doses was effective in lowering cholesterol and β-lipoprotein in 10 patients with hyperlipidemia and serum triglycerides as well. Increases in PBI and red cell L-T$_3$-^{131}I binding and suppression of thyroidal-^{131}I uptake occurred without alteration of TBG capacity. Increased BMR, pulse rate, and weight loss were observed.

Moses et al. (1964) fed Proloid at 3 up to 25 grains daily for 2-week intervals. Decreases in serum total and α- and β-lipoprotein cholesterols were noted at the 10-grain level, and eventually decreases of 20–30% were observed. α-Lipoprotein triglycerides decreased, but total and β remained unchanged.

Nejad and Chaikoff (1964) reported that glucocorticoids depressed the conversion of acetate carbon to cholesterol in the liver of hypophysectomized rats. The injection of L-T$_4$ for 14 days increased the capacity. When the two hormones were administered conversion was not observed.

Duncan et al. (1964) studied the body cholesterol of the male rat. It contained 1.72 mg/gm. Injection of either D- or L-T$_4$ resulted in an increase mainly in the skin. Thyroidectomy had no effect on total body cholesterol. Cholesterol in the diet increased the body cholesterol to 2.25 mg/gm. In cholesterol-fed rats hyperthyroidism resulted in a reduced body cholesterol due to a lower concentration in the liver.

Ruegamer (1965) reported that plasma cholesterol concentrations were reduced slightly by Diac feeding. Triac and Triprop were found to be more calorigenically active and more toxic than L-T$_4$ when fed in a high fat-cholesterol diet whereas they are known to be only 20 and 10% as active as L-T$_4$.

Felt (1966) administered L-T$_3$ to 3 age groups. In young persons serum cholesterol was low and no further lowering was observed. The level was about 165 mg/100 ml. In older age groups the initial levels were higher and were lowered in most cases by L-T$_3$.

In Vitro Technique for Detecting Cholesterol Synthesis Inhibitors

Eades and Phillips (1963) described a method for the in vitro detection of cholesterol synthesis inhibitors. In the method acetate-1-^{14}C is added to rat liver homogenate with the test compound. The degree of inhibition of the incorporation of the acetate into the nonsaponifiable fraction is used as the index. ToP and its iodinated analogs were studied. All markedly inhibited synthesis except T$_4$P.

M. Effect of L-T$_4$ on α-Glycerophosphate Dehydrogenase and Malic Enzymes

A number of rat tissue enzymes increase as a result of thyroid hormone administration but the mitochondrial α-glycerophosphate dehydrogenase (GPD) enzyme and the soluble malic enzyme show the greatest response. The largest GPD enzyme increases were observed in liver, kidney, heart, and pancreas with smaller increases in skeletal muscle, stomach, colon, and skin. No changes were detected in testis, brain, lung, spleen, and small intestine.

Comparison of BMR with GPD

Ruegamer et al. (1964) compared the BMR and liver Q_{O_2} with liver and kidney GPD. When liver and kidney GPD activities were plotted against either BMR or liver slice Q_{O_2} values, a rather good correlation was obtained as well as when the thyroid hormone level was changed. The liver and kidney GPD response was much larger than that of either BMR or the Q_{O_2} and appeared to be more sensitive and accurate for assessing the tissue response to varying levels of thyroid hormone.

Propylthiouracil (PTU) partially blocked all these effects except the kidney GPD response, and it obviously interfered with the action of L-T$_4$ by some mechanism that was separate from its inhibition of L-T$_4$ synthesis.

X. Comparison of Oral Effectiveness of Thyroid, USP and L-T$_4$ in Man

Starr and Liebhold-Schueck (1954) reported that 0.1 mg of Na L-T$_4$ had the clinical effect of 0.5 (32.5 mg) to 1 grain (65 mg) of desiccated thyroid.

Selenkow and Asper (1955) reported that doses of Na L-T$_4$ of 0.2–0.5 mg daily by mouth produced the same metabolic effects as 128–192 mg (2–3 grains) of desiccated thyroid.

Sturnick and Lesses (1961) compared desiccated thyroid (USP) and Na L-T$_4$ in 28 myxedematous patients, using PBI levels as an index: 0.1–0.2 mg of L-T$_4$ produced normal PBI levels whereas 195 mg (3 grains) of desiccated thyroid were required for the same effect.

Lavietes and Epstein (1964) reported that 60 mg thyroid USP or thyroglobulin, 0.1 mg L-T$_4$ and 0.025 mg L-T$_3$ were equally effective orally.

Oddie et al. (1964) reported that 73% of an oral dose of L-T$_4$-^{131}I was absorbed by the average subject. In a later study of 7 subjects, Oddie et al. (1965) observed a mean of 63.4%. Na L-T$_4$ was fed in doses of 100 and 200 μg/day to determine the level of total ^{131}I blockage. It was calculated that 280 μg would be required.

Fisher and Oddie (1964) noted that 85% of an oral dose of L-T$_3$ was absorbed.

XI. Comparison of Oral and Subcutaneous Administration

L-T$_3$ and L-T$_4$, desiccated thyroid tissue, thyroglobulin, and thyroactive iodinated casein are all biologically active when administered orally since the active molecule is an iodinated amino acid. The oral effectiveness of these compounds in various species differs considerably. These differences may depend upon the completeness of their absorption from the digestive tract of single-stomach species compared to ruminant animals. It may depend upon the rate of passage of food through the digestive tract, the presence of antithyrotoxic substances in the diet which bind L-T$_4$ and cause increased excretion in the feces, of soybean products, and bulk in diet.

1. Rat

Bauman and Turner (1966b) compared the biological activity of L-T$_4$, L-T$_3$, and thyroprotein (a synthetic thyroactive iodinated casein containing 1% L-T$_4$) when administered orally and by subcutaneous injection to mature male rats. With subcutaneous administration of L-T$_4$ as a standard, it was shown that L-T$_4$ given orally was 37.9% as effective. In other words, 2.5 times as much L-T$_4$ must be given orally to be as effective as by injection.

L-T$_3$ was 95% as effective as L-T$_4$ on an equimolar basis when administered orally. Since L-T$_3$ is 2.6 times as active as L-T$_4$ by injection, its oral effectiveness would be 36.9%. Thus the absorption of L-T$_3$ and L-T$_4$ is nearly the same, but since L-T$_3$ is 2.6 times as active as L-T$_4$, its biological activity is greater.

In comparison with injected thyroprotein, the oral effectiveness was 30.7% but in comparison with L-T$_4$ by injection, the oral effectiveness was 36.2%.

With these data available it is possible to determine the oral requirement of these hormones to provide dosage within the physiological range.

2. Dairy Cattle

Mixner and Lennon (1960) studied the efficiencies of absorption of orally administered L-T$_4$, thyroprotein, and porcine thyroglobulin from the gastrointestinal tracts of lactating cows by comparing the relative increase of plasma PBI from oral administration with the corresponding PBI increase due to intravenous administration of L-T$_4$.

In two trials using 7 and 6 lactating cows, the efficiency of absorption of thyroprotein was 12.3 and 13.9%, respectively. In 5 lactating cows the oral efficiency of L-T_4 and porcine thyroglobulin was 11.6 and 15.9%, respectively.

Premachandra *et al.* (1960) utilized the L-T_4 secretion rate technique for the estimation of the oral effectiveness of thyroprotein with L-T_4 by subcutaneous injection. It was shown that thyroprotein given orally was 10% as effective as when injected. Thus the feeding of 1 gm of thyroprotein is comparable to the injection of 1 mg of L-T_4.

Premachandra *et al.* (1960) compared the mean L-T_4 secretion rate of 22 milking and dry cows with their equivalent requirement of L-T_3 by injection. It was shown that L-T_3 was 2.14 times as effective biologically as L-T_4.

Bauman and Turner (1965) determined the TSR of 10 nonlactating cows using L-T_4 and thyroprotein by injection and then by oral administration. When L-T_4 was given orally, it was found to be only 9.4% as effective. L-T_3 given orally was 21.4% as effective as injected L-T_3. Thyroprotein given orally was as effective as L-T_4 given orally. The biological effectiveness was 9.9%. The oral administration of thyroprotein was found to be 11.8% as efficient as injected thyroprotein.

The low oral effectiveness of thyroprotein or L-T_4 in ruminant animals of about 10%, in comparison with effectiveness in the rat of about 36% and in fowls of about 60%, has not been explained.

Premachandra and Turner (1961) studied the rate of absorption of L-T_4-^{131}I from a subcutaneous site whereas Pipes *et al.* (1962) studied the rate of absorption after oral administration. It was shown that essentially all the L-T_4 injected subcutaneously was absorbed within a period of 24 hours, in contrast to much slower absorption from the gastrointestinal tract.

3. Fowls

Srivastava and Turner (1967b) determined the thyroid hormone secretion rate (TSR) equivalent of L-T_4, L-T_3, and thyroprotein in 4-year-old male and female New Hampshire fowls. In male birds, if the mean TSR of L-T_4 is considered 100%, L-T_3 was observed to be 2.2 times as active biologically whereas thyroprotein (containing 1% L-T_4) was 1.1 times as active. In comparison of subcutaneous and oral administration and using the former as 100%, in two trials, L-T_4 orally was 96.2 and 88.8% as active. L-T_3 was 67.5% as active, and thyroprotein 58.2%.

In females, if the mean TSR of L-T_4 is considered 100%, L-T_3 was 1.5 times as active, and thyroprotein was 1.3 times as active. In the comparison of subcutaneous and oral administration, in two trials L-T_4 was 40.7 and 68.7% as effective orally, L-T_3 was 55.9% as effective orally, and thyroprotein 62.1% as effective.

Since the oral effectiveness of males was 58.2% and of females 62.1%, it was suggested that a value of 60% be used for thyroprotein in estimating the amount required to be added to.a poultry ration within the physiological range.

A. ANTITHYROTOXIC SUBSTANCES

Earlier studies of antithyrotoxic substances were based upon their ability to improve the poor growth rate of rats fed high levels of L-T_4. Westerfeld et al. (1962) and Richert et al. (1964) showed that the calorigenic response to dietary L-T_4 was also blocked. In a preliminary study Ruegamer (1963) reported that the antithyrotoxic factor in liver residue (LRF) interfered with the oral absorption of L-T_4-^{131}I from the gut. Plasma levels of L-T_4 were only one-half those of normal rats, and the amount of L/T_4 excreted into the feces was doubled. Ruegamer et al. (1964) reported that the antithyrotoxic effect of liver residue was evident since it partially blocked all the L-T_4 effects including the kidney GPD response. Intact rats fed chow had lower liver GPD activities than rats fed the purified basal diet. The chow probably contained some antithyrotoxic activity since the addition of L-T_4 to chow gave smaller responses than to the purified diet. These observations were confirmed and extended by Ruegamer and Wallace (1965) with both liver residue and hemoglobin. They suggest that the poor absorption is due to a more rapid passage of L-T_4 through the lower ileum and large intestine and to the formation of L-T_4 with LRF into an unavailable complex which is not absorbed.

Ruegamer et al. (1967) reported that the extent to which PBI is reduced depends upon the relative potency and dietary concentration of the antithyrotoxic substance. The reduction in PBI accounts for the decrease in the peripheral activity of the L-T_4.

Bergman et al. (1967) reported that the absorption of Na ^{131}I was diminished when cholestyramine, but not when charcoal, was,added to the diet of hamsters. When L-T_4-^{131}I was injected, body radioactivity decreased more rapidly when the diet was supplemented with charcoal because of greater excretion into the feces.

Girard et al. (1966) fed cholesterol and cholic acid in an iodine-deficient diet to young male rats. There was a great degree of thyroid enlargement. There was an increased fecal excretion of radioactivity in the supplemental diet. Since the thyroid enlargement is prevented by iodine supplementation, the cholesterol-cholic acid supplement is thought to accentuate iodine depletion either by increasing biliary excretion of L-T_4 or by interfering with intestinal resorption of L-T_4.

B. OTHER SUBSTANCES

Van Middlesworth (1957) reported that rats fed a diet rich in soy flour became goitrous and excreted 3 times as much ^{131}I in the feces after a tracer dose of L-T_4-^{131}I as did rats fed a starch-casein control diet.

Beck (1958) reported fecal excretion of more than 100% of the injected dose of L-T_4-^{131}I in soy-fed rats, while the control rats fed starch-casein excreted 70% of the dose after 90 hours.

McPherson and Albert (1961) suggest that the differences may be due to the bulk of the feces. An increase in the bulk increases and decreased bulk reduces the loss in the feces.

Sasaki and Nakajima (1962) reported increased fecal excretion of L-T_4 when young rats were fed powdered cellulose, barium sulfate, or clay to the basal diet.

Chung and Van Middlesworth (1964) studied the rate of absorption of thyroxine-^{131}I from intestine loops in the rat. From 20–50% of a tracer dose was absorbed during the first hour with little additional absorption during 3 subsequent hours. The L-T_4 remaining appeared to be bound to a large molecule, possibly plasma albumin. It was suggested that plasma proteins are constantly secreted into the intestinal lumen, to which L-T_4 becomes bound, impeding absorption. The addition of 0.1 ml of plasma to L-T_4 in the intestinal loop almost prevented absorption of L-T_4.

Bauman et al. (1967) reported that 48% of orally administered L-T_4 was effective compared to subcutaneous administration. The addition of rat blood plasma to the L-T_4 before oral administration reduced its biological effectiveness to 34%, a significant reduction of 30%.

XII. Bioassay of Thyroidal Substances

The earlier methods of bioassay of thyroidal substances are reviewed in the previous edition (Turner and Premachandra, 1962). The methods depended upon changes in metabolic rate (mouse anoxia), goiter prevention, thyroid hormone secretion rate (TSR), depression of ^{131}I uptake by the thyroid, and tadpole metamorphosis.

Wiberg et al. (1963) compared the bioassay of thyroactive material by the mouse anoxia and goiter prevention test in the same animals. They report that the goiter prevention test was the more sensitive. However, the precision reported for the mouse was not as good as that reported for the rat.

Some question was raised in regard to the use of antithyroid drugs in the goiter prevention test due to the extrathyroidal effect of thiouracil and related compounds. For a recent review of this problem, the reader is referred to Morreale de Escobar and Escobar del Rey (1967). They present evidence that thiouracil depresses both the deiodination and biological activity of L-T$_4$. They are not sure whether or not the same is true for L-T$_3$ and other analogs.

Hoffman *et al.* (1966) determined the effect of L-T$_4$, L-T$_3$, Tetrac, Triac, Tetraprop, Triprop, and isopropyl on the GPD content of various tissues of weanling male rats when fed 2-thiouracil, 6-propylthiouracil, and methimazole. L-T$_4$ reduced the response, but the other analogs were unaffected. Methimazole had no effect on L-T$_4$.

Short and Ruegamer (1966) used the GPD method to assay the relative activity of L-T$_4$ and several analogs that were either injected or fed to rats on a diet containing 10% hemoglobin (Hb). It was reported that Triac and Triprop were more active when fed in either the basal diet or with Hb than when injected whereas the converse was found for L-T$_4$ and L-T$_3$. Triac was as active as T$_3$ when both were fed in the basal diet. Dietary Hb inhibited the activity of all analogs, but marked differences were observed. L-T$_4$ fed with Hb was only 6% of that fed in the basal diet whereas oral L-T$_3$ and Triac were reduced to 30 and 64%, respectively.

Lee *et al.* (1967) reported that the level of GPD of the rat liver is greatly decreased after hypophysectomy. The level was rapidly restored after administration of a single dose of L-T$_3$. TSH given to such animals gradually increased enzyme activity depending on dose and duration. Comparison of thyroxine isomers indicated that L-T$_3$ was most active. Tetraiodothyroacetic acid and L-T$_4$ were about 80% as effective in a 24-hour period. D-T$_4$ was about one-fifth as active as L-T$_4$. MIT and DIT were inactive.

Wiberg *et al.* (1964) studied the effect of various goitrogens in the goiter prevention assay due to the claim that thiouracil-type goitrogens influence the peripheral metabolism of L-T$_4$. Assays employing either thiouracil, thiourea, aminotriazole or perchlorate led to statistically equivalent potency estimates of swine thyroids. Thiocyanate proved to be toxic at 1% of drinking water.

In the use of the TSR method, methimazole has been used to block the recycling of ^{131}I. Since it has been claimed by Grosvenor (1962) to be a goitrogen without extrathyroidal effect, its use would avoid the problem raised by the use of other goitrogens.

For those wishing to use the tadpole metamorphosis assay, the review of this problem by Frieden (1967) is suggested.

The only new method for the bioassay of thyroidal substances is based on the glycerophosphate dehydrogenase (GPD) response in the liver and kidney. Westerfield *et al.* (1965) described the method and

Hoffman *et al.* (1966), Short and Ruegamer (1966), and Lee *et al.* (1967) report results of its use with L-T$_4$ and its analogs.

XIII. Comparison of L-T$_4$ with Its Analogs

The reader is referred to the earlier edition for comparisons up to 1960 (Turner and Premachandra, 1962). Frieden (1967) has presented an excellent review on thyroid hormones and the biochemistry of amphibian metamorphosis. Frieden and Westmark (1961) pointed out that the tadpole as an assay animal showed much greater activity when immersed in the test solution. When the tadpoles were injected their relative activities were more comparable to the response of the rat.

Henriques (1962) assayed L-T$_4$ and L-T$_3$ by the use of *Xenopus* larvae made hypothyroid by the administration of thiourea. L-T$_4$ and L-T$_3$ were added as the sodium salt to the water for 3 days, and the stage of metamorphosis was determined after 7 days. L-T$_3$ was found to be 7–12 times as active as L-T$_4$. In a later study (1964) he reported that diiodotyrosine had no effect and L-T$_2$ only a small effect. The potency of Triprop was greater than that of Triac and Triac was more active than Tetrac. The relative activity of D-T$_4$ was one-seventh that of L-T$_4$. By injection L-T$_3$ was 4.5 : 1 compared to L-T$_4$.

Henriques (1964) compared the activity of thyroxine analogs by injection and immersion. Diiodotyrosine had no effect, and DIT only a small effect. The activities of Triprop, Triac, and Tetrac were difficult to estimate. D-T$_4$ was only one-seventh as active as L-T$_4$. L-T$_3$ was 9 times as active by immersion, but only 5 times as active by injection, compared to L-T$_4$.

Wahlborg *et al.* (1964) compared triiodothyronine analogs by injection and immersion in tadpoles. 3'-Isopropyl-T$_2$ was observed to be 3 times as active as L-T$_3$ by injection. All other compounds were less active.

Comparisons have been made also using the goitrogen technique and by substituting other analogs for L-T$_4$ in the TSR method.

Stasilli *et al.* (1961) fed 0.2 or 0.3% thiouracil in the diet of weanling rats to inhibit growth. Perceptible growth was induced with a minimum of 0.04 μg/100 gm body weight per day with L-T$_4$ or 3,5,3'-triiodothyropropionic acid.

Greenberg *et al.* (1963) reported that 3,5-diiodo-3'-isopropyl-L-thyronine (isopropyl L-T$_2$) was more active than L-T$_3$ by several indices. Bauman *et al.* (1965b) by the thyroid hormone secretion rate (TSR) method reported that isopropyl-L-T$_2$ was slightly more active than L-T$_3$ and 2.9 times as active as L-T$_4$.

Jorgensen and Reid (1965) using thiouracil as the goitrogenic agent reported that $3'$-Cl-L-T_2 was 27% as active as T_4 and $3',5'$-Cl$_2$-L-T_2 as less than 27 but greater than 15% by an antigoitrogen test in the rat.

Barker *et al.* (1965) evaluated a number of L-T_4 analogs primarily involving alterations in the iodo-hydroxyl-diphenyl ether portion of the L-T_4 molecule by their effect on BMR and resting heart rate in thyroid-ectomized rats. They reported that L-T_3 was 4–5 times as active as L-T_4 and that $3'$-isopropyl-3,5-diiodothyronine was 50% more potent than L-T_3.

Taylor *et al.* (1967) reported that the biological potency of an iodine-free thyroxine analog, $3'$-isopropyl-3,5-dihomo-L-thyronine, was about 7 times that of L-T_4 when estimated from its effect on the resting heart rate of thyroidectomized rats, but only about twice that of L-T_4 in its action on the tadpole or its goiter-preventing action in rats. The corresponding diiodo analog generally showed greater potency than the bromo compound.

A new method of estimating biological activity of L-T_4 and its analogs by the glycerophosphate dehydrogenase (GPD) response has been reported.

Westerfeld et al. (1965) *Method.* Groups of 8 weanling rats (50 gm) are fed a purified basal diet (see Richert *et al.*, 1964) and injected subcutaneously with 3, 6, 9, or 40 μg of L-T_4/100 gm body weight daily for 11–12 days. This provides a standard response curve. The rats are decapitated, and the GPD of the liver and kidney are determined. Enzyme values are expressed as microliters of O_2/150 mg of fresh tissue in 10 minutes.

XIV. Methods of Determining Thyroxine Secretion Rate

A. THE GOITER-PREVENTION METHOD

Dempsey and Astwood (1943) first showed that the depression of thyroid weight in thiouracil-treated rats bore a quantitative relation to the thyroxine dosage. This technique was used to determine the estimated thyroxine secretion rate at several environmental temperatures. Subsequently, the method was used extensively to determine the estimated thyroxine secretion rate of poultry, rats, mice, and goats. Data were presented by Reineke and Turner (1950) concerning these studies.

By substituting various analogs of thyroxine, the comparative biological activity in respect to goiter prevention can be determined. This technique has been used extensively.

The chief drawback in the use of this method has been the need of sacrifice of groups of animals to obtain thyroid weight (or thyroidectomy).

It is thus limited to experimental animals. Further, the estimated thyroxine secretion rate applies to groups of animals rather than to individuals, so no idea of the range in secretion rate may be obtained.

B. The Thyroidal-^{131}I Blockage Method

A technique was proposed by Pipes et al. (1950) to measure the daily output of thyroxine in rats using ^{131}I as a tracer. It was shown that the release of thyroidal-^{131}I by the rat was proportional to the amount of thyroxine daily administered. The daily level of thyroxine which inhibited TSH secretion, and thus inhibited thyroidal-^{131}I output, was estimated as the thyroxine secretion rate.

The method does not involve the sacrifice of the animals and individual thyroxine secretion rates may be determined. Domestic as well as experimental animals may be used and successive determinations under varying or constant environmental, physiological, and nutritional conditions may be made.

The details of the method as applied to various types of animals have been presented by Pipes et al. (1957) for cattle; by Henneman et al. (1952) for sheep; by Flamboe and Reineke (1957) for goats; by Biellier and Turner (1957) and Pipes et al. (1958) for fowls; by Grosvenor and Turner (1960) for pigeons; by Reineke and Singh (1955) and Grosvenor and Turner (1958) for rats; by Amin et al. (1957) and Wada et al. (1959) for mice; by Brown-Grant (1955) for rabbits.

Tanabe and Komiyama (1962) suggested a modified method of determining TSR. The TSR is estimated as that amount of L-T_4 which inhibits thiouracil-induced acceleration of ^{131}I release and returns the thyroidal-^{131}I release to the rate before thiouracil administration. It is stated that by this method TSR is about 60% of that obtained by complete ^{131}I blockage by L-T_4. It is difficult to understand how a measurement based on the recycling of ^{131}I (which thiouracil prevents) would be satisfactory for the measurment of TSR.

C. Other Methods

Post and Mixner (1961) compared several methods of measuring TSR in cattle. One method was an isotope dilution procedure based on the decline in specific activity of PBI following the injection of L-T_4-^{131}I. The normal L-T_4 turnover method was a chemical procedure based on the decline in plasma PBI after the injection of L-T_4.

TSR determined by the isotope dilution and chemical PBI methods in 14 young bull calves were 0.40 and 0.39 mg/100 lb per day, respectively. In 4 nonlactating cows the TSR was 0.14 and 0.13 mg, respectively. When the inhibition of thyroidal-^{131}I release method was used the TSR averaged 0.13 mg/100 lb.

Sorensen (1961) used a method in which the release rate of thyroidal-^{131}I and the specific activity of the circulating thyroid hormone were used for TSR calculations.

Robertson and Falconer (1961) studied several parameters of thyroid function in a group of Cheviot ewes of increasing age. Using Sorensen's TSR method, they reported that the rate constant for ^{131}I uptake and release were highly correlated with TSR. While most other students of the problem have found little relation of TSR to these indices, Robertson and Falconer suggest that they are of value when the environment and diet are controlled.

In Irving's (1967) study of the TSR of horses, he injected L-T$_4$-^{131}I and measured the radioactivity of jugular blood at 24-hour intervals, comparable to one of the methods suggested by Post and Mixner (1961).

D. GLYCEROPHOSPHATE DEHYDROGENASE RESPONSE

Ruegamer *et al.* (1964) suggested the estimate of TSR in the rat (Holtzman) by the GPD response to administered L-T$_4$. Theoretically the amount of L-T$_4$ required to reestablish euthyroid GPD levels in thyroid-ectomized rats should equal the amount of L-T$_4$-like activity produced endogenously by normal euthyroid rats. However, the liver and kidney GPD responses to small doses of L-T$_4$ were greater in thyroidectomized than in intact rats and any estimate of endogenous L-T$_4$ output from the dose-response curves for thyroidectomized rats would be too low.

This can be avoided by using the dose-response curve for intact rats because this curve reflects the sensitivity of the tissues to administered L-T$_4$. The maximum amount of L-T$_4$ that can be administered to intact rats without producing any increase in tissue GPD activity should be equivalent to the daily endogenous L-T$_4$ production because it just balances off and replaces the endogenous thyroid hormone production.

The estimated TSR by this enzyme procedure for 5 tissues was 1.0–1.5 μg/100 gm body weight per day. The average value for these adult rats was 1.25 μg.

1. Effect of Temperature on GPD

Ruegamer *et al.* (1964) estimated the TSR of male Holtzman rats by their GPD method. Rats maintained at a temperature of 5°C were more sensitive to L-T$_4$ than were rats maintained at 23°C, and the latter were more sensitive than those kept at 35°C. The TSR of normal rats was estimated at about 1 μg L-T_4/100 gm body weight per day. The TSR was increased about 50% at 5°C and practically ceased at 35°C.

2. TSR of Sheep

Griffin *et al.* (1962) determined the TSR of 6 Hampshire and 6 Shropshire rams, all 2 years of age. The mean TSR was 0.07 mg L-T_4 daily for the Shropshires, and 0.09 mg for the Hampshires. There was a 4- or 5-fold decline in TSR from the mean value in December compared to July. The decline in TSR in spring and early summer was followed by a similar decline in semen quality.

Brooks *et al.* (1962) studied the effect of varying temperature (46°–87°F) upon the TSR of 21 Hampshire rams varying in age between 1 and 3 years and in body weight between 100 and 200 lb. The 64 estimations ranged from 0.2–0.7 mg L-T_4/100 lb body weight, with a mean of 0.36 mg. Based on a regression line, the TSR ranged from 0.45 mg at 45°F to about 0.3 mg at 85°F.

Falconer and Robertson (1961) used the Sorensen method of TSR determination in a group of 5–7-year-old Cheviot ewes. They ranged from 0.132–0.564 mg/100 lb body weight, with a mean of 0.323 mg.

Brooks *et al.* (unpublished) determined the TSR of 25 Northwest ewes while they were dry, pregnant, or lactating. The TSR ranged from 0.1 to 0.6 mg/100 lb body weight, with a mean of 0.26 mg. No significant difference in TSR was found due to pregnancy or lactation.

TSR of Lambs. The TSR of 5 Cheviot and Dorset Horn lambs from 5 to 8 weeks of age were estimated by Falconer and Robertson (1961). They ranged from 0.32–1.34 mg L-T_4/100 lb body weight per day, with a mean of 0.70 mg/day. In a group of 7 lambs 5–12 months of age of the same 2 breeds, the range in TSR varied from 0.47–1.08 mg/100 lb body weight per day, with a mean of 0.84 mg L-T_4/day. On the basis of these limited observations, it was suggested that the TSR of lambs increase rapidly to the age of 6–8 months, then decline slightly with increasing age.

Brooks *et al.* (unpublished) determined the TSR of 20 lambs out of Northwest ewes in May. The lactating ewes showed a mean of TSR in April of 0.26 mg T_4/100 lb body weight. The lambs ranged from 0.3–0.5 mg/100 gm body weight per day with a mean of 0.43 mg/day. Their mean secretion rate was significantly higher than that of their dams.

3. TSR of Swine

Sorensen and Moustgaard (1957) reported the mean TSR of 60-kg pigs to be 0.7 mg per head daily. Frape *et al.* (1958) found the TSR of young pigs to be about 0.2 mg/100 lb body weight. Sorensen (1961) observed the TSR of Danish Landrace pigs to be 1.09 mg/100 kg body weight. He reported a 10-fold increase in TSR when pigs maintained at 24°C were shifted to 3°C.

Romack *et al.* (1964) determined the TSR of 213 animals of Poland China, Hampshire, Yorkshire, and Duroc breeds. The mean TSR of 60 Poland Chinas was 0.52 mg/100 lb; of 94 Hampshires, 0.40 mg; 71 Yorkshires, 0.34 mg; and 8 Durocs, 0.40 mg. The TSR of 233 determinations of pigs 2–8 months of age was 0.41 mg, compared to 24 animals 10–14 months of age of 0.19 mg. A significant positive correlation between TSR and daily rate of gain was found in Poland China males and Yorkshire pigs, but not in Poland China females or Hampshires.

4. TSR of Horses

Irvine (1967) determined the TSR of standard and thoroughbred horses under conditions in Southern New Zealand. No effect of age (over 2 years), breed, or sex was observed. The TSR was determined from the rate of degradation of $L\text{-}T_4\text{-}^{131}I$.

The TSR of resting horses was 0.49 mg $L\text{-}T_4$/1000 lb body weight. At a temperature of 2.8°C, 10 untrained horses had mean TSR of 0.58 mg. The effect of training was determined. Untrained had a TSR of 0.49 mg, in partly trained horses TSR increased to 0.67 mg (38%), and in fully trained horses it increased to 0.81 mg (65%). When horses were acutely exposed to cold the TSR increased to 1.09 mg, an increase of 66%. The TSR of 8 pregnant horses was 0.58 mg, a nonsignificant increase of 18%.

5. TSR of Cattle

Premachandra *et al.* (1960) determined the TSR of dairy cattle during the winter and summer of 4 breeds. The Jersey cows had a TSR of 0.55 mg/100 lb in winter, 0.20 mg in summer; Guernsey, 0.4 mg and 0.15 mg; Holstein 0.50 mg and 0.23 mg; and Brown Swiss 0.50 and 0.21 mg, respectively. The mean TSR in 106 observations was 5.4 mg during winter and, in 73 trials, 2.0 mg in summer. The total range in TSR of the cattle was from 0.1–1.0 mg/100 lb.

Mixner *et al.* (1962) used the chemical $L\text{-}T_4$ turnover method to estimate the TSR of 12 lactating cows. The mean TSR in 48 determinations was 0.142 mg/100 lb/day. TSR was highest at the beginning of lactation (0.155 mg) and lowest at the ninth month (0.132 mg). The TSR was highest in the spring (0.165 mg) and lowest in the fall (0.129 mg).

Mixner *et al.* (1966) used the chemical $L\text{-}T_4$ turnover method to determine the relation of TSR to body weight of 36 growing Holstein heifers from birth to 2 years of age. The TSR was highest in the 0–3 month group (0.828 mg/100 kg body weight) and declined steadily to 0.326 mg/100 kg in the oldest group. An equation $Y = 0.033 \, X^{0.64}$ where

Y is the TSR and X, body weight was calculated. The exponent of X indicates that for a 1% increase in body weight there was an increase of 0.64% in daily TSR.

Hendrich and Turner (1964) determined the TSR of 5 Holstein-Hereford crossbred and 1 each of Holstein and Guernsey calves, ranging in age from 3 weeks to 3 months of age during early spring. The mean TSR was 0.214 mg L-T_4/100 lb/day. The mean TSR measured in the fall was the same. The TSH secretion rate (TSH-SR) was determined simultaneously. The TSH-SR was 829 mU/100 lb/day in the spring and 764 mU in the fall. The estimations of TSH-SR were highly correlated with TSR, $r = +0.62$ in spring and $r = +0.78$ in the fall.

Pipes et al. (1963) studied the TSR of beef cattle. The mean TSR of the Shorthorns was 0.29 mg/100 lb body weight, Angus 0.24 mg, and Herefords 0.24 mg. In the group of 68 heifers, 33 steers, and 74 bulls, no significant difference was found due to sex, castration, breed, or season. Individual variations ranged from 0.1–0.7 mg, with a mean of 0.27 mg/100 lb body weight.

6. TSR in Man

Fisher and Oddie (1963) estimated the TSR of infants 24–65 days of age as 18.6 μg/kg/day. It was suggested that estradiol benzoate increased the TSR. On the basis of earlier estimations in adults of 2.54 μg/kg/day, the TSR of the infants is about 7 times that of the adult. However, Beckers et al. (1966) estimated the L-T_4 secretion rate of children from 9 to 16 years of age as 34.3 $\pm$ 4.6 μg/day or 0.94 $\pm$ 0.1 μg/kg body weight.

7. TSR of Fowls

Stahl et al. (1961a) determined the TSR of New Hampshire chickens from 6–28 weeks of age. At 8 weeks of age, the mean TSR of 40 males was 1.65 μg L-T_4/100 gm/day, while 52 females had a mean of 1.58 μg. TSR remained the same until sexual maturity when the males showed a slight drop to 1.48 μg at 24 weeks. The pullets showed a slight rise to 1.99 μg at 26 weeks of age.

The mean TSR of the high TSR line in August was 2.08 μg whereas the low TSR line had a mean of 1.17 μg. It was suggested that high summer temperatures have less depressing effects on TSR in growing as compared to mature birds.

Stahl and Turner (1961) studied the seasonal variation in New Hampshire fowls of high and low TSR strains during the first laying year. The mean TSR of the 2 sexes during the winter season (September–April) was 2.97 μg L-T_4/100 gm/day, whereas during the summer months (May–September) the TSR was reduced to 1.24 μg, a decline of 58.3%.

The mean TSR of the low TSR group during the winter months was 1.01 μg, and during the summer months 0.59 μg, a decline of 41.6%.

Stahl et al. (1961b) placed a group of fowls in a room maintained at 40°F in September and a second group in January. Periodic estimations of TSR were made. In the September group, 5 birds reached maximum TSR within 32 days, 14 between 32 and 54, 2 between 85 and 112, whereas 2 showed increases for 190 days.

In the second group subject to lowering environmental to January, 7 reached a maximum TSR within 14 days, 2 within 49 days, 5 within 78 days, and 4 beyond 108 days. These observations indicate that TSR may increase gradually for a considerable time at low temperatures.

Tanabe (1965) determined the TSR of White Leghorn and cross-bred cockerels of 2–14 weeks of age by the goitrogen prevention and his ^{131}I assay method. TSR on the basis of unit body weight was highest at 2 weeks of age, and decreased with advancing age and declining growth rate. Highly significant positive correlation was observed between TSR and growth rate.

Hahn et al. (1966) took a group of 19 New Hampshire hens which had been held at 40°F for 2 years and returned them to room temperature. The TSR in the cold was 0.91 μg L-T_4/100 gm/day, whereas after 17 days at higher temperatures, the TSR was 0.53 μg, a reduction of 41.8%. This level was comparable to that for a group of 23 hens, held at room temperature for 2 years, of 0.52 μg. These studies indicate that a cold environment may cause a gradual rise in TSR but that a warm environment causes a very rapid decline in TSR.

Hendrich and Turner (1967b) studied the effect of increasing age on TSR of New Hampshire hens. The TSR of 16 birds in their first laying year was 0.89 μg L-T_4/100 gm/day; 12 birds 2 years old were 1.06 μg; 14 birds 3 years old, 0.91 μg; and 11 birds 4 years old, 0.91 μg. The mean TSR of the 53 birds was 0.94 μg. No significant change of TSR with increasing age was observed.

Stahl et al. (1962) studied the mode of inheritance of TSR in high and low TSR lines. The TSR of the parental lines and progeny were determined during the growing period. Matings of birds of low TSR produced progeny with low mean TSR, whereas birds of high TSR produced progeny of high TSR. Matings of cockerels with high TSR with pullets of increasing TSR produced progeny with graded increases in TSR. The heritability estimates obtained indicate TSR could be rapidly changed by selection.

Srivastava and Turner (1967a) determined the TSR of two strains of cockerels developed by the Hy-Line Poultry Farms characterized as "docile" and "flighty" as to temperament during June. The "flighty" strain had a mean TSR of 0.82 μg L-T$_4$/100 gm/day whereas the "docile" strain had a TSR of 0.58μg, a difference of 67.6%. When the TSR was determined during a hot period (90–95°F), the TSR of the "flighty" birds was reduced to 0.58 μg, but the other group was unaffected.

8. TSR of Ducklings

Von Faber and Schreiber (1966) estimated the TSR by the goiter prevention method of 4-week-old ducklings. Muscovy males weighing 954 gm secreted L-T$_4$ at a level of 0.78 μg/100 gm body weight. Females weighing 718 gm secreted 0.97 μg. Pekin males weighing 1212 gm secreted 1.46 μg, and females weighing 1213 gm secreted 1.76 μg, per 100 gm body weight.

TABLE VI

SPECIES VARIATION IN THYROID SECRETION RATE (TSR) (MAMMALS)

Animal	Sex	No.	Range of TSR	Mean (μg/L-T$_4$/ 100 gm bw)	Environ- mental condition	Reference
Albino mouse (Swiss Webster)	F	16	—	1.38	78°F	Pipes *et al.* (1960)
P. maniculatus graulis	—	12	—	1.45	July	Elefthereon and Zarrow (1962)
	—	8	—	1.93	Dec.	,,
P. maniculatus baridii	—	12	—	0.75	July	,,
	—	8	—	1.12	Dec.	,,
Hamster	—	—	0.5–0.75	0.62	Room temp.	Premachandra (1962)
	F	88	0.45–0.70	0.58	Room temp.	Bauman *et al.* (1968)
Guinea pig	—	—	0.1–0.75	0.48	Room temp.	Premachandra (1962)
Albino rat (Sprague-	F	66	0.4–1.2	0.88	78°F	Djojoroebagio and Turner (1964)
Dawley)	F	25	—	0.97	78°F	Anderson *et al.* (1961)
	M	34	—	0.97	78°F	,,
Mole, *Scalopus* aquaticus	M+F	20	1.75–2.5	1.96	78°F adult and juvenile	Leach *et al.* (1962)
	M+F	8	1.75–2.5	1.86	78°F adult	,,
	M+F	8	1.75–2.5	2.03	78°F, juvenile	,,
Oppossum, *Didelphis*	M+F	51	0.75–2.5	1.72	Feb.–May, adult	Bauman and Turner (1966)
virginianus	M+F	50	1.0–5.75	2.66	Feb.–May, juveniles	,,
Raccoon, *Procyon lotor*	M+F	29	0.03–0.4	0.12	Room temp., adult and juvenile	Bauman *et al.* (1965a)
	M+F	22	0.03–0.4	0.12	Adult	,,
	M+F	7	0.08–0.15	0.10	Juvenile	,,

REFERENCES

Adams, R., Specht, N., and Woodward, I. (1960). *J. Clin. Endocrinol. Metab.* **20**, 1366.
Amin, A., Chai, C. K., and Reineke, E. P. (1957). *Am. J. Physiol.* **191**, 34.
Anbar, M., Inbar, M., and Tata, J. R. (1965). *Acta Endocrinol.* **48**, 506.
Anderson, R. R., Grossie, J. A., and Turner, C. W. (1961). *Proc. Soc. Exptl. Biol. Med.* **107**, 571.
Anderson, R. R., Bauman, T. R., Coffman, W. J., and Turner, C. W. (1968). Unpublished.
Balfour, W. E., and Tunnicliffe, H. E. (1960). *J. Physiol.* **153**, 179.
Barker, S. B., Shimada, M., and Makiuchi, M. (1965). *Endocrinology* **76**, 115.
Barrett, O., Berman, A., and Maier, J. G. (1960). *J. Clin. Endcocrinol. Metab.* **20**, 1467.
Barrington, E. J. W., Barron, N., and Piggins, D. J. (1961). *Gen. Comp. Endocrinol.* **1**, 170.
Bauman, T. R., and Turner, C. W. (1965). *J. Dairy Sci.* **48**, 1353.
Bauman, T. R., and Turner, C. W. (1966a). *Gen. Comp. Endocrinol.* **6**, 109.
Bauman, T. R., and Turner, C. W. (1966b). *Proc. Soc. Exptl. Biol. Med.* **123**, 9.
Bauman, T. R., Clayton, F. W., and Turner, C. W. (1965a). *Gen. Comp. Endocrinol.* **5**, 261.
Bauman, T. R., Pipes, G. W., and Turner, C. W. (1965b). *Endocrinology* **76**, 537.
Bauman, T. R., Srivastava, L. S., and Turner, C. W. (1967). *Proc. Soc. Exptl. Biol. Med.* **124**, 553.
Bauman, T. R., Anderson, R. R., and Turner, C. W. (1968). *Gen. Comp. Endocrinol.* **10**, 92.
Beck, R. N. (1958). *Endocrinology* **62**, 587.
Beckers, C., Malvaux, P., and DeVisscher, M. (1966). *J. Clin. Endocrinol. Metab.* **26**, 202.
Beierwaltes, W. H. (1967). *Endocrinology* **80**, 545.
Bergman, F., Halvorsen, P., and van der Linden, W. (1967). *Acta Endocrinol.* **56**, 521.
Bhagat, B., and Lockett, M. F. (1961). *J. Endocrinol.* **23**, 227.
Biellier, H. V., and Turner, C. W. (1957). *Missouri Univ. Agr. Expt. Sta. Res. Bull.* **622**.
Blomstedt, B. (1965). *Acta Endocrinol.* **48**, 481.
Blomstedt, B., and Einhorn, J. (1965). *J. Clin. Endocrinol. Metab.* **25**, 181.
Blomstedt, B., and Einhorn, J. (1967). *Metabolism* **16**, 319.
Blomstedt, B., and Neujahr, H. Y. (1964a). *Acta Endocrinol.* **46**, 473.
Blomstedt, B., and Neujahr, H. Y. (1964b). *Acta Endocrinol.* **47**, 343.
Bois, I., and Larsson, L. G. (1958). *Acta Endocrinol.* **28**, 262.
Bois-Svensson, I., Einhorn, J., and Wicklund, H. (1966). *Acta Endocrinol.* **51**, 1.
Boyd, G. S., and Oliver, M. F. (1960a). *J. Endocrinol.* **21**, 25.
Boyd, G. S., and Oliver, M. F. (1960b). *J. Endocrinol.* **21**, 33.
Brasch, J. W., Albert, A., Keating, F. R., and Black, B. M. (1955). *J. Clin. Endocrinol.* **15**, 732.
Braverman, L. E., and Ingbar, S. H. (1967). *J. Clin. Endocrinol. Metab.* **27**, 389.
Braverman, L. E., Foster, A. E., and Ingbar, S. H. (1967). *J. Clin. Endocrinol. Metab.* **27**, 227.
Bray, G. A., and Goodman, H. M. (1965). *Endocrinology* **76**, 323.
Bray, G. A., and Hildreth, S. (1967). *Endocrinology* **81**, 1018.
Brooks, J. R., Pipes, G. W., and Ross, C. V. (1962). *J. Animal Sci.* **21**, 414.
Brown, D. M. (1966). *Endocrinology* **78**, 1252.
Brown-Grant, K. (1955). *J. Physiol.* **127**, 352.
Brown-Grant, K. (1963). *J. Physiol.* **168**, 599.
Brown-Grant, K., and Gibson, J. G. (1955). *J. Physiol.* **127**, 341.
Buchanan, J., and Tapley, D. F. (1966). *Endocrinology* **79**, 81.
Campbell, P. L., Deibler, G. E., Gelber, S., and Sokoloff, L. (1964). *Endocrinology* **75**, 304.
Carter, A. C., Schwartz, H. L., Kydd, D. M., and Kologlu, S. (1964). *Endocrinology* **74**, 689.

Christensen, L. K. (1960). *Acta Endocrinol.* **33**, 111.

Chung, S. J., and Van Middlesworth, L. (1964). *Endocrinology* **74**, 694.

Clark, F. and Crispell, K. R. (1967). *J. Clin. Endocrinol. Metab.* **27**, 153.

Clark, F., and Horn, D. B. (1965). *J. Clin. Endocrinol. Metab.* **25**, 39.

Clark, F., and Horn, D. B. (1966). *J. Clin. Endocrinol. Metab.* **26**, 352.

Cowan, J. W., and Margossian, S. (1966). *Endocrinology* **79**, 1023.

Cuaron, A. (1966). *J. Clin. Endocrinol. Metab.* **26**, 53.

Cuaron, A., and Fucugauchi, M. E. (1964). *Acta Endocrinol.* **46**, 161.

Cutherbertson, W. F. J., Elcoate, P. V., Ireland, D. M., Mills, D. C. B., and Shearley, P. (1960). *J. Endocrinol.* **21**, 45 and 69.

D'Angelo, S. A. (1966). *Proc. Soc. Explt. Biol. Med.* **121**, 555.

Daniel, P. M., Pratt, O. E., Roitt, I. M., and Torrigiani, G. (1966). *J. Physiol. (London)* **183**.

Daniel, P. M., Pratt, O. E., Roitt, I. M., and Torrigiani, G. (1967). *Quart. J. Exptl. Physiol.* **52**, 184.

Danowski, T. S. and Moses, C. (1965). *Metabolism* **14**, 99.

Dempsey, E. W., and Astwood, E. B. (1943). *Endocrinology* **32**, 509.

De Nayer, P. H., Malvaux, P., Van Den Schrieck, H. G., Beckers, C., and De Visscher, M. (1966). *J. Clin. Endocrinol. Metab.* **26**, 233.

Devlin, W. F., and Stephenson, N. R. (1962). *J. Pharm. Pharmacol.* **14**, 597.

Djojosoebagio, S., and Turner, C. W. (1964). *Proc. Soc. Exptl. Biol. Med.* **116**, 1099.

Donati, R. M., Warnecke, M. A., and Gallagher, N. I. (1964). *Proc. Soc. Exptl. Biol. Med.* **115**, 405.

Donati, R. M., Warnecke, M. A., and Gallagher, N. I. (1966). *Proc. Soc. Exptl. Biol. Med.* **122**, 1199.

Dowling, J. T., Razevska, D., and Goodner, C. J. (1964). *Endocrinology* **75**, 157.

Duncan, C. H., Best, M. M., and Lubbe, R. J. (1964). *Metabolism* **13**, 1.

Dunn, J. T., and Werner, S. C. (1964). *J. Clin. Endocrinol. Metab.* **24**, 460.

Dutoit, C. H. (1952). *In* "Phosphorus" (W. D. McElroy and B. Glass, eds.), Vol. II, p. 597. Johns Hopkins, Baltimore, Maryland.

Eades, C. H., Jr., and Phillips, G. E. (1963). *Endocrinology* **72**, 514.

Eades, C. H., Jr., and Stasilli, N. R. (1963). *Endocrinology* **72**, 509.

Eichoff, W., and Herberhold, C. (1965). *Acta Endocrinol.* **49**, 466.

Eleftherion, B. E., and Zarrow, M. X. (1962). *Proc. Soc. Explt. Biol. Med.* **110**, 128.

Ellefson, R. D., and Mason, H. L. (1962). *Endocrinology* **71**, 425.

Ellefson, R. D., and Mason, H. L. (1964). *Endocrinology* **75**, 179.

Emrich, D., Pfannenstiel, P., Hoffmann, G., and Keiderling, W. (1966). *Acta Endocrinol.* **53**, 151.

Evans, E. S., Taurog, A., Koneff, A. A., Potter, G. D., Chiakoff, I. L., and Simpson, M. E. (1960). *Endocrinology* **67**, 619.

Evans, E. S., Rosenberg, L. L., Evans, A. B., and Koneff, A. A. (1964). *Endocrinology* **74**, 770.

Evans, E. S., Schooley, R. A., Evans, A. B., Jenkins, C. A., and Taurog, A. (1966). *Endocrinology* **78**, 983.

Falconer, I. R., and Hetzel, B. S. (1964). *Endocrinology* **75**, 42.

Falconer, I. R., and Robertson, H. A. (1961). *J. Endocrinol.* **22**, 23.

Farer, L. S., Robbins, J., Blumberg, B. S., and Rall, J. E. (1963). *Endocrinology* **70**, 686.

Farran, H. E. A., and Evans, K. (1965). *J. Endocrinol.* **32**, 265.

Favino, H., Emrich, D., and von zur Muhlen, A. (1967). *Acta Endocrinol.* **54**, 362.

Feldman, E. B., and Carter, A. C. (1963). *Metabolism* **12**, 1132.

Feldman, J. D. (1960). *Proc. Soc. Exptl. Biol. Med.* **103**, 860.

Fell, H. B., and Mellanby, E. (1955). *J. Physiol.* **127**, 427.

Felt, V. (1966). *J. Clin. Endrocrinol. Metab.* **26**, 683.

Fisher, D. A., and Oddie, T. H. (1963). *J. Clin. Endocrinol Metab.* **23**, 811.

Fisher, D. A., and Oddie, T. H. (1964). *J. Clin. Endocrinol. Metab.* **24**, 733.

Fisher, D. A., Lehman, H., and Lackey, C. (1964). *J. Clin. Endocrinol. Metab.* **24**, 393.

Flamboe, E. E., and Reineke, E. P. (1957). *J. Animal Sci.* **16**, 1061.

Fletcher, K., and Myant, N. B. (1958). *J. Physiol.* **144**, 361.

Fletcher, K., and Myant, N. B. (1962). *Endocrinology* **71**, 870.

Flock, E. V., Bollman, J. L., and Grindlay, J. H. (1957). *Am. J. Physiol.* **189**, 420.

Flock, E. V. Bollman, J. L., and Grindlay, J. H. (1958). *Am. J. Physiol.* **194**, 33.

Flock, E. V., Bollman, J. L., and Grindlay, J. H. (1960). *Endocrinology* **67**, 419.

Flock, E. V., Bollman, J. L., Grindlay, J. H., and Stobie, G. H. (1961). *Endocrinology* **39**, 626.

Flock, E. V., David, C. Hallenbeck, G. A., and Owen, C. A., Jr. (1963a). *Endocrinology* **73**, 764.

Flock, E. V., David, C., Stobie, G. H., and Owen, C. A., Jr. (1963b). *Endocrinology* **73**, 442.

Florsheim, W. H., Faircloth, M. A., Corcorran, N. L., and Rudko, P. (1966). *Acta Endocrinol.* **52**, 375.

Ford, D. H., and Rhines, R. (1964). *Acta Endocrinol.* **45**, 211.

Frape, D. L., Gage, J. W., Jr., Hays, V. W., Speer, V. C. and Catron, D. V. (1958). *J. Animal Sci.* **17**, 1225.

French, F. S., and Van Wyk, J. J. (1964). *J. Pediat.* **64**, 589.

Friedberg, W., and Reineke, E. P. (1962). *Federation Proc.* **11**, 50.

Frieden, E. (1967). *Rec. Prog. Hormone Res.* **23**, 139.

Frieden, E., and Westmark, G. W. (1961). *Science* **133**, 1487.

Gabbiani, G., Tuchweber, B., and Cote, G. (1967). *Endocrinology* **81**, 798.

Galton, V. A. (1965). *Endocrinology* **77**, 278.

Galton, V. A., and Ingbar, S. H. (1965). *Endocrinology* **77**, 169.

Ganju, S. N., and Lockett, M. F. (1958). *J. Endocrinol.* **16**, 396.

Geloso, J. P., and Bernard, G. (1967). *Acta Endocrinol.* **56**, 561.

Girard, A., Andrus, S. B., and Hegsted, D. M. (1966). *Metabolism* **15**, 714.

Gittes, R. F., and Irvin, G. L., III (1966). *Endocrinology* **79**, 1033.

Godden, J. D., and Garnett, E. S. (1964). *J. Endocrinol.* **29**, 167.

Goldsmith, R. E., Rauh, J. L., Kloth, R., and Dahlgren, J. (1967). *Acta Endrocrinol.* **54**, 494.

Goolden, A. W. G., Gartside, J. M., and Osorio, C. (1965). *J. Clin. Endocrinol Metab.* **25**, 127.

Goolden, A. W. G., Gartside, J. M., and Osorio, C. (1967). *Acta Endocrinol.* **56**, 146.

Gordon, A. H., Gross, J., Connor, D., and Pitt-Rivers, R. (1952). *Nature* **169**, 19.

Gorman, C. A., Flock, E. V., Owen, C. A., Jr., and Paris, J. (1966). *Endocrinology* **79**, 391.

Greenberg, C. M., Blank, B., Pfeiffer, F. R., and Pauls, J. F. (1963). *Am. J. Physiol.* **205**, 821.

Gregerman, R. I., and Solomon, N. (1967). *J. Clin. Endocrinol. Metab.* **27**, 93.

Griffin, S. A., Henneman, H. A., and Reineke, E. P. (1962). *Am. J. Vet. Res.* **23**, 109.

Grossie, J., Hendrich, C. E., and Turner, C. W. (1965). *Proc. Soc. Exptl. Biol. Med.* **120**, 413.

Grosvenor, C. E. (1961). *Endocrinology* **69**, 1092.

Grosvenor, C. E. (1962). *Endocrinology* **70**, 934.

Grosvenor, C. E., and Turner, C. W. (1958). *Proc. Soc. Exptl. Biol. Med.* **99**, 517.

Grosvenor, C. E., and Turner, C. W. (1960). *Am. J. Physiol.* **198**, 1.

Hahn, D. W., Ishibashi, T., and Turner, C. W. (1966). *Poultry Sci.* **45**, 31.

Haibach, H., and McKenzie, J. M. (1967). *Endocrinology* **81**, 435.

Hall, P. F., and Myant, N. B. (1956). *J. Physiol.* **133**, 181.

Hamolsky, M. W., Stein, M., and Freedberg, A. S. (1957). *J. Clin. Endocrinol.* **17**, 33.

Hegsted, D. M. (1967). *Endocrinology* **81**, 673.

Hendrich, C. E., and Turner, C. W. (1964). *J. Dairy Sci.* **47**, 1007.

Hendrich, C. E., and Turner, C. W. (1966). *Gen. Comp. Endocrinol.* **7**, 411.

Hendrich, C. E., and Turner, C. W. (1967a). *Poultry Sci.* **46**, 3.

Hendrich, C. E., and Turner, C. W. (1967b). *Proc. Soc. Exptl. Biol. Med.* **124**, 616.

Hendrich, C. E., and Turner, C. W. Unpublished.

Heninger, R. W., and Albright, E. C. (1966). *Endocrinology* **79**, 309.

Heninger, R. W., and Newcomer, W. S. (1964). *Proc. Soc. Exptl. Biol. Med.* **116**, 624.

Henneman, H. A., Griffin, S. A., and Reineke, E. P. (1952). *J. Animal Sci.* **11**, 704.

Henriques, U. (1962). *Acta Endocrinol.* **41**, 143.

Henriques, U. (1964). *Acta Endocrinol.* **45**, 187.

Hershman, J. M. (1963). *Endocrinology* **72**, 799.

Hershman, J. M. (1964). *J. Clin. Endocrinol. Metab.* **24**, 173.

Hirvonen, L., and Lang, H. (1962). *Proc. Soc. Exptl. Biol. Med.* **109**, 284.

Hirvonen, L., and Lybeck, H. (1956). *Acta Physiol. Scand.* **36**, 17.

Hodges, R. E., Evans, T. C., Bradbury, J. T., and Keettel, W. C. (1955). *J. Clin. Endocrinol. Metab.* **15**, 661.

Hoffman, W. W., Richert, D. A., and Westerfeld, W. W. (1966). *Endocrinology* **78**, 1189.

Hollander, C. S., Odak, V. V., Prout, T. E., and Asper, S. P. (1962). *J. Clin. Endocrinol. Metab.* **22**, 617.

Hollander, C. S., Scott, R. L., Burgess, J. A., Rabinowtiz, D., Merimee, T. J., and Oppenheimer, J. H. (1967a). *J. Clin. Endocrinol. Metab.* **27**, 1219.

Hollander, C. S., Thompson, R. H., Barrett, P. V. D., and Berlin, N. I. (1967b). *Endocrinology* **81**, 1007.

Hum, R. F., Goldberg, R. C., and Chaikoff, I. L. (1951). *Endocrinology* **49**, 21.

Hunter, O. R., Jr., and Chow, C. C. T. (1962). *Am. J. Clin. Pathol.* **37**, 355.

Hutchins, Max O. (1956). *Proc. Soc. Exptl. Biol. Med.* **120**, 581.

Imarisio, J. J., and Greco, J. (1964). *Metabolism* **13**, 897.

Inada, M., and Sterling, K. (1967). *J. Clin. Endocrinol. Metab.* **27**, 1019.

Inada, M., Koshiyama, K., Torizuka, K., Akagi, H., and Miyake, T. (1964). *J. Clin. Endocrinol. Metab.* **24**, 775.

Ingbar, S. H. (1958). *Endocrinolgy* **63**, 256.

Ingbar, S. H., Braverman, L. E., Dawber, U. A., and Lee, G. Y. (1965). *J. Clin. Invest.* **44**, 1679.

Inoue, K., and Taurog, A. (1967). *Endocrinology* **81**, 319.

Inoue, K., Grimm, Y., and Greer, M. A. (1967). *Endocrinology* **81**, 946.

Irvine, C. H. G. (1967). *J. Endocrinol.* **39**, 313.

Jablonski, J. R., Neilan, B., Sunder, J. H., Zara, C. C., and Moses, C. (1962). *Metabolism* **11**, 935.

Johnson, C. A., and Smith, K. L. (1961). *J. Pharm. Pharmacol.* **13**, Suppl. 113T-135T.

Jones, J. E., and Seal, U.S. (1967). *J. Clin. Endocrinol. Metab.* **27**, 1521.

Jorgensen, E. C., and Reid, J. A. W. (1965). *Endocrinology* **76**, 312.

Knobil, E., and Josimovich, J. B. (1939). *Ann. N.Y. Acad. Sci.* **75**, 895.

Kologlu, S., Schwartz, H. L., and Carter, A. C. (1966). *Endocrinology* **78**, 231.

Kritchevsky, D., Moynishan, J. L., and Sachs, M. L. (1961). *Proc. Soc. Exptl. Biol. Med.* **108**, 254.

Kuhl, W. J., Halper, I. S., and Dowben, R. M. (1961). *J. Clin. Endocrinol. Metab.* **21**, 1592.

Lachiver, F., and Leloup, J. (1955). *Compt. Rend. Acad. Sci.* **241**, 573.

Lavietes, P. H., and Epstein, F. H. (1964). *Ann. Internal Med.* **60**, 79.

Leach, B. J., Bauman, T. R., and Turner, C. W. (1962). *Proc. Soc. Exptl. Biol. Med.* **110**, 681.

Lee, N. D., Henry, R. J., and Golub, O. J. (1964), *J. Clin. Endocrinol. Metab,* **24**, 486.

Lee, K. L., Sellinger, O. Z., and Miller, O. N. (1967). *Proc. Soc. Exptl. Biol. Med.* **126**, 169.

Leloup, J., and Lachiver, F. (1955). *Compt. Rend. Acad. Sci.* **241**, 509.

Lemarchand-Beraud, T., Assayah, M. R., and Vannotti, A. (1964). *Acta Endocrinol.* **45**, 99.

Levine, R. J., Oates, J. A., Vendsalu, J. A., and Sjoerdsma, A. (1962). *J. Clin. Endrocrinol. Metab.* **22**, 1242.

Levy, R. P., Marshall, J. S., and McGuire, W. L. (1964). *Metabolism* **13**, 557.

Lew, M., Lépp, A., and Starr, P. (1963). *Endocrinology* **72**, 160.

Liewendahl, K., and Lamberg, B. A. (1965). *J. Clin. Endocrinol. Metab.* **25**, 991.

Lightfoot, R. W., and Christian, C. L. (1966). *J. Clin. Endocrinol. Metab.* **26**, 305.

Lissitzky, S., Codaccioni, J. L., Bismuth, J., and Depieds, R. (1967). *J. Clin. Endocrinol. Metab.* **27**, 185.

Loewenstein, J. E., and Wollman, S. H. (1967). *Endocrinology* **81**, 1086.

London, W. T., Money, W. L., Rawson, R. W. (1963). *Endocrinology* **73**, 205.

Lundgren, R. G., and Johnson, H. D. (1964). *J. Animal Sci.* **23**, 28.

Maayan, M. L. (1964). *Endocrinology* **75**, 747.

Maayan, M. L. (1966). *Endocrinology* **78**, 471.

Maayan, M. L., and Rosenberg, I. N. (1963). *Endocrinology* **73**, 38.

McClure, J., de Mowbray, R., and Gilliland, I. C. (1961). *J. Endocrinol.* **22**, 87.

Mack, R. E., Hart, K. T., Druet, D., and Bauer, M. A. (1961). *Am. J. Med.* **30**, 323.

Maclagan, N. F., Bowden, C. H., and Wilkinson, J. H. (1957). *Biochem. J.* **67**, 5.

MacLeod, R. M. (1965). *Endocrinology* **77**, 96.

McPherson, J. R., and Albert, A. (1961). *Endocrinology* **69**, 856.

Malamos, B., Miras, C. J., Karli-Samoiulidou, J. N., and Kontras, D. A. (1966). *J. Endocrinol.* **35**, 223.

Malkasian, G. D., and Tauxe, W. N. (1965). *J. Clin. Endocrinol. Metab.* **25**, 923.

Malvaux, P., DeNayer, Ph., Beckers, C., Van Den Schrieck, H. G., and DeVisscher, M. (1966). *J. Clin. Endocrinol. Metab.* **26**, 459.

Marks, J. F. (1965). *J. Clin. Endocrinol. Metab.* **25**, 852.

Matsuda, K., and Greer, M. A. (1965). *Endocrinology* **76**, 1012.

Meineke, H. A., and Crafts, R. C. (1959). *Proc. Soc. Biol. Med.* **102**, 121.

Meineke, H. A., and Crafts, R. C. (1964). *Proc. Soc. Exptl. Biol. Med.* **117**, 520.

Melmon, K. L., Rivlin, R. S., Oates, J. A., and Sjoerdsma, A. (1964). *J. Clin. Endocrinol. Metab.* **24**, 691.

Meyer, Y. N., and Evans, E. S. (1964). *Endocrinology* **74**, 784.

Michels, R., Cason, J., and Sokoloff, L. (1963). *Science* **140**, 1417.

Miller, B. F., Sanford, P. E., and Clegg, R. E. (1962). *Poultry Sci.* **41**, 989.

Mitchell, M. L. (1958). *J. Clin. Endocrinol. Metab.* **18**, 1437.

Mitchell, M. L., and O'Rourke, M. E. (1959). *Clin. Res.* **7**, 241.

Mitchell, M. L., Harden, A. B., and O'Rourke, M. E. (1960). *J. Clin. Endocrinol. Metab.* **20**, 1474.

Mitchell, M. L., Bradford, A. H., and Collins, S. (1964). *J. Clin. Endocrinol. Metab.* **24**, 867.

Mixner, J. P., and Lennon, H. D. (1960). *J. Dairy Sci.* **43**, 1480.

Mixner, J. P., Kramer, D. H., and Szabo, K. T. (1962). *J. Dairy Sci.* **45**, 999.

Mixner, J. P., Szabo, K. T., and Mather, R. E. (1966). *J. Dairy Sci.* **49**, 199.

Morreale de Escobar, G., and Escobar del Rey, F. (1967). *Rec. Prog. Hormone Res.* **23**, 87.

Moses, C., Sunder, J. H., Vester, J. W., and Danoweki, T. S. (1964). *Metabolism* **13**, 717.

Murphy, B. E. P., and Pattee, C. J., (1964). *J. Clin. Endocrinol. Metab.* **24**, 187.

Murphy, B. E. P., Pattee, C. J., and Gold, A. (1966). *J. Clin. Endocrinol. Metab.* **26**, 247.

Myant, N. B. (1958). *J. Physiol.* **142**, 329.

Nagataki, S., Shizume, K., and Nakao, K. (1966). *Endocrinology* **79**, 667.

Nakajima, H., Kuramochi, M., Hoiguchi, T., and Kubo, S. (1966). *J. Clin. Endocrinol. Metab.* **26**, 99.

Nataf, B., Sfez, M., Michel, R., and Roche, C. R. (1956). *J. Soc. Biol.* **150**, 1088.

Nava, M., and De Groot, L. J. (1962). *New Engl. J. Med.* **266**, 1307.

Nejad, N. S., and Chaikoff, I. L. (1964). *Endocrinology* **75**, 396.

Nichols, F. L. (1962). *J. Am. Med. Assoc.* **181**, 134.

Nicoloff, J. T., Dowling, J. T., and Patton, D. D. (1964). *J. Clin. Endocrinol. Metab.* **24**, 294.

Nikolai, T. F., and Seal, U. S. (1966). *J. Clin. Endocrinol. Metab.* **26**, 835.

Oddie, T. H., Fisher, D. A., and Rogers, C. (1964). *J. Clin. Endocrinol. Metab.* **24**, 628.

Oddie, T. H., Fisher, D. A., and Epperson, D. (1965). *J. Clin. Endocrinol. Metab.* **25**, 1196.

Oddie, T. H., Meade, J. H., Jr., and Fisher, D. A. (1966). *J. Clin. Endocrinol. Metab.* **26**, 425.

Oppenheimer, J. H., and Surks, M. I. (1964). *J. Clin. Endocrinol. Metab.* **24**, 785.

Oppenheimer, J. H., and Werner, S. C. (1966). *J. Clin. Endocrinol. Metab.* **26**, 715.

Oppenheimer, J. H., Squef, R., Surks, M. I., and Hauer, H. (1963). *J. Clin. Invest.* **42**, 1769.

Osorio, C., and Myant, N. B. (1965). *Endocrinology* **76**, 938.

Peterson, R. N., and Young, W. C. (1952). *Endocrinology* **50**, 218.

Pileggi, V. J., Segal, H. A., and Golub, O. J. (1964). *J. Clin. Endocrinol. Metab.* **24**, 273.

Pileggi, V. J., Golub, O. J., and Lee, N. D. (1965). *J. Clin. Endocrinol Metab.* **25**, 949.

Pipes, G. W., and Dale, H. E. (1963). *Federation Proc.* **22**, 621.

Pipes, G. W., Blincoe, C. R., and Hsieh, K. (1950). *J. Dairy Sci.* **33**, 384.

Pipes, G. W., Premachandra, B. N., and Turner, C. W. (1957). *J. Dairy Sci.* **40**, 340.

Pipes, G. W., Premachandra, B. N., and Turner, C. W. (1958). *Poultry Sci.* **37**, 36.

Pipes, G. W., Grossie, J. A., and Turner, C. W. (1960). *Proc. Soc. Exptl. Biol. Med.* **104**, 491.

Pipes, G. W., Bauman, T. R., and Turner, C. W. (1962). *J. Diary Sci.* **45**, 1253.

Pipes, G. W., Bauman, T. R., Brooks, J. R., Comfort, J. E., and Turner, C. W. (1963). *J. Animal Sci.* **22**, 476.

Pittman, C. S., and Shimizu, C. (1966). *Endocrinology* **79**, 1109.

Pittman, C. S., Shinobara, M., and McCraw, E. F. (1964). *Endocrinology* **74**, 611.

Pitt-Rivers, R. (1962). *Biochem. J.* **82**, 108.

Pitt-Rivers, R. (1966). *J. Endocrinol.* **36**, 203.

Pitt-Rivers, R., and Rall, J. E. (1961). *Endocrinology* **68**, 309.

Post, T. B., and Mixner, J. P. (1961). *J. Dairy Sci.* **44**, 2265.

Premachandra, B. N., and Turner, C. W. (1961). *Proc. Soc. Exptl. Biol. Med.* **106**, 818.

Premachandra, B. N., Pipes, G. W., and Turner, C. W. (1960). *Missouri Univ. Agr. Exptl. Sta. Res. Bull.* **727**.

Premachandra, B. N., Ray, A. K., and Blumenthal, H. T. (1962). *Proc. Soc. Exptl. Biol. Med.* **110**, 277.

Purves, H. D., and Griesbach, W. E. (1946). *Brit. J. Exptl. Pathol.* **27**, 170.

Querido, A., Schut, K., and Terpstra, J. (1957). *Ciba. Found. Colloq. Endocrinol.* **10**, 124.

Rabinowitz, J. L., and Myerson, R. M. (1967). *Metabolism* **16**, 69.

Ray, A. K., and Premachandra, B. N. (1964). *Endocrinology* **74**, 800.

Reineke, E. P. (1954). *J. Dairy Sci.* **37**, 1227.

Reineke, E. P., and Singh, O. N. (1955). *Proc. Soc. Exptl. Biol. Med.* **88**, 203.

Reineke, E. P., and Turner, C. W. (1950). *In* "Hormone Assay" (C. W. Emmens, ed.). Chapter 19. Academic Press, New York.

Reineke, E. P., and Turner, C. W. (1942). *Missouri Univ. Agr. Exptl. Sta. Res. Bull.* **355**.

Reineke, E. P., and Turner, C. W. (1945). *J. Biol. Chem.* **161**, 613.

Reineke, E. P., and Turner, C. W. (1946). *J. Biol. Chem.* **162**, 369.

Reineke, E. P., Turner, C. W., Kohler, G. O., Hoover, R. D., and Beezley, M. B. (1945). *J. Biol. Chem.* **161**, 599.

Richert, D. A., Schenkman, J., and Westerfeld, W. W. (1964). *J. Nutr.* **83**, 332.

Riekstniece, E., and Asling, C. W. (1966). *Proc. Soc. Exptl. Biol. Med.* **123**, 258.

Rivlin, R. S., and Levine, R. J. (1963). *Endocrinology* **73**, 103.

Rivlin, R. S., and Kaufman, S. (1965). *Endocrinology* **77**, 295.

Robertson, H. A., and Falconer, I. R. (1961). *J. Endocrinol.* **21**, 411.

Roche, J., Michel, O., Michel, R., and Tata, J. R. (1954). *Biochem. Biophys. Acta* **13**, 471.

Roitt, I. M., and Torrigiani, G. (1967). *Endocrinology* **81**, 421.

Romack, F. E., Turner, C. W., Lasley, J. F., and Day, B. N. (1964). *J. Animal Sci.* **23**, 1143.

Rosenberg, L. L., and La Roche, G. (1964). *Endocrinology* **75**, 776.

Rosenberg, L. L., La Roche, G., and Ehlert, J. M. (1966). *Endocrinology* **79**, 927.

Rosenman, R. H., Byers, S. O., and Friedman, M. (1952). *J. Clin. Endocrinol. Metab.* **12**, 1287.

Ross, J. E., and Tapley, D. F. (1966). *Endocrinology* **79**, 493.

Roy, S. K., and Kobayashi, Y. (1962). *Proc. Soc. Exptl. Biol. Med.* **110**, 699

Rubino, F., and Pennetti, V. (1957). *Arch. Sci. Biol. (Bologna)* **41**, 444.

Ruegamer, W. R. (1963). *Federations Proc.* **22**, 359.

Ruegamer, W. R. (1965). *Proc. Soc. Exptl. Biol. Med.* **118**, 37.

Ruegamer, W. R., and Silverman, F. R. (1961). *Endocrinology* **68**, 564.

Ruegamer, W. R., and Wallace, C. W. (1965). *Endocrinology* **77**, 433.

Ruegamer, W. R., Westerfeld, W. W., and Richert, D. A. (1964). *Endocrinology* **75**, 908.

Ruegamer, W. R., Wagner, B. J., Barstow, M., and Keran, E. E. (1967). *Endocrinology* **81**, 49.

Rupp, J. J. and Paschkis, K. E. (1961). *Am. J. Med.* **30**, 472.

Rupp, J. J., Chavarria, C., Paschikis, K. E., and Chublarian, E. (1959). *Ann. Internal Med.* **51**, 359.

Sasaki, T., and Nakajima, H. (1962). *Endocrinology* **71**, 520.

Saxena, K. M., Crawford, J. D., and MacGilliosay, M. H. (1964). *Endocrinology* **74**, 415.

Schatz, D. L., Sheppard, R. H., Polter, H. C., and Jaffri, M. H. (1967). *Metabolism* **16**, 1075.

Schussler, G. C., and Plager, J. E. (1967). *J. Clin. Endocrinol. Metab.* **27**, 242.

Selenkow, H. A., and Asper, S. P. (1955). *J. Clin. Endocrinol. Metab.* **15**, 285.

Shalet, M., Coe, D., and Reissmann, K. R. (1966). *Proc. Soc. Exptl. Biol. Med.* **123**, 443.

Shambaugh, G. E., III, and Beisel, W. R. (1967). *J. Clin. Endocrinol. Metab.* **27**, 1667.

Shellabarger, C. J., and Tata, J. R. (1961). *Endocrinology* **68**, 1056.

Shepard, T. H., (1967). *J. Clin. Endocrinol. Metab.* **27**, 945.

Shimoda, S. (1964). *Acta Endocrinol.* **46**, 653.

Shimaoka, K. (1963). *Acta Endocrinol.* **43**, 285.

Shimaoka, K., and Jasani, B. M. (1965). *J. Endocrinol* **32**, 59.

Short, S. H., and Ruegamer, W. R. (1966). *Endocrinology* **79**, 90.

Siegel, E., and Sachs, B. A. (1964). *J. Clin. Endocrinol. Metab.* **24**, 313.

Slebodzinski, A. (1965a). *J. Endocrinol.* **32**, 65.

Slebodzinski, A. (1965b). *J. Endocrinol.* **32**, 45.

Sokoloff, L., and Kaufman, S. (1959). *Science* **129**, 569.

Sokoloff, L., and Kaufman, S. (1961). *J. Biol. Chem.* **236**, 795.

Sorensen, P. H. (1962). *Proc. Conf. Use Radioisotopes Animal Biol. Med. Sci., Mexico City,* 1961, *Intern. Atom. Energy Agency.*

Sorensen, P. H., and Moustgaard, J. (1957). *Royal Vet. Agr. Coll. Yearbook, Copenhagen, Denmark.* p. 83.

Srivastava, L. S., and Turner, C. W. (1967a). *Proc. Soc. Exptl. Biol. Med.* **124**, 325.

Srivastava, L. S., and Turner, C. W. (1967b). *Proc. Soc. Exptl. Biol. Med.* **126**, 157.

Stahl, P., and Turner, C. W. (1961). *Poultry Sci.* **40**, 239.

Stahl, P., Pipes, G. W., and Turner, C. W. (1961a). *Poultry Sci.* **40**, 1036.

Stahl, P., Pipes, G. W., and Turner, C. W. (1961b). *Poultry Sci.* **40**, 646.

Stahl, P., Pipes, G. W., Turner, C. W., and Stephenson, A. B. (1962). *Poultry Sci.* **41**, 570.

Starr, P. (1961). *Acta Endocrinol.* **37**, 110.

Starr, P., and Liebhold-Schueck, R. (1954). *J. Am. Med. Assoc.* **155**, 732.

Starr, P., and Nicoloff, J. (1967). *Acta Endocrinol.* **56**, 577.

Starr, P., Roen, P., Freibrun, J. L., and Schleissner, L. A. (1960). *Arch. Internal Med.* **105**, 830.

Stasilli, N. R., and Kroc, R. L. (1956). *J. Clin. Endocrinol.* **16**, 1595.

Stasilli, N. R., Kroc, R. L., and Nemith, P. J. (1961). *Endocrinology* **68**, 1068.

Stein, O., and Gross, J. (1962). *Proc. Soc. Exptl. Biol. Med.* **109**, 817.

Sterling, K., and Brenner, M. A. (1966). *J. Clin. Invest.* **45**, 153.

Sterling, K., and Hegedus, A. (1962). *J. Clin. Invest.* **41**, 1031.

Sterling, K., and Tabachnick, M. (1961). *J. Clin. Endocrinol. Metab.* **21**, 456.

Sterling, K., Lashof, J. E., and Mann, E. B. (1954). *J. Clin. Invest.* **33**, 1031.

Stolc, V. (1962). *Endocrinology* **71**, 564.

Strand, O. (1962). *Proc. Soc. Exptl. Biol. Med.* **109**, 668.

Sturnick, M. I., and Lesses, M. F. (1961). *New Engl. J. Med.* **264**, 608.

Surks, M. I., and Oppenheimer, J. H. (1964). *J. Clin. Endocrinol. Metab.* **24**, 794.

Surks, M. I., Beckwitt, H. J., and Chidsey, C. A. (1967). *J. Clin. Endocrinol. Metab.* **27**, 789.

Szabo, K. T., and Mixner, J. P. (1964). *Proc. Soc. Exptl. Biol. Med.* **115**, 521.

Tanabe, Y. (1965). *Poultry Sci.* **44**, 591.

Tanabe, Y., and Komiyama, T., (1962). *Endocrinology* **70**, 142.

Tata, J. R. (1963a). *J. Endocrinol.* **27**, i.

Tata, J. R. (1963b). *Nature* **197**, 1167.

Tata, J. R., and Shellabarger, C. J. (1959). *Biochem. J.* **72**, 608.

Taurog, A., and Evans, E. S. (1967). *Endocrinology* **80**, 915.

Taurog, A., Wheat, J. D., and Chaikoff, I. L. (1956). *Endocrinology* **58**, 121.

Taurog, A., Porter, J. C., and Thio, D. T. (1964). *Endocrinology* **74**, 902.

Taylor, R. E., Tu, T., Barker, S. B. and Jorgensen, E. C. (1967). *Endocrinology* **80**, 1143.

Tepperman, H. M., and Tepperman, J. (1964). *Am. J. Physiol.* **206**, 357.

Thorson, S. C., Tauxe, W. N., Taswell, H. F. (1966). *J. Clin. Endocrinol. Metab.* **26**, 181.

Tong, W., Raghupathy, E., and Chaikoff, I. L. (1963). *Endocrinology* **72**, 931.

Tonoue, T., and Yamamoto, K. (1967a). *Endocrinology* **81**, 101.

Tonoue, T., and Yamamoto, K. (1967b). *Endocrinology* **81**, 1029.

Turner, C. W., and Premachandra, B. N. (1962). *In* "Methods in Hormone Research" (R. I. Dorfman, ed.), 1st ed., Vol. II, p. 385, Academic Press, New York.

Van Middlesworth, L. (1957). *Endocrinology* **61**, 570.

Volpert, E. M., Martinez, M. and Oppenheimer, J. H. (1967). *J. Clin. Endocrinol. Metab.* **27**, 421.

von Faber, H., and Schreiber, H. (1966). *Acta Endocrinol.* **53**, 462.

Wada, H., Berswordt-Wallrabe, R. V., and Turner, C. W. (1959). *Proc. Soc. Exptl. Biol. Med.* **102**, 608.

Wahlborg, A., Bright, C., and Frieden, E. H. (1964). *Endocrinology* **75**, 561.

Walfish, P. G., Britton, A., Melville, P. H., and Ezrin, C. (1961). *J. Clin. Endocrinol. Metab.* **21**, 582.

Webb, F. W. (1961). *J. Pharm. Pharmacol.* **13**, Suppl. 1367.

Weiss, W. P., and Sokoloff, L. (1963). *Science* **140**, 1324.

Werner, S. C. (1967). *J. Clin. Endocrinol. Metab.* **27**, 1637.

Werner, S. C., Row, V. V., and Radichevich, I. (1960). *J. Clin. Endocrinol.* **20**, 1372.

West, C. D., Chavre, V. J., and Wolfe, M. (1965). *J. Clin. Endrocrinol. Metab.* **25**, 1189.

West, C. D., Chavre, V. J., and Wolfe, M. (1966). *J. Clin. Endocrinol. Metab.* **26**, 986.

Westerfeld, W. W., Doisy, R. J., and Richert, D. A. (1962). *J. Nutr.* **78**, 393.

Westerfeld, W. W., Richert, D. A., and Ruegamer, W. R. (1965). *Endocrinology* **77**, 802.

Wiberg, G. S., and Stephenson, N. R. (1961). *J. Pharm. Pharmacol.* **13**. Suppl. 136T.

Wiberg, G. S., Devlin, W. F., Stephenson, N. R., Carter, J. R., and Bayne, A. J. (1962). *J. Pharm. Pharmacol.* **14**, 777.

Wiberg, G. S., Carter, J. R., and Stephenson, N. R. (1963). *Acta Endocrinol.* **43**, 609.

Wiberg, G. S., Carter, J. R., and Stephenson, N. R. (1964). *Acta Endocrinol.* **45**, 370.

Wise, E. M., and Ball, E. G. (1964). *Proc. Natl. Acad. Sci. U.S.* **52**, 1255.

Wiswell, J. G., and Coronbo, V. (1962). *J. Clin. Endocrinol. Metab.* **22**, 657.

Woeber, K. A., and Ingbar, S. H. (1964). *Endocrinology* **75**, 917.

Woldring, M. G., Bakker, A., and Doorenbos, H. (1961). *Acta Endocrinol.* **37**, 607.

Woods, J. W., Wayt, H. J., and Baker, H. J. (1966). *Proc. Soc. Exptl. Biol. Med.* **122**, 211.

Chapter 9

Insulin

K. L. Smith

I. Introduction

Since insulin is unique in that it is a potent drug possessing rapid action and that under or over dosage outside narrow limits is betrayed by unpleasant symptoms, it is unfortunate that a specific chemical test with high inherent accuracy is not available to ensure the uniformity of material issued for clinical use.

However, the qualitative effect of insulin can be demonstrated readily in laboratory animals by the exhibition of falls in blood sugar level indicated either by actual blood sugar determinations or by the incidence of convulsions relieved by the ingestion of glucose. Through the years insulin has been reliably assayed by methods employing these reactions.

During recent years physicochemical methods using paper chromatography and biological methods using new systems have been applied to the assay of insulin.

Both groups already have great value, the former as a domestic tool for those interested in problems relating to optimum yield, stability, etc., and the latter for those interested in determining insulin at physiological levels. Neither, however, has yet supplanted the classic methods using animals, which are still the methods officially called for in the examinations of insulin intended for clinical use. It will be appreciated however, that the physicochemical methods have a distinct value in supplementing the biological assay of such insulins.

Great interest has been shown in the application of an isotope dilution method using insulin labeled with ^{131}I to measure the combination of insulin with guinea pig anti-insulin serum. Although in the main this method has been used to detect insulin at physiological levels, it has obvious application to all aspects of insulin assay. Baum *et al.* (1964) have published results to suggest that it could be used to control the potencies of insulin for clinical use.

II. The Standard Preparation

It is essential that when a biological assay is being conducted the assay should be so designed that a simultaneous comparison with a standard preparation may be made.

The first international standard for insulin was established in 1925 and contained by definition 1 unit in 0.125 mg, this unit being intended to approximate the clinical unit defined by Macleod and Orr (1924). The preparation and assay of the second standard set up in 1935 is described in the Quarterly Bulletin of the Health Organisation of the League of Nations (1936). It was accepted as having a potency of 22 U per milligram, this value being approximately that yielded by the assays on rabbits and somewhat lower than that obtained by the mouse method in 4 out of 5 of the laboratories. It is not surprising that on this occasion the two methods yielded different results when it is considered that the comparisons were made between preparations of widely different purities. Such differences in potency between the two methods should not occur when preparations having the same degree of purity are being compared.

A third international standard for insulin containing 24.5 U per milligram was established in 1952, and the fourth and present international standard containing 24.0 U per milligram was established in 1959 and was obtained by recrystallizing a mixture of purified ox insulin (52%) and purified pig insulin (48%).

Unlike the previous standards for insulin which had been stored under nitrogen and dried over P_2O_5, the fourth standard has been filled over air and contains 5.65% moisture but nevertheless is still hygroscopic.

In this instance the report by Bangham and Mussett (1959) indicates that the potencies by mouse and rabbit methods agreed well (mouse method 24.1 U per milligram; rabbit twin cross-over tests 23.8; rabbit triplet cross-over tests 23.4).

In use the weighed standard may be dissolved in 0.9% saline acidified with hydrochloric acid to pH 2.5 and containing 0.3% tricresol (or 0.5% phenol) to prevent the growth of microorganisms. If this solution is prepared to contain 20 U per milliliter and stored at a temperature near to its freezing point it can be considered to be stable for 6 months.

Following their usual custom, the Reference Standards Committee of the United States Pharmacopeial Organization issue their own reference standard for insulin. This is now identical material to that used for the fourth international standard.

The U.S. Pharmacopeia XVI instructs that a solution to contain 40 U per milliliter be effected in water containing 0.1–0.25% w/v of phenol or cresol, between 1.4 and 1.8% glycerin, and sufficient hydrochloric acid to produce a pH between 2.5 and 3.5

III. The Rabbit Method of Assay

A. DESIGN AND INTERPRETATION

1. Early Designs

A report on the preparation of the first international standard for insulin and the definition of the unit of activity (League of Nations, 1926) contained considerations of the principles involved in the assay of this hormone and recorded the test designs that had hitherto been used.

The use of the rabbit for the assay had been suggested (Banting *et al.*, 1922) since it had been observed that the degree of hypoglycemia produced in rabbits by insulin paralleled its clinical effect on diabetes mellitus.

Since the incidence of hypoglycemic convulsions was usually associated with a blood sugar level of 45 mg/100 ml, the unit of activity had been defined as the smallest amount that would cause this blood sugar level to be reached within 4 hours of injection.

The earliest designs therefore consisted of attempts to establish this value with regard to the sample under examination without any reference to a standard preparation. When a reference standard has been established the simultaneous comparison with it was made in tests completed in one day.

2. The Cross-over Test

When small numbers of animals are used in comparative assays, completed in one day, the appearance of a particularly sensitive or insensitive animal among those receiving either the standard or the test preparation will bias the result unduly.

To overcome this, Marks (1925) suggested that the animals used on one day should be tested again in the same groupings, and that on this occasion those which had previously received injections of the standard preparation should receive injections of the test preparation and vice versa. He made this suggestion since he had observed that whereas the level of sensitivity of a colony of rabbits might vary from day to·day the comparative sensitivities of the individuals remained fairly constant.

He suggested that the response of each rabbit be measured as the percentage of blood sugar reduction and that an indication of relative activity could be obtained by summing the responses yielded by the rabbits receiving the test preparation and expressing it as a ratio of the corresponding responses to the standard preparation. For this purpose he expressed the percent blood sugar reduction as

$$\% \text{ (blood sugar) reduction} = 100 \, \frac{(\text{I.B.S.} - \text{F.B.S.})}{\text{I.B.S.}}$$

where I.B.S. and F.B.S. are the initial and final blood sugar levels. Marks (1925) used for F.B.S. the mean blood sugar level, after injection, in samples of blood taken at hourly intervals for 5 hours.

The cross-over test carried out thus could only show whether, at the potency assumed, the sample was or was not equal in activity to the standard. Many workers (Macleod and Orr, 1926; Culhane et al., 1929; Hershey and Lacey, 1936) considered that reliance could be placed only on tests that indicated equal activity of the standard and test preparations, and apparently only used indications of departures from this identity to enable suitable adjustments to be made so that it could be reached in subsequent tests.

Marks (1926) considered that the cross-over test to be efficient should be capable of demonstrating known differences and showed how by testing known dilutions of standard a curve relating the ratio to true activity could be constructed. In the light of later experience (Marks, 1932), he modified this curve to overcome the correlation exhibited between assumed and estimated potencies and recommended that, to avoid such bias introduced by the use of a curve the slope of which did not strictly apply, an assay should consist of a series of cross-over tests aimed to yield ratios both greater and less than unity.

Marks (1926) had suggested that if the response of a rabbit appeared discordant in view of the previous history of the animal it might be necessary to discard the response of that rabbit altogether, but if this were done a corresponding rabbit should be removed from the other dosage group to compensate for it. The practice of discarding a response because it does not appear satisfactory is gravely suspect. Compensation for the loss of a response through death or convulsions appears to be most satisfactorily provided by working with group averages rather than with sums.

3. The Interpretation of a Series of Cross-over Tests

A review (Fieller et al., 1939a,b) was made of accumulated data from certain laboratories which had followed Marks' suggestion to assay each sample at assumed potencies so as to yield ratios greater than and less than unity. It demonstrated how such data, whether the relative effect was measured by the ratios of the responses to standard and test preparations or by their differences, could be treated to supply an estimate of the log dose-response line (l.d.r.l.) obtaining in the laboratory and to indicate the degree of precision to be expected under those conditions.

Fieller (1940) gave an extensive description of the arithmetic procedures involved in this treatment, using response differences as the criterion of relative efficiency and taking as an example a series of 7 cross-over tests carried out on one sample at assumed potencies ranging from 100 to 160 U/ml.

The series of cross-over tests taken as an example by Fieller had not been carried out with a view to the subsequent calculations, which were enumerated. In a planned assay much computational labor may be saved by arranging that the assumed potencies have equal logarithmic intervals, for then the main calculations may be carried out using logs to the base of the dose interval, suitably reduced to yield whole numbers for x, and the necessary correction made later.

4. The Three-Assumption Cross-over Design

Marks (1936) suggested that in the course of a cross-over test the animals receiving the test preparation should be split so that they received it at one of two dose levels, a suggestion which in effect meant the simultaneous conduct of two cross-over tests at two assumed potencies.

Lacey (1941) described a procedure used in the Insulin Committee Laboratory of the University of Toronto which called for a comparison with the standard at three assumed potency levels. Lacey (1946), describing the interpretation of data from such tests, implied that the index of relative activity calculated for each test as

$$\text{Index} = \frac{\text{mean \% reduction effected by test preparation} \times 100}{\text{mean \% reduction effected by standard preparation}}$$

should be plotted against log assumed potency and calculated the regression line by the method of least squares.

The data presented by him will be used to show the arithmetic steps needed in the interpretation of a three-assumption cross-over test.

To preserve the similarity with Fieller's treatment of a series of cross-over tests the response will be taken as $y = 100 - \text{index}$, a value suggested by Fieller *et al.* (1939b), and a weight ascribed to each test equal to $2n_1 n_2/(n_1 + n_2)$ where n_1 and n_2 are the numbers of rabbits, respectively, in each cell of the test.

Lacey (1946) recorded the indexes from three cross-over tests each using 8 rabbits and carried out at assumed potencies of 200, 100, and 50% of the standard (at 40 U/ml).

As y is to be related to log assumed potencies, then, since the assumed potencies are equally spaced on the log scale, whole numbers may be scored for the value $x = \log$ assumed potency as given in Table I, suitable correction being made later to convert to common logarithms.

TABLE I

ARITHMETIC STEPS IN INTERPRETATION OF A THREE-ASSUMPTION CROSS-OVER TEST

Test	Assumed potency (%)	w	$x = \log_2 a$ Assumed potency	Index	$y = 100 - \text{Index}$	wx	wx^2	wy	wxy
1	200	4	+1	67.8	32.2	4	4	128.8	128.8
2	100	4	0	105.0	−5.0	0	0	−20.0	0
3	50	4	−1	126.8	−26.8	−4	4	−107.2	107.2
		12				0	8	1.6	236.0

^{a} Suitably reduced to yield integers:

$$\bar{x} = Swx \div Sw = 0$$
$$Sw(x - \bar{x})^2 = Swx^2 - \bar{x}Swx = 8 - 0 = 8$$
$$\bar{y} = Swy \div Sw = 1.6 \div 12 = 0.1333$$
$$Swx(y - \bar{y}) = Swxy - \bar{y}Swx = 236.0 - 0 = 236.0$$

Then working in logs to base 2 (2 is the ratio between successive assumed potencies)

$$b = \frac{Swx(y - \bar{y})}{Sw(x - \bar{x})^2} = \frac{236}{8} = 29.5$$

and the log activity ratio is

$$M = \bar{x} - \frac{\bar{y}}{b} = \frac{-0.1333}{29.5} = -0.0045$$

On converting to common logarithms,

$$M = -0.0045 \times 0.301 = -0.0014 \text{ or } \bar{1}.9986 = \log 0.9968$$

Hence the potency is estimated to be 99.7% of that assumed, or 39.9 U/ml.

In this case, of course, a similar result would have been obtained if w had been taken as unity, but it may often occur that the constituent cross-over tests are not, by reason of lost responses, exactly balanced. The fuller arithmetic procedure has therefore been included.

In contradistinction to the treatment by differences as described by Fieller, there is no value comparable to s^2 (the variance of a single response as described in Chapter 1) and hence the linearity of the l.d.r.l. cannot be checked, nor can the significance of the calculated slope and the limits of error to be attached to the estimate be assessed.

5. The Establishment of l.d.r.l. from Multidose Tests

In the designs so far considered the slopes of the l.d.r.l. have been determined wholly from changes in response level effected by changes in the injected dose of the test preparation. Test designs in which consideration is given to the parallelism of the l.d.r.l. for the standard and the test preparations have also been described.

Practical difficulties may make it impossible to consider at the same time the linearity of each l.d.r.l., and it may become necessary to establish the relationship of the response to the dose by means of special experiment. Especially is this so if a new criterion of response is being examined.

Bliss and Marks (1939a) described their investigation into the characteristics of the l.d.r.l. for insulin in rabbits when percentage reductions were used as the response criterion. For this they used the data from 8 rabbits, arranged for treatment by means of 2 randomized 4×4 Latin squares, so that each rabbit received during four testings each of four doses of insulin (equally spaced on a logarithmic scale), each dose being equally represented on each day.

6. The Six-Point Assay

Bliss and Marks (1939b) also illustrated how this design could be applied to the assay of an unknown sample of insulin against a standard. Their treatment has become a pattern for most of the biological assays in which the response is graded. It has not, however, been applied generally to the assay of insulin, solely because of the time needed to collect the data. Under the normal conditions allowing a week to elapse between the separate testings, the time needed to conduct such an assay using two doses of standard and two of test preparations would be 3 weeks. In view of the more recent suggestions that single blood sugar levels without reference to the initial level provide a satisfactory measure of response to insulin (see Chapter 1 and Young and Romans, 1948), it

TABLE II

PROTOCOLS FROM THE ASSAY OF CRYSTALLINE INSULIN 9224B AT 22 UNITS/MG

Ratio between successive doses = 1.667[a]

Rabbit	Standard			Test preparation			Sums
	2 U/ml	1.2 U/ml	0.72 U/ml	2 U/ml	1.2 U/ml	0.72 U/ml	
18	117	116	150	151	158	207	899
23	135	142	146	101	142	191	857
Sums	252 (1)	258 (2)	296 (3)	252 (4)	300 (5)	398 (6)	
64	115	148	163	97	99	160	782
48	134	145	159	137	149	165	889
Sums	249 (6)	293 (1)	322 (2)	234 (3)	248 (4)	325 (5)	
35	159	172	184	155	173	196	1039
8	132	163	147	116	130	157	845
Sums	291 (5)	335 (6)	331 (1)	271 (2)	303 (3)	353 (4)	
46	117	131	135	105	133	157	778
29	169	220	220	138	176	189	1112
Sums	286 (4)	351 (5)	355 (6)	243 (1)	309 (2)	346 (3)	
4	127	144	146	102	123	166	808
21	144	177	240	149	151	178	1039
Sums	271 (3)	321 (4)	386 (5)	251 (6)	274 (1)	344 (2)	
42	133	138	161	139	146	152	869
17	158	188	196	101	142	138	923
Sums	291 (2)	326 (3)	357 (4)	240 (5)	288 (6)	290 (1)	
Total sums	1640	1884	2047	1491	1722	2056	10840

Days	1	2	3	4	5	6
Sums	1683	1795	1766	1817	1893	1876

[a] Figures in parentheses indicate day of dosing.

does become practicable to apply this design even with the use of three doses each of the standard and the test preparations.

To illustrate the interpretation, the data shown in Table II have been taken from such an assay using three doses of standard and three of test preparations, in which the responses were measured as the blood sugar levels (the sum of duplicate readings) at 1½ hours after the subcutaneous injection of the insulins. The test was completed in 6 consecutive days, injections being made at 9:30 AM, bleedings made at 11 AM, and the animals being fed uniformly from 12 noon to 4:30 PM, at which time the uneaten food was removed. The rabbits were allowed access to water during the whole test.

The data were submitted to an analysis of variance. The results of this analysis are shown in Table III.

TABLE III

ANALYSIS OF VARIANCE FOR DATA IN TABLE II

Source of variation	Sum of squares	Correction term	Reduced sum of squares	df	Variance
Total	$117^2 + \cdots + 138^2$	$10840^2/72$	61140	71	
Between rabbits	$(899^2 + \cdots + 923^2) \div 6$	$10840^2/72$	21202	11	1927.5
Between days	$(1683^2 + \cdots + 1876^2) \div 12$	$10840^2/72$	2395	5	479
Between doses	$(1640^2 + \cdots + 2056^2) \div 12$	$10840^2/72$	21708	5	4341.6
Residual error			15835	50	$316.7 = s^2$

The significant variance ratio for doses showed that changes in dose were accompanied by real change in response level. A partition of the reduced sum of squares for between doses was made using polynomial coefficients as suggested by Bliss and Marks (1939a).

TABLE IV

EXAMINATION OF DOSE RESPONSE RELATION FOR EXPERIMENTAL DATA IN TABLE II

	St_{100}	St_{60}	St_{36}	T_{100}	T_{60}	T_{36}	$NS(x)^2$	$S(xYp)$	Variance $\dfrac{S^2(xYp)}{NS(x^2)}$	Variance ratio
Difference between samples	-1	-1	-1	$+1$	$+1$	$+1$	72	-302	$1266.7 = D^2$	3.999
Slope of l.d.r.l.	$+1$	0	-1	$+1$	0	-1	48	-972	$19683 = B^2$	62.15
Departure from parallelism	$+1$	0	-1	-1	0	$+1$	48	158	520.1	1.64
Curvature of combined line	$+1$	-2	$+1$	$+1$	-2	$+1$	144	22	3.36	0.01
Opposed curvature of separate lines	-1	$+2$	-1	$+1$	-2	$+1$	144	184	235.11	0.75
Total response in 12 rabbits $= Yp$	1640	1884	2047	1491	1722	2056		Sum	21708.27	

Residual variance $= 316.7$
$s = 17.8$

The results of this examination are shown in Table IV. From it, it can be concluded that the individual lines relating response to log dose are linear and parallel and that the mean slope differs significantly from zero. Then the log activity ratio may be calculated as

$$M = \frac{kID}{B}$$

where $I = \log_{10}$ of dose interval $= \log 1.667 = 0.2218$ and in an assay using three doses of each preparation

$$k = \sqrt{8/3} = 1.633$$

i.e.,

$$M = \frac{(1.633)(0.2218)(35.6)}{(140.3)} = 0.0919 = \log 1.236$$

Calculation of Fiducial Limits of Error. When $C_p = B^2/(B^2 - t^2 s^2)$ is small, the fiducial limits of M are approximately given by the expressions

$$M + ts_m \quad \text{and} \quad M - ts_m$$

where $s_m = skI\sqrt{B^2 + D^2}/B^2$. In the example given

$$s_m = \frac{(17.8)(1.633)(0.2218)\sqrt{19683 + 1266.7}}{19683}$$

$$= \frac{933.1533}{19683} = 0.0474$$

and

$$t(P = 0.05) = 2.01$$

The fiducial limits of M are then $0.0919 \pm 0.0953 = 0.1872$ and $\bar{1}.9966$ or $\log 1.539$ and $\log 0.9922$. These formulas are modified by C_p as follows. The true fiducial limits are then

$$C_p M + t_p s_m \quad \text{and} \quad C_p M - t_p s_m$$

where

$$_p s_m = \sqrt{C_p}\, skI \sqrt{B^2 + C_p D^2}/B^2$$

They may also be calculated by applying a simplified formula which is the appropriate modification of that given by Smith et al. (1944).

$$C_p M \pm \sqrt{(C_p - 1)(8/3\,I^2 + C_p M^2)}$$

By using the simplified formula in the given example, $C_p(P = 0.05) = 1.0695$ and the true fiducial limits $(P = 0.95)$ of M are $(1.0695)(0.0919) \pm \sqrt{(0.0695)(0.1312 + 0.0090)} = 0.1970$ and $\bar{1}.9996$, or $\log 1.574$ and $\log 0.9910$.

7. The Twin Cross-over Design

The possibility of designing cross-over tests enabling the slopes of the l.d.r.l. for the standard and the test preparations to be compared was referred to by Fieller (1940). He made brief mention of cross-over designs using two or three doses of both standard and test preparations which had been carried out and which used eight and eighteen dosage groups, respectively. Ultimately these were replaced by the twin cross-over test (Smith *et al.*, 1944) which is considered in Chapter 1 and is the design described in the "British Pharmacopoeia 1963" (B.P. 1963) and the "United States Pharmacopeia 1960 XVI" (U.S.P. XVI).

The Combination of a Series of Cross-over Tests. It was indicated (Smith *et al.*, 1944) that if a series of twin cross-over tests were carried out on one sample of insulin at the same assumed potency and using the same dose ratio, a condition that is most likely to apply if a sample is being assayed in accordance with the requirements of pharmacopeias, then, providing the separate estimates of s^2 are homogeneous (Barlett, 1937), the mean activity and its fiducial limits could be calculated by the following method.

TABLE V

SUMMARY OF DATA OF A SERIES OF TWIN CROSS-OVER TESTS[a]

Test No.	n_1; n_2; n_3; n_4	$1/w$	$1/w'$	T	U
1	3; 3; 3; 2	1.5000	−0.1667	+3.30	28.30
2	3; 3; 3; 3	1.3333	0.0	−15.77	26.10
3	3; 3; 3; 3	1.3333	0.0	−1.73	44.67
4	3; 3; 3; 3	1.3333	0.0	+8.60	46.07

[a] In each test the assumed strength was 22 U/mg and d 0.3010.

TABLE VI

CALCULATIONS ON DATA OF TABLE V AND VALUES OF s^2

Test No.	w	wT	wU	w^2/w'	df	S. of sq.	s^2
1	0.6667	+2.20	18.87	−0.074	7	142.46	20.35
2	0.7500	−11.83	19.57	0.0	8	303.74	37.97
3	0.7500	−1.30	33.50	0.0	8	534.65	66.83
4	0.7500	+6.45	34.55	0.0	8	650.81	80.35
Sums (1–4)	2.9167	−4.48	106.49	−0.074	31	1631.66	52.63
	= W	= Y	= X	= W'			= $\bar{s}^2$

$$t^2(P = 0.05, n = 31) = 4.16$$

For illustration the data from four tests were taken (see Tables V and VI). The mean log activity ratio was calculated as

$$\bar{M} = Yd/X = (-4.48)(0.301)/106.49$$

$$= -0.0127 = \bar{1}.9873 = \log 0.971$$

The mean activity of the sample was calculated as $22 \times 0.971 = 21.4$ U per milligram. The fiducial limits of the mean log activity ratio were calculated as the roots of the equation

$$X'^2 m^2 - 2(XY)' \, dm + Y'^2 d^2 = 0$$

where $X'^2 = X^2 - t^2 \bar{s}^2 W = 10701.5$

$(XY)' = XY - t^2 \bar{s}^2 W' = -460.88$

$Y'^2 = Y^2 - t^2 \bar{s}^2 W = -618.51$

whence $(XY)' d = (-460.88)(0.301) = -138.72 = -0.0130 \, X'^2$

$$Y'^2 d^2 = (-618.51)(0.0906) = -56.037 = -0.00524 \, X'^2$$

The quadratic reduces to the form

$$m^2 + 2(0.0130) \, m - 0.00524 = 0$$

or $(m + 0.0130)^2 = 0.00524 + (0.0130)^2$

$$= 0.005409 = (0.07354)^2$$

The fiducial limits $P = 0.95$ of the mean log activity ratio were calculated to be -0.0130 ± 0.0735, i.e., -0.0865 and 0.0605 or $\log 0.819$ and $\log 1.150$, and the fiducial limits of the activity of the sample to be $22 \times 0.819 = 18.0$ and $22 \times 1.15 = 25.3$ U per milligram.

A simplified formula was also given that could be applied to those examples in which responses for both days were obtained from all the animals tested or that losses occurred so to render the term $W' = 0$.

This formula necessitates the calculation of the value C_p (Fieller, 1940) which in these instances may be obtained as

$$C_p = X^2/X^2 - t^2 \bar{s}^2 W$$

The fiducial limits of the log activity ratio are then

$$C_p M \pm \sqrt{(C_p - 1)(d^2 - C_p M^2)}$$

8. The Triplet Cross-over Design

The logical extension of both the twin cross-over test and the three-assumption cross-over test, the triplet cross-over test, was applied in a collaborative assay of a freeze-dried preparation of globin insulin, under-taken by the Department of Biological Standards, National Institute of Medical Research, and the British Insulin. Manufacturers Biological Standardisation Committee (1952).

The layout of this design is shown in Table VII. Since it consists of three cross-over tests carried out at different assumed potencies it would be interpreted by the method described by Fieller (1940).

TABLE VII

ARRANGEMENT OF THE TRIPLET CROSS-OVER TEST

	Treatment in test	
Dosage group	Day 1	Day 2
1	Standard (high)	Test (low)
2	Standard (middle)	Test (middle)
3	Standard (low)	Test (high)
4	Test (high)	Standard (low)
5	Test (middle)	Standard (middle)
6	Test (low)	Standard (high)

It can also be interpreted by a method comparable to that for a twin cross-over test already described. The data to be extracted may be symbolized as in Table VIII.

TABLE VIII

DATA TO BE EXTRACTED FROM A TRIPLET CROSS-OVER TEST

Group of rabbits	Mean response to		Observed mean sum	Observed mean difference $T - St$	Number of animals
	Standard	Test			
1	St_3	T_1	Y_1	y_1	n_1
2	St_2	T_2	Y_2	y_2	n_2
3	St_1	T_3	Y_3	y_3	n_3
4	St_1	T_3	Y_4	y_4	n_4
5	St_2	T_2	Y_5	y_5	n_5
6	St_3	T_1	Y_6	y_6	n_6

Values of S^2 (mean square between rabbits) and s^2 (mean square within rabbits) are calculated by the methods already considered with regard to the twin cross-over test; both will be determined with $(Sn - 6)$ degrees of freedom.

The important aspects of the assay may be checked by computing the quantities and their sampling variances shown in Table IX.

TABLE IX

VALUES TO BE OBTAINED FROM A TRIPLET CROSS-OVER TEST

	Quantity to be calculated	Sampling variance
Agreement between slope	$(Y_1 + Y_6) - (Y_3 + Y_4)$	$S^2 \left(\dfrac{1}{n_1} + \dfrac{1}{n_6} + \dfrac{1}{n_3} + \dfrac{1}{n_4} \right)$
Departure from linearity	$(Y_1 + Y_3 + Y_4 + Y_6) - 2(Y_2 + Y_5)$	$S^2 \left(\dfrac{1}{n_1} + \dfrac{1}{n_3} + \dfrac{1}{n_4} + \dfrac{1}{n_6} + \dfrac{4}{n_2} + \dfrac{4}{n_5} \right)$
Common slope (U)	$- y_1 + y_3 + y_4 - y_5$	$s^2 \left(\dfrac{1}{n_1} + \dfrac{1}{n_3} + \dfrac{1}{n_4} + \dfrac{1}{n_6} \right)$
Differences in responses (T)	$y_1 + y_2 + y_3 + y_4 + y_5 + y_6$	$s^2 \left(\dfrac{1}{n_1} + \dfrac{1}{n_2} + \dfrac{1}{n_3} + \dfrac{1}{n_4} + \dfrac{1}{n_5} + \dfrac{1}{n_6} \right)$

Working in logs to the base of the *extreme* dose ratio, U is an estimate of 4 times the slope of the l.d.r.l. and T is an estimate of 6 times the mean difference between standard and test.

The estimate of $\log_{10}$ activity ratio of the standard and test preparations is $M = 2Td/3U$ where $d = \log_{10}$ of the *extreme* dose ratio.

Calculation of fiducial limits. The calculation of fiducial limits may be made in a similar manner to that recorded for the twin cross-over test.

First the values

$$\frac{1}{w_u} = \frac{1}{n_1} + \frac{1}{n_3} + \frac{1}{n_4} + \frac{1}{n_6}$$

$$\frac{1}{w_t} = \frac{1}{n_1} + \frac{1}{n_2} + \frac{1}{n_3} + \frac{1}{n_4} + \frac{1}{n_5} + \frac{1}{n_6}$$

$$\frac{1}{w'} = -\frac{1}{n_1} + \frac{1}{n_3} + \frac{1}{n_4} - \frac{1}{n_6}$$

are calculated.

Then the fiducial limits are the roots of the equation

$$U'^2 m^2 - 2(UT)' \, dm + T'^2 d^2 = 0$$

where $U'^2 = U^2 - t^2 s^2/w_u$

$(UT)' = 2UT/3 - t^2 s^2/w'$

$T'^2 = 4/9(T^2 - t^2 s^2/w_t)$

9. Relative Efficiency of the Designs

The most efficient test design based on a given number of responses, will be that which yields at the proposed probability level the smallest fiducial range to be attached to the potency estimate extracted from the data.

The formula derived by Fieller (1940) measures the square of the half-fiducial range as

$$\frac{t^2 s^2 C_p}{b^2}\left[\frac{1}{n_{St}}+\frac{1}{n_T}+\frac{C_p}{Sw(x-\bar{x})^2}\frac{(\bar{y}_{St}-\bar{y}_T)^2}{b^2}\right]$$

where

$$C_p=b^2\Big/\left[b^2-\frac{t^2 s^2}{Sw(x-\bar{x})^2}\right]$$

and n_{St} and n_T are the number of responses on standard and test preparations.

If $\bar{y}_{St}-\bar{y}_T=0$, and deviations from this cannot be attributed to animal arrangement this reduces to

$$\frac{t^2 s^2 C_p}{b^2}\left(\frac{1}{n_{St}}+\frac{1}{n_T}\right)$$

The portion

$$\left(\frac{1}{n_{St}}+\frac{1}{n_T}\right)$$

is a minimum when $n_{St}=n_T$ a condition which is imposed by those designs using a cross-over technique or modifications of it. In such cases the expression is reduced to $t^2 s^2 C_p/b^2 N$ where $N=\frac{1}{4}$ the total number of responses.

A measure of the efficiency is given by the value $Wf=Nb^2/t^2 s^2 C_p$ which may be written

$$\frac{Nb^2}{t^2 s^2}-\frac{N}{Sw(x-\bar{x})^2}$$

since $1/C_p$ may be written

$$\left(\frac{b^2}{s^2}-\frac{t^2}{Sw(x-\bar{x})^2}\right)\Big/\frac{b^2}{s^2}$$

The values in Table X have been extracted by examining the varying designs which have been discussed, keeping the number of responses constant $(=4N)$ and considering the extreme log-dose interval $(=d)$ (and equal for both standard and unknown if both are split).

From this it would be concluded that with a given number of responses the smallest fiducial range is yielded by those designs in which both standard and test preparations are injected at two dose levels, and that the inclusion of an intermediate dose while allowing for a check on linearity to be made widens this range.

TABLE X

VALUES OF $Sw(x - \bar{x})^2$ AND Wf IN VARIOUS CROSS-OVER DESIGNS USING $4N$ RESPONSES

Design	Doses of standard	Dose of unknown	$Sw(x - \bar{x})^2$	Wf	df for s^2
Bliss and Marks	2	2	Nd^2	$(Nb^2/t^2 s^2) - (1/d^2)$	$3N - 6$
Bliss and Marks	3	3	$2Nd^2/3$	$(Nb^2/t^2 s^2) - (3/2d^2)$	$3N - 10$
Twin cross-over	2	2	Nd^2	$(Nb^2/t^2 s^2) - (1/d^2)$	$2N - 4$
Triplet cross-over	3	3	$2Nd^2/3$	$(Nb^2/t^2 s^2) - (3/2d^2)$	$2N - 6$
Three-assumption cross-over	1	3	$Nd^2/6$	$(Nb^2/t^2 s^2) - (6/d^2)$	$2N - 6$

The apparent difference in efficiency of the designs, however, will be small if $1/d^2$ itself is small compared with $Nb^2/t^2 s^2$.

If the average value of b^2/s^2, encountered in insulin assay on rabbits, is taken to be of the order 40, tables may be constructed to show the approximate number of responses necessary to yield fiducial limits of given order at the probability levels $P = 0.95$ and $P = 0.99$, when the various designs are used and the extreme dose ratio is that described in the official tests of the B.P. 1963 and the U.S.P. XVI (see Table XI).

The conclusions to be drawn from Table XI are that when $b^2/s^2 = 40$,

TABLE XI

APPROXIMATE NUMBER OF RABBIT RESPONSES NEEDED TO YIELD FIDUCIAL LIMITS OF GIVEN ORDER WHEN $b^2/s^2 = 40$

Design	Doses of standard	unknown	Error Wf	10% 583.22 $P = 0.99$	10% $P = 0.95$	15% 271.26 $P = 0.99$	15% $P = 0.95$	25% 106.50 $P = 0.99$	25% $P = 0.95$	50% 32.25 $P = 0.99$	50% $P = 0.95$
Bliss and Marks	2	2		404	233	196	112	84	49	34	22
Bliss and Marks	3	3		407	235	200	115	88	51	38	25
Twin cross-over	2	2	$d = 0.3010$	404	233	197	114	85	51	35	23
Triplet cross-over	3	3		407	235	201	116	89	53	40	26
Three-assumption cross-over	1	3		441	255	233	135	123	72	73	44

all designs are roughly of equal efficiency when high orders of precision are aimed at and the dose ratio is 2 to 1. The three-assumption cross-over design is the least efficient and would become more so if the dose ratio is narrowed.

Figure 1 illustrates the number of responses needed for varying values of b^2/s^2 for certain conditions.

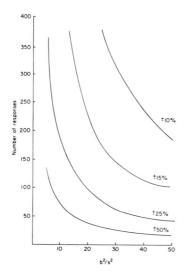

Fig. 1. Graphs showing the number of responses needed to achieve certain degrees of precision ($P = 0.95$) for different values of b^2/s^2, using optimal conditions in design and a dose interval of 2 ($d = 0.301$).

10. Test for Delayed Activity

Although the clinical action of the insulin preparations which possess delayed activity may not be reflected identically in the response of the normal unfed rabbit, a test for delayed action may be performed on rabbits which gives some indications of the relative efficiency of such preparations and may be used to examine them for uniformity either by making comparison with soluble insulin or preferably with a standard preparation of like composition.

In such tests the cross-over principle may also be employed. The data recorded are the mean blood sugar levels of the groups of rabbits at fixed intervals after injection, and may or may not be expressed as a percentage of the initial level. There seems some advantage in expressing the level in this way since if it is then plotted against time, the resulting curves will have a common origin.

It is customary to carry out the comparison at one assumed level only, and since the character of the delayed-action insulins may be otherwise impaired the injection is made without dilution and at equal levels of concentrations for both standard and test preparations. For this reason the volumes to be injected will be very small and of the order 0.01 or 0.02 ml for preparations containing 80 or 40 U per milliliter. Injections of such volumes may be readily made by means of the micrometer syringe designed by Trevan (1925). Lacey (1946) has also referred to the use of 0.25-ml syringe graduated to 0.01 ml for this purpose.

The precision of the U.S.P. XIII test for delayed activity was examined by Bliss (1949); he considered that the test could distinguish finer differences than it was called upon to make in practice.

Thorp (1944a) has shown that the handling of the rabbits during the course of the assay affects considerably the speed with which their blood sugars return to normal. His results, shown in Fig. 2, indicate that this is more marked in the case of soluble insulin than in the case of delayed-action preparations.

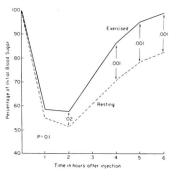

FIG. 2. Graph to show the reliability of the differences between the responses of "exercised" and "resting" rabbits after injection of soluble insulin. The significance of the differences at each hour is shown by the arrows. (From Thorp, 1944a.)

Stewart and Smart (1953) described the use of guinea pigs in tests for delayed activity. Guinea pigs of one sex that weigh 200–500 gm are considered suitable, but in any one test the weight range is restricted to 160 gm. The blood samples are removed by heart puncture and no cross-over technique is adopted, the test being completed in one day.

B. Manipulative Procedures

1. Rabbit Colony

If it were possible to set aside sufficient space for breeding or to purchase such animals, the use of one breed of rabbits for the purpose of insulin assay might be preferable.

Bliss and Marks (1939b) considered the ways in which the reactions of individual rabbits could affect the precision of the assay. They concluded in their experiment that those of the Sandy Lop breed were less sensitive to insulin than the 12 Himalayans which were retained and on which their subsequent calculations were made. A valid treatment in which individual sensitivities are allowed for will be referred to later (dosage of animals); its use here might have made all animals in this group equally suitable.

Among the Himalayans retained by Bliss and Marks, however, there was no evidence that the rabbits varied in their reactions either to dose changes or to differences in days although there was still evidence of a wide variation in their overall susceptibility. Certain rabbits showed more erratic responses than others, and it was suggested that it might be profitable to replace such animals in future tests. Retaining the Himalayans the estimate of variance was $s^2 = 41.4$ (77 df), but if the erratic rabbits were removed this was reduced to 28.7 (49 df).

In the conduct of cross-over tests, variations in the slopes of the l.d.r.l. of individual rabbits would produce larger effects on the value of s^2 when the doses administered to the rabbit were more widely spaced. Fieller (1940) noted that in the simple cross-over tests he had examined and which had been carried out on mixed breeds there was no evidence of this. From similar tests carried out from 1933 to 1938 a mean estimate of $s^2 = 35.18$ (5825 df) was recorded (Fieller et al., 1939b). Data from the same laboratory, for the period 1941 to 1945, when larger differences in the doses were effected by the use of the twin cross-over design, gave an estimate of variance of 48.16 (3749 df).

This higher variance could indicate that variations in the slopes of l.d.r.l. for individual rabbits did occur, but such an assumption could not be substantiated, nor could it be assumed that the use of rabbits of one breed would have obviated this.

In all the assay laboratories with which we are acquainted the colonies used for insulin assay are composed of mixed breeds purchased from reputable dealers and animals weigh 2–3 kg.

Often it is found that on arrival the rabbits' ears are infested with mites, a condition which may be successfully treated with phenolized oil, the use of which as a prophylactic for this purpose is also to be recommended.

2. Selection for Test

When animals are being selected for test the record cards of those considered suitable may be shuffled and dealt into heaps, corresponding in number to the number of dosage groups, until the number decided as convenient for use has been selected.

The doses to be assigned to these groups are decided by further randomization. In cross-over tests the dose on the second day is determined by that administered on the first.

In 4- or 6-day tests a more elaborate randomization may be employed such as is described by Bliss and Marks (1939a) using the basic patterns tabulated by Fisher and Yates (1938).

The pattern must be further randomized by interchanging rows and columns by use of shuffled numbered tags or by use of random numbers. The doses are assigned to the letters and finally the groups of rabbits or individual rabbits assigned to the rows.

Since this procedure is laborious, it has been worth while to record all the 4 × 4 combinations possible, paying due regard to the relative frequency to be applied to the basic patterns, and to assign a consecutive number by randomization to each combination, and to make the final selection by a method similar to that used above to select the basic pattern.

Although theoretically similar frequencies in the 6 × 6 design should be considered, in practice it is adequate to randomize the interchange of rows and columns from one block.

It is a normal practice, on the completion of a test, to split up the groups of animals used so that random selections for a new test may be made. In the conduct of cross-over tests this may be modified so that, on the day a test is completed, further groups of animals are injected with dilutions of a new test preparation and these groups, together with the original groups receiving standard, form the beginning of a new test. The economy in animals is considerable and the procedure has only the objection that the groups retain their identity for three consecutive appearances, losing it when they have received the test preparation on the day the second test is completed.

3. Colony Diet

It does not seem that the nature of the colony diet, providing it is adequate, has a marked effect on the precision of insulin assay. In practice it was found that feeding a mixture of bran and oats supplemented with fresh green food and allowing access to water continuously gave results roughly parallel to those obtaining in other laboratories. In another laboratory, the use of cubed diet without supplements of fresh green food (Bruce and Parkes, 1946) proved equally satisfactory.

4. Dosage of Animals

In single-day tests it is imperative that the doses be administered on a strictly defined basis (e.g., units per kilogram), and as has been noted previously the presence of an unduly sensitive or insensitive rabbit would materially affect the result obtained.

Use of the cross-over technique, or modifications of it, allows for animals of widely differing sensitivities to be used without bias, but even so it is wise to avoid using those animals that respond only slightly to the defined dose or to an extent approaching convulsive levels. This could be achieved by submitting all animals to a prior standardization and discarding those that respond outside certain predetermined levels.

Marks (1925) considered that, although doses could be related to the weight of the animal, the dose received by an animal throughout a test should be constant and not fluctuate with its weight changes, which would of course be small if they occurred at all. This principle is also implied in the conditions specified in the U.S.P. XVI.

Constancy of dose in a test is also maintained in a practice followed to render a greater proportion of the colony available for test. In this method the dose that will produce a satisfactory response is determined for each animal and is expressed in millimeters of a standard solution containing 2 U per milliliter. This volume is called the "standard volume" and may vary from 0.3 to 0.8 ml. Whenever an animal appears on test it receives its "standard volume" of the preparation suitably diluted to allow for different levels of dosage to be employed.

This procedure has been examined critically (Fieller *et al.*, 1939b) and shown to be valid.

It has been customary to make the injection of insulin in concentrations of the order 2 U per milliliter using 1-ml tuberculin syringes. These are usually of high order of accuracy, but it will be appreciated that, if the method of dosage employing use of "standard volumes" is followed, inaccuracy in graduations of the syringe, providing it is used without change for the whole test, will be of no importance.

Lacey (1946) has reported that satisfactory results may be achieved by making injections without dilution by means of a micrometer syringe or by using a 0.25-ml syringe graduated to 0.01 ml. This, it is claimed, does not mask the difference in action between insulins of differing purities which has greater importance in experimental work than in the routine assay of insulin solutions for clinical use.

It has also been customary to make the injections subcutaneously. Young and Romans (1948) have reported experiments which show that intravenous injections, with blood sugar levels determined at 50 minutes after injection, are perfectly satisfactory. Experience shows that the levels of dosage required for intravenous or subcutaneous injections are the same and that one route has little advantage over the other from the point of view of precision, although the subcutaneous injection has the advantage of manipulative simplicity.

5. Blood Samples

The method adopted for the taking of blood samples will depend on individual preferences. The following procedure which has been used quite satisfactorily over a long period is recorded in some detail.

The blood is removed via the ear by venipuncture. The ear of the rabbit is first shaved, a small paper clip fastened to the base, and the veins are further dilated by means of a 32-candle power carbon filament lamp which serves also to illuminate the venous pattern of the ear (Fig. 3). The vein is punctured by means of a No. 13 triangular surgical needle, the incision being made in the external vein and in the first instances as near to the base of the ear as is convenient. The external vein should preferably be used, since incision of the larger mid-veins soon renders the ear unsuitable for the taking of further samples. The blood is encouraged to flow by a minimum of massage and is collected into a small pot containing a few crystals of potassium oxalate, from which it is pipetted into suitable deproteinizing solutions. Subsequent bleedings are induced at this puncture by the same operations and usually, but not always, necessitate reopening of the puncture by means of the needle. There are are other means by which the necessary dilation of the vein may be induced. It can be accomplished by the use of xylol; this does, however, tend to harden the ear.

Although the use of heparin or special resins will suggest themselves for the purpose of rendering shed blood noncoagulable, the use of potassium oxalate as described has been found quite satisfactory. If more accurate oxalation is desired it may be obtained by pipetting exact volumes of potassium oxalate solution into clean tubes and then drying off the liquid in an oven.

It is to be expected that excitement, with the consequent liberation of adrenaline, will cause a considerable rise in blood sugar level and it is therefore desirable that a minimum amount of disturbance to the animals should be allowed.

It has been found satisfactory to allow the animals freedom of movement between bleedings by housing them in suitable cages whence they are removed in turn to a restraining box so that the bleeding may be more easily accomplished (Fig. 3). The front of this box is in the form of stocks secured by means of a sliding lid. The box is also fitted with a movable partition so that rabbits of varying sizes may be accommodated.

This removal from the cage to the box cannot be done without some disturbance, and the effect of the treatment on the blood sugar level of untreated fasting animals has been studied.

It was concluded that removing the animals for the taking of blood samples at hourly intervals would not affect the response unduly,

FIG. 3. The restraining box for bleeding rabbits.

especially when it was considered that each animal would receive equivalent treatment.

Another procedure consists of restraining the animals for the duration of the test either by tying the animals in a bundle by means of a cloth square so that only the head is visible, a condition which is endured without struggle, or by confining them to the restraining box. For this purpose Thorp (1944b) found a specially designed metal box, reproduced diagrammatically in Fig. 4, to be most convenient. It has the advantage

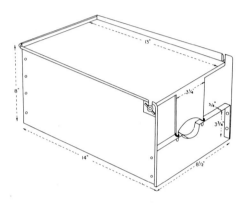

FIG. 4. Details of the rabbit box. (From Thorp, 1944b.)

that it was readily cleaned and so designed that damage to the spine was practically impossible. Thorp found that the animals soon accustomed themselves to remaining in such boxes for long periods without struggling. It is our experience that struggling does occasionally occur; the disturbance then is more severe than that caused by removal to a separate bleeding box and is, of course, less uniform for the group of animals.

Thorp (1944a) compared the effect of this procedure with that in which a uniform amount of exercise was applied to each rabbit before each bleeding and showed that the curves relating blood sugar to time differed markedly between the exercised and nonexercised rabbits when treated with soluble insulin. The graph prepared by him is reproduced in Fig. 2.

6. Blood-Sugar Determinations

Methods that specifically assay glucose are available and are used to assay blood sugar levels in insulin assays. The author is not aware that such methods improve the accuracy or the precision of insulin assays.

The method of Hagedorn and Jensen (1923) using Somogyi's (1930) method of protein precipitation lends itself most readily to multi-blood sugar analyses, and relatively unskilled workers soon attain a high degree of accuracy in its use.

Whether to contribute to greater accuracy or to avoid lost readings through accident it is customary to determine blood sugars in duplicate. Actually our practice has been to make the bleedings in duplicate and make one determination on each filtrate. From data available to him and which had been obtained in this manner, but using the Shaffer and Hartman (1921) method of blood sugar determination, Fieller (1940) considered the standard error of a single determination to be of the order 3.7 mg and calculated that with an I.B.S. of 120 mg/100 ml and a F.B.S. ranging from 70 to 100, values ranging from 6.4 to 8.1 would be contributed to the residual variance of a percentage reduction. If only single determinations were made we would expect the residual variance to be increased by a further amount ranging from 6.4 to 8.1 under similar conditions.

Since the efficiency of an assay is inversely proportional to the residual variance of a single response but proportional to the number of responses obtained, any loss of efficiency resulting from the use of single in place of duplicate determinations could be allowed for, in the extreme of the case quoted above, by multiplying the number of responses by $(s^2 + 8.1)/s^2$.

If a value of s^2 of the order 36 (Fieller, 1940) is to be expected, this factor would then be 1.225.

7. Criterion of Response

The early concept that the most informative response is the blood sugar level measured over 5 hours after injection related to the I.B.S. was preserved in the B.P. 1958.

It has been shown (Bliss and Marks, 1939a; Fieller, 1940) that a linear relationship exists between the percent reduction and the log dose. Many workers (Hemmingsen and Marks, 1932; Fieller, 1940; Bliss and Marks, 1939a) have shown, however, that if the F.B.S. is related to the I.B.S. in this manner a correlation still exists between the resulting percent reduction and the I.B.S., and methods have been described by which this degree of correlation may be assessed and corrected.

Since it was found in one laboratory that the correlation factor had remained stable over a number of years, it was suggested that adjusted responses should replace the percent reductions, and for this purpose percent reductions −0.3 I.B.S. (in mg/100 ml) were used.

It has been suggested (Emmens, 1948; Young and Romans, 1948) that an efficient response is the blood sugar level determined at that time at which experience suggests the lowest level is reached. Thus with intravenous injections Young and Romans were content to take single blood samples after 50 minutes had elapsed. Pugsley and Rampton (1948) have confirmed that the use of the single reading following intravenous injections, as a measure of response compares very favorably with that of the mean blood sugar level, over 5 hours, related to I.B.S. following subcutaneous injections. Data presented in this chapter to illustrate the interpretation of Bliss and Marks show that with subcutaneous injection blood sugars at $1\frac{1}{2}$ hours yield a satisfactory response. The U.S.P. XVI uses as the measure of response the summed blood-sugar levels at 1 and $2\frac{1}{2}$ hours after injection without reference to the I.B.S. In the B.P. 1963, the measure of response is the blood sugar level $1\frac{1}{2}$ hours after injection without reference to the I.B.S.

8. Fasting Period and Frequency with Which Animals May Be Used

The frequency with which animals may be used will depend to a large extent on the fasting period imposed and the bleeding schedule. A 6-day interval between usage will allow for almost any accepted fasting period and for any bleeding schedule to be applied.

With this interval it has been found convenient to arrange that the animals are not fed on the day before the test or on the day of the test until the last bleeding, 5 hours after injection, has been made. On occasions, to accommodate the use of animals twice in one week, the animals have been fed in the morning of the day before the test and the remaining food removed at 4:30 PM. A similar pretesting treatment has been imposed for the completion of the test with a 2-day interval between the two halves of the test.

No great differences in reaction were noted on these occasions except that it was found necessary to increase the dose of insulin injected by approximately 30%.

If the bleeding schedule is such that only one blood sample is taken (Young and Romans, 1948), the frequency of use may be greatly increased. The data quoted in Table III, were obtained on 6 successive days by taking blood samples $1\frac{1}{2}$ hours after the subcutaneous injection of insulin and arranging that the animals were fed uniformly from noon to 4:30 PM.

It is not considered that this treatment is too severe: in fact animals used in this way are fed more uniformly, and the number of bleedings per rabbit in one week is less than the number carried out in one day if the method followed is that which has hitherto been considered normal. Young and Romans (1948) reported that with a week's rest between successive tests it was possible to use each animal in this manner for 4 to 5 tests.

IV. The Mouse Method of Assay

A. DESIGN AND INTERPRETATION

1. Early Designs

The fact that mice, though able to withstand the effects of large doses of insulin at normal environmental temperatures, showed characteristic convulsive symptoms at elevated temperatures led to their extensive use.

The dose needed to cause 50% convulsions, the mouse dose of insulin, was estimated by Hemmingsen and Krogh (1926) under their conditions to have 1/600 of the value of the original Toronto rabbit unit. It was reported purely for the sake of interest since the inadequacy of this measure of response was appreciated.

Construction of dose-response curves resulted sooner with this response than had been the case with the rabbit response although as first described some differences in the nature of the relationship of percent convulsions to dose were recorded.

Hemmingsen and Krogh (1926) presented graphs in which the percent convulsions were linearly related to log dose. Trevan and Boock (1926) plotted percent convulsions against dose, but this was done for expediency in calculation since they considered the ratio of the doses necessary to induce identical changes in response level on different days to be equal.

A uniform treatment of data supplied by animals yielding "all-or-none responses" was suggested by Gaddum (1933) which indicated that a mathematical function of the response, its normal equivalent deviation (NED) was linearly related to log dose. To avoid negative values, Bliss (1934) suggested that the NED values should be increased by 5 and called probits.

Hemmingsen (1933) applied this treatment specifically to insulin assays using data from his own laboratory and that published by others (Trevan and Boock, 1926; Trevan, 1927). He showed that not only was the probit of the response of mice to insulin linear to log dose but the variation in the slopes of the l.d.r.l. so calculated exceeded that expected by the random sampling of mice.

2. The 2 + 2 Test

Tests using two doses of the standard and two of the test preparations at the same time enable checks to be made on the parallelism of the slopes of the l.d.r.l. for standard and test preparations.

Table XII shows the responses which were obtained in the course of such an assay and records the probits, the weighting factors appropriate to them ($= B$) and the overall weighting factor to be attached to the points ($= nB$).

TABLE XII

RESPONSES FROM THE 2 + 2 TEST

Dose	Standard high	Standard low	Test high	Test low
Response	18/24	1/24	15/24	4/24
Probit	5.674	3.269	5.319	4.033
B	0.54	0.20	0.61	0.45
n	24	24	24	24
nB	12.96	4.80	14.64	10.80

The calculations to be applied to the responses to the standard preparation are shown in Table XIII, and similar treatment of the responses to the test preparation will also be necessary. Since the dose ratios for the standard and the test preparations are equal, the calculations may again be simplified by using integers for $x =$ log dose, writing 1 for log high dose and 0 for log low dose and making suitable correction later to convert to terms of common logarithms.

TABLE XIII

CALCULATIONS APPLIED TO 2 + 2 TEST RESPONSES

Dose	Response	Probit $= y$	$nB = N$	x	Nx	Nx^2	Ny	Nxy
60	1/24	3.269	4.8	0	0	0	15.6912	0
100	18/24	5.674	12.96	1	12.96	12.96	73.5350	73.5350
Sum			17.76		12.96	12.96	89.2262	73.5350

$$\bar{x} = SNx \div SN \qquad 12.96 \div 17.76 = 0.7294$$
$$\bar{y} = SNy \div SN \qquad 89.2262 \div 17.76 = 5.0240$$
$$SN(x - \bar{x})^2 = SNx^2 - \bar{x}SNx \qquad 12.96 - 9.4569 = 3.5031 = p$$
$$SNx(y - \bar{y}) = SNxy - \bar{x}SNy \qquad 73.5350 - 65.1084 = 8.4266 = q$$
$$[SNx(y - \bar{y})]^2 \div SN(x - \bar{x})^2 \qquad (8.4266)^2 \div 3.5031 = 20.2699$$
$$1/SN \qquad 1 \div 17.76 = 0.0563$$

These values together with those obtained by similar treatment of the data for the test preparation are collected together in Table XIV where the additions and subtractions subsequently called for may be conveniently made.

On working in common logarithms, the log activity ratio of unknown to standard is

$$M = d[(\bar{x}_{S_t} - \bar{x}_T) - (\bar{y}_{S_t} - \bar{y}_T)/b]$$

where $d = $ log dose ratio which in the example $= \log 1.667 = 0.2218$.

Thus $M = 0.2218 [0.1542 - (0.2509/1.683)] = 0.0016 = \log 1.003$

We therefore estimate the potency of the unknown to be 100.3% of that assumed. The rest of the calculations follow as indicated in Chapter 1.

TABLE XIV

COMBINATION OF VALUES ARISING FROM CALCULATIONS ON DATA FROM $2 + 2$ TEST

	$1/SN$	q	p	q^2/p	$\bar{y}$	$\bar{x}$
Standard	0.0563	8.4266	3.5031	20.2699	5.0240	0.7297
Test	0.0393	7.9892	6.2147	10.2704	4.7731	0.5755
Sum	0.0941	$16.3577 = Q$	$9.7178 = P$	30.5403	—	—
Difference	—	—	—	—	0.2509	0.1542

$b = Q/P = 1.683 \qquad Q^2/P$	27.5345
$Sq^2/p - Q^2/P \; (\chi^2 \; \text{Slopes})$	3.0058

Although simplified calculations have been suggested for the interpretation of $2 + 2$ assays, the more extensive method described is preferable. If certain conditions are standardized, much computational labor may be saved by the preparation of suitable tables.

Treatment of Zero or Total Convulsions. It may happen that zero or total convulsions are encountered in a test. When using groups of 24 mice the convention of treating such responses as $\frac{1}{2}$ or $23\frac{1}{2}$ out of 24 has been adopted by the author. If in any test two total or two zero responses have been recorded, these responses have only been used to estimate the slope of the l.d.r.l. and the estimate of relative potency has been based on the remaining two responses.

A more elaborate method involving iteration has also been described and would overcome the criticism that can be raised against the suggested treatment for zero and total convulsions. When tests with zero or total convulsions provide a large part of the information, resort should be made to the iterative method, but it is the author's experience that when their appearance is occasional the procedure suggested is satisfactory.

3. Cross-over Tests with Mice

Hemmingsen (1939) has described the application of the cross-over technique to the mouse method of assay.

A unit cross-over test using a single dose each of standard and test preparations was conducted so that on the second day those mice which had previously received the standard preparations now received the test preparation and vice versa.

Hemmingsen imposed a further restriction in that the group was preserved intact and used for a series of cross-over tests at varying assumed potencies.

He interpreted the data simply by recording the difference in the proportion of mice convulsing on standard and test preparations in each test and relating this difference to the l.d.r.l. calculated by dividing the range of the differences effected by extreme change in assumed potency by the log of the ratio of these assumed potencies.

He pointed out that if the convulsion rates were between 10 and 90% this result would be practically the same as would have been obtained if probits had been used.

He assessed precision by recording the standard deviation of the estimated potencies and concluded that by making the comparison between standard and test preparations in a series of cross-over tests on the same mice the standard deviation of a test comprising 160 mice was reduced from 12–25 to 7–10%.

B. MANIPULATIVE PROCEDURES

The assay of insulin in mice has been successfully applied using animals purchased from dealers and those bred within the laboratory.

1. Mouse Colony

It could be expected that the laboratory-bred mice would have the advantage for the animals are likely to be more uniform, but we have no evidence to suggest that this is so. Certaintly they are not subjected to the disturbances associated with the delivery journey and with the change in colony diet but it appears that the effects of such disturbances, if they exist, are nullified by allowing an interval of 7 days to elapse between the receipt of the animals and their use for test purposes.

It is a satisfactory practice to house the animals on sawdust in sheet metal boxes with a mesh lid, in a room having a temperature range of 65° to 70°F. Boxes with dimensions $12 \times 12 \times 6$ inches are considered adequate to hold 35 mice weighing up to 30 gm.

2. Colony Diet

Rowlinson and Lesford (1948) suggested that a change in colony diet can cause a real change in the slope of the l.d.r.l. and hence, of course, affect the overall efficiency of the test. The data indicated that with a diet consisting of bread the mean slope of the l.d.r.l. was 4.68 whereas with a mixed diet, fed in the form of cubes and containing more protein and fat but less carbohydrate, the slope of the l.d.r.l. was 3.96. The difference between these two values was stated to be significant at $P = 0.95$ level. With both diets the animals received water ad libitum.

The slope of the l.d.r.l. was examined by us over two periods while the animals were being maintained on a typical mixed diet supplemented by crushed oats which were fed in a very moist state with no extra water. In the period November 1944 to July 1945, covering 269 tests, the mean slope was estimated to be 5.44, significant heterogeneity being indicated ($\chi^2 = 407$). During the first half of 1948 the mean slope from 231 tests was estimated to be 5.32 ($\chi^2 = 284$).

3. Fasting Periods

It is possible that the use of some precise fasting period would provide more uniform animals for test purposes.

A more convenient procedure however, has been satisfactorily followed for several years. Using a powdered diet, mixed to a crumble with water and supplemented with soaked bread and crushed oats, the animals set aside for insulin assay are fed each day at noon and supplied with water ad libitum.

On the next morning all are considered equally fasted and suitable for test. Those required are removed to clean boxes and subjected to test at 1–6 hours later.

The influence of this difference in the fasting period on the CD_{50} (the dose causing 50% convulsions) and on the slope of the l.d.r.l. during 231 tests has been examined by comparing those tests carried out during the morning with those carried out during the afternoon. The summarized results of this examination are shown in Table XV. They indicate that the extended fasting period imposed by delaying the

TABLE XV

THE INFLUENCE OF EXTENDED PERIOD OF FASTING ON CD_{50} AND SLOPE OF l.d.r.l.

Time tested	No. of tests	Log CD_{50} in mU/gm and SE	χ^2 between tests	Slope of l.d.r.l. and SE	χ^2 between tests
Morning	97	1.7409 (0.011)	769.9	5.470 (0.143)	6.43
Afternoon	134	1.7407 (0.009)	870.7	5.193 (0.116)	155.95

χ^2 between times   0.00 χ^2 between times   2.27
Critical $\chi^2 P = 0.05$ $n = 133$ $n = 96$ $n = 1$
                                166.35   124.50   3.84

tests until the afternoon has no effect on the sensitivity level of the mice and no significant effect on the slope of the l.d.r.l.

4. Selection of Animals for Test

a. Selection on Basis of Weight. The fasted mice are weighed and sorted into groups with restricted weight ranges.

Hemmingsen (1939) has reported the use of mice weighing 12 gm, but we limit our use to those weighing 17–30 gm, segregating them into groups weighing 17/20, 20/25, and 25/30 gm.

The mice for any one test are taken from one only of these weight groups, and for the purpose of this test are considered to be of equal weight.

The influence of different weight groupings on the CD_{50} and on the slope of the l.d.r.l. during 231 tests has been examined.

The summarized results of this examination are shown in Table XVI. They indicate that while in the case of the 20/25 and 25/30 gm groups dosing may be based on the mean of the weight range, in the case of

TABLE XVI

INFLUENCE OF WEIGHT GROUPS ON THE CD_{50} AND ON THE SLOPE OF THE l.d.r.l.

Weight group (gm)	No. of tests	Log CD_{50} (mU/gm and SE)	χ^2 between tests	Slope of l.d.r.l. and SE	χ^2 between tests
17/20	80	$\bar{1}$.7040 (0.012)	535.8	5.156 (0.151)	101.88
20/25	123	$\bar{1}$.7604 (0.009)	868.3	5.385 (0.125)	125.46
25/30	28	$\bar{1}$-7518 (0.016)	129.9	5.396 (0.259)	35.79

	χ^2 between groups	14.7		χ^2 between groups	1.51
Critical χ^2 $P = 0.05$	$n = 122$	$n = 79$	$n = 27$	$n = 2$	
	154.0	104.98	40.113	5.99	

the 17/20 gm some extra compensation is called for to allow for their greater sensitivity. The different weight groupings have no effect on the slope of the l.d.r.l.

b. Selection on Basis of Previous Use. Mice surviving the test may be used again, but those chosen for test should be segregated according to whether they are new mice, mice which have been used once, used twice, etc.

The effect of previous usage of mice on their reactions to insulin during 231 tests has been examined. The summarized results of this examination are shown in Table XVII. They show that the prior usage of mice has a significant effect on the CD_{50}, which is lower for new mice and those used once.

A possible explanation of this is that the mice lost through deaths during the early tests are the more sensitive ones. It would also appear permissible to telescope the groups of mice after they have been used twice previously. The prior use of mice has no significant effect on the slope of the l.d.r.l.

TABLE XVII

INFLUENCE OF PREVIOUS USE ON THE CD_{50} AND ON THE SLOPE OF THE l.d.r.l.

Times used previously	No. of tests	Log CD_{50} in (mU/gm and SE)	χ^2 between tests	Slope of l.d.r.l. and SE	χ^2 between tests
0	85	$\bar{1}.6842$ (0.012)	634.5	5.154 (0.148)	109.68
1	58	$\bar{1}.7316$ (0.012)	356.9	5.639 (0.181)	52.33
2	45	$\bar{1}.8023$ (0.010)	136.6	5.323 (0.206)	52.02
3	27	$\bar{1}.8038$ (0.014)	90.04	5.394 (0.266)	35.85
4	13	$\bar{1}.7867$ (0.025)	50.0	4.782 (0.115)	4.73
5	3	$\bar{1}.7983$ (0.049)	11.38	4.549 (0.257)	2.53

	χ^2 between use 43.5		χ^2 between use 7.49
Critical $\chi^2 P = 0.05$	$n = 84$ $n = 67$ $n = 44$ $n = 26$	$n = 12$ $n = 2$ $n = 5$
	110.71 79.25 63.70 38.88	21.03 5.99 11.07

c. *Selection on Basis of Sex.* For practical reasons the use of one sex is to be preferred.

The influence of sex on the reactions of mice to insulin during 231 tests has been examined. The summarized results are shown in Table XVIII. They indicate that sex has some effect on the CD_{50} but not on the slope of the l.d.r.l.

TABLE XVIII

INFLUENCE OF SEX ON THE CD_{50} AND ON THE SLOPE OF THE l.d.r.l.

Sex	No. of tests	Log CD_{50} in (mU/gm and SE)	χ^2 between tests	Slope of the l.d.r.l. and SE	χ^2 between tests
Male	182	$\bar{1}.7482$ (0.008)	1389.2	5.3093 (0.102)	198.88
Female	49	$\bar{1}.7106$ (0.013)	232.9	5.2863 (0.193)	65.75

	χ^2 between sexes 6.3	χ^2 between sexes 0.0108
	Critical $\chi^2 P = 0.05$ $n = 181$ $n = 48$	$n = 1$
	219.66 68.527	3.841

However, although one sex has no advantage over the other insofar as the precision of the assay is concerned, there is practical advantage in the choice of males.

5. *Preparation of Solutions for Test and Their Injection*

It has been considered preferable to effect change in the doses of insulin by changing the concentration and to administer all doses in the same volume. It is felt that it should not exceed 0.5 ml, and in practice a volume of 0.25 ml per mouse has been found quite convenient.

It is customary to make the injections subcutaneously. Trevan and Boock (1926) reported that they found intravenous and subcutaneous injections equally efficient.

6. *Treatment of Mice during the Test*

After injection and for the duration of the test the animals are normally maintained at an elevated temperature. Trevan and Boock (1926) used for this purpose a thermostatically controlled water bath in which heavy containers were placed to hold the mice. Hemmingsen and Krogh (1926) described the use of an air incubator with a glass front, and it is with such an apparatus that we have been accustomed to work. It has the advantage that the mice may be observed during the test; those which convulse can be removed quickly and given a therapeutic injection of glucose.

Our testing cabinet (Fig. 5) is a shallow cupboard in which access to 6 shelves is provided separately by means of glass slides. It is warmed by electric heater wires fitted below each shelf, the temperature is thermostatically controlled, and the air within the cabinet is mixed by means of a fan placed in the space at the rear of the shelves.

The cabinet holds 48 glass jars to house 96 treated mice; those jars which are to hold mice having the same dose are similarly colored and distributed throughout the cabinet so that the small temperature gradient which exists is applied equally to all doses.

The positions of these colored jars in the cabinet are constant and in each test the doses are assigned to the various colors at random.

Thorp (1948) has referred to the construction of a glass-fronted cabinet of cubic form. Air warmed by passage over suitable heating pads is supplied through the roof of the cabinet by means of a fan and the temperature is thermostatically controlled. The jars to hold the mice are placed on small movable racks and the apparatus has the distinct advantage in that it is readily cleaned.

Thompson (1946) has described the use of an inclined wire for the observation of mice showing the hypoglycemic reactions. This mesh screen, 24 × 36 inches, which will hold 100 or more mice, is fitted at an

FIG. 5. An insulin testing cabinet for mice.

angle of 60 degrees and so arranged that the injected mice placed on it can only leave the screen over an edge which is 8 inches or more from any other surface. Mice with advanced symptoms fall from the screen into a tray from which they may be removed to be injected with glucose.

A modification has been described by Young and Lewis (1947): the screen is replaced by a wire mesh drum of 8 inches diameter that is caused to revolve continuously, rotating once every 40 seconds. Under these conditions the mice apparently lose their hold before severe hypoglycemia has developed and feed on a suitable diet in the receiving tray so rendering the injection of glucose unnecessary.

7. Temperature for the Conduct of the Test

Elevated temperatures are necessary if mice are to exhibit the characteristic convulsions associated with hypoglycemia. The use of varying temperatures for the assay of insulin in mice has been described.

Trevan reported results using a temperature of 37°C while Hemmingsen preferred a temperature of 29°C, for at this temperature he found that his losses of animals were less. For many years we have used a temperature of 32°C, at which temperature the mice did not display the signs of discomfort shown at 37°C and appeared to respond more consistently than when a temperature of 29°C was applied.

Differences in the slopes of the l.d.r.l. obtained in the various laboratories may have been attributed to the temperature used, but it is certain that other factors have also contributed to these differences.

Data supplied by Trevan and Boock (1926) working at 37°C indicated a slope (probit *vs.* log dose) of the order 5, but a review (Irwin, 1943) of data accumulated later in the same laboratory while this temperature was still maintained indicated a slope of 3.0. Hemmingsen (1933) working at 29°C has recorded a slope of 4.9. In our own laboratory the mean slopes recorded for 269 tests during the period 1944 to 1945 was 5.43, and during 1948 the mean slope in 231 tests was 5.32. These tests were carried out at 32°C, but the slope value is higher than that reported by Rowlinson and Lesford (1948) working at 34°C.

The use of wire meshes, either fixed or revolving, since it determines the onset of less severe hypoglycemic symptoms has particular application in the conduct of insulin assays at temperatures lower than those normally applied.

Even though temperature may not have marked effect on the slope of the l.d.r.l., and therefore on the precision of the assay, it is certain that it has marked effect on the level of sensitivity, and for this reason it is important that whatever temperature is applied it should be controlled as closely as possible.

8. Convulsive Symptoms

The reacting mice mostly convulse violently; often, however, a mouse may pass into a state of collapse determined by the failure of the animal to right itself when placed on its back.

Both symptoms are considered equally positive. The animals are removed from the cabinet, and injected with 0.5 ml. of a 15% glucose solution. They are not separated on removal, for the final scores may be easily made by counting the empty spaces in the cabinet.

9. *Duration of the Test*

At 32°C convulsions may commence within 20 minutes of injection, reach their peak incidence in $\frac{3}{4}$ to 1 hour but rarely occur after $1\frac{1}{2}$ hours. For this reason it is adequate to observe the mice for $1\frac{1}{2}$ hours after injection. When the injection of one dose is completed the time is noted and readings taken from that point. Since the injection of 96 mice may be completed in 15 minutes the overall time taken for a test is $1\frac{3}{4}$ hours.

10. *Frequency of Use of Mice*

Animals on test on any day are fed at the completion of the test. They are suitable for test after a further 2 days of normal feeding. Thus, mice which have been used for test on Monday can be used again on Thursday.

11. *Number of Times To Be Used*

Mice can be satisfactorily used up to 6 times: their use on more occasions than this is seldom possible since at that time it is difficult to obtain sufficient mice of the correct weight range and "times used" to give full groups. The information in Table XVII, however, suggests that segregation on the basis of use may be abandoned after the mice have been used twice previously.

Table XVII also indicates that during these tests 85 groups of new mice were taken and 231 tests conducted. This means that on the average, under these conditions, each mouse was used 2.70 times, although the value would in fact be higher than this since some of the mice would have been used for other approximate assays. The magnitude of this value will naturally depend on the amount of testing to be done since a larger float of animals and pressure of testing allows them to be used more efficiently. Estimates made on two other occasions indicated that on the average the mice are used 3.7 and 4.1 times. These two estimates were from periods in which the mice used were of one sex.

V. Comparison of Rabbit and Mouse Methods of Assay

A. AGREEMENT BETWEEN THE METHODS

The results obtained in 4 out of 5 laboratories during the standardization of the second international standard against the first suggested that the mouse method yielded results different from those obtained by the rabbit method. This has been explained by the fact that in this case comparison was being made between preparations of widely

differing purities, and it has been considered that such differences should
not occur when samples of similar purities were being examined.

A comparison of results obtained in one laboratory under these conditions using both rabbit and mouse methods of assay is shown in Table
XIX. The rabbit tests used were the twin cross-over tests, each was
weighted inversely as the variance of the estimated potency, and this
weight was used to calculate a weighted mean potency. The individual
mouse tests were weighted similarly.

TABLE XIX

AGREEMENT BETWEEN RABBIT AND MOUSE METHODS OF ASSAY

	Rabbit method					Mouse method					
Sample	Estimated potency	No. of rabbit responses	No. of tests	Sw	χ^2 between tests	Estimated potency	No. of mice	No. of tests	Sw	χ^2 between tests	χ^2 between methods
H487	63.96	96	3	536.6	1.26	66.22	524	5	860.8	2.89	0.07
H488	168.5	160	5	2204.3	1.03	147.2	452	4	1259.0	1.88	2.76
H489	217.0	128	4	624.8	0.82	203.2	560	4	1182.1	1.49	0.33
H490	190.8	160	5	1845.1	8.41	195.4	1120	7	2199.7	8.08	0.11
H491	220.1	160	5	688.9	1.69	248.5	384	2	870.8	0.10	1.09
Sum		704		5899.7			3040		6372.4		

For each sample the agreement of the individual results obtained by
each method was checked by means of the χ^2 test, and a further χ^2 test
was made to check the agreement between the two methods.

Only with sample 488 was there a somewhat wide difference between
the mean potencies estimated by the two methods, but this was not
significant at $P = 0.95$ level.

B. RELATIVE EFFICIENCY OF THE TWO METHODS

On ignoring all other factors that must be considered in assessing
the relative efficiency of the two methods, the data summarized in
Table XIX indicate that the average contribution to Sw made by one
rabbit $= 5899.7/704 = 8.38$ and that the corresponding contribution
made by one mouse $= 6372.4/3040 = 2.10$. It would, therefore, be
concluded in this instance that 4 mice had an efficiency equivalent to 1
rabbit.

From the point of view of the labor and space required for the
housing and the feeding of the animals and for the conduct of the assay,
reliance on the mouse method has distinct advantages; but perhaps its
greatest values lies in the speed with which a result may be obtained.

Since, however, it is most probable that a colony of rabbits will be maintained in any case, the possibility of using this to the full to supplement the mouse method of assay must be considered.

This possibility will be approached with hesitancy if the method proposed involves blood sugar readings over 5 hours and the use of a 7-day interval between the separate stages of the test. It becomes more attractive, however, when it is considered that each member of the colony could supply a response to insulin on each day if the response were measured by means of a single blood sugar reading taken $1-1\frac{1}{2}$ hours after injection.

VI. Biological Assay of Insulin at Physiological Levels

Until the development of the radioimmunoassay of insulin a specific and sufficiently sensitive chemical or immunological method was not available for the assay of the small amounts of insulin to be found in blood, and the methods used were biological ones based on the effect of insulin both *in vivo* and *in vitro*.

A. *In Vivo* METHODS

Anderson *et al.* (1947) and Anderson and Long (1947a, b, 1948) described the use of the glucose-fed, alloxan diabetic, hypophysectomized, adrenodemedullated rat (A.D.H.A. rat) and used it for detecting the presence of insulin in perfusates from the isolated rat pancreas (Anderson and Long, 1948).

A.D.H.A. rats were given 5 ml of 20% glucose by stomach tube, submitted to pentobarbitone anesthesia, and, after 29 minutes at 38.3°C, were injected with the sample under test *via* the exposed jugular vein. Blood samples were taken 1, 15, and 30 minutes after injection, i.e., 30, 45, and 60 minutes after the glucose was given, and falls of blood sugar of about 50% were produced by the injection of 1 mU of insulin.

A method employing A.D.H.A. rats has also been described by Bornstein (1950) and has been widely used. A.D.H.A. rats are placed in individual cages in an incubator at 37°C with access to water but not to food. After 1 hour a blood sample is taken from the tail vein and the sugar is determined. Injections of test solutions are made subcutaneously and a further blood sugar determination is made after 1 hour. Bornstein showed that over the range 0.5–0.05 mU the blood sugar concentration was linearly related to the log insulin concentration by the equation $D = 75 + 49.1\ L$ where $L = \log$ insulin in milliunits. His results indicated that b^2/s^2 had a value of the order 25 (see Fig. 1).

Biegelman *et al.* (1956) refer to the use of hypophysectomized alloxanized mice (H.A. mice) and in experiments using H.A. rats obtained a value for b^2/s^2 of 10.7 with insulin in an albumin solution but indicate that it is too imprecise for use with aqueous solutions of insulin.

B. *In Vitro* METHODS

Gemmill (1941) reported that insulin acting on the isolated rat diaphragm caused increased synthesis of glycogen from glucose. Assays measuring glucose uptake of the hemidiaphragm under the influence of insulin have been described (Groen *et al.*, 1952; Vallance-Owen and Hurlock, 1954; Randle, 1954). Randle examined the precision of the method under the following conditions. Normal male rats weighing 100 to 150 gm, deprived of food for 18–24 hours before use, are killed by a blow and exsanguinated. The diaphragms are removed, divided, and washed for exactly 5 minutes in ice-cold buffer glucose. [Buffer (Gey and Gey, 1936) containing 2.5 mg of glucose per milliliter previously saturated with 93% O_2 and 7% CO_2.] The hemidiaphragms are removed, blotted dry, and transferred to the main compartments of Warburg manometer flasks containing the appropriate quantity of insulin in 1 ml of glucose buffer. Incubation is allowed to proceed for 3 hours at 37°C at a shake rate of 100 cycles per minute, the gas phase during incubation being 93% O_2 and 7% CO_2.

After incubation the flasks are cooled and the glucose is estimated on 0.2 ml by the method of Somogyi (1945). The hemidiaphragms are blotted dry and weighed on a torsion balance; the glucose uptake is expressed as milligrams of glucose per gram wet weight of diaphragm per hour. The cube root of this uptake is linearly related to the log insulin concentration. The value for b^2/s^2 in Randle's examination was 7.7 (see Fig. 1).

Martin *et al.* (1958) described the use of rat epididymal adipose tissue for the *in vitro* assay of insulin.

Rats fed ad libitum are killed by a blow and rapidly exsanguinated. The epididymal adipose tissue is lifted gently at the base and removed with a single cut. Without further manipulation or chilling it is divided into 3 parts and each piece, weighing 80–200 mg, is transferred separately to 10-ml preweighed rubber-stoppered flasks, containing 2 ml of plasma or Kreb's bicarbonate buffer containing 2 mg of gelatin per milliliter and with the glucose adjusted to be 3 mg per milliliter containing 0.2 μCi of glucose-1-^{14}C (1.9 ml of buffer or plasma +0.1 ml of glucose-1-^{14}C. After reweighing to obtain the tissue weight, the flasks are gassed with 5% CO_2 95% O_2 through hypodermic needles inserted through rubber-sealed ports in the rubber stopper. Below one port a small plastic cup is suspended. The needles are withdrawn, leaving the system airtight, and the flasks are incubated for 2 hours at 72°C at a shake rate of 72 cycles per minute.

After incubation, 0.2 ml of NaOH (freshly diluted 1:10 from saturated NaOH with CO_2-free water) is injected into the cup and 0.2 ml of 10 N H_2SO_4 into the medium. After at least 2 hours the contents of the cup are quantitatively transferred to a weighed centrifuge tube containing $BaCl_2$ and the precipitated $BaCO_3$ is washed 3 times with CO_2-free water, dried, and reweighed to give the total $BaCO_3$ present.

An aliquot is transferred to a weighed planchette and the specific activity is determined in a proportional flow counter. The results are expressed in counts per minute per total CO_2 as $BaCO_3$ per 100 mg of adipose tissue, the square root of which has been found to be linearly related to the log concentration of insulin.

Martin *et al.* (1958) also indicated that the method may be used by making measurements of the glucose uptake. Then, only 0.8 ml of buffer or plasma is used, the glucose concentration is 2 mg/ml, incubation is for 4 hours, and a sample solution of buffer or plasma is run concurrently without tissue.

The glucose concentration is determined in duplicate on 0.5-ml aliquots using the method of Nelson (1944).

The results are expressed as micromoles of glucose uptake per gram adipose tissue. The value of b^2/s^2 in Martin's experiments was 10.4 (see Fig. 1).

Using insulin-^{131}I, Piazza *et al.* (1959) have assessed the degradation of insulin during the *in vitro* assays using the rat diaphragm methods of Randle (1954), Willibrands and Groen (1956), and Vallance-Owen and Hurlock (1954) and the rat adipose tissue method of Martin *et al.* (1958). Degradation was appreciable in all systems but greatest in the rat muscle preparations, and proteolytic enzymes were leached into the medium. Insulin degradation was least in the adipose tissue preparation and the leaching phenomena minimal. In all cases the degradation was proportional to the mass of incubated tissue and to the extracellular concentration of insulin and was significantly inhibited by factors present in normal plasma.

VII. Methods Using Insulin Antiserum

Sera containing insulin antibodies have been produced in the guinea pig, the horse, the rabbit, and the sheep (Moloney and Coval, 1955; Moloney and Goldsmith, 1957), and its production in the fowl has been described by Patterson *et al.* (1964). Moloney and Coval produced it in guinea pigs by making successive injections spread over two sites of 1 mg crystalline insulin contained in a stable water in oil emulsion together with Freund's adjuvant (Freund and McDermott, 1942).

Some collections of guinea pig antiserum raised against ox insulin exhibit species specificity as described by Berson and Yalow (1959) and Berson *et al.* (1964). When such is the case, ox insulin will be bound more strongly than pig insulin, which itself will bind more strongly than human insulin. The strength of binding of a mixture of ox and pig insulin as presented in the International and U.S.P. reference standards will be intermediate between that of ox and pig, and their competition for antibody binding sites will be in the same order.

Ideally therefore the standard preparation, test preparation, and insulin for immunization should be of the same species. Although this is possible when commerical samples are being examined, it will probably not be possible when examinations on serum samples are being made. In such circumstances it will perhaps be best to work with an antiserum raised against a single crystalline insulin and to use this insulin as the reference standard.

A. Immunoassay

1. Using Ouchterlony Plates

The reaction between insulin and antiserum is not always a precipitating one. Moloney and Aprile (1959) showed that their antiserum from horse, rabbits and guinea pigs produced precipitin bands by the Ouchterlony (1948) plate technique, and this has been the experience of Steigerwald *et al.* (1960), Jones and Cunliffe (1961), Birkinshaw *et al.* (1962), as is that of Patterson *et al.* (1964) using fowl antiserum. The intensity of these bands and their shape and position under electrophoresis may be used to assess the potency of insulin when it is present in concentrations of the order 2 units per milliliter.

2. Using Tagged Red Cells

Arquilla and Stavitsky (1956) described how insulin antiserum could be used to assay microgram quantities of insulin in pure solutions. In principle, their method measured the release of hemoglobin produced by the residual amounts of antiserum after incubation with graded quantities of insulin acting in the presence of guinea pig complement on insulin-sensitized erythrocytes, prepared by coupling insulin to washed rabbit erythrocytes by means of bisdiazobenzidine. The method required optimally that the antiserum dilution should be that which shows the greatest inhibition of lysis when it is incubated with 10 μg of insulin, and under these conditions the hemoglobin released is inversely and linearly related to the log of the insulin concentration.

B. RADIOIMMUNOASSAY

1. Principles of the Radioimmunoassay

The binding of insulin labeled with ^{131}I and insulin antibodies has been used as a tracer system for unlabeled insulin.

In a mixture of radiolabeled insulin and insulin antiserum with the insulin in excess, added unlabeled insulin will compete with the radioactive insulin for the available antibody, and in a system where the amounts of radioactive insulin and insulin antibody are kept constant the radioactivity of the separated insulin antibody complex will vary with the amount of unlabeled insulin added.

Assay methods which have been described differ in the means which they employ to separate insulin antibody complex (bound insulin) from the free insulin (unbound insulin).

These methods fall into three main groups in which separation is accomplished by means of paper chromatoelectrophoresis, salt precipitation, or immunoprecipitation.

2. Radioimmunoassay Using Paper Chromatoelectrophoresis

This method employing paper chromatoelectrophoresis has been described and used extensively by Berson et al. (1956) and Berson and Yalow (1960). When a mixture of free insulin and insulin bound to antibody is subjected to paper electrophoresis, the free insulin remains at the point of application while the insulin antibody complex migrates with the globulins. Thus in the presence of insulin-^{131}I, two peaks of radioactivity corresponding to free and antibody-bound insulin-^{131}I appear.

The areas enclosed by these peaks are relative to the proportion of bound and free insulin present, and their ratio (bound/free) may be plotted against concentration of unlabeled insulin used.

In all calculations correction should be made for damaged insulin-^{131}I which would migrate with the serum proteins in the same manner as antibody-bound insulin. The proportion of damaged insulin may be estimated by means of a control strip in which the immune serum is replaced by nonimmune serum or by antiserum the binding capacity of which has been saturated by standard insulin.

The following is a brief outline of the method used by Berson *et al.* (1956).

Using Veronal buffer pH 8.6, ionic strength 0.1, solutions containing a constant amount of insulin-^{131}I (50–150 $\mu\mu$Ci/ml) and varying concentrations of standard insulin and the sample under test are prepared. To each is added antiserum diluted in the Veronal buffer and the mixtures refrigerated at 4°C for 4 days.

The mixtures are subjected to chromatoelectrophoresis for 60–90 minutes at 4°C in the same buffer on Whatman 3MM paper strips (37 × 550 mm) at a constant voltage of 20–25 V/cm, the cover of the apparatus being left open to allow hydrodynamic flow to occur during the run.

After drying at 45–60 minutes at 115°C the strips are assayed for radioactivity in an automatic strip counter.

3. Radioimmunoassay Using Salt Precipitation

The method using salt precipitation has been described by Grodsky and Forsham (1960), who used it to investigate levels of circulating insulin in man. Baum *et al.* (1964) have used it to assay commercial samples of insulin and protamine zinc insulin which had been stored for 20 years and had become mildly degraded. The results agreed well with those obtained by bioassay, and it was considered that the method discriminated between natural and denatured forms of insulin.

The following is a brief description of the method as used by Baum *et al.* (1964).

Into a series of tubes are pipetted 20 μ/ml volume dilutions of standard insulin and the sample under test together with 20 μ/ml of diluted insulin-^{131}I (0.04 μCi/20 μ/ml) all dilutions been made in 5% human serum albumin. Then 2.04 ml of a solution consisting of equal volumes of 0.2 M glycine and 30% urea in 5% albumin solution and containing antiserum is added to each tube, and the tubes are gently agitated for 1 hour at 24°C. To provide a carrier protein, there is then added 0.8 ml of a suitable dilution of human plasma (which had had its insulin content destroyed by storage at 5°C for 24 hours after adjustment to pH 10.5 with sodium hydroxide and then centrifugation in the cold after adjustment to pH 7.4 with hydrochloric acid).

After a further 15 minutes' agitation 6.0 ml of 27.32% sodium sulfite is added to each tube. The tubes are agitated for 1 hour at 24°C, then centrifuged in a refrigerated angle-head centrifuge at 2400 g for 45 minutes. The radioactivity of the supernatant fluid is measured and expressed as a percentage of that in the supernatant of a similarly treated control tube (containing no unlabeled insulin and no antibody). This percentage can be plotted against concentration of unlabeled insulin.

4. Radioimmunoassay Using Immunoprecipitation

The immunoprecipitation method, also described as the two-anti-body method, depends on the use of anti-γ-globulin serum to precipitate the insulin–antibody complex. It was used initially by Skom and Talmage (1958) and has also been described by Morgan and Lazarow (1962) and Hales and Randle (1963).

The reaction is usually carried out in two stages. In the first stage the solution of insulin-^{131}I with or without unlabeled insulin is allowed to react with a suitable dilution of anti-insulin serum. After a suitable time interval a dilution of a second serum containing antibodies raised against the γ-globulin of the anti-insulin serum is added, and precipitation is allowed to proceed. The precipitate is separated either by centrifugation or by filtration through cellulose acetate membranes, and the radio-activity of the supernatant fluid or the precipitate is measured.

The use of various buffer systems and of various periods of incubation has been described.

The following method has proved to be suitable.

Antiserum raised in guinea pigs against ox insulin is suitably diluted in 0.04 M phosphate buffer pH 7.4 containing thiomersalate (0.06 M) and bovine plasma albumin (0.1%), and 0.1 ml is placed in series 10×75 Pyrex tubes containing 0.1 ml of suitable concentration of the standard and sample under test contained in the buffer solution containing 0.9% sodium chloride. Then 0.0025 μg of insulin-[131]I (specific activity 10–150 μCi/μg) is added to all tubes, and a similar quantity is transferred to a circlet of lens tissue in the centre of a counting planchet so that the radio-active count added to each tube may be determined. The tubes are refrigerated (0–4°C) for 4 hours, after which 0.1 ml of a suitable dilution of serum raised in rabbits against either whole guinea pig serum or guinea pig γ-globulin is added to all tubes. After mixing, the refrigeration is continued for a further 22–24 hours. The precipitates are collected by filtration through a cellulose acetate membrane mounted on a micro-analysis filter holder, washed by the addition of 2×0.75 ml of the phosphate buffer containing increased bovine plasma albumin (4%). The membranes are attached to card circlets using rubber solution and dried at 37°C for 90 minutes. The radioactivity count is then measured in a suitable apparatus.

For a successful assay, zero tubes containing buffer in place of unlabeled insulin and treated similarly should bind 40–50% of the total insulin-^{131}I, and when control tubes containing no antiserum are included to check the efficiency of the washing procedure, only 2% or less of the total count rate should be recorded.

The count has been related to insulin concentration in various ways.

The simplest is to express count rate observed against concentration of insulin when, if the system obeys the rules for isotope dilution analysis, a linear relationship applies. This depends on a restriction that the antibody binds the same quantity of antigen irrespective of concentration, and though this is not the case it has been stated that in practice a linear relationship seems to hold. If this is so the results may be suitably interpreted by the slope-ratio method.

Some workers modify the count rate (C_i) by dividing it by the count (C_o) in the absence of unlabeled insulin yielding (C_i/C_o) by using it to divide the count yielding (C_o/C_i) or by using the difference between these counts $(C_o - C_i)$. Such procedures add nothing to the value of the count, although there may be some advantage if the difference method ensures that the plotted line passes through the origin.

Hales and Randle (1963) have described variants of the assay procedure outlined above which makes the method more suitable for assaying the low concentrations of insulin in serum and also removes any interference in serum assays caused by the reaction between γ-globulin in the serum being assayed and the rabbit anti-γ-globulin serum.

It has been stressed by various workers using immunoprecipitation methods that all buffer solutions should be prepared with deionized distilled water as the variation in the quality of ordinary distilled water gives rise to variable antigen/antibody binding.

VIII. Chromatographic Methods

Chromatographic methods using columns have been described for the separation of insulin from its associated impurities (Porter, 1953; Porath and Li, 1954; Dickinson, 1956). Robinson and Fehr (1952) used a paper chromatographic method to estimate the insulin present in protamine-zinc-insulin preparations. Paper chromatographic methods have also been described by Grodsky and Tarver (1956) and Light and Simpson (1956).

Bouman and Homan (1958) and Fenton (1959) have described the systemized application of paper chromatographic methods applicable to the routine comparison of insulins with a standard preparation.

Fenton (1959), using a micrometer syringe, applies quantities of the order 50 μg of insulin as standard and test preparations as spots at distances of 2.5 cm along a line drawn 4 cm from the bottom edge of a sheet of Whatman No. 1 paper 28 × 13 cm wide in the order A.B.B.A. The paper is allowed to dry at room temperature for 2–24 hours. A fold is made 2.5 cm from the top and punched centrally to allow the paper to be suspended in chromatographic tanks (dimensions: height 42 cm, base 27 × 9 cm) above the development solvent described by Light and Simpson (1956). [Butan-2-ol, 1% acetic acid (1:1 v/v) is shaken vigorously for several minutes in a large separating funnel and placed in the chromatography room for 24 hours. The lower phase is discarded and the upper phase run into the tank to a depth of 1 to 1.5 cm.] The tanks are covered with a glass lid, the joint being sealed with silicone grease. The lid is drilled centrally so that the glass frame carrying the papers may be raised or lowered without breaking the seal. After equilibration for 4–6 hours the papers are lowered so that the 2–4 mm of the bottom edge are immersed in the solvent. Development is allowed to continue until the solvent front has moved 20 cm up the paper. The papers are removed, blotted, and dried in an air oven at 80°C for 10 minutes. They are then immersed in a protein-staining solution (0.02% bromocresol green in a mixture prepared by diluting 12 ml of acetic acid to 2 liters and adding 125 ml of 0.1 N sodium hydroxide). After staining for 15 hours, the papers are removed, blotted dry, and washed by immersion for 3 minutes with occasional agitation in 4 successive quantities of 1% (v/v) acetic acid solution. The papers are pressed between clean blotting paper and returned to the drying oven for 10 minutes.

The staining of the specific insulin spots is intensified by holding them above 5 N ammonia, while their location is circumscribed by means of a pencil. These areas, together with an area of similar size to serve as a blank which is taken at a point removed from the spots, are cut out and placed in a series of test tubes 12 × 1.5 cm. To each tube is added 5 ml of eluent [0.1 N sodium hydroxide and ethanol (1:1 v/v)], the tube is agitated at intervals during 30 minutes, and the extinctions are compared with that of the blank at 625 mμ in 10-cm cells.

Fenton (1959) showed that the lines relating extinction to concentration passed through the origin so that the relative activity using single levels of test and standard was proportional to the extinction values.

Since this condition may not always apply, there would be some advantage in using two or more levels of each preparation to establish this point in each assay. The data so obtained would be amenable to the treatment applied for slope ratio assays.

Garratt (1957) has noted that paper chromatography does not separate insulin from its gelled form and hence the usefulness of this method is limited when applied to stored insulin solutions. When the purity of the component insulin is known, its concentration in solutions could be determined by applying measured quantities to filter paper and carrying out the drying, staining, and elution procedures but omitting the development. Such a method could certainly be applied to limit the concentration of insulin in the supernatant fluids of precipitated insulins.

REFERENCES

Anderson, E., and Long, J. A. (1947a). *Endocrinology* **40**, 92.

Anderson, E., and Long, J. A. (1947b). *Endocrinology* **40**, 98.

Anderson E., and Long, J. A. (1948). *Recent Progr. Hormone Res.* **2**, 209.

Anderson, E., Lindner, E., and Sutton, V. (1947). *Am. J. Physiol.* **149**, 350.

Arquilla, E. R., and Stavitsky, A. B. (1956). *J. Clin. Invest.* **35**, 458.

Bangham, D. R., and Mussett, M. V. (1959). *Bull. World Health Organ.* **20**, 1209.

Banting, F. G., Best, C. H., Collip, J. B., Macleod, J. J. R., and Noble, E. C. (1922). *Am. J. Physiol.* **62**, 162.

Bartlett, M. S. (1937). *Proc. Roy. Roc.* **A160**, 268.

Baum, W. E., Brown, W. F., and Crabtree, R. E. (1964). *J. Pharm. Sci.* **53**, 738.

Berson, S. A., and Yalow, R. S. (1959). *J. Clin. Invest.* **38**, 2017.

Berson, S. A., and Yalow, R. S. (1960). *J. Clin. Invest.* **39**, 1157.

Berson, S. A., Yalow, R. S., Bauman, A., Rothschild, M. A., and Newerly, K. (1956). *J. Clin. Invest.* **35**, 170.

Berson, S. A., Yalow, R. S., Glick, S. M., and Roth, J. (1964). *Metabolism, Clin. Exptl.* **13**, 1135.

Biegelman, P. M., Goetz, F. C., Antoniades, H. N., and Thorn, G. W. (1956). *Metabolism, Clin Exptl.* **5**, 35.

Birkinshaw, V. J., Randall, S. S., and Risdall, P. C. (1962). *Nature* **193**, 1089.

Bliss, C. I. (1934). *Science* **79**, 38.

Bliss, C. I. (1949). *J. Am. Pharm. Assoc., Sci. Ed.* **38**, 560.

Bliss, C. I., and Marks, H. P. (1939a). *Quart. J. Pharm. Pharmacol.* **12**, 82.

Bliss, C. I., and Marks, H. P. (1939b). *Quart. J. Pharm. Pharmacol.* **12**, 182.

Bornstein, J. (1950). *Australian J. Exptl. Biol. Med. Sci.* **28**, 87.

Bouman, J., and Homan, J. D. H. (1958). *Biochim. Biophys. Acta* **29**, 417.

"British Pharmacopoeia 1963." General Medical Council, London.

Bruce, H. M., and Parkes, A. S. (1946). *J. Hyg.* **44**, 501.

Culhane, K., Marks, H. P., Scott, D. A., and Trevan, J. W. (1929). *Biochem. J.* **33**, 397.

Department of Biological Standards. N.I.M.R. and British Insulin Manufacturers Biological Standardisation Committee (1952). *J. Pharm. Pharmacol.* **4**, 382.

Dickinson, W. (1956). *Nature* **178**, 994.

Emmens, C. W. (1948). "Principles of Biological Assay," p. 191. Chapman & Hall, London.

Fenton, E. L. (1959). *Biochem. J.* **71**, 507.

Fieller, E. C. (1940). *Suppl. J. Roy. Statist. Soc.* **7**, 63.

Fieller, E. C., Irwin, J. O., Marks H. P. and Shrimpton E. A. G. (1939a). *Quart. J. Pharm. Pharmacol.* **12**, 206.

Fieller E. C., Irwin, J. O., Marks, H. P., and Shrimpton, E. A. G. (1939b). *Quart. J. Pharm. Pharmacol.* **12**, 724.

Fisher, R. A., and Yates, F. (1938). "Statistical Tables for Biological Agricultural and Medical Research," pp. 44–45. Oliver & Boyd, Edinburgh.

Freund, J., and McDermott, K. (1942). *Proc. Soc. Exptl. Biol. Med.* **49**, 548.

Gaddum, J. H. (1933). *Med. Res. Council (Brit.) Spec. Rept. Ser.* **183**.

Garratt, D. C. (1957). *Proc. Congr. Modern Anal. Chem. Ind., Univ. St. Andrews*, p. 77.

Gemmill, C. L. (1941). *Bull. Johns Hopkins Hosp.* **68**, 50.

Gey, G. O., and Gey, M. K. (1936). *Am. J. Cancer* **27**, 45.

Grodsky, G. M., and Forsham, P. H. (1960). *J. Clin. Invest.* **39**, 1070.

Grodsky, G., and Tarver, H. (1956). *Nature* **177**, 223.

Groen, J., Kamminga, O. E., Willebrands, A. F., and Blickman, J. R. (1952). *J. Clin. Invest.* **31**, 97.

Hagedorn, H. C., and Jensen, B. N. (1923). *Biochem. Z.* **135**, 46.

Hales, C. N., and Randle, P. J. (1963). *Biochem. J.* **88**, 137.

Hemmingsen, A. M. (1933). *Quart. J. Pharm. Pharmacol.* **6**, 39.

Hemmingsen, A. M. (1939). *Skand. Arch. Physiol.* **82**, 105.

Hemmingsen, A. M., and Krogh, A. (1926). Pubs. *League Nations*, III Health III, C. H. 398.

Hemmingsen, A. M., and Marks, H. P. (1932). *Quart. J. Pharm. Pharmacol.* **5**, 245.

Hershey, J. M., and Lacey, A. H. (1936). *Quart. Bull. Health Organ. League Nations* (Nov.), p. 584.

Irwin, J. O. (1943). *Quart. J. Pharm. Pharmacol.* **14**, 352.

Jones, V. E., and Cunliffe, A. C. (1961). *Nature* **192**, 136.

Lacey, A. H. (1941). *Endocrinology* **29**, 866.

Lacey, A. H. (1946). *Endocrinology* **39**, 344.

League of Nations. (1926). III, Health III, C. H. 398.

Light, A., and Simpson, M. V. (1956). *Nature* **177**, 223.

Macleod, J. J. R., and Orr, M. D. (1924). *J. Lab. Clin. Med.* **9**, 591.

Macleod, J. J. R., and Orr, M. D. (1926). Pubs. *League Nations*, III Health III, C. H. 398.

Marks, H. P. (1925). *Brit. Med. J.* **II**, 1102.

Marks, H. P. (1926). Pubs. *League Nations*, III Health III, C. H. 398.

Marks, H. P. (1932). *Quart. J. Pharm. Pharmacol.* **5**, 255.

Marks, H. P. (1936). *Quart. Bull. Health Organ. League Nations, Spec. No.*, November.

Martin, D. B., Renold, A. E., and Dagenesis, Y. M. (1958). *Lancet* **II**, 76.

Moloney, P. J., and Aprile, M. A. (1959). *Can. J. Biochem. Physiol.* **37**, 793.

Moloney, P. J., and Coval, M. (1955). *Biochem. J.* **59**, 179.

Moloney, P. J., and Goldsmith, L. (1957). *Can. J. Biochem. Physiol.* **35**, 79.

Morgan, C. R., and Lazarow, A. (1962). *Proc. Soc. Exptl. Biol. Med.* **110**, 29.

Nelson, N. (1944). *J. Biol. Chem.* **152**, 375.

Ouchterlony, O. (1948). *Acta Pathol. Microbiol. Scand.* **25**, 186.

Patterson, R., Colwell, J. A., Gregor, W. H., and Carey, E. (1964). *J. Lab. Clin. Med.* **64**, 399.

Piazza, E. A., Goodner, C. J., and Frienkel, N. (1959). *Diabetes* **8**, 459.

Porath, J., and Li, C. H. (1954). *Biochim. Biophys. Acta* **13**, 268.

Porter, R. R. (1953). *Biochem. J.* **53**, 320.

Pugsley, L. I., and Rampton, S. (1948). *Endocrinology* **42**, 31.

Quart. Bull. Health Organ. League Nations (Nov. 1936).

Randle, P. J. (1954). *Brit. Med. J.* **I**, 1237.

Robinson, F. A., and Fehr, K. L. A. (1952). *Biochem. J.* **51**, 298.

Rowlinson, H. R., and Lesford, J. M. (1948). *Quart. J. Pharm. Pharmacol.* **21**, 259.

Shaffer, P. A., and Hartman, A. F. (1921). *J. Biol. Chem.* **45**, 365.

Skom, J. H., and Talmage, D. W. (1958). *J. Clin. Invest.* **37**, 783.

Smith, K. W., Marks, H. P., Fieller, E. C., and Broom, W. A. (1944). *Quart. J. Pharm. Pharmacol.* **17**, 108.

Somogyi, M. (1930). *J. Biol. Chem.* **86**, 655.

Somogyi, M. (1945). *J. Biol. Chem.* **160**, 61.

Steigerwald, H., Spielman, W., Fries, H., and Grebe, S. T. (1960). *Klin. Wochschr.* **38**, 973.

Stewart, G. A., and Smart, J. V. (1953). *J. Pharm. Pharmacol.* **5**, 939.

Thompson, R. E. (1946). *Endocrinology* **39**, 62.

Thorp, R. H. (1944a). *Quart. J. Pharm. Pharmacol.* **17**, 75.

Thorp, R. H. (1944b). *J. Pathol. Bacteriol.* **54**, 270.

Thorp, R. H. (1948). Ph.D. Thesis. University of London.

Trevan, J. W. (1925). *Biochem. J.* **19**, 1111.

Trevan, J. W. (1927). *Proc. Roy. Soc.* **B101**, 483.

Trevan, J. W., and Boock, E. (1926). Pubs. *League Nations*, III Health III, C. H. 398.

"United States Pharmacopeia." (1960). Sixteenth Revision. Mack Publ., Easton, Pennsylvania.

Vallance-Owen, J., and Hurlock, B. (1954). *Lancet* **I**, 68.

Willebrands, A. F., and Groen, J. (1956). *Diabetes* **5**, 378.

Young, D. M., and Lewis, A. H. (1947). *Science* **105**, 368.

Young, D. M., and Romans, R. G. (1948). *Biometrics* **4**, 122.

Chapter 10

Glucagon

WILLIAM W. BROMER

I. Introduction

Although the existence of glucagon was suggested in 1924, shortly after the discovery of insulin, only in the past few years has glucagon gained general recognition as a second hormone of the pancreas. Undoubtedly, much of the early apathy toward glucagon may be attributed to the overshadowing interest in insulin because of its role in the control of diabetes; nevertheless, faster progress on glucagon might have been expected if a convenient and precise assay method had been available. Within the past decade refinements of existing methods have facilitated advances in the chemistry and physiology of glucagon: the hormone has been prepared in crystalline form, and its structure has been determined; the mechanism of the hyperglycemic-glycogenolytic effect of glucagon has been well characterized. Knowledge of the effects of glucagon and epinephrine on adenyl cyclase to form adenosine 3′,5′-phosphoric acid has led to the recognition that the nucleotide is an important intermediary in a wide variety of hormonal systems. In addition, with the availability of crystalline glucagon, many and diverse biological effects of the hormone have been established. Recent advances in immunoassay technique have helped clarify the physiological function of glucagon, although many of the interesting biological effects of the hormone cannot yet be adequately integrated into a unified hypothesis of function.

A. Chemical Aspects of Glucagon

The discussion of the chemistry of glucagon is intended to serve as a background for the assay methods. A more detailed review may be found elsewhere (Behrens and Bromer, 1958).

1. Homogeneity of Glucagon

The isolation of a virtually homogeneous glucagon preparation is a prerequisite for the application of analytical methods based on physico-chemical properties of the hormone and for use of the hormone as a standard for all assay systems. Staub et al. (1955) demonstrated the high purity of crystalline glucagon preparations by means of chemical end-group analysis. Repeated crystallizations afforded no increase in biological activity, and the protein in the mother liquor was as active as the isolated crystals. Zone electrophoresis with starch granules (Staub et al., 1955), ion exchange chromatography in urea buffers (Cole, 1960), and electrophoresis in acrylamide gel (Heiney, 1965) all indicate the presence of a minor component in crystalline glucagon preparations. All available data suggest that the minor fraction is a desamido form of glucagon.

2. Properties of Glucagon

Glucagon contains many functional groupings capable of binding small ions; however, the active hormone can be isolated in crystalline form without significant contamination from metals or other charged substances (Staub et al., 1955). On the basis of zone electrophoretic data the isoelectric region of glucagon lies between pH 7 and 8. Evidence exists (Bromer, 1965) that fibrils, freshly prepared from a 1% glucagon solution at pH 1.5, retain full biological potency. However, fibrils formed over a period of months from a 0.1% solution, pH 2.5, at 37°–50°C appear to be inactive and cannot be regenerated by alkaline treatment. Additional work will be required to elucidate the differences between fibril types and to evaluate the effect of fibril formation on biological activity.

3. Structure of Glucagon

Porcine glucagon is composed of a single chain of 29 amino acids (Bromer et al., 1957) containing N-terminal histidine and C-terminal threonine. The hormone has a molecular weight of 3485 on the basis of structural studies. The structure was elucidated through (1) digestion with enzymes into small fragments, (2) isolation of the fragments by means of Dowex 50 columns, (3) characterization of the peptide fragments, and (4) correlation of the data in an unequivocal manner. The following amino acid sequence was established: His·Ser·Glu(—NH$_2$)·

Gly · Thr · Phe · Thr · Ser · Asp · Tyr · Ser · Lys · Tyr · Leu · Asp · Ser · Arg · Arg · Ala · Glu(–NH₂) · Asp · Phe · Val · Glu(–NH₂) · Trp · Leu · Met · Asp(–NH₂)·Thr. The bovine hormone was found to have biological activity, physicochemical properties, and a quantitative amino acid composition identical to porcine glucagon, but it is not known whether the amino acid sequence is the same (Bromer, 1965).

The high concentration of functional groupings in glucagon is noteworthy. For example, the single tryptophan and two tyrosine residues in the chain absorb strongly in the ultraviolet at 276 mμ, providing a convenient assay for crystalline glucagon in solution. Other amino acids present in glucagon, such as the single residues of methionine and histidine, also provide a basis for analysis of purified samples. Clearly, such chemical methods can be employed only in conjunction with a physiological assay.

B. Physiological Aspects of Glucagon

Early in the history of insulin, investigators noted that the injection of some pancreatic extracts into animals produced a rapid transitory hyperglycemia. The liver was implicated as the site of this hyperglycemic action by several lines of evidence. Then, in 1945 Shipley and Humel noted that insulin preparations stimulated glycogenolysis in liver slices. Sutherland and Cori (1948) showed that the glycogenolysis was attributable to a "glycogenolytic factor" in the insulin preparations and thus prepared the way for intensive study of the mechanism of the effect. Since the advent of crystalline glucagon (Staub et al., 1955) the hormone has been shown to affect a wide variety of systems in addition to glycogenolysis in the liver. For an extensive treatment of the biological effects of glucagon the reader is referred to the excellent monograph of Foà and Galansino (1962).

1. Effects in Liver

After Sutherland and Cori (1948, 1951) showed that glucagon affected the rate-limiting phosphorylase step of liver glycolysis, much attention was focused on the phosphorylase system. Largely through the efforts of Sutherland and his collaborators (Wosilait, Rall, Berthet, and Makman), many of the details of the glycogenolytic action of glucagon in liver have been elucidated. Liver phosphorylase (LP) concentration depends on a balance between a phosphorylase-activating enzyme (dephosphophosphorylase kinase) and a LP-inactivating enzyme (phosphorylase phosphatase). Rall et al. (1957) and Sutherland and Rall (1957, 1958) further demonstrated in a cell-free system that either glucagon or epinephrine acts on a particulate liver fraction to form adenosine-$3',5'$-phosphoric acid (cyclic $3',5'$-AMP), which in turn stimulates phosphorylase activation. The particulate liver fraction was found to contain adenyl cyclase (Sutherland *et al.*, 1962; Rall and Sutherland, 1962a) which appears to be activated directly by glucagon (Makman and Sutherland, 1964), thus stimulating the synthesis of cyclic $3',5'$-AMP from ATP. Contrary to the interpretation of Foa (1964) it is not yet clear whether the cyclic nucleotide acts to enhance the kinase-catalyzed conversion of inactive to active phosphorylase or to depress the phosphatase that inactivates phosphorylase (cf. Sutherland and Rall, 1960; Rall and Sutherland, 1961). In any case the increased phosphorylase activity results in glycogenolysis and hyperglycemia. The glycogenolytic system, in either a direct or indirect fashion, provides the basis for nearly all the methods of glucagon bioassay presently in use.

2. Effects in Other Systems

A few of the striking effects of glucagon in other systems are cited since these actions could be used as a basis for glucagon assay. The now well-documented actions of glucagon probably not mediated by hyperglycemia include (1) marked reduction in intestinal motility and gastric secretion, (2) enhanced excretion of electrolytes by the kidney, and (3) increased urinary nitrogen and decreased blood amino nitrogen levels. The lowering of blood amino acids has been used as a semiquantitative test for comparing the duration of action of various glucagon preparations (cf. Section II, B, 3).

II. Methods of Assay

Various methods for the assay of glucagon are outlined that may be applicable to the crystalline hormone or to crude mixtures containing very small concentrations. An attempt has been made to consider methods critically, and the limits of applicability and sensitivity are discussed. Many of the methods of assay are cited, but only a few have been selected for detailed consideration.

A. Physical Methods

Methods dependent on the physical properties of glucagon are useful with highly purified hormone preparations, but require confirmation and correlation with a bioassay. Such procedures are applicable principally to the determination of the concentration of crystalline glucagon in solution, to the analysis of purity, and in some instances to the separation of glucagon from complex mixtures. Most of the methods have not been developed as quantitative assay procedures, although all may be suitable for such development.

1. Ultraviolet Absorption

The concentration of crystalline glucagon in aqueous solution (pH 1–9) may readily be obtained by measurement of the ultraviolet absorption at 276 mμ, followed by comparison with the $E_{1\,\mathrm{cm}}^{1\%}$ value of glucagon: 21.15, with a standard deviation of 0.54 (Kuzel and Holzer, 1959). This value was obtained from measurements on 12 different lots of crystalline glucagon.

2. Electrophoretic Methods

Light and Simpson (1956) have suggested that the paper electrophoretic separation of insulin and glucagon may be useful in determining small amounts of glucagon in insulin. Glucagon remained immobile after electrophoresis for 24 hours at about 6.7 V/cm, 2°C, on Whatman No. 1 paper in 0.03 M pH 7.5 sodium phosphate buffer; insulin moved toward the anode. No indication of the sensitivity of the method was offered.

Starch electrophoresis has been employed by Staub et al. (1955) to provide data on purity of glucagon. Five milligrams of crystalline glucagon was applied to starch troughs using 0.075 M glycine buffer, pH 9.9. The electrophoresis was conducted for 40 hours at 4°C, 160–170 V, 13–15 milliamperes.

Lochner et al. (1964) described a cellulose acetate electrophoresis method that may prove useful in preparing small amounts of glucagon from tissues and in helping identify glucagon in crude extracts.

3. Chromatographic Methods

Wiesel et al. (1963) demonstrated that glucagon and insulin can be separated from serum proteins by descending chromatography on (30%) Amberlite IRC-50-impregnated paper in butanol–water–acetic acid (12:5:6).

B. BIOASSAY METHODS

1. Measurement of the Hyperglycemic Effect of Glucagon

The rise in blood sugar in an experimental animal is measured after the injection of glucagon. The methods differ primarily in the species of animal employed, in the experimental design, and in the procedure for handling the data. For example, the hyperglycemic response of rats (von Holt et al., 1956), rabbits (Rowlinson and Lesford, 1951; Lazarus *et al.*, 1957), chicks (Beekman, 1958), and cats (Staub and Behrens, 1954) has been used as a quantitative measure of glucagon. The chief virtues of the *in vivo* methods lie in the simplicity and the reproducibility of the procedures. The difficulties encountered with such methods include individual variation, lack of specificity, slowness, and the need for large numbers of animals. Several of the above methods have been tried in the Lilly Laboratories. The one selected for detailed consideration is a recent modification (Smith and Robbins, 1965) (cf. U.S.P., XVII, p. 268) of the cat method of Staub and Behrens (1954).

Sixteen hours prior to assay, cats weighing 2–4 kg are injected intraperitoneally with 2.5 gm of glucose and are deprived of food but not water. Just prior to assay the animals are placed under surgical anesthesia with an intraperitoneal injection of 170 mg of 10% phenobarbital per kilogram and are then covered to prevent hypothermia. Both femoral veins are exposed; one is used for injection of the test solutions and the other for removal of blood samples. A normal blood sample (0.8 ml) is taken and added immediately to 0.2 ml of a solution containing 4 mg of sodium fluoride and 20 units of heparin; all subsequent blood samples are handled in similar fashion. Immediately after removal of the normal blood, a glucagon solution is injected by vein, and blood samples are taken at 8 and 16 minutes. After an additional 74 minutes (about 1 hour and 30 minutes between injections), another normal blood sample is taken and another glucagon solution is injected. The procedure is continued until 4 samples have been injected. Recrystallized glucagon is employed as a standard, at both 0.1 (SL) and 0.2 (SH) μg/kg. The unknown samples are prepared in corresponding low (UL) and high (UH) concentrations. The assay is based on a double 4×4 Latin square design using 4 animals per group with a series of 4 randomized injections per animal. The accompanying schedule is customarily employed for each series of 8 cats.

Dose No.	Dose regimen for animal number							
	1	2	3	4	5	6	7	8
1	SH	SL	UL	UH	SH	SL	UH	UL
2	UL	UH	SH	SL	UH	UL	SH	SL
3	SL	SH	UH	UL	SL	SH	UL	UH
4	UH	UL	SL	SH	UL	UH	SL	SH

The blood sugar analyses are performed routinely using a Technicon AutoAnalyzer. The analytical method of Hoffman (1937) has been adapted by Technicon for the apparatus. All values are compared to a standard glucose curve determined for each experiment using standard solutions of 0.25–2.0 mg/ml (in 0.25 mg/ml increments). The net rise in blood sugar is found for the higher of the two samples by subtraction of the appropriate preinjection control value.

The potency of the unknown sample is calculated according to the U.S. Pharmacopeia XVII, page 269, 1965. The standard preparation (lot 258-234B-167-1), when assayed in 31 cats as above at 0.1 and 0.2 μg/kg, provided a blood sugar rise of 31 ± 8.3 (SD) and 50 ± 17.7 (SD) mg per 100 ml, respectively. When 12–16 animals are employed, a standard error of approximately $\pm 20\%$ or less is expected. With 8 animals the error may be about $\pm 30\%$. If the sample is injected at 1 ml/kg, as little as 0.035 μg of glucagon per milliliter $(1 \times 10^{-5}$ μmoles/ml) can be measured. Although quite sensitive for a bioassay procedure, the method is not sensitive enough to measure glucagon in blood without prior extraction.

One of the major disadvantages of the method stems from the requirement that any substance which affects blood sugar levels, such as insulin, must first be removed from the glucagon sample. In the analysis of glucagon in insulin preparations, selective destruction of most of the insulin activity can readily be accomplished by incubation with cysteine (Staub and Behrens, 1954). In addition, the exclusion of nonspecific effects is inherently more difficult in the intact animal than in an *in vitro* system. The possibility that changes in blood sugar may be mediated by obscure secondary effects cannot be completely eliminated. Despite these objections, the usefulness of the hyperglycemic assay cannot be denied. Since hyperglycemia per se is often the response desired from glucagon when injected into humans or animals, an assay based on measurements of increased levels of blood sugar has special merit. The value of the method was demonstrated in facilitating the isolation of glucagon in crystalline form (Staub *et al.*, 1955) from crude pancreas fractions.

2. Measurement of the Glycogenolytic Effect of Glucagon

As previously discussed, glucagon promotes the formation of cyclic 3',5'-AMP; the nucleotide activates liver phosphorylase, which, in turn, is responsible for glycogenolysis. Thus, measurement of the nucleotide, of phosphorylase, or of glucose provides a basis of assay for the pancreatic hormone.

a. Liver Slice Method. Sutherland and Cori (1948) first utilized the glycogenolytic reaction in liver slices as a means of assay for the "glycogenolytic factor" (glucagon) in insulin preparations. Since that time the method has been modified by Audy and Kerly (1952a, b), Please (1952),

Vuylsteke *et al.* (1952), de Duve and Vuylsteke (1953), and Tyberghein and Williams (1958). An extensive treatment of the liver slice method was published by Vuylsteke and de Duve (1957). Their method will be considered in some detail, although a full appreciation of the technique can best be obtained from the original publication.

In essence the procedure involves measurement of the glucose liberated into the medium by the action of glucagon on liver slices. In view of the degree of variability observed, the assay has been designed to include an internal standard and to utilize the 2- × 3-point method (Bliss and Marks, 1939) so that statistical analysis may be employed. Each unit cell is composed of 6 matched liver slices added randomly to 6 flasks, each containing a different amount of standard or unknown. In other unit cells it is advisable to provide for control slices without glucagon and for slices with an excess of the hormone so that the maximal response can be ascertained.

Healthy adult rabbits are sacrificed by bleeding under pentobarbital anesthesia and a portion of the liver, preferably the middle lobe, is quickly removed. Only apparently normal livers that contain qualitatively a reasonable amount of glycogen are used. (The amount of glycogen precipitate is estimated from the addition of 1.1 volumes of 95% ethanol to a hot 20% NaOH digest of a small amount of liver.) The liver is placed in ice-cold saline and the suspension is stirred for 5 minutes. The chilled liver is cut freehand parallel to the capsule into slices about 2 × 3 cm. The large slices are further cut into 6 smaller slices, as nearly alike as possible, of about 40–60 mg each, which are used together as a unit cell. Precautions should be taken to keep the tissue cold before and after slicing. The slices are weighed and are added at random, each to 1 of the 6 flasks of a unit cell previously prepared with medium and sample. A minimum of 3 unit cells is suggested per sample.

Each unit cell of 6 flasks contains 3 logarithmically spaced concentrations of sample and of standard; e.g., suitable concentrations for crystalline glucagon are 4×10^{-3}, 8×10^{-3}, and 1.6×10^{-2} $\mu g/ml$.

The procedure employing 20-ml beakers shaken in air in a Dubnoff metabolic incubator is described; equally satisfactory results may be obtained with 2.5- × 15-cm test tubes in a Warburg bath. The 2.4 ml of medium per beaker is 0.02 M, pH 7.4 potassium phosphate buffer (Sutherland and de Duve, 1948) containing 0.12 M sodium chloride and 100 μg of glucagon-free insulin. The slices of a unit cell are incubated simultaneously for 40 or 45 minutes at 37°C; the incubation is stopped by adding 5 ml of 0.15 M barium hydroxide followed by 5 ml of 0.15 M zinc sulfate. The mixture is filtered, and glucose is determined on the filtrate according to the method of Nelson (1944). Alternatively, glycogen or phosphate may be determined if appropriate adjustments are made in the procedure. The amount of inorganic phosphate liberated is used as a measure of phosphorylase activity. The results are generally reported as milligrams of glucose formed per gram of liver per 40 minutes. The data are treated by the method of factorial coefficients as described by Emmens (1948).

Advantages of the method include sensitivity and economy of time, animals, and labor. The variability observed in 10 unit cells compares well with that observed for 16 animals in the cat assay (Staub and Behrens, 1954), and the livers from only 2 or 3 rabbits are needed. A probable saving of nearly 50% in time and labor is effected. Like the *in vivo* assays, the slice method is also beset with difficulties from non-specific glycogenolytic effects and from occasional extreme variability in response. That the glycogenolytic response is due to glucagon may be partially verified by determining whether or not the response is potentiated by insulin and is insensitive to ergotamine. Vuylsteke and de Duve (1957) pointed out that the standard deviation is not completely independent of the response, a finding in conflict with one of the criteria set forth by Gaddum (1931) for a reliable bioassay. However, the standard deviation varies over a limited range, making possible a variance analysis if the assay is well balanced. Another difficulty is the lack of parallel response when crystalline glucagon as a standard is compared with crude glucagon-containing materials. The authors suggested the use of an arbitrary standard comparable in purity to the unknowns.

b. Liver Homogenate Method. While elucidating the interesting series of reactions leading to the formation of liver phosphorylase (LP), Rall *et al.* (1957) discovered that certain liver homogenates were capable of supporting the same series of reactions that occur in slices. Shortly thereafter Berthet *et al.* (1957) published a method of assay for glucagon and epinephrine based on the use of liver homogenates. Cat or dog liver homogenates were found to be satisfactory, whereas rabbit and rat liver homogenates gave relatively poor responses.

Makman and Sutherland (1964) have since devised a more specific homogenate method based on the effect of glucagon to increase the formation of cyclic $3',5'$-AMP.

Cats are anesthetized with chloroform or ether and the livers are perfused *in situ* via a portal vein cannula with cold 0.9% NaCl. The liver is immediately removed, cooled in saline, and sliced in pieces about $25 \times 20 \times 2$ mm. The slices are washed with cold 0.9% NaCl, followed by incubation with 3 volumes of medium for 15 minutes at 37°C. The washed slices are chilled, forced through a fine-mesh screen, and homogenized in 2 volumes of 0.001 M $MgSO_4$ and 0.002 M glycylglycine, pH 7.4.

The homogenate is centrifuged at 2200 g, 3°C, for 20 minutes and the particulate fraction containing adenyl cyclase is washed in the homogenization medium, resuspended in the same diluent, frozen rapidly in small portions, and stored at −70°C.

For the standard incubation (30°C, 15 minutes), 0.2 ml of cat liver cyclase is added to 0.4 ml of media containing glucagon, blank, or unknown. According to Makman and Sutherland (1964), the final incubation mixture is composed of: "... particulate fraction equivalent to 50–100 mg/ml of cat liver, 0.0027 M ATP, 0.0033 M MgSO$_4$, 0.1 mg/ml of casein, 0.0067 M caffeine, 0.022 mg/ml of erogtamine tartrate, 0.02 M Tris buffer (pH 7.8), and 0.0002 M 8-hydroxyquinoline." To stop the formation of cyclic 3′,5′-AMP, the tubes are heated in boiling water for 3 minutes, chilled, and centrifuged to remove insoluble material.

The nucleotide formed is determined indirectly by two subsequent incubations (Rall and Sutherland, 1962b): (1) active phosphorylase is formed by the addition of cyclic 3′,5′-AMP to a system containing dephosphophosphorylase, ATP, and a supernatant fraction of cat liver, (2) inorganic phosphate is finally measured as a result of the action of phosphorylase in a system containing glucose 1-phosphate, glycogen, NaF, and AMP.

As little as 5 mμg of glucagon per milliliter may be detected in this manner, and the assay appears to be more specific for glucagon than any other bioassay. Further specificity studies will be required before this aspect can be critically appraised, as is the case regarding precision. The method is laborious, requiring the use of several purified enzymes and a high order of technical skill, and for these reasons has not gained widespread use. Makman and Sutherland (1964), using the assay, found significant concentrations of glucagon in extracts of dog and human gastrointestinal tract and of pancreas, but not of blood. This apparently reflects the extremely low content of glucagon in blood.

   c. Slice-Homogenate Method. Prior to the development of the homogenate assay, Fodden and Read (1955) and Ui *et al.* (1956) made the very interesting observation that glucagon could be assayed in a two-step procedure: (1) phosphorylase was activated by glucagon in liver slices, and (2) after homogenization of the slices, added glycogen was degraded by the activated phosphorylase. Details of the method have been published by Ui and colleagues (1956).

   Rabbits about 1 month old are sacrificed under pentobarbital anesthesia by severing the carotid artery. The liver is removed rapidly and is placed in a cold solution of 0.75% sodium chloride in 0.02 M phosphate buffer pH 7.4. Rectangular blocks of tissue with an end area of about 1 cm^2 are prepared from which are cut slices of about 150 mg each. Two or three slices are shaken aerobically for 10 minutes at 37°C (110 oscillations per minute) in 3 ml of the above medium containing the glucagon sample. The contents of the flask are homogenized in a Potter-Elvehjem homogenizer and 2 mg of glycogen are added per 100 mg of tissue. Medium is added to a final concentration of 25 mg of tissue per milliliter. The homogenate is centrifuged at low speed, and the supernatant fluid is divided into five 2-ml aliquots which are incubated for 3 hours under conditions described above. A 0.6-ml aliquot is removed, is diluted with 2.9 ml water, and is deproteinized by 0.2 ml each of 5% zinc sulfate and 0.3 N barium hydroxide. Glucose is determined on 2 ml of the supernatant fluid by the Nelson (1944) method.

When the above procedure was performed with 5 different levels of cysteine-inactivated insulin, 2 assumed to be the "standard," the other 3 the "unknown," the relative potency of the unknown was reported as 103%, with 95% fiducial limits of 96.2–110.5%. Ui has indicated that the addition of crystalline glucagon in quantities of 0.2, 0.3, and 2.0 μg per flask caused an increase in glucose output of 10, 16, and 65%, respectively; thus, as little as 0.2–0.5 μg of glucagon can be detected.

This blending of techniques appeared to eliminate many of the variables associated with the slice method, and the design of the slice-homogenate method provided excellent reproducibility within a single liver preparation. A high blank value possibly may be minimized by preincubation of the slices according to Sutherland and colleagues. Apparently the gain in precision is accompanied by about a tenfold loss in sensitivity. The fact that insulin provided a better response (two- to fivefold) but gave a lower slope of the dose-response curve than cysteine-inactivated insulin has been interpreted on the basis of (a) a partial destruction of glucagon by cysteine and/or HCl, and (b) an inhibition of insulin on glucagon activity. These data may be compared to the findings of Vuylsteke and de Duve (1957) that a 100-fold increase in the activity of crystalline glucagon was found when 100 μg of insulin was added per flask. In addition, in the latter study, the log dose-response lines were reasonably parallel. Vuylsteke and de Duve (1957) have further shown that the potentiation effect of insulin may most likely be ascribed to the protection of glucagon from proteolysis. Thus, although the slice-homogenate assay appears to be a relatively simple and precise method, additional evaluation work is needed.

3. Measurement of the Protein Catabolic Effect of Glucagon

Glucagon has been found to lower blood amino acids, to increase urine nitrogen, and to inhibit the uptake of labeled amino acids into protein. Although none of these effects has yet been developed into a quantitative bioassay, Bromer and Chance (1967) have utilized the blood amino acid effect as the basis for a quantitative comparison of the duration of action of glucagon modifications.

Control blood samples are obtained from an ear vein of fed New Zealand white rabbits weighing 3–5 kg. The glucagon preparation (5 mg/ml) is injected subcutaneously at 100 μg/kg, and blood samples are obtained as before at regular intervals up to about 8 hours. A cross-over design is used, in which the animals are allowed to rest about 1 week between injections. A minimum of 10 animals per sample is used. Blood "amino acids" are determined as dialyzable, ninhydrin-reactive substances using the Technicon AutoAnalyzer, and data are calculated as leucine equivalents based on a leucine standard curve.

C. Immunochemical Methods

The immunochemical assay methods are based on the same basic principles, the primary difference being the procedure for separation of free and antibody-bound glucagon-^{131}I. Glucagon in the sample and glucagon-^{131}I are allowed to compete for binding with anti-glucagon serum. Free and antibody-bound glucagon-^{131}I are separated, usually by electrophoresis or precipitation, and the amount of labeled glucagon is determined with great sensitivity in either or both fractions. A large amount of free labeled glucagon is observed as a result of its displacement from the antibody by a large amount of glucagon in the test sample, and vice versa. In such manner a daily standard curve is prepared, against which the result from the glucagon unknown may be compared. The basic design is similar to the immunological assays for insulin, pioneered particularly by Berson et al. (1956, 1957).

1. Production of Antibodies

The small molecular size of glucagon makes it a predictably poor antigen, and considerable difficulty has been encountered in several laboratories in developing antisera of sufficiently high titer. Unger and co-workers (1959a,b) successfully produced antisera in a small percentage of rabbits by employing complete Freund's adjuvant. Recently, Probst and Colwell (1966) described what would appear to the the best method available, using alum-precipitated glucagon in complete Freund's adjuvant.

To 12.5 ml of isotonic saline containing 800 mg of crystalline egg albumin is added 30 ml of a dilute NaOH solution (ca. pH 10) containing 5 mg of crystalline beef-pork glucagon per milliliter. Then 45 ml of 10% alum [AlK(SO$_4$)$_2$·12H$_2$O] in water is added; the solution is adjusted to pH 6.5 with 5 N NaOH, and 4 ml of excess alkali is added. The resulting precipitate is recovered by low speed centrifugation at 5°C for 5 minutes, is washed twice with 50 ml of 0.0004 M sodium borate, and is suspended in 50 ml isotonic saline. This suspension of alum-precipitated glucagon is mixed with 45 gm of mineral oil (Drakeol 6-VR), 5 gm of Arlacel A, and 250 mg of heat-killed *Mycobacterium tuberculosis* (BP-088) cells, and an emulsion is prepared in a Virtis homogenizer.

New Zealand white male rabbits weighing 2–3 kg each are injected subcutaneously (s.c.) with 2 ml (ca. 3 mg glucagon) of the emulsion, given in 10 divided 0.2-ml doses in 9 different hindquarter sites and in one rear foot pad. After 15 days, 4 0.25-ml doses of emulsion are administered s.c. in 4 different sites in the scapular region. Thirty days after the initial treatment and each 30 days thereafter, the rabbits are given 0.5 ml of antigen s.c. in the right thorax. Antibody titers of serum from the ear vein are determined 37 days after treatment, and, if the titer is adequate, 50 ml of blood is obtained by heart puncture. This regimen was reported (Probst and Colwell, 1966) to produce antibodies in 80% of the animals, either rabbits or guinea pigs.

2. Immunoassay

Most of the methods currently in use (e.g., Grodsky *et al.*, 1961; Unger *et al.*, 1963; Probst and Colwell, 1966) appear to be modifications of the salt-precipitation method devised by Grodsky *et al.* (1961). Although the technique of Probst and Colwell appears to have a distinct advantage over other methods (and this will be discussed below), the method of Unger *et al.* (1963) will be described in some detail since it alone has been applied to glucagon in blood, and since it differs from the original method of Unger *et al.* (1959a,b) described in the first edition of this work.

One milliliter of antiserum is incubated at 25°C for 1 hour either with 1 ml of glucagon standard (0 to 2×10^{-3} μg/ml) or test solution. After addition of 0.1 ml of a solution containing about 50 $\mu\mu$g of glucagon-^{131}I, the mixture is incubated 3 days at 4°C. The total radioactivity is determined in a well-type scintillation counter, and 2 ml of normal human plasma is added to the glucagon standard solutions and 2 ml of 2% albumin to the glucagon test solutions. Immediately 4.1 ml of 30% Na_2SO_4 is added with stirring, followed by a 15-minute incubation of the tubes at room temperature. The solution is centrifuged at low speed for 20 minutes, and the precipitate is washed once with 5 ml of 15% Na_2SO_4, redissolved in distilled water to 2.1 ml total volume, and counted as before to determine the labeled glucagon bound to antibody. The percentage of glucagon-^{131}I in the precipitate is calculated and is

corrected for nonspecific binding (never $>6\%$) as determined by substituting normal rabbit sera for the immune sera and carrying out the
usual procedure. The potency of unknown samples is determined by
comparison with a standard curve constructed by plotting glucagon
concentration versus percentage of glucagon-^{131}I precipitated. The
standard error of the method, based on 116 replicate analyses of glucagon
in serum, is $\pm 13.4\%$. In the range 0–1000 $\mu\mu$g/ml, differences can apparently be observed, using duplicate analyses, between two glucagon
samples that differ by 250 $\mu\mu$g/ml. Data are presented in micromicrogram-
equivalents since crystalline human glucagon is not available for use as
a standard, and since human serum degrades more glucagon-^{131}I than
does 2% albumin. Thus, absolute comparisons between standards and
serum unknowns is impossible, but comparative data are apparently
valid. A great premium is placed upon the quantitative precipitation and
counting of the glucagon-^{131}I bound to antibody, since, due to the
extreme slope of the curve in the usable range for serum analysis (ca.
22–36% glucagon-^{131}I precipitated), a small error in analysis would
markedly affect the final result. Glucagon added to serum is recovered
reasonably well up to 1 mμg/ml, but recovery is quite variable above
this concentration.

Probst and Colwell (1966), using a similar salt-precipitation assay,
noted that glucagon-^{131}I, when diluted for use in albumin solutions and
either kept frozen or at 5°C, progressively deteriorated over a 2-week
period in such a manner as to markedly increase the amount of radioactivity that did not bind to antibody (e.g., from about 45% to 65% in
14 days); the standard curve shifted almost daily, resulting in a loss of
sensitivity and lack of reliability. To rectify this problem, apparently
unnoticed by other laboratories, Probst and Colwell prepared an antibody–glucagon-^{131}I complex that stabilized the labeled hormone and
was useful as a reagent in the assay.

Glucagon-^{131}I (1 ml containing 1 μCi) is mixed with 4 ml of appropri-
ately diluted antiserum (e.g., 1 : 10) and the solution is gently agitated for
30 minutes at room temperature. To the mixture is added 5 ml of 4 M
$(NH_4)_2SO_4$, and after 30 minutes the suspension is centrifuged at 2400 g
for 20 minutes. The pellet, representing the glucagon–antibody complex,
is carefully washed once with 5 ml of 2 M $(NH_4)_2SO_4$, and is dissolved
in 70 ml of borate buffer (pH 8.3, 0.1 Γ) containing 0.25% human serum.
When stored at 5°C, the complex remains stable for at least 2 weeks.
However, throughout this period a rather constant 20% of the radioactivity of the diluted complex is not precipitable later in the assay by
Na_2SO_4, suggesting that some nonglucagon radioactive substance(s) in
the original glucagon-^{131}I is coprecipitated with the specific complex or

that some glucagon-^{131}I dissociates on dilution of the complex. The useful range of the assay at present is about 6–100 mμg of glucagon per sample, which is not sensitive enough to determine the concentration of glucagon in blood. However, all glucagon immunoassays leave something to be desired, and this commendable basic approach to the problem may lead to further improvements in methodology as well as to a better understanding of radioiodinated hormones and their interaction with antibody.

III. Applications of the Methods

A. CRYSTALLINE GLUCAGON

By definition, any of the physical, biological, or immunological methods may be used with highly purified or crystalline glucagon. Specificity and sensitivity requirements are minimized, and a high premium is placed on precision and ease of performance such as is found in the physical methods. Since the desired action of the hormone is biological, however, a physical or immunoassay must always be supplemented with a bioassay, such as the cat method or the liver slice assay. However, once approximate biological potency is established, the physical or immunological methods may often be used for routine tests on large numbers of samples.

B. TISSUE EXTRACTS

With less pure hormone preparations, e.g., crude extracts of tissue, somewhat greater demands are made on the specificity and sensitivity of the methods used. Because of the inherent physicochemical specificity of the antigen-antibody interaction, coupled with a high order of sensitivity and precision, the immunoassay remains a good choice for measurement of crude glucagon extracts. Again the method should not stand alone because immunological and biological specificities are not necessarily identical. Until proved otherwise, it is entirely possible that biologically inert, glucagon-like substances may interact with anti-glucagon serum in a manner indistinguishable from glucagon. Thus, a bioassay should also be employed, and the choice may be promulgated largely on the basis of sensitivity and relative specificity. The adenyl cyclase (liver homogenate) method, although laborious, would appear to exhibit adequate sensitivity and specificity, admirably complementing the immunoassay. Using this method Makman and Sutherland (1964) corroborated and extended their earlier findings that glucagon-like activity could be extracted from dog and human gastric mucosa as

onio as pancreas. This situation provides an excellent example of the need for application of two assay methods based on separate parameters. Immunological identity of the extract to glucagon, along with the bioassay result, would provide a basis for establishing the identity of the intestinal factor beyond reasonable doubt. Preliminary experiments in a different laboratory (Jackson *et al.*, 1965), using the cat and immunoassays, have confirmed that glucagon is present in gastrointestinal extracts.

C. Glucagon in Serum

Measurement of the minute amounts of glucagon in blood has proved to be a difficult problem; in fact no technique is available for measuring directly the absolute concentration of glucagon in blood. However, the relative measurements by Unger *et al.* (1963) using the immunoassay have provided useful data.

Assay specificity and sensitivity are the major stumbling blocks in the case of the bioassays. The sensitivity problem may be eased somewhat through extraction of glucagon from serum, but the fact remains that a bioassay is sorely needed that is sensitive enough to measure glucagon directly in serum. Many problems of specificity have also arisen with the bioassay methods (cf. Makman *et al.*, 1958, 1960; Tyberghein and Williams, 1958; Makman and Sutherland, 1964), and these are at least as serious as sensitivity. The groups of Williams and of Sutherland both noted unknown seral factors that inhibited the action of glucagon in liver slices or homogenates. Furthermore, Sutherland and his colleagues made extensive studies that seemed to demonstrate that serum glucagon was being measured in the homogenate system (finding ca. 5 μg of glucagon per 100 ml of human plasma). Makman *et al.* (1960) later described a substance in blood that is not identical with glucagon but that exhibits glucagon-like activity in respect to phosphorylase activation. This was identified as protein-bound calcium (Makman *et al.*, 1960; Makman and Sutherland, 1961). Makman and Sutherland (1964) have since introduced the use of adenyl cyclase for the assay of glucagon; this method is not affected by calcium and appears to be the most specific bioassay available. If the enzyme preparation can be freed of glucagon-inhibitors, the sensitivity of the assay might be improved so that endogenous glucagon can be measured in the range reported by immunoassay.

Many improvements are still needed in the immunoassay before unequivocal measurements of glucagon in serum can be made. Nevertheless, Unger and his collaborators have provided an interesting insight into the relative changes of serum glucagon concentration in response to various stimuli. For example, glucagon levels were found to increase in a somewhat predictable manner following insulin- or phlorizin-induced hypoglycemia (Unger *et al.*, 1962), and after starvation (Unger *et al.*, 1963). Advances in the assay methods are anticipated that should provide the tools needed to further elucidate the hormonal role of glucagon.

ADDENDUM

The readers' attention is directed to a few of the pertinent publications that have appeared since this chapter was written, and that would have appreciably changed the content of a particular section.

Section I, A

Total synthesis of pancreas hormone glucagon, Wünsch, E. (1967). *Z. Naturforsch.* **22b**, 1269.

A conformational study of glucagon, Gratzer, W. B., Beaven, G. H., Rattle, H. W. E., and Bradbury, E. M. (1968). *European J. Biochem.* **3**, 276.

Section I, B

Cyclic AMP, Robison, A., Butcher, R. W., and Sutherland, E. W. (1968). *Ann. Rev. Biochem.* **37**, 149.

Section II, A

Quantitative electrophoretic separation of insulin and glucagon, Ziegler, M., and Lippmann, H. G. (1968). *Naturwissenschaften* **55**, 181.

Section II, C

Production of antibodies of high binding affinities to glucagon in rabbits, Worobec, R., Locke, R., Hall, A., and Ertl, R. (1967). *Biochem. Biophys. Res. Commun.* **29**, 406.

A double antibody immunoassay for glucagon, Hazzard, W. R., Crockford, P. M., Buchanan, K. D., Vance, J. E., and Williams, R. H. (1968). *Diabetes* **17**, 179.

Section III, B

Demonstration and characterization of a second fraction of glucagon-like immunoreactivity in jejunal extracts, Valverde, I., Rigopoulou, D., Exton, J., Ohneda, A., Eisentraut, A., and Unger, R. H. (1968). *Am. J. Med. Sci.* **255**, 415.

Immunologic discrimination between pancreatic glucagon and enteric glucagon-like immunoreactivity in tissues and plasma, Eisentraut, A., Ohneda, A., Parada, E., and Unger, R. H. (1968). *Diabetes* **17**, 321.

Section III, C

Radioimmuno assayable glucagon levels in man. Effects of starvation, hypoglycemia, and glucose administration, Lawrence, A. M. (1966). *Proc. Natl. Acad. Sci. U.S.* **55**, 316.

Rise in serum immunoreactive glucagon after intrajejunal glucose in pancreatectomized dogs, Buchanan, K. D., Vance, J. E., and Williams, R. H. (1967). *Proc. Soc. Exptl. Biol. Med.* **126**, 813.

Characterization of the responses of circulating glucagon-like immunoreactivity in intraduodenal and intravenous administration of glucose, Unger, R. H., Ohneda, A. Valverde, I., and Eisentraut, A. M. (1968). *J. Clin. Invest.* **47**, 48.

Effect of glucose concentration on insulin and glucagon release from isolated Islets of Langerhans of rat, Vance, J. E., Buchanan, K. D., Challoner, D. R., and Williams, R. H. (1968). *Diabetes* **17**, 187.

New ideas concerning physiologic roles of glucagon, Unger, R. H. (1968). *Am. J. Sci.* **255**, 273.

REFERENCES

Audy, G., and Kerly, M. (1952a). *Biochem. J.* **52**, 70.

Audy, G., and Kerly, M. (1952b). *Biochem. J.* **52**, 77.

Beekman, B. E. (1958). *Poultry Sci.* **37**, 595.

Behrens, O. K., and Bromer, W. W. (1958). *Vitamins Hormones* **16**, 263.

Berson, S. A., Yalow, R. S., Bauman, A., Rothschild, M. A., and Newerly, K. (1956). *J. Clin. Invest.* **35**, 170.

Berson, S. A., Yalow, R. S., and Volk, B. W. (1957). *J. Lab. Clin. Med.* **49**, 331.

Berthet, J., Sutherland, E. W., and Rall, T. W. (1957). *J. Biol. Chem.* **229**, 351.

Bliss, C. I., and Marks, H. P. (1939). *Quart. J. Pharm. Pharmacol.* **12**, 182.

Bromer, W. W. (1965). Unpublished data.

Bromer, W. W., and Chance, R. E. (1967). *Abstr. 27th Meeting Am. Diabetes Assoc.* p. 38.

Bromer, W. W., Sinn, L. G., Staub, A., and Behrens, O. K. (1957). *J. Am. Chem. Soc.* **79**, 2807.

Cole, R. D. (1960). *J. Biol. Chem.* **235**, 2300.

de Duve, C., and Vuylsteke, C. A. (1953). *Arch. Intern. Physiol.* **61**, 252.

Emmens, C. W. (1948). "Principles of Biological Assay." Chapman & Hall, London.

Foà, P. P. (1964). *In* "The Hormones" (G. Pincus, K. V. Thimann, and E. B. Astwood, Eds.), Vol. IV, pp. 531–556. Academic Press, New York.

Foà, P. P., and Galansino, G. (1962). "Glucagon: Chemistry and Function in Health and Disease." Thomas, Springfield.

Fodden, J. H., and Read, W. O. (1955). *Am. J. Physiol.* **182**, 513.

Gaddum, J. H. (1931). *Biochem. J.* **25**, 1113.

Grodsky, G. M., Hayashida, T., Peng, C. T., and Geschwind, I. I. (1961). *Proc. Soc. Exptl. Biol. Med.* **107**, 491.

Heiney, R. E. (1965). Personal communication.

Hoffman, W. S. (1937). *J. Biol. Chem.* **120**, 51.

Jackson, R. L., Probst, G. W., and Bromer, W. W. (1965). Unpublished data.

Kuzel, N. R., and Holzer, F. H. (1959). Unpublished data.

Lazrus, S. S., Volk, B. W., and Lew, H. (1957). *J. Clin. Endocrinol. Metab.* **17**, 542.

Light, A., and Simpson, M. V. (1956). *Biochim. Biophys. Acta* **20**, 251.

Lochner, J. de V., Esterhuizen, A. C., and Unger, R. H. (1964). *Diabetes* **13**, 387.

Makman, M. H., and Sutherland, E. W. (1961). *Federation Proc.* **20**, 189.

Makman, M. H., and Sutherland, E. W. (1964). *Endocrinology* **75**, 127.

Makman, M. H., Makman, R. S., and Sutherland, E. W. (1958). *J. Biol. Chem.* **233**, 894.

Makman, M. H., Makman, R. S., and Sutherland, E. W. (1960). *In* "Hormones in Human Plasma" (H. N. Antoniades, ed.), p. 119. Little, Brown, Boston, Massachusetts.

Nelson, N. (1944). *J. Biol. Chem.* **153**, 375.

Please, N. W. (1952). *Biochem. J.* **52**, 75.

Probst, G. W., and Colwell, R. W. (1966). *Biochemistry* **5**, 1209.

Rall, T. W., and Sutherland, E. W. (1961). *Cold Spring Harbor Symp. Quant. Biol.* **26**, 347.

Rall, T. W., and Sutherland, E. W. (1962a). *J. Biol. Chem.* **237**, 1228.

Rall, T. W., and Sutherland, E. W. (1962b). *In* "Methods in Enzymology," (S. P. Colowick and N. O. Kaplan, eds.), Vol. V, pp. 384–387. Academic Press, New York.

Rall, T. W., Sutherland, E. W., and Berthet, J. (1957). *J. Biol. Chem.* **224**, 463.

Rowlinson, H. R., and Lesford, J. M. (1951). *J. Pharm. Pharmacol.* **3**, 887.

Shipley, R. A., and Humel, E. J., Jr. (1945). *Am. J. Physiol.* **144**, 51.

Smith, F. A., and Robbins, E. B. (1965). Unpublished data.

Staub, A., and Behrens, O. K. (1954). *J. Clin. Invest.* **33**, 1629.

Staub, A., Sinn, L., and Behrens, O. K. (1955). *J. Biol. Chem.* **214**, 619.

Sutherland, E. W., and Cori, C. F. (1948). *J. Biol. Chem.* **172**, 737.

Sutherland, E. W., and Cori, C. F. (1951). *J. Biol. Chem.* **188**, 531.

Sutherland, E. W., and de Duve, C. (1948). *J. Biol. Chem.* **175**, 663.

Sutherland, E. W., and Rall, T. W. (1957). *J. Am. Chem. Soc.* **79**, 3608.

Sutherland, E. W., and Rall, T. W. (1958). *J. Biol. Chem.* **232**, 1077.

Sutherland, E. W., and Rall, T. W. (1960). *Pharmacol. Rev.* **12**, 265.

Sutherland, E. W., Rall, T. W., and Menon, T. (1962). *J. Biol. Chem.* **237**, 1220.

Tyberghein, J. M., and Williams, R. H. (1958). *Metabolism, Clin. Exptl.* **7**, 635.

Ui, M., Kobayashi, B., and Ito, Y. (1956). *Endocrinol. Japon.* **3**, 191.

Unger, R. H., Eisentraut, A. M., McCall, M. S., Keller, S., Lanz, H. C., and Madison, L. L. (1959a). *Proc. Soc. Exptl. Biol. Med.* **102**, 621.

Unger, R. H., Eisentraut, A. M., McCall, M. S., Keller, S., and Madison, L. L. (1959b). *J. Lab. Clin. Med.* **54**, 952.

Unger, R. H., Eisentraut, A. M., McCall, M. S., and Madison, L. L. (1962). *J. Clin. Invest.* **41**, 682.

Unger, R. H., Eisentraut, A. M., and Madison, L. L. (1963). *J. Clin. Invest.* **42**, 1031.

von Holt, C., von Holt, L., Kroner, B., and Kuhnau, J. (1956). *Ciba Found. Colloq. Endocrinol.* **9**, 14.

Vuylsteke, C. A., and de Duve, C. (1957). *Arch. Intern. Pharmacodyn.* **111**, 437.

Vuylsteke, C. A., Cornelis, G., and de Duve, C. (1952). *Arch. Intern. Physiol.* **60**, 105.

Wiesel, L. L., Positano, V., Kologlu, Y., and Anderson, G. E. (1963). *Proc. Soc. Exptl. Biol. Med.* **112**, 515.

Chapter 11

Parathyroid Hormone

R. H. THORP

I. Introduction

Parathyroid hormone has been isolated in a highly purified form from bovine glands by Aurbach (1959a,b) and Rasmussen and Craig (1961) and has been shown to be a single-chain polypeptide containing the common amino acids with the exception of cystine. It has a molecular weight of approximately 9000 but the sequence of the amino acid moieties in the chain is not yet established. The hormone from human parathyroid glands has not yet been isolated although the bovine material is active in man and other species and it has been shown by immunochemical methods that the structures of the bovine and human hormones are similar although not identical.

The parathyroid hormone plays a major part in calcium and phosphorus metabolism, and in deficiency states an abnormally low concentration of calcium is present in the blood serum together with elevation of the renal threshold to phosphate excretion; there is also reduction in the amount of phosphate lost from the body in the urine. The most predominant effect of parathyroid hormone deficiency is an increase in the ratio of phosphate to calcium in the serum and, conversely, the administration of extracts of the hormone causes an increase in serum calcium together with a slight reduction in the phosphate ion concentration. Many methods used for the assay of parathyroid hormone have been based upon the rise in blood calcium, and various devices using this criterion have been employed, ranging from direct measurement of the blood calcium concentration to the antagonism of magnesium anesthesia, which had previously been observed after injection of ionizable calcium preparations.

Studies of the excretion of calcium in the rat or phosphate in rats and mice have also been used as bases for assays, and Gellhorn (1935) has suggested the possibility of using the sensitivity to calcium of hypodynamic skeletal muscle in an isolated preparation as an indicator of parathyroid extract potency.

Attempts to use methods of this kind for the estimation of parathyroid hormone levels in human blood or urine have been attended with little success in view of the large doses of the hormone required to produce such effects, and the lack of specificity of methods involving urinary phosphate excretion.

More recently immunological assay methods have been developed that offer greatly increased sensitivity. Whereas the older methods required doses of several units of parathyroid hormone for each animal these methods can be performed with milliunit quantities.

II. Possibilities of a Standard Preparation

There is no international standard for the parathyroid hormone, and the assays that have been described either define the potency of the preparation in terms of response or by comparison with a private standard, adopted by that particular laboratory and which has itself been standardized in terms of a biological response.

It is now universally appreciated that a standard preparation of similar constitution to that of the material under examination is essential for any biological assay, and now that highly potent preparations of the bovine hormone are available it would seem likely that an international standard could be established.

In 1936 Dyer described the preparation of a stable powder with an activity of 80 Collip units per gram, and L'Heureux et al. (1947) prepared a powder with a potency of 200–300 U.S.P. units per milligram of N.

More recently much more active preparations have been prepared by Friedman and Munson (1958, 1959), Aurbach (1959a, b), and Rasmussen and Craig (1959). The material prepared by these workers had an activity of 1250–3000 units per milligram of peptide.

Rasmussen and Craig called their product "parathormone C," since they had previously isolated two other peptides called A and B that could have been degradation productions of Preparation C. It is possible that these highly active preparations represent the pure polypeptide hormone.

III. The Unit of Parathyroid Activity

In the absence of a standard preparation the activity of parathyroid preparation has been stated in terms of the biological response, and two units were described in this way.

Collip and Clark (1925) originally defined that unit as 1/100 part of the amount of an extract required to raise the serum calcium of a dog weighing 20 kg by 5 mg/100 ml, but Hanson (1928) proposed a smaller unit consisting of 1/100 of the amount causing a rise of 1 mg/100 ml, in the serum of parathyroidectomized dogs.

The unit described in the U.S. Pharmacopeia (XVI revision) is similar to that of Hanson (1928) except that the rise in the serum calcium is that produced in normal dogs within 16–18 hours after administration of the hormone preparation.

IV. Methods of Assay

A. METHODS BASED ON THE ELEVATION OF SERUM CALCIUM

1. Methods Using Dogs

The method originally used by Collip and Clark (1925) involved the measurement of the rise in serum calcium after dosage with parathyroid extracts in groups of 10 dogs.

Blood samples were taken from the ear veins of 10 normal dogs of approximately 20 kg weight, and the calcium content of the serum was determined. In the late afternoon of the same day (6:00 PM) the dogs were given a subcutaneous injection of the parathyroid extract under examination and the serum calcium was again determined at 9:00 AM the following day. The calculation of potency in this case was a simple arithmetic proportion based on a rise of 5 mg/100 ml being produced by 100 units of parathyroid activity.

The method originally described by Collip and Clark has been the subject of many modifications and improvements of which probably the most significant are the investigations of this method by Miller (1938) and Bliss and Rose (1940).

Miller first examined the dose-response relationship for the para-thyroid elevation of serum calcium and showed, as one would expect, that the linear part of this relationship was small and corresponded only to a threefold change in dose. He found that when no account was taken of this relationship very variable results were obtained, and one of the samples examined gave results varying from 75–222 U.S.P. units per milliliter when the dose given was varied from 2–6 ml per dog. Efforts to extend the dose range, over which a steep response relationship would be obtained by modifications of the diet of the dogs, were without success. Miller concluded that the dose given must be one producing a significant response, which is submaximal, using a group of at least 5 dogs. In his experiments a rise of serum calcium of approximately 5 mg/100 ml was a maximal response.

The examination of the method by Bliss and Rose (1940) followed upon the work of Miller and was directed principally toward determining the accuracy and reproducibility of the results obtained in such assays. These authors pointed out the great variation in sensitivity from dog to dog and the necessity for the use of a standard preparation. They examined data supplied by Miller as well as those derived from their own experiments.

Two experimental designs were used in the experiments which Bliss and Rose made, either 5 groups of 4 dogs each being tested 4 times in a Latin square arrangement or 3 groups of 12 dogs each being tested twice in an arrangement of symmetrical pairs. In order to achieve comparable results the standard employed was that used in the Lilly Research Laboratories. Their investigations can best be discussed under several headings.

a. The Dose-Response Curve for Parathyroid Extract. By using Miller's data obtained on 12 dogs each treated with 7 doses of the extract ranging from 0.5–6.0 ml, and with determinations of serum calcium 7 hours before and 17 hours after injection, separate dose-response curves were plotted for each of 10 dogs that had contributed results all through the experiments.

The data used were both the absolute values of serum calcium after the hormone and the rise in serum calcium above the initial value for each dog. Using the latter data, Bliss and Rose showed that the slope of the dose-response curves varied from $b = 4.30–9.49$ with a combined value of 6.846. They calculated an analysis of the variance of the results and they showed that computations from responses within dogs were more consistent than between different dogs. The slope of the dose-response curve for individual dogs agreed within normal experimental limits.

When these results were plotted as the rise in serum calcium against log dose and constant terms were added to reduce individual curves to a common basis, it was shown that the relationship was linear and maximal, for the extract employed, with doses of 6 ml per dog. The relationship obtained in this way could not be reconciled with the implied relationship of the U.S.P. (XIth revision).

When only the final serum calcium data were used, the combined slope was $b_c = 7.330$ and ranged from $b = 4.27-10.22$. In this case the variation between animals was more marked, but the authors concluded that no criterion involving the initial serum calcium gave better results than using the final serum calcium value alone.

These findings were confirmed by the experiments conducted by Bliss and Rose themselves, and again, the final serum calcium level was a satisfactory criterion. Separate estimates of slope did not vary to significantly lower values than those from Miller's data. The combined slopes in Bliss's experiment being $b_c = 4.133$ for the increase in serum calcium and $b_c = 4.082$ for final serum calcium alone, emphasized the importance of an integral determination of slope in such an assay.

b. *Suggested Assay Design.* Bliss and Rose proposed that a satisfactory assay should be a comparative test with a standard preparation, should have an internal determination of slope and error, and the difference in overall sensitivity should be separated from the estimates of potency and error. They proposed the use of a Latin square design to encompass these requirements (Bliss and Marks, 1939a,b) and consequently investigated an arrangement of five 4×4 squares in parallel, with all 5 squares conducted on each day.

Analysis of variance showed that the difference between days was small, between dogs large, and once again, the final serum calcium value was an adequate criterion. The sums of squares for treatments were subdivided by factorial analysis, and it was shown that differences in dosage contributed mostly to the value, while the divergence from parallelism of the curves for the standard and test materials was of no significance.

With 40 observations on both standard and test preparations the standard error exceeded $\pm 10\%$ partly because of the smaller slope in Bliss and Rose's experiments and partly because the strength of the sample used as the test material in these experiments was 30% more potent than postulated.

Using the design of symmetrical pairs described by Yates (1936), these workers obtained a result with a standard error of $\pm 13\%$ (when the determined potency was 113% of that of the standard material) using 36 dogs with two tests on each. They described the application of this design quite fully and also pointed out that unless the body weight of the animals is uniform throughout the group, it is essential to make a correction for the different values.

On using Miller's data, accuracy of a similar order was obtained with 11 dogs for both standard and test preparations because of the steeper slope obtained in his laboratory.

The actual technique of the dog serum calcium method has been examined by Allardyce (1931), who stated that a meat diet with cod liver oil gave better results but that the addition of calcium as calcium lactate did not result in an increased response to parathyroid hormone. Since the more recent statistical designs were not current at this time, further work on these lines might reduce slope variation between dogs and reduce the number of observations required for a given degree of accuracy in this assay. Allardyce found incidentally that cats did not show appreciable hypercalcemia after parathyroid injection and hence could not be used as test objects for this purpose.

c. Method of United States Pharmacopeia. The method that follows is that described in the U.S. Pharmacopeia (XVIth revision, 1960) and embodies the considerations which Miller showed to be important.

Select male dogs free from gross evidence of disease and accustomed to venipuncture, but which have not been used during the previous 4 weeks for the purposes of this assay. The dogs selected are mature, as indicated by the presence of their second teeth, and weigh between 8 and 16 kg but do not differ in weight by more than 5 kg. Employ not less than 10 dogs in each test. During the assay, maintain the dogs under similar conditions with respect to diet and environmental influences.

Select, by preliminary trial, a dose of the preparation to be assayed such that its injection will be expected to produce increases in the serum calcium content of the dogs selected of between 2 and 5 mg/100 ml.

Withdraw 10 ml of blood from each dog, using a clean, dry syringe containing no anticoagulant. Transfer the blood immediately to a centrifuge tube, and allow it to clot. Free the clot with a glass rod, and centrifuge sufficiently to yield the serum as a clear supernatant layer. Siphon off the serum by suitable means, and if necessary centrifuge the serum again after its separation from the clot to ensure the removal of cellular material. Determine the serum calcium.

Inject subcutaneously into each dog the selected dose of parathyroid sample. Between 16 and 18 hours after the injection, again determine the serum calcium.

Determine for each dog the increase in serum calcium (milligrams per 100 ml of serum) and determine the average of these values for all the animals injected. The potency of a sample of parathyroid injection is required to be such that the average increase is not less than 1 mg/100 ml of serum per milliliter of parathyroid injection.

The method for the determination of serum calcium requires little comment and a suitable one is described in the U.S. Pharmacopeia (XVIth revision, 1960) in the description of the assay.

2. The Use of Rabbits

Hamilton and Schwartz (1932) described a method using rabbits in which parathyroid hormone caused a delay in the rise of serum calcium after administration of calcium chloride by mouth.

Dyer (1935a) examined the method in a detailed manner and found that the variations in normal serum calcium values in rabbits and the values after parathyroid injections were very great so that it was not possible to give an average figure for the response to a given dose of parathyroid hormone or to compare the potency of two extracts by measuring the increase in serum calcium.

Methods based on elevation of serum calcium are therefore satisfactory when used as described by Bliss and Rose (1940) but can have little meaning without the use of a standard preparation and an adequate statistical design.

3. The Use of Parathyroidectomized Rats

The normal rat has been shown to be very insensitive to injected parathyroid hormone, and Biering (1950) found that large doses of parathyroid extract up to approximately 1000 U.S.P. units were necessary to produce a rise in serum calcium of 3 mg/100 ml of serum. Tweedy and Chandler (1929) showed that parathyroidectomy produced an increase in sensitivity, and Davies and her colleagues (1954) studied the use of such animals for an assay. These workers used hooded rats weighing 200–250 gm and performed parathyroidectomy by cauterization (Davies and Gordon, 1953), using the animals 3–21 days later. They used a method for plasma calcium determination which makes use of chelation of calcium by sodium Versenate, the end point being the loss of the pink color of the indicator Eriochrome T. The method is described in full in their paper. These workers showed that the response of the rat is best found at 21 hours after injection and they used this interval in subsequent experiments. It was also shown that 50 units of Parathormone produced approximately the same rise in operated rats as 200 units in normal animals so that there was approximately a fourfold increase as a result of the operation. Since the rise of plasma calcium is dependent upon the initial plasma calcium + magnesium level which is very variable from rat to rat, these workers used a corrected response which measured the effect of the hormone free from this dependence. The use of this corrected response resulted in a reduction of the spread of the experimental values and an increase in accuracy of the assay together with a simplification of the method of calculation.

These authors concluded that the parathyroidectomized rat has advantages over the dog in that it is a cheaper and more convenient experimental animal, the level of accuracy using the same number of animals is about the same as that for the dog, and less hormone is required.

Rasmussen and Westall (1956) showed that if crude parathyroid extracts were fractionated, the time duration of the rise of plasma calcium in the rat differed according to the fraction; and the method of Davies *et al.* (1954) showed apparent inactivity in some of their samples, but if plasma samples were taken earlier after injection the plasma calcium value reached a peak at 5–7 hours in these cases and had returned to normal after 12–14 hours. They concluded therefore that assay methods in which the plasma calcium determinations are made after 16–18 hours can easily give an incorrect result when fractionated preparations are studied.

Munson (1955) has also studied the use of parathyroidectomized rats for assay purposes, and an assay technique is described using calcium-depleted rats and giving a good dose/response relationship with doses of 5–20 U.S.P. units of parathyroid extract per 100 gm of body weight.

Male rats of the Sprague-Dawley strain 40–45 days old are kept on a normal diet until 4 days before the assay. They are then given the calcium-deficient diet of Shaw (1947), and the parathyroid glands are destroyed 4 days later by cauterization. The rats are arranged in groups of five or six in a random fashion and immediately after the operation are injected with parathyroid hormone. Two groups of rats receive 5 and 20 U.S.P. units, respectively, of Lilly parathyroid extract per 100 gm as a standard. Other groups of rats are given doses of the test extracts. Six hours after operation and injection, the rats are anesthetized with ether and bled by cardiac puncture. Blood samples are removed and centrifuged, and the calcium content is determined. In rats not treated with parathyroid hormone the serum calcium level falls to about 5 mg/100 ml and to about 8–9 mg/100 ml when the rats have been given 20 U.S.P. units of parathyroid extract at the time of operation.

In a series of 15 assays, the index of precision was 0.27. In an assay using 4 groups of 5 rats, two groups being given doses of the standard preparation and the remaining two groups doses of the test material, the potency estimate has a standard error of about ±30%.

B. Antagonism of Magnesium Anesthesia by the Rise in Serum Calcium Produced by Parathyroid Hormone

The reversal of magnesium depression by calcium ions has been known since 1905 (Meltzer and Auer, 1905, 1908, 1913), and Simon

(1935) showed that in normal mice subcutaneous injections of parathyroid hormone had the same effect upon magnesium narcosis as injections of calcium chloride due to the rise in serum calcium produced by the hormone. He also found that there was an optimal dose of parathyroid hormone which prevented magnesium narcosis in the greatest number of mice. Simon suggested the assay of parathyroid hormone by comparison of this optimal dose for different preparations in comparison with that obtained with a standard preparation.

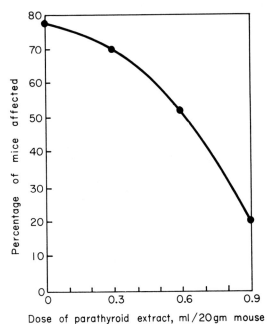

Dose of parathyroid extract, ml/20 gm mouse

FIG. 1. The effect of parathyroid extract in preventing narcosis in mice produced by injections of magnesium sulfate. (From Dyer, 1935b.)

Dyer (1935b) examined this method in detail, making use of the observations of Wokes (1931), who constructed a curve relating the percentages of mice affected by different doses of magnesium sulfate. When magnesium sulfate is injected subcutaneously into mice they become drowsy and unconscious, and unless a fatal dose has been given, respiration continues in a regular manner. Dyer used as his criterion of narcosis the inability of a mouse to right itself when turned on its back.

Dyer first investigated the effect of single and repeated doses of parathyroid hormone prior to magnesium narcosis and showed that a given dose of parathyroid extract was much more effective in antagonizing magnesium narcosis when injected in three increments at intervals of 3 hours, the dose totaling 0.09 ml of parathyroid extract, than when given as a single dose. In fact a single dose had practically no effect on magnesium narcosis $2\frac{1}{2}$ hours later, in both cases over 80% of the mice remaining narcotized an hour later. The same dose given in three injections reduced the percentages narcotized at this time to below 10%. In this experiment also, Dyer showed that the effect of a total dose of 0.09 ml, of parathyroid extract given in two or three doses was greater than that produced by 0.18 ml given as a single dose, although this produced a more marked antagonism than a single dose of 0.09 ml. By using doses ranging from 0.3–0.9 ml of an extract given in three divided doses to groups of mice at 2-hour intervals, Dyer showed that the percentage of mice narcotized was related to the dose of parathyroid extract and a smooth curve could be drawn relating the two. Dyer's curve is reproduced in Fig. 1. For this experiment he used the percentage of mice narcotized 1 hour after the injection of magnesium sulfate when this was given in a dose of 1.5 mg per gram of body weight at $1\frac{1}{2}$ hours after the last injection of parathyroid hormone.

Dyer compared the potency of two extracts, assayed by another method, by the use of this technique and although it happened that the percentage of mice narcotized was the same in each case, and thus the potency was in inverse ratio of the doses given, the results agreed very well with those previously obtained. A statistical evaluation of this method has not been described, but it has the advantage of simplicity and rapidity and would appear worthy of extension.

C. Assay Methods Using the Fall of Serum Phosphate

Tepperman et al. (1947) were interested in assaying large numbers of samples of parathyroid hormone and fractions derived from it and found the serum calcium method in dogs too costly and time consuming for this purpose. These workers developed a method using the fall in serum inorganic phosphorus in the rat after parathyroid hormone and obtained a linear relationship between response and log dose over the range 12.5–100 U.S.P. units and a similar degree of accuracy to that obtained by the dog serum and calcium method.

Tepperman and her colleagues described two designs for the assay of parathyroid hormone by this method, one in which a previously established standard dose-response curve is used and a more complete design in which an integral determination of the slope of the dose-response curve is made by using two doses of each preparation.

The general technique, applicable in each case, consists of using groups of male albino rats fed on Purina dog chow for at least 2 weeks before use, but not fasted prior to the experiment, although during the experiment only water is allowed. Blood samples are taken from the cut tip of the tail and 0.6 ml is collected from each rat into centrifuge tubes, centrifuged for 10 minutes and 0.2 ml samples of the serum are pipetted into 6 ml of 10% trichloroacetic acid; this is centrifuged and 5-ml aliquots from the supernatant protein-free solution are used for the estimation of inorganic phosphorus by the method of Fiske and Subba-Row. Tepperman *et al.* used an Evelyn photoelectric colorimeter for the final reading of the color.

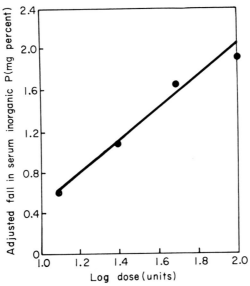

Fig. 2. Dose-response curve obtained on rats using parathyroid hormone to produce a fall in serum inorganic phosphorus. (From Tepperman *et al.*, 1947.)

In their experiments Tepperman and co-workers used parathyroid extract (Lilly) as a standard in the absence of any official preparation and they measured the serum phosphorus initially and 3 hours after subcutaneous injection of parathyroid hormone.

Figure 2 shows the dose-response curve obtained by this method; it will be seen that the relationship between log dose and response is substantially linear. The number of observations at each point varied from 121 at a dose of 50 U.S.P. units per rat to 22 in the case of the 100-unit dose.

For assay of relative potency by the shorter technique, these workers described a design in which two doses of the test preparation are used with a group of 3 rats for each dose. The fall in serum phosphorus is determined 3 hours after injection, and an adjustment is made for differences in the initial serum phosphorus level since it had been shown earlier that this factor influenced the fall to a considerable extent and that regressions of the fall in serum phosphorus on initial level had similar slope values for different dose levels of the hormone. This adjustment corrects all responses for an initial value of 9.15 mg/100 ml, the mean value obtained by these authors. The log ratio of the potencies of the unknown and standard preparation is then calculated by the standard procedure using a modification that incorporates the use of a predetermined standard curve. This modification involves a test of parallelism of the regression lines for each preparation and correction for any difference that may be found before calculating the variances of the mean response to the test sample. The potency of the unknown sample and its standard error can then be calculated. A sample assayed in this way gave a value of 173 U.S.P. units per milligram of nitrogen with a standard error of ± 33 U.S.P. units.

In view of the crudity of many of the preparations these workers were testing, such a method was adequate, but they also described in detail the complete assay mentioned earlier in which Yates' design of "symmetrical pairs" is used. This design enables the rat serum phosphorus method to give results comparable with the results obtained by Bliss and Rose (1940) by the dog method, but with much less technical effort and expense. In an experiment using 12 rats in the symmetrical pairs design, calculation of confidence limits ($P = 0.95$) indicated that upon repetition, only 1 assay in 20 would be expected to give an estimate outside the limits 60–142%, the potency being 93% of that of the standard in this case. In Bliss and Rose's experiments 36 dogs gave confidence limits of 87–140% at $P = 0.95$ when the standard and unknown were of identical potency. The use of the same number of rats, therefore, should produce results of accuracy comparable to those of the dog method.

The methods were found to be successful only with fed rats, the fall in serum inorganic phosphate being erratic and ill defined in fasted animals. This has not been further reported upon but may mean that increased sensitivity could be produced by dietary modifications.

D. Methods Based on the Urinary Excretion of Phosphate

Since it was suggested (Stewart and Bowen, 1952) that the two actions of parathyroid preparations in causing an elevation of plasma calcium and inhibiting the renal reabsorption of phosphate might be separable, Davies and her colleagues (1955) examined assay methods based on phosphate excretion in the urine. They studied the increase of urinary phosphate excretion which occurs during a period of $3\frac{1}{2}$ hours after the injection of parathyroid hormone.

Using albino mice weighing 20–25 gm and hydrated by giving 1 ml of 0.9% saline intraperitoneally per 5 gm of body weight at the commencement of the experiment, these workers collected urine from 15 minutes to $3\frac{1}{2}$ hours after giving parathyroid extracts subcutaneously. They showed that the output of phosphate was high when the urine volume was high and therefore they devised a correction for the milligrams of phosphorus excreted per hour, to remove the dependence of this upon urine volume. The use of this correction gave higher slope values, smaller error variance, and smaller limits of error to the estimate of potency. It was shown that this assay was better than that of Tepperman et al. (1947) on the fall in serum phosphate in the rat and comparable in accuracy with the dog plasma calcium assay or the parathyroidectomized rat plasma calcium assay. Davies et al. (1955) used this method to study the ratio of renal phosphate activity to calcium-mobilizing activity for various different parathyroid extracts. They found that this ratio differed in these cases from that given by Parathormone and they suggested that standardization in terms of both activities is desirable.

The use of radiophosphorus (^{32}P) excretion as a basis for an assay technique was suggested by Tweedy et al. (1947), and this method was examined by Rubin and Dorfman (1953), who showed that the use of thyroparathyroidectomized rats given ^{32}P enabled doses of 0.5 U.S.P. unit or more of parathyroid hormone to be detected.

These authors collected the urine for 3 hours and pointed out that the elimination of tedious chemical work and the increased sensitivity over the plasma calcium dog method, together with the rapidity of this method were features which render it an improvement over those previously described.

It would seem that the mouse phosphate excretion methods of Davies et al. (1955) could be simplified by using radioactive phosphate in this way in preference to chemical estimation.

E. Methods Based on the Urinary Excretion of Calcium

In some preliminary experiments with parathyroid hormone Dyer (1932) found an increase in calcium excretion in the urine of the rat and tentatively suggested that this might form the basis for a method of assay. Later, however, Dyer performed a number of experiments in which no rise in calcium excretion was observed, and this observation was also made by Pugsley (1932), who found that daily injections of the hormone were necessary to ensure a rise in urinary calcium.

In a later paper Dyer (1933) described further experiments in which he used rats weighing 120–160 gm in groups of 10 animals and fed upon a diet containing 1% calcium carbonate. The effect of parathyroid extract was much greater with the high calcium diet. The normal excretion for a group of 5 rats Dyer found to be approximately 1.3 mg per day, and this rose to 7.8 mg per day when the parathyroid hormone was injected.

The test as Dyer used it comprised two groups of at least 5 rats, and he used one group for each of the materials under comparison. The doses used were 0.4 ml of an extract equivalent to Parathormone (Lilly), and by retaining the rats for a further period of 4 days after the last injection it was possible to perform a cross-over test by giving the two samples to opposite groups for another period of 3 days.

The relationship between the dose of parathyroid hormone and the rise in calcium excretion appeared to be a linear one.

Truszkowski *et al.* (1939) reinvestigated methods for the assay of parathyroid hormone and considered that Dyer's method could be useful. They used larger rats weighing 150–200 gm and housed them in groups of 5 in glass metabolism cages. The diet used in this case contained approximately 0.3% of calcium carbonate and was fed to the rats in different cages once daily.

These workers found the normal calcium excretion to be 0.404 mg/100 gm per day and they showed that the standard deviation of the difference between two groups treated at the same time was less than half that for the same animals at different times; so, they suggested that the rise in the difference in calcium excretion between two similar groups of rats at the same time is more significant than for the same group of rats at different times.

The method favored by Truszkowski and his colleagues, therefore, was to record the daily excretion of calcium for about 7 days and then to give an injection of parathyroid hormone to one of two groups. This produced a steep rise in calcium output followed by a rapid fall, and the extra excretion was complete in 72 hours. The control group was then used to provide a baseline for the treated group, and the area of the curve due to the injection of parathyroid hormone was plotted against the dose given.

It was shown that there was a linear dose-response relationship for a 6× change in dose, although the exact doses given cannot be stated since the extract used was not described in terms of a unit but given by weight.

F. GELLHORN'S WORK WITH PARATHYROID HORMONE ON HYPODYNAMIC MUSCLE

The use of an isolated tissue preparation that would respond to varying doses of parathyroid hormone would present a very desirable assay method, and Gellhorn (1935) studied hypodynamic skeletal muscle in this way.

Skeletal muscle is highly sensitive to calcium ions when in a hypodynamic state, and Gellhorn set up hindlimb preparations of *Rana esculenta* arranged for perfusion through the abdominal aorta. The tendons of the gastrocnemius muscles were attached to isotonic levers magnifying the contraction 7 times. Nerve stimulation was given at a rate of 40 per minute until the height of contraction was reduced by 50%. After 15–30 minutes rest, stimulation was resumed at 15 per minute and the preparation was used for experiments as soon as it had settled to a steady response.

Gellhorn used dilutions of 1 in 100 in 1 in 1000 of Parathormone (Lilly; 20 Collip units per milliliter) in phosphate-buffered Ringer's solution of pH 7.2 and found that there was always an increase in the height of contraction and this increase was graded according to the concentration of the hormone.

The effect took about 2–5 minutes to commence, and periods of 5–10 minutes stimulation were used alternately with the same periods of rest. Gellhorn did not find this effect when the hormone was inactivated; although it had been shown earlier that similar effects could be produced by calcium ions, this was not the mechanism in Gellhorn's experiments. He therefore concluded that the hormone aided recovery from fatigue and augmented the height of contraction by its action in raising the calcium level.

The method has not been developed for assay purposes but might well be worthy of further consideration as it would have the advantages of speed and simplicity.

G. IMMUNOASSAYS BY COMPLEMENT FIXATION

The methods already described suffer from lack of precision and the necessity for large amounts of the hormone for the performance of the assay.

It has been shown by Tashjian, Levine, and Munson (1962) that bovine parathyroid hormone can produce a precipitating antibody in the rabbit, and an assay method has been developed from this (Tashjian *et al.*, 1966) for which it is claimed that the precision is greater than that of any method previously described. The method is sensitive, and as little as 24 ng (84 mU) gave a reliable result. This method is briefly described below.

1. Preparation of Antiserum

Antiserum to parathyroid hormone is prepared in a rabbit by the use of a highly purified preparation of bovine parathyroid hormone with an activity of approximately 40,000 units per milligram of N.

The rabbit is injected with a solution of this product containing 1.0 mg in 1.0 ml of 0.005 N acetic acid and 1.0 ml of complete Freund's adjuvant. A dose of 0.2 ml is injected into the toe pads of each hind paw and the remainder given intramuscularly. Three weeks later the first bleeding takes place when the blood contains precipitating antibody. Immediately after the bleeding doses of 150 μg of the initial antigen dissolved in 0.005 N acetic acid can be injected daily for 5 days to increase the antibody titer to approximately twice that at the time of the first bleeding. The antiserum may be stored at −20°C without preservative.

2. Complement Fixation

The rabbit serum is heated to 60°C for 20 minutes to destroy endogenous complement activity and is then diluted in the isotonic NaCl–barbital buffer of Osler et al. (1952) containing 5×10^{-4} M $MgCl_2$, 1.5×10^{-4} M $CaCl_2$, and 0.1% of bovine serum albumin. The dilution is 1/400 at which concentration freezing at −20°C permits the storage, without loss of activity, of a sufficient quantity for several assays on different days. The assay is performed in 40-ml centrifuge tubes in an ice bath, and to these are added in order the diluted antiserum, buffer, diluted guinea pig complement, and finally the antigen (the hormone standard or unknown) diluted in a 2-fold series in buffer.

Appropriate controls for antigen, antibody, and complement are included, and details of an experimental protocol are given by the authors in their description of this method.

After incubation at 2–4°C for 14–18 hours, 1.0 ml of hemolysin-sensitized sheep red cells (5×10^7 cells/ml) is added to each tube and hemolysis is allowed to proceed in a water bath at 35–37°C for 40–60 minutes or until 80–90% hemolysis has taken place in the control tubes as estimated visually. The tubes are next cooled in ice and centrifuged for 10 minutes to sediment the unlysed red cells. The optical density of the supernatant fluid is then determined in a spectrophotometer at 413 mμ. Provided that the controls do not show pro- or anticomplement activity the results are expressed in one of a number of ways: (1) directly as optical density, (2) the difference between the mean optical density of the controls, provided they are similar, and that of the experimental tubes, or (3) as the percentage of complement fixed.

3. Parathyroid Hormone Standard

For the development and evaluation of this method of assay the authors used a purified sample of the hormone as a standard. The activity was approximately 22,000 units per milligram of N which was stored frozen in 0.2 M ammonium acetate buffer.

4. Dose-Response Curve

Figure 3 shows a complement fixation dose response curve. To the left is the zone of antibody excess followed by a region of equivalence and then antigen excess inhibition to the right.

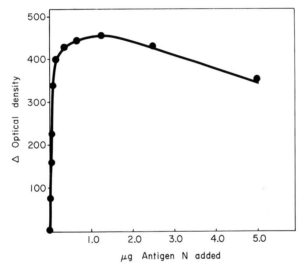

FIG. 3. Complement fixation curve of highly purified bovine parathyroid hormone and its homologous rabbit antibody. (From Tashjian, Levine and Munson, 1964.)

The segment of the curve between ΔOD_{50} to OD_{400} of antibody excess is most sensitive to small changes in antigen concentration and is the linear portion of the curve used for assay purposes. This semi-logarithmic plot results in a straight line with a good negative slope value, and Fig. 4 shows such dose response curves relating the optical density to the dose of hormone added.

In estimations of the potency of unknown samples, standard antigen was included in each assay in a range of 5–100 ng of nitrogen. It was found that the smallest amount of hormone consistently detectable was

3.75 ng of hormone nitrogen corresponding to 24 ng of hormone or 84 mU.

In a series of determinations of potency of parathyroid hormone preparations of widely differing biological activity both by the bioassay method of Munson (1961) and the immunoassay described here, the two sets of results were in good agreement.

Storage of the hormone in the frozen state for periods of 24 hours results in a loss in the amount of complement fixed although storage for longer periods produces only further losses of a minor amount so that this decrease is largely complete at 24 hours. The decrease was fully

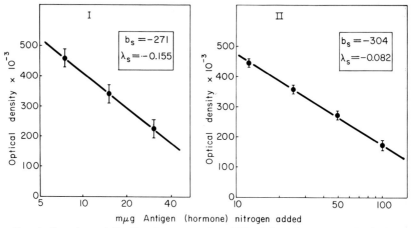

FIG. 4. Complement fixation (represented as OD) of the reference standard plotted semilogarithmically. Each point represents the mean of 2 determinations in I and of 3 determinations in II. The vertical lines represent the standard errors. (From Tashjian, Levine and Munson, 1964.)

restored by exposure to sonic oscillation for 3 minutes. The loss of activity was the same in the case of standard and test preparation and although the slope of the dose response curve is less steep under these circumstances the estimated potency is not affected.

The loss of activity on freezing is only seen in dilute solutions of the hormone (<1 μg/ml). Solutions of 100 μg/ml or more withstood repeated freezing and thawing without loss over a period of more than a year.

The immunoassay offers an increase in precision over the bioassay on parathyroidectomized rats and requires far less hormone. There are substantial variations in the absolute amounts of complement fixed between assays of the same substance but the overall precision of the method still exceeds that of any other assay method yet described. Although the immunoassay can replace the bioassay in many applications, the bioassay will still be needed as a means of identifying the activity of parathyroid preparations by means of their characteristic properties *in vivo*.

The amount of parathyroid hormone in human serum appears to be less than the smallest amount that can be determined reliably by the complement fixation method and since no satisfactory method for separation of the hormone from blood has been described there is need for more delicate assay methods to measure endogenous circulating hormone.

An immunoassay based upon the competitive inhibition of the binding of ^{131}I-labeled hormone to specific antibody has been developed by Berson, Yalow, Aurbach, and Potts (1963). This method was originally employed for the assay of insulin by these workers and consists of labeling a highly purified preparation of bovine parathyroid hormone with [131]I.

Rabbits or guinea pigs are then immunized with bovine parathyroid hormone at intervals of 2–4 weeks, and those animals given 2000 U or less in two injections show parathyroid binding antibodies in the serum.

If the iodine-labeled hormone is then added to the immune serum and subjected to paper electrophoresis it is bound to the antibody and migrates with the globulins whereas if nonimmune serum is used the labeled hormone remains at the starting line.

If mixtures are prepared containing constant amounts of labeled parathyroid hormone and antiserum and variable concentrations of unlabeled hormone and are incubated for 3 days at 4°C, there is separation of the unbound ^{131}I-labeled hormone from that which is bound and migrates with the serum proteins. The ratio B:F falls as the concentration of unlabeled parathyroid hormone is increased as a result of competitive inhibition of the binding of the labeled hormone.

By analyzing the dried paper strips in an automatic strip counter the B:F ratio can be determined, and this is plotted against the concentration of unlabeled hormone to give a dose-response curve, from which the hormone concentration in unknown solutions can be determined.

The degree of purity of unknown hormone preparations does not appear to be of great importance since extracts varying almost 300-fold in purity gave results of the same order for the parathyroid hormone content. Human parathyroid hormone was shown also to inhibit the binding of the labeled bovine preparation, but higher concentrations were required so that some degree of species specificity is apparent. It was possible to obtain a definite decrease in the B:F ratio with 1.5–6 mU/ml of human hormone.

Provided the test antigen is purified to the extent that contaminating proteins exist only in trace amounts, serious interference from non-hormonal protein antibodies can be avoided.

This method extends the range of sensitivity sufficiently to enable detection of endogenous parathyroid hormone in the plasma of hyperparathyroid subjects and some normal subjects, but not in hypoparathyroid patients.

REFERENCES

Allardyce, W. J. (1931). *Am. J. Physiol.* **98**, 417.
Aurbach, G. D. (1959a). *Arch. Biochem. Biophys.* **80**, 467.
Aurbach, G. D. (1959b). *J. Biol. Chem.* **234**, 3179.
Berson, S. A., Yalow, R. S., Aurbach, G. D., and Potts, J. T., Jr. (1953). *Proc. Natl. Acad. Sci. U.S.* **49**, 613.
Biering, A. (1950). *Acta Pharmacol. Toxicol.* **6**, 59.
Bliss, C. I., and Marks, H. P. (1939a). *Quart. J. Pharm. Pharmacol.* **12**, 82.
Bliss, C. I., and Marks, H. P. (1939b). *Quart. J. Pharm. Pharmacol.* **12**, 182.
Bliss, C. I., and Rose, C. L. (1940). *Am. J. Hyg.* **31**, 79.
Collip, J. B., and Clark, E. P. (1925). *J. Biol. Chem.* **64**, 485.
Davies, B. M. A., and Gordon, A. H. (1953). *J. Endocrinol.* **9**, 292.
Davies, B. M. A., Gordon, A. H., and Mussett, M. V. (1954). *J. Physiol. (London)* **125**, 383.
Davies, B. M. A., Gordon, A. H., and Mussett, M. V. (1955). *J. Physiol. (London)* **130**, 79.
Dyer, F. J. (1932). *J. Physiol. (London)* **75**, 13P.
Dyer, F. J. (1933). *Quart. J. Pharm. Pharmacol.* **6**, 426.
Dyer, F. J. (1935a). *Quart. J. Pharm. Pharmacol.* **8**, 197.
Dyer, F. J. (1935b). *Quart. J. Pharm. Pharmacol.* **8**, 513.
Dyer, F. J. (1936). *J. Physiol. (London)* **86**, 3P.
Friedman, S., and Munson, P. L. (1958). *Biochim. Biophys. Acta* **28**, 204.
Friedman, S., and Munson, P. L. (1959). *Biochim. Biophys. Acta* **35**, 509.
Gellhorn, E. (1935). *Am. J. Physiol.* **111**, 466.
Hamilton, B., and Schwartz, C. (1932). *J. Pharmacol. Exptl. Therap.* **46**, 285.
Hanson, A. M. (1928). *J. Am. Med. Assoc.* **90**, 747.
L'Heureux, M. V., Tepperman, H. M., and Wilhelmi, A. E. (1947). *J. Biol. Chem.* **158**, 167.
Meltzer, S. J., and Auer, J. (1905). *Am. J. Physiol.* **14**, 361.
Meltzer, S. J., and Auer, J. (1908). *Zentr. Physiol.* **21**, 788.
Meltzer, S. J., and Auer, J. (1913). *Zentr. Physiol.* **27**, 632.
Miller, L. C. (1938). *J. Am. Pharm. Assoc., Sci. Ed.* **27**, 90.
Munson, P. L. (1955). *Ann. N.Y. Acad. Sci.* **60**, 776.
Munson, P. L. (1961). "The Parathyroids" (R. O. Greep and R. V. Talmage, eds.), p. 94. Thomas, Springfield, Illinois.
Osler, A. G., Strauss, J. H., and Mayer, M. M. (1952). *Am. J. Syph.* **36**, 140.
Pugsley, L. I. (1932). *J. Physiol. (London)* **76**, 315.
Rasmussen, H., and Craig, L. C. (1959). *J. Am. Chem. Soc.* **81**, 5003.
Rasmussen, H., and Craig, L. C. (1961). *J. Biol. Chem.* **236**, 759.
Rasmussen, H., and Westall, R. G. (1956). *Nature* **178**, 1173.
Rubin, B. L., and Dorfman, R. I. (1953). *Proc. Soc. Exptl. Biol. Med.* **83**, 223.
Shaw, J. H. (1947). *J. Dental Res.* **26**, 47.

Simon, A. (1935). *Arch. Exptl. Pathol. Pharmakol.* **178**, 57.

Stewart, G. S., and Bowen, H. F. (1952). *Endocrinology* **51**, 80.

Tashjian, A. H., Jr., Levine, L., and Munson, P. L. (1962). *Biochem. Biophys. Res. Commun.* **8**, 259.

Tashjian, A. H., Jr., Levine, L., and Munson, P. L. (1964). *Endocrinology* **74**, 244.

Tepperman, H. M., L'Heureux, M. V., and Wilhelmi, A. E. (1947). *J. Biol. Chem.* **168**, 151.

Truszkowski, R., Blauth-Opienska, J., and Iwanowska, J. (1939). *Biochem. J.* **33**, 1, 1005.

Tweedy, W. R., and Chandler, S. B. (1929). *Am. J. Physiol.* **88**, 754.

Tweedy, W. R., Chilcote, M. E., and Patras, M. C. (1947). *J. Biol. Chem.* **168**, 597.

"U.S. Pharmacopeia" (1935, 1955, 1960). Eleventh, Fifteenth and Sixteenth Revisions. Mack Publ. Co., Easton, Pennsylvania.

Wokes, F. (1931). *J. Pharmacol. Exptl. Therap.* **43**, 531.

Yates, F. (1936). *Ann. Eugenics* **7**, 121.

Chapter 12

Posterior Pituitary Hormones

R. H. Thorp

I. Introduction

In 1928 Kamm and his colleagues prepared fractions of posterior pituitary extract with nearly complete separation of the oxytocic and pressor components, and Livermore and du Vigneaud (1949) isolated pure oxytocin from the pituitary gland some 20 years later. This substance was later synthesized by du Vigneaud and his colleagues (1953), and a method was developed for the synthesis of oxytocin on a commercial scale by Boissonnas *et al.* (1955) so that it is now available for therapeutic use in this form.

Vasopressin was also studied by du Vigneaud *et al.* (1953), who showed that both these substances were octapeptide amides differing only in the nature of two of the amino acids present.

The chemical structures of vasopressin and oxytocin are discussed in a monograph by Berde (1959), who also reviews the work on the

457

relation between chemical structure and pharmacological activity in these compounds and their synthetic analogs.

Since the two compounds oxytocin and vasopressin are so closely related chemically, it is not surprising that pure vasopressin possesses some oxytocin activity and vice versa (van Dyke *et al.*, 1955).

Correlated with the chemical studies on these hormones from the posterior pituitary gland, improved assay methods have been developed and more extensive pharmacological studies have been made.

There are two different fields of work requiring assay methods for posterior pituitary hormones. The first is in the quality control of pharmaceutical preparations for therapeutic use where the amount .of material available for assay is large but the degree of accuracy required in the assay is high.

The second field is in the study of the physiological role of these hormones for which methods of extreme sensitivity are desirable at the expense of high precision. Notable advances have been made recently in the assay of small amounts of oxytocin in circulating blood, but these methods are still rendered difficult by reason of the very low concentrations of the hormones, the formation of pharmacologically active substances after the blood samples have been withdrawn, and the rapid inactivation of oxytocin which occurs *in vitro* in human blood obtained during pregnancy.

The development of the superfused rat uterus preparation by Fitzpatrick (1961) and milk-ejection response studies by Tindal and Yokoyama (1962) provide notable improvements in this field.

For the quality control of posterior pituitary preparations both the U.S. Pharmacopeia (1960) and the British Pharmacopoeia (1963) now recommend for the assay of oxytocin a procedure based upon the method described by Coon (1939) using the depressor response in the anesthetized chicken as a commercial assay method although the British Pharmacopoeia also suggests the isolated rat uterus preparation of Holton (1948) as an alternative method.

Earlier methods involving the use of the isolated uterus of the guinea pig are superseded because this preparation often proved erratic and unreliable and was incapable of giving a sufficient number of responses to permit of adequate statistical analysis being applied to the results.

These two official methods can be regarded as the basic assay techniques for the control of oxytocin preparations industrially, and methods based on the elevation of the rat blood pressure or the antidiuretic response in rats serve a similar purpose in the case of vasopressin.

None of these official methods is very sensitive and they are unsuitable for the estimation of very small quantities of these hormones in blood or biological fluids, but methods have been developed for studies of this kind, and these are considered separately. The use of paper chromatography as a preliminary means of purifying the preparations has recently been introduced and has enabled further increases in sensitivity to be made.

II. Standard Preparations

A. INTERNATIONAL STANDARD

In order to achieve uniformity, an international standard was set up for posterior pituitary lobe extracts in 1925 from a powder prepared by Smith and McClosky (1924), but at this time it was suggested that workers might prepare a similar powder using the same methods and regard such a preparation as equivalent to the international standard.

In 1935 it was decided by the Commission on Biological Standardisation of the Health Organisation of the League of Nations to have only one international standard, and such material is now held at national centers in the various countries concerned. The international standard has an activity of 2000 units per gram and the unit is defined as the activity of 0.5 mg of this material both for oxytocic and pressor assays.

B. PREPARATION OF SUBSIDIARY STANDARD

It is sometimes convenient to prepare material for use as a subsidiary standard, particularly in a laboratory concerned with the large-scale preparation of extracts of posterior pituitary lobe for clinical use. The following method can conveniently be employed.

The pituitary glands should be collected as fresh as possible at a slaughterhouse and frozen in a jar surrounded by solid carbon dioxide. Upon arrival in the laboratory, the posterior lobes are dissected from the remainder of the gland. This is not very easily done unless the glands are allowed to thaw a little as there is an optimum hardness at which the removal is most readily accomplished. The posterior lobes are then placed in cold acetone, about 4 ml of acetone is used for each lobe and the container is kept surrounded by refrigerant. After about 3 hours the lobes can be cut up and transferred to a similar volume of fresh acetone and left overnight. The acetone is then poured off and the glandular material is dried in a desiccator over phosphorus pentoxide. The dried material is next powdered to the size of a No. 40 mesh sieve and further dried in the desiccator. Fat removal is next completed by extraction with pure acetone in a Soxhlet extractor for 3 hours; after drying, the powder may be stored in ·a desiccator or in sealed tubes at low temperature.

After adequate assays in comparison with the international standard preparation, such material may be adopted as a working standard for the particular laboratory. It is unlikely to be as potent as the international standard but an activity of 1200–1600 units per gram is typical of powders prepared in this way.

C. Preparation of Standard Extracts

In order to use the standard preparations an extract must be prepared by weighing out a portion of the solid of approximately 10 mg in a stoppered weighing bottle taking great care to avoid undue exposure of the powder to air in view of its hygroscopic nature (Gaddum, 1927). The weighed sample of the powder is then transferred quantitatively to a hard-glass boiling tube with the aid of 0.25% acetic acid and the volume adjusted to 1 ml for each milligram of the powder. The tube is plugged with cotton wool and placed in a boiling water bath for 2 minutes, cooled, and the contents filtered through a small filter paper. The filtrate contains an activity of 2 units per milliliter. It is essential to prepare the standard extract in exactly this way since slight variations produce differences which can be detected in differential assays of the component activities.

D. Potency of the Synthetic Substances

The potency of synthetic oxytocin is such that 1 mg corresponds to 500 international units (IU), and for vasopressin 1 mg is equivalent to 600 IU.

III. Methods of Assay for Oxytocin in Pharmaceutical Quality Control

The potency of the crude extract of posterior pituitary lobe can be assayed by means of any of the three characteristic properties described previously, although it is usual to assay simple extracts by means of the oxytocic action alone, especially as this is the action most frequently employed in therapeutics.

The methods of assay most commonly employed are the rat uterus assay and the chicken blood pressure method for oxytocic activity, the anesthetized rat method for pressor activity, and the delay in water diuresis in the rat for the antidiuretic activity. There are various more recent methods and modifications of the standard ones which are described in proximity to the description of the relevant usual methods.

A. The Isolated Rat Uterus Method

This method comprises a comparison of the action of the test and standard preparations upon rat uterine muscle suspended in a modified Ringer's solution and arranged to record quantitatively changes in length upon a kymograph.

A convenient arrangement of the apparatus is shown in Fig. 1 and consists of a water bath surrounding 2 glass inner vessels in which the muscle strips are suspended. The apparatus illustrated uses a 250-W

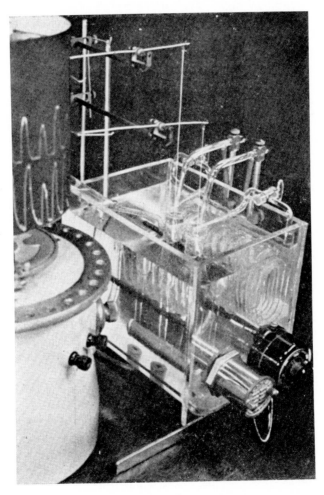

Fig. 1. General arrangement of isolated organ bath for use in rat uterus assay of oxytocic activity.

immersion heater controlled by a bimetal thermoregulator, and the bath capacity is about 10 liters. The temperature in the outer bath is thus regulated to 32°C with a differential of approximately ±0.5°, and the mixing of the water is achieved by aeration through a metal tube perforated with a number of small holes and extending the full width of the bath.

The inner vessels may be of any convenient size but those depicted hold approximately 20 ml. Filling and emptying is controlled by glass stopcocks and there is a glass spiral of large capacity in the outer bath to ensure that the Ringer's solution enters the inner chambers already warmed.

The lower end of the uterine segment is held at the botton of the bath by hooking it over a sharp prong on a bent glass tube which is also used to oxygenate the saline solution. The upper end of the uterus is attached by cotton to an isotonic frontal-writing lever recording on a kymograph. The lever should have a magnification of about 4× and should load the uterus to about 1.2 gm.

The composition of the Ringer's solution used in this assay is as follows:

Sodium chloride (NaCl)	9.00	gm
Potassium chloride (KCl)	0.42	gm
Calcium chloride (CaCl$_2$)	0.12	gm
Sodium bicarbonate (NaHCO$_3$)	0.5	gm
Dextrose	0.25	gm
Magnesium chloride (MgCl$_2$)	0.0025	gm
Water to	1.0	liter

The distilled water used should preferably be obtained by condensation in glass although a stainless steel condenser tube also gives satisfactory results. It is essential to avoid contamination with copper and alloys containing copper since this element is quite toxic to preparations of this kind.

The solution is oxygenated with a mixture of 95% oxygen and 5% carbon dioxide (carbogen). To set up the preparation, a female rat in diestrus, weighing between 120 and 200 gm, is killed and one horn of the uterus is suspended in each of the baths, thus allowing a duplicate assay to be performed. Two dilutions of the standard preparation are then found that produce clearly discriminated submaximal contractions, and when these are complete the solution in the bath is replaced by fresh solution and the muscle is allowed to relax. The unknown solution is then diluted suitably to give 2 responses similar to those obtained with the standard when similar volumes are added to the bath.

The ratio between the high and low doses of both the test preparation and the standard should be the same and must be kept constant throughout the assay.

The two doses of the standard preparation and the two doses of that under test are then given in random order, and at least 4 responses to each dose are recorded. It is usually found that these may be given at

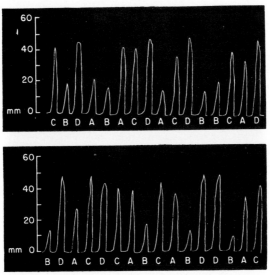

Fig. 2. An assay of posterior pituitary extract on the isolated rat uterus. The record shows 32 recordings of the contraction of the uterus in response to 4 different doses of posterior pituitary extract A, B, C, and D, each of which is given in each group of 4 contractions. A = 0.05 unit, B = 0.04 unit, C = 0.064 unit, and D = 0.08 unit. B and C were regarded as "standard" and A and D as "unknown." A/D = B/C = 5/8. Estimate of unknown/standard = 1.25. True value unknown/standard = 1.25. A dose was put into the bath every 4 minutes and washed out after 45 seconds. The temperature of the bath was 34–36°C, and the load on the uterus (from a 140-gm rat) was 1.3 gm. (From Holton, 1948.)

intervals of 3–5 minutes depending on the rate of relaxation of the muscle. The responses are then measured on the kymograph record, and the result of the assay is calculated by the standard statistical methods applicable to a (2 + 2) dose assay.

This method was originally described by Holton (1948), who found that, out of 9 rats, 6 gave good responses. The doses of pituitary extract were given at intervals of 3 or 4 minutes and 2 doses were found, such that the contraction for the higher dose was at least twice as great as that of the lower. The ratio usually employed for these 2 doses was 4:3, but only contractions below 80% of the maximal could be employed in order to ensure a linear relationship between response and log dose:

Little trouble was experienced due to spontaneous contractions, but when these did occur they were often overcome by reducing the temperature of the bath, or the interval between successive doses.

One of Holton's tracings is reproduced in Fig. 2 and shows the results obtained in one assay. This method enables an estimate of potency to be obtained with an integral determination of the slope of the dose-response curve. The error of the assay is calculated by variance analysis, and the slopes of the dose-response curves for the standard and test preparations are tested for concordance. The calculated standard error for a series of 8 assays, using this method, was 2.84%, approximately half the value found by Gaddum (1938) for the older guinea pig uterine assay.

B. The Chicken Depressor Method

Of the methods for oxytocic activity other than by uterine contraction, the principal research has been upon the utilization of the transient fall of blood pressure which oxytocin produces upon injection into birds. This phenomenon was first observed by Paton and Watson (1912) after injection of pituitary extracts and was attributed by Gaddum (1928) principally to oxytocin. The development of an assay method on this basis was due to Coon (1939); the method produces results very close to those of the older guinea pig uterus method and is quicker and technically simpler. Coon described the following technique, which has proved very satisfactory and is the basis of the assay method of the British Pharmacopoeia (1958).

White Leghorn chickens are used weighing 1.8–2.2 kg, although owing to difficulties of supply the author has used Light Sussex birds, of a similar weight, satisfactorily, whereas Rhode Island Reds proved of little use. The bird is anesthetized by intravenous injection of 200 mg of sodium phenobarbital per kilogram via the brachial vein and arranged for recording blood pressure from the ischiadic artery. The ischiadic artery is exposed by removing the feathers from the outer surface of the left thigh, an incision 7–8 cm long is made in the skin, parallel to and about 1.5 cm below the femur, exposing the gluteus primus muscle. The lower edge of this incision is retracted to expose the edge of the gluteus primus muscle overlying the semitendinosus muscle. This edge is then freed for the length of the incision, and when the free edge is lifted, the ischiadic artery, ischiadic vein, and crural vein can be seen lying along the edge of semitendinosus muscle. The gluteus primus muscle is cut at right angles near the proximal end of the incision, and the resulting flap is deflected and secured to the upper thigh. Lengths of the ischiadic artery and crural vein are dissected free, and the artery is cannulated.

For recording blood pressure a mercury manometer with an inside diameter of 2.5–3 mm may be used: a hollow ebonite float is used to operate the recorder pointer, and the manometer is filled with a 5–8.5% solution of sodium citrate as coagulant. The blood pressure recorded should be approximately 105 mm Hg and will quickly settle down to a constant level. It is convenient to use a slow-moving recording drum with a surface speed of approximately 1 cm per minute, since injections are made every 3–5 minutes. Injections are made directly into the crural

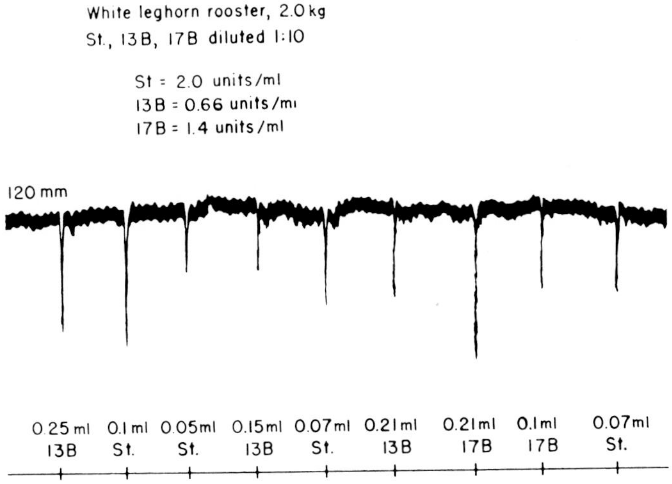

FIG. 3. A typical tracing of the assay of 2 unknown samples of posterior pituitary extract by the chicken depressor method. Injections were given at intervals of 3–4 minutes. (From Coon, 1939.)

vein by means of a 1-ml tuberculin syringe and fine needle, using the same puncture hole for subsequent injections and covering the hole with a pledget of absorbent cotton between each pair of injections. The standard posterior pituitary extract (2 units per milliliter) is diluted 1:10 with 0.9% saline, and such injections are made that a graded fall in blood pressure results from graded doses. The illustration of Fig. 3 from Coon's paper show the effects observed in a good preparation. The fall in blood pressure should be between 20 and 40 mm Hg. A suitable dose for preliminary trial should be 0.2 ml of the diluted extract. After a suitable dose has been determined, doses of the test and standard can be injected at 3- to 5-minute intervals according to the suitability of the bird. The doses can be injected in any suitably arranged sequence. Coon endeavored to produce matched responses and to obtain the potency of the unknown sample by direct comparison, but a suitable experimental arrangement is a random block design with 2 doses of the test and standard preparations as used in the rat uterine assay.

Further work on this method has been reported by Smith (1942) and Smith and Vos (1943) and most recently by Thompson (1944). Smith and Vos showed that the depressor response in the chicken increases linearly with the logarithm of the dose of pituitary extract given, and they used a randomized arrangement similar to that referred to above. Since this arrangement eliminates the variations in sensitivity over long periods of time, but is still subject to influence by changes in sensitivity within the period of an individual group of 4 doses, Thompson (1944) made use of an experimental design developed by Vos (1943) for use in the assay of ergonovine upon the rabbit uterus. In this arrangement, the dose of the standard preparation is kept constant and administered alternately with three varied doses of the test sample giving responses above, below, and equivalent to that of the standard. The dose of the test preparation giving a response greater than that of the standard should not be more than twice as great as the dose producing the smallest response. This assay must be run to an accurate time schedule, and an interval of 3 minutes between doses is recommended unless this allows insufficient time for the blood pressure to return to normal between doses. The accuracy obtained by Smith and Vos was such that a mean error of 6.9% was obtained using "unknown" dilutions from a standard preparation, and results obtained by Thompson showed even better agreement.

Coon found that the presence of large amounts of vasopressin caused a secondary rise in blood pressure, after the initial fall, but this did not introduce appreciable errors with pressor to oxytocic ratios of less than 4:1. In addition to this secondary pressor action, however, the presence of large amounts of the pressor principle was shown to produce some degree of enhancement of the oxytocic depressor response. A slightly higher apparent potency would therefore be obtained in comparison with the isolated uterus preparation. In practice it was found that ratios of pressor to oxytocic principle of less than 2.5:1 did not produce significant deviation from the uterine value. As the assay continues, the animal becomes tolerant to the depressor response, and it may be advisable to leave the bird to recover for an hour or so, if the sensitivity becomes greatly reduced. If the blood pressure falls to an undesirably low level the injection of 4–8 mg of ephedrine sulfate per kilogram frequently restores the pressure to a useful level. A chicken prepared in this way can constitute a stable preparation for 6–12 hours and may be used to assay several unknown samples. Approximately 90% of these preparations prove suitable for assay purposes.

IV. Sensitive Methods of Oxytocin Assays in Research

For estimation of oxytocin in extracts rich in this hormone the methods just described are very suitable, but since vasopressin has quite a strong oxytocic effect, as shown by van Dyke and his colleagues (1955) (see Table I) allowance must be made for this where the quantity of vasopressin is likely to be appreciable. Robertson (1960) used the rat uterus assay for the estimation of oxytocin in hypothalamic and pituitary extracts and was able to estimate 0.25 mU added to a 5-ml bath using uteri from rats pretreated with stilbestrol.

TABLE I

POTENCY OF PURIFIED OXYTOCIN AND VASOPRESSIN IN TERMS OF INTERNATIONAL STANDARD[a,b]

Compound	Oxytocic (rat uterus)	Avian depressor (fowl)	Milk-ejecting (rabbit)	Pressor (rat)	Antidiuretic (dog)
Oxytocin	500	500	500	7	3
Vasopressin	30	85	100	600	600

[a] van Dyke et al. (1955).
[b] All figures are U.S.P. units per milligram.

Fitzpatrick (1961) has reviewed methods that may be used to estimate small amounts of oxytocin in blood. He has pointed out that none of the assay methods presently available are both sensitive and specific, and he therefore suggests that parallel assays on two or more organs are desirable. The most suitable methods are reported to be the isolated superfused rat uterus method originally described by Gaddum (1953) and the milk-ejection method in the rabbit.

A. SUPERFUSION PREPARATION OF ISOLATED RAT UTERUS

Gaddum (1953) described a process of superfusion of the rat uterus suitable for the assay of oxytocin in which the effective dose is about 0.02 mU. This method consisted of suspending a segment of rat uterus in a warmed bath similar to the arrangement used by Holton (1948) but without the saline solution bathing the tissue. Down the thread attaching the muscle to the writing lever a steady flow of 1–5 ml of solution per minute (Gaddum et al., 1949) was arranged from a glass tube having a spoon-shaped tip, and to this tip is added the substance under test in a volume of 0.2 ml. The flow of saline solution is turned off during the period (10–60 seconds) in which the drug is allowed to act on the muscle.

The uteri used by Gaddum were taken from rats prepared by the injection of stilbestrol (0.1 mg/kg) the day before the experiment.

Fitzpatrick (1961) also used pretreatment with stilbestrol dipropionate in a dose of 25–50 μg/kg given to intact rats 17–18 hours prior to the assay. He found, even so, that fewer than 50% of the uteri were sufficiently sensitive for the assay.

Bisset and Walker (1954) also used the isolated bathed uterus in the manner described by Holton, but they reduced the temperature of the organ bath to 33°C and also used a Lock solution with one-fourth of the normal calcium content in order to reduce spontaneous rhythm. With an organ bath capacity of 2 ml, the doses of oxytocin used were 0.5–4.0 mU. In the superfusion method, however, Fitzpatrick obtained good responses with amounts of oxytocin greater than 1–2 μU in 0.3 ml. In check assays with solutions of oxytocin of known concentration the estimates were within the range of 96.9–100.6% of the true value, and the fiducal limits ($P = 0.05$) were within $\pm 5\%$ of the estimated potency. If limits of $\pm 7.5\%$ were acceptable then only 8–12 responses to each sample were necessary. Fitzpatrick found that his preparations would give consistent responses for 30–60 applications of the test solutions, and he was therefore able to assay several samples on the same preparation.

B. MILK EJECTION IN THE LACTATING RABBIT

Another sensitive method for the estimation of oxytocin makes use of the milk-ejecting property of oxytocin in the lactating rabbit, but in this test vasopressin also shows appreciable activity and is approximately one-sixth as active as oxytocin (Cross and van Dyke, 1953) so that content of vasopressin must be known.

This method is very specific and a dose of 0.5 mU can be detected after intravenous injection into an anesthetized lactating rabbit weighing 1.8 kg.

The method is fully described by van Dyke and his colleagues (1955) and makes use of rabbits in lactation anesthetized with urethan and pentobarbital. One of the ducts in the rabbit's nipple is cannulated with a hypodermic needle connected to a condenser manometer of high sensitivity. The apparatus used by these workers was such that 1 mm on the record corresponded to a pressure of 0.4 mm. of water at maximum sensitivity. Figure 4 shows a record obtained in such an assay and illustrates the degree of discrimination which is given between doses of 0.5, 0.75, and 1.0 mU of standard posterior pituitary extract.

Two significant improvements have recently been made in developing an assay based on the milk-ejection response. The first of these is

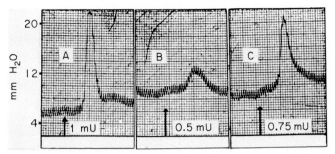

FIG. 4. The effect of intravenous injection of standard posterior pituitary extract on the pressure in the lactating mammary gland of the rabbit which weighed 1.8 kg and was in the eighth day of lactation. The small regular waves represent respiratory movements. Abscissa: 1 mm = 2 seconds. Ordinate: 1 mm = 0.4 mm water pressure.

the use of retrograde intra-arterial injection as described by Fitzpatrick (1961) using rabbits, the second is the use of the guinea pig in a similar manner by Tindal and Yokoyama (1962).

By using the intravenous route for the administration of the test material, van Dyke and his colleagues were able to detect about 0.5 mU of oxytocin, but Fitzpatrick obtained nicely graded responses with doses of 50–1000 μU, as shown in the graph of Fig. 5.

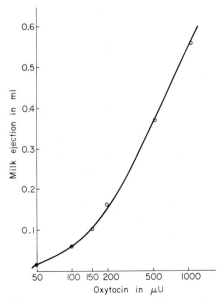

FIG. 5. Milk ejection in response to Syntocinon. The volume of milk ejected from a posterior mammary gland of a lactating rabbit is plotted against the logarithm of the dose of Syntocinon given intra-arterially. (From Fitzpatrick, 1961.)

The intra-arterial injection in the rabbit is made into the femoral artery just distal to the junction of the subcutaneous abdominal artery which supplies the posterior mammary glands. The main branches of the femoral artery are ligated, and an injection of 0.1 ml is made as rapidly as possible. This volume fills the arterial trunk back to the aorta and hence constitutes a consistent volume to be carried to the mammary

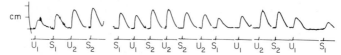

FIG. 6. Intra-arterial assay of oxytocin (No. 1). S_1, $U_1 = 16 \ \mu\mu$; S_2, $U_2 = 32 \ \mu\mu$; $\rho = 1.00$; $R = 0.97$. (From Tindal and Yokoyama, 1962.)

gland. In a series of 10 rabbits the sensitivity ratio of the response to intra-arterial compared with intravenous injection varied from 20 to 100 with a mean value of 37.1, and the mean dose in this series giving a response of sufficient magnitude for assay purposes was 149 μU.

In five of the animals the femoral artery was occluded proximal to the branching of the mammary artery, but there was no very obvious increase in sensitivity as a result of this.

Tindal and Yokoyama used guinea pigs, and essentially a similar

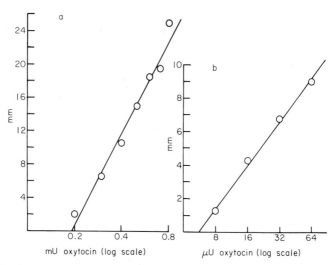

FIG. 7. Log dose-response relationships, together with calculated regression lines, obtained from recording of milk-ejection responses in 2 lactating guinea pigs when oxytocin was administered: (a) intravenously; (b) intra-arterially. Each point is the mean of 2 responses. (From Tindal and Yokoyama, 1962.)

procedure but the injection was made into the internal saphenous artery after ligation of the main branches supplying the limb. In the guinea pig the mammary glands are supplied with blood from the external pudendal arteries which branch from the internal saphenous artery just as it enters the leg. The milk ejection response was measured by means of a Statham strain-gauge pressure transducer recording on a Grass polygraph.

The guinea pig presents the advantage over the rabbit that each teat has only a single large galactophore and cannulation with thin polythene tubing is not difficult. The milk output is also proportionately greater than in the rabbit for this reason.

This paper of Tindal and Yokoyama (1962) gives precise details of the method; Fig. 6 shows a record obtained in a four-point assay and Fig. 7 gives the dose-response relationship obtained by these workers by both the intravenous and intra-arterial routes of administration.

This method represents the most sensitive and specific assay method for the determination of oxyticin, and doses within the range 15–60 μU gives responses suitable for assay.

Isolated strips of the mammary gland from the lactating rabbit also have been used for the assay of oxytocin by Mendez-Bauer, Cabot, and Caldeyro-Barcia (1960), who showed that such strips contract in linear relationship to the concentration of oxytocin added to the organ bath containing Tyrode's solution. The sensitivity of this method is less than that obtained *in vivo*, and good responses required concentrations of 1–10 mU/ml.

V. Sources of Error in Oxytocic Assays

It has been shown by a number of workers that the concentration of magnesium in the saline solution bathing isolated organs used for the assay of preparation of oxytocin can influence the result obtained when the preparation also contains vasopressin. Stewart (1949) showed that the guinea pig uterus assay for oxytocic activity could give results that were quite erroneous when the concentration of vasopressin in the mixture was high. He examined mixtures in which the oxytocin: vasopressin ratio varied from 4:1 to 1:4 but in each case the oxytocic potency was known. When Stewart used the Ringer's solution (British Pharmacopoeia, 1948) prescribed for the assay he obtained very good agreement between the assay result and the known values, but when extra magnesium was added to the Ringer's solution errors up to 25% high were observed when the ratio of oxytocin: vasopressin was less than 1:1.

The effect of magnesium concentration upon the rat uterus preparation has recently been examined by Munsick (1960), who, using pure oxytocin and vasopressin provided by du Vigneaud *et al.* (1953), showed that arginine vasopressin, which has an oxytocic potency of 9U per milligram in the absence of magnesium, 15 U per milligram in 0.5 mM per liter of magnesium, 42 U per milligram in the chicken depressor assay, and 51 U per milligram by the rabbit milk-ejection reaction, gave the least oxytocic action in the absence of magnesium. Munsick reported the rat uterus preparation under magnesium-free conditions to be the most specific assay of this type for oxytocin. In these experiments Munsick (1960) showed that valyl oxytocin was most potentiated by magnesium, but since this sample was an impure analog he did not attach great importance to this result. He also pointed out that assays performed with and without magnesium added to the bath could provide a useful qualitative tool since oxytocin is the only octapeptide not showing increased potency in the presence of this ion.

VI. Methods for the Assay of Vasopressin Activity

For the assay of vasopressin by its pressor properties, three animal preparations may be used; the spinal cat, the anesthetized dog, and the anesthetized or spinal rat. The rat preparation is the most economical, sensitive, and reliable of these, and it forms the basis of the official methods described in the British Pharmacopoeia (1963) and the U.S. Pharmacopeia (XVIth Revision) and is the method of choice today.

A. The Rat Blood Pressure Method

In view of the expense and protracted nature of assays upon cats or dogs, attempts have been made to use the rat for this assay, and this work has largely been described by Landgrebe *et al.* (1946). These workers used anesthetized male rats, and in some cases spinal animals, and found the following procedure to be the most satisfactory.

Rats weighing more than 380 gm, and preferably above 450 gm, should be used; then are anesthetized with 0.3 ml per kilogram of "Dial" liquid intraperitoneally ("Dial" Ciba, or a liquid prepared by taking 0.4 gm monoethyl urea, 0.4 gm urethan, 0.1 gm diallylbarbituric acid and making up to 1 ml with water). The animal is kept warm and given a total of 400–500 mg of urethan in doses of 100 mg after an interval of 1 or 2 hours. After a further 30 minutes the animal is prepared for operation on a warm table, keeping the rectal temperature at 33°C. The trachea is cannulated, the pharyngeal extremity is plugged with cotton wool, and the vagi and associated spinal nerves are cut. The central nervous system is next pithed caudally from the anterior tip of the pelvic girdly to eliminate fluctuations of the blood pressure when injections are made via the femoral vein. The femoral vein is then cannulated for injection and 1–2 mg of heparin is injected. One carotid artery is next ligated, and the second is cannulated and arranged for recording the blood pressure by means of a narrow-bore mercury manometer, using 3.8% sodium citrate as an anticoagulant. The preparation is next given 12–18 mg of soluble pentobarbitone by the venous cannula, and artificial respiration is given

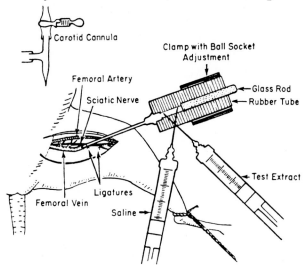

FIG. 8. Details of the apparatus and femoral cannulation in the pressor assay of vasopressin on the rat. The external and internal diameters of the carotid cannula are 1.0 and 0.7 mm, respectively. (From Landgrebe *et al.*, 1946.)

at 40 strokes per minute. Pentobarbitone in that dosage causes cessation of normal respiration without increasing the degree of general anesthesia or lessening the blood pressure. The pituitary preparation is injected at 15-minute intervals via the venous cannula, and the authors suggest the arrangement illustrated in Fig. 8, which ensures that the whole of a dose of a hormone is washed into circulation.

Animals prepared in this way have a relatively steady blood pressure baseline and survive for 12–15 hours. Figure 9 from this paper shows the pressure difference produced by 30% changes in dose, and a 10% difference is usually easily discriminated even in the less sensitive preparations. Figure 10 shows the dose-response relationship for this preparation. The best discrimination occurs between 6 and 8 mU of posterior pituitary lobe extract. When much larger doses are given, up to 32 mU, irregular responses are produced, but this effect is not normally serious since it occurs only with 4–5 times the most suitable dose.

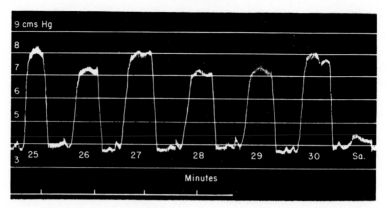

FIG. 9. Pressor responses to injection of posterior pituitary lobe extracts using the rat preparation. (From Landgrebe *et al.*, 1946.)

Key: 25 = 8 mU posterior pituitary extract; 26 = 6 mU posterior pituitary extract; 27 = 8 mU posterior pituitory extract; 28 = 6 mU posterior pituitary extract; 29 = 6 mU posterior pituitary extract; 30 = 8 mU posterior pituitary extract; *Sa* = 0.2 ml of saline.

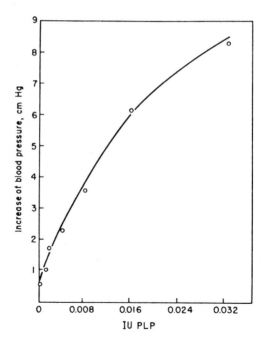

FIG. 10. Dose-response curve obtained for the pressor response in the rat using posterior pituitary lobe extract (PLP). (From Landgrebe *et al.*, 1946.)

The response of the rat preparation to histamine is small; hence the amount normally present in commercial powders is insufficient to interfere with the pressor assay. In fact, histamine contamination up to 2% by weight in a posterior pituitary lobe powder has no effect upon the pressor assay. The rat preparation is normally 15–20 times as sensitive as a good spinal cat and will often detect 10% and certainly discriminate 20% dose intervals, which is again, as good or better than, the cat.

Dekanski (1952) has shown that the rat need not be pithed, but that equally good results may be obtained by treatment with dibenzylamine (Dibenamine). For this modification the rat is anesthetized with urethan (175 mg/kg) and the trachea is cannulated; the femoral vein is also cannulated for injection, and heparin (2000 units per kilogram) is then given. The carotid artery is cannulated for the recording of blood pressure by means of a narrow-bore mercury manometer. Dibenzylamine is then injected in 2 doses of 100 μg/100 gm of body weight at intervals of 10 minutes. The pressor effect of an injection of saline at 0.3—0.5 ml should then be very reduced, and if this does not occur a third dose of dibenzylamine should be given. Dekanski showed that doses of posterior pituitary standard ranging from 1–38 mU gave a linear relationship between log dose and the increase in blood pressure. He suggested that doses of 4–12 mU be given at intervals of 6–10 minutes and reported that the preparation can be used for up to 40 injections. An experimental arrangement such as the (2 + 2) assay design is again applicable to this preparation.

The procedure described in the U.S. Pharmacopeia is similar except that an injection of 10 mg of phenoxybenzamine hydrochloride per kilogram is made about 18 hours previously. This injection is prepared by dissolving 5 mg of phenoxybenzamine hydrochloride in 0.1 ml of alcohol, adding one drop of sulfuric acid and diluting to 5 ml with saline. The British Pharmacopoeia has also adopted the rat blood pressure method as the official pressor assay, but in this case hexamethonium is used to produce a level blood pressure of about 50 mm Hg and to abolish the volume effect of injected solutions. Doses of 6–10 mU are suggested as a suitable range of dose of pituitary extract to be tried at the commencement of the assay.

B. METHODS FOR THE DETERMINATION OF ANTIDIURETIC ACTIVITY

The first attempt to utilize the antidiuretic activity of preparations from the posterior pituitary lobe as a method of biological assay was described by Gibbs (1930), using mice. Groups of 8 mice were used for these experiments, and each animal was placed in a glass funnel on a gause mesh disk and covered with a second funnel. Beneath each was placed a graduated cylinder for the collection of the urine. Each mouse was given an injection of warm tap water intraperitoneally and then 4 of the mice were given a dose of pituitary extract by subcutaneous injection. The actual dose Gibbs used is not exactly described but was presumably 0.1 ml of a 10-unit per milliliter preparation. Gibbs indicated the flow of urine by one or more plus signs and noted that after about 2 hours the control mice were excreting increasing quantities of urine whereas there was a marked delay in the urinary excretion of the pituitary treated mice.

Burn (1931) followed up this work and first suggested the use of rats instead of mice since the former animals could be used in a cross-over test, and also because they produce an easily measurable volume of urine, thus converting the method from a quantal to a continuous variate one.

The technique used by Burn employed a group of 16 male rats each weighing 120–240 gm housed in gauze-floored cylindrical cages supported over large funnels with 4 rats in each cage. The rats were starved at least 12 hours before the test was commenced, although free access to water was still permitted. This procedure results in a greater change in the delay in diuresis with a given incremental change in dose, than is the case with rats fed up to the time of the experiment.

The rats were weighed for the test and given 5 ml/100 gm of warm tap water by stomach tube. They were then given the dose of posterior pituitary extract by subcutaneous injection and placed in the cages; the urine was collected in 10-ml graduated cylinders placed below the funnels. Time was recorded for each group from the mean time of injection of the pituitary preparation, and when the excretion of urine was first observed the amount produced was recorded every 15 minutes until it became consistently small.

Burn recorded these amounts in tabular form and determined the time of maximum water excretion by adding together the separate volumes, with the exception of the first collection, dividing by 2, and obtaining the corresponding time interval to this volume from the table. The first collection was rejected because it often occurred as an isolated urine excretion and not the forerunner of the main diuresis. The test was repeated 2 or 3 days later with the same group of animals in a cross-over arrangement, so that which received the standard received the test and vice versa. This was done to compensate for any inherent difference in sensitivity between groups.

The relative potency of the unknown sample Burn determined from a graph for that particular colony of rats, by previous determinations of the time of diuresis delay with several known doses.

During the ensuing years many other workers have used and modified Burn's antidiuretic assay. Gilman and Goodman (1937) found that a more consistent response was obtained after the administration of a preliminary hydrating dose of water. This consisted of tap water given by mouth in a volume equal to 2.5% of the body weight, and, 3 hours later, at the commencement of the test, all urine previously collected was rejected and twice this dose of water was given at the same time as the dose of posterior pituitary lobe extract. Silvette (1940) gave a single dose of 10 ml of 0.2% saline/100 gm by intraperitoneal injection but used a method of calculation based upon the measurement of the total volume of urine excreted per 100 gm of body weight during a period of 6 hours after the fluid intake. Krieger and Kilvington (1940) used a different method of interpretation again and plotted the actual amounts of urine after intervals of 15 minutes against time for a period of 6 hours from the fluid intake. They then measured the area enclosed by the curve with a planimeter and used this as the response criterion. They gave less water, using only 12 ml for a rat weighing 200 gm, Robinson and Farr (1940) measured the time taken to excrete 2.5% of the original body weight of water.

It will be seen therefore that, at this time, there was a diversity of slight modifications but there was little evidence as to which was the most accurate.

Burn's method was reexamined by Ginsburg (1951), who pointed out that it had disadvantages in that the cross-over test could not be completed in less than 2 or 3 days and also the error of a single assay could not easily be calculated. Ginsburg modified the method so that it could be completed in 4–4½ hours and described a statistical procedure for the calculation of the fiducial limits of the assay. The doses of the test material were given subcutaneously, but Ginsburg and Heller (1953) then showed that intravenous injection is more satisfactory since it is free from tissue reactions and more sensitive. These workers inserted a cannula of polythene tubing into the right external jugular vein 18 hours before the test and externalized the end of the cannula between the ears of the rat. When the test was to be performed the rats were placed singly in metabolism cages and the cannula was extended to permit injections to be made without disturbing the animals. Each rat was next given 2 doses of water (5% of the body weight) by stomach tube at intervals of 50 minutes, and the urinary output was measured at intervals of 10 minutes thereafter. For rats to be included in the test these workers required the urinary excretion to be at least 1.5 ml/10 minutes, and if this were so, doses of vasopressin were given and washed in with 0.2 ml of heparin solution in saline (10 U/ml in 0.9% NaCl). The first injection was usually heparin solution alone, and this should produce no anti-diuresis. For the subcutaneous injection route Ginsburg (1951) found that 0.4 mU of vasopressin would normally produce a satisfactory response whereas by the intravenous route Ginsburg and Heller (1953) state that significant antidiuretic responses were frequently observed with 12.5 μU/100 gm of body weight. They usually gave doses greater than this, and with a series of doses between 50 and 200 μU/100 gm a graded response was obtained.

In these antidiuretic assays a most important point is to maintain a constant rate of urine flow during the control periods, although this is usually done by the repeated oral administration of water whenever the urine flow decreases, this results in the assay being performed against a background of a gradually decreasing water load. Boura and Dicker (1953) therefore devised a very ingenious method whereby the water load could be maintained constant by using the urinary output to control the administration of water by stomach tube automatically and employing a correction for the extrarenal water loss. In this method records are made on a kymograph of each 0.1 ml of urine excreted, the number of drops of urine flowing from the bladder catheter per unit time, and the deviation of body weight of the rat during the experiment. They showed a very level urinary output in their results and also a very clear antidiuretic effect with a dose of 5 μU/100 gm of body weight.

Dicker in a subsequent paper (1953) described the use of this apparatus in the assay of small amounts of antidiuretic activity and showed that the useful range of the method was 3.5–50 μU/100 gm of body weight. They also added ethanol to the water given to the rat since van Dyke and Ames (1951) had shown that ethanol suppresses the excretion of endogenous antidiuretic hormone. By this technique, the same dose of vasopressin produced a similar response each time, not only in the same animal, but in all the animals these workers used. This method is extremely elegant and undoubtedly represents a major advance in the assay of vasopressin by means of the antidiuretic response. It formed the basis of the method which was included in the British Pharmacopoeia (1958).

VII. Chromatographic Methods for the Separation of Oxytocin and Vasopressin Prior to Assay

Studies have been made on the chromatography of hypophyseal polypeptides, and Heller and Lederis (1958) reported a technique of paper chromatography using butanol–acetic acid–water in the ascending manner on Whatman No. 1 paper. After location of the spots by chlorination and spraying with potassium iodide–starch solution (Reindel and

Hoppe, 1954), these workers cut out and eluted spots from parallel chromatograms and assayed the extracts biologically using the isolated rat uterus method for oxytocin and the pressor response in the rat for vasopressin. They showed that 10 mU of oxytocic or pressor activity could be eluted or assayed in this way.

Arimura and Dingman (1959) described an improved technique of chromatography for these substances which is complete in 30–50 minutes. They used glass-fiber paper strips (6 × 15 cm) impregnated with silica acid according to the method of Dieckert et al. (1958), but with double the concentration of potassium silicate. The papers were dried at 150–200°C and stored in a desiccator prior to use. Two different solvent mixtures were used, one for vasopressin comprising butanol, ethanol, and ammonium hydroxide in a ratio 60:30:10 (solvent A) and a second of n-amyl alcohol and acetic acid, 80:5, saturated with water (solvent B) for oxytocin.

The chromatograms were run by the ascending method in closed glass jars without previous equilibration and then dried by means of a fan and sprayed on the reverse side with Folin's phenol reagent which detects as little of $0.5\,\mu g$ of a polypeptide.

With solvent A, synthetic oxytocin runs to the solvent front and lysine vasopressin gives a clear spot at R_f 0.71. With solvent B, synthetic oxytocin showed two spots, one very faint at the solvent front and one very strong at R_f 0.71. Pitressin did not move at all, and the spot remained at the starting line.

When 1.0-mU spots of Pitressin or of synthetic oxytocin were applied to the paper and the appropriate areas were eluted into Ringer solution for biological assay, 93% of the activity of the Pitressin was recovered from the spot at R_f 0.71 corresponding to the lysine vasopressin, and 99% of the activity of synthetic oxytocin was recovered from the chromatogram in solvent B again at position R_f 0.71.

The biological assays were performed using Gaddum's superfused rat uterine strip for oxytocic assays and Dicker's antidiuretic method (1953) for vasopressin.

These authors concluded that quantities less than 1.0 mU of each substance could be estimated after minor modifications of the method in view of the great sensitivity of the biological assays they employed.

REFERENCES

Arimura, A., and Dingman, J. F. (1959). *Nature* **184**, 1874.

Berde, B. (1959). "Recent Progress in Oxytocin Research," pp. 6–20. Thomas, Springfield, Illinois.

Bisset, G. W., and Walker, J. M. (1954). *J. Physiol. (London)* **126**, 588.

Boissonnas, R. A., Guttmann, St., Jaquenoud, P. A., and Waller, J. P. (1955). *Helv. Chim. Acta* **38**, 1491.

Boura, A., and Dicker, S. E. (1953). *J. Physiol. (London)* **122**, 144.

British Pharmacopoeia (1948). Pharmaceutical Press, London.

British Pharmacepoeia (1963). Pharmaceutical Press, London.

Burn, J. H. (1931). *Quart. J. Pharm. Pharmacol.* **4**, 517.

Coon, J. M. (1939). *Arch. Intern. Pharmacodyn.* **62**, 79.

Cross, B. A., and van Dyke, H. B. (1953). *J. Endocrinol.* **9**, 232.

Dekanski, J. (1952). *Brit. J. Pharmacol.* **7**, 567.

Dicker, S. E. (1953). *J. Physiol. (London)* **122**, 149.

Dierkert, J. W., Carney, W. B., Ory, R. L., and Morris, N. J. (1958). *Anal. Chem.* **30**, 1442.

du Vigneaud, V., Ressler, C., Swan, J. M., Roberts, C. W., Katsoyannis, P. G., and Gordon, S. (1953). *J. Am. Chem. Soc.* **75**, 4879.

Fitzpatrick, R. J. (1961). *In* "Oxytocin" (R. Caldeyro-Barcia and H. Heller, eds.), p. 358. Pergamon Press, Oxford, 1961.

Gaddum, J. H. (1927). *Pharm. J.* **119**, 580.

Gaddum, J. H. (1928). *J. Physiol. (London)* **65**, 434.

Gaddum, J. H. (1938). *Quart. J. Pharm. Pharmacol.* **11**, 697.

Gaddum, J. H. (1953). *Brit. J. Pharmacol.* **8**, 321.

Gaddum, J. H., Peart, W. S., and Vogt, M. (1949). *J. Physiol. (London)* **108**, 467.

Gibbs, O. S. (1930). *J. Pharmacol. Exptl. Therap.* **40**, 129.

Gilman, A., and Goodman, L. (1937). *J. Physiol. (London)* **90**, 113.

Ginsburg, M. (1951). *Brit. J. Pharmacol.* **6**, 411.

Ginsburg, M., and Heller, H. (1953). *J. Endocrinol.* **9**, 267.

Heller, H., and Lederis, K. (1958). *Nature* **182**, 1231.

Holton, P. (1948). *Brit. J. Pharmacol.* **3**, 328.

Kamm, O., Aldrich, T. B., Grotte, I. W., Rowe, L. W., and Bugbee, E. P. (1928). *J. Am. Chem. Soc.* **50**, 573.

Krieger, V. I., and Kilvington, T. B. (1940). *Med. J. Australia* **1**, 575.

Landgrebe, F. W., Macaulay, M. H. E., and Waring, H. (1946). *Proc. Roy. Soc. Edinburgh* **B62**, 202.

Livermore, A. H., and du Vigneaud, V. (1949). *J. Biol. Chem.* **180**, 365.

Mendez-Bauer, C., Cabot, H. M., and Caldeyro-Barcia, R. (1960). *Science* **132**, 299.

Munsick, R. A. (1960). *Endocrinology* **66**, 451.

Paton, D. N., and Watson, A. (1912). *J. Physiol. (London)* **44**, 413.

Reindel, F., and Hoppe, W. (1954). *Chem. Ber.* **87**, 1103.

Robertson, P. A. (1960). Personal communication.

Robinson, F. H., Jr., and Farr, L. E. (1940). *Ann. Internal Med.* **14**, 42.

Silvette, H. (1940). *Am. J. Physiol.* **128**, 747.

Smith, M. J., and McClosky, W. T. (1924). *Hyg. Lab. Bull.* **138**.

Smith, R. B., Jr. (1942). *J. Pharmacol. Exptl. Therap.* **75**, 342.

Smith, R. B., Jr., and Vos, B. J., Jr. (1943). *J. Pharmacol. Exptl. Therap.* **78**, 72.

Stewart, G. A. (1949). *J. Pharm. Pharmacol.* **1**, 436.

Tindal, J. S., and Yokoyama, A. (1962). *Endocrinology* **71**, No. 2, 196.

Thompson, R. E. (1944). *J. Pharmacol. Exptl. Therap.* **80**, 373.

U.S. Pharmacopeia (1960). Sixteenth Revision. Mack. Publ. Co., Easton, Pennsylvania.

van Dyke, H. B., and Ames, R. G. (1951). *Acta Endocrinol.* **7**, 110.

van Dyke, H. B., Adamsons, K., Jr., and Engel, S. L. (1955). *Recent Progr. Hormone Res.* **11**, 1.

Vos, B. J., Jr. (1943). *J. Am. Pharm. Assoc., Sci. Ed.* **32**, 138.

Chapter 13

Bioassay of Relaxin

Bernard G. Steinetz, Vivian L. Beach, and Robert L. Kroc

I. Introduction

Increasing international interest in the nonsteroidal hormone relaxin has underscored the need for a practical and reproducible method of bioassay and for a well-characterized reference standard.

All available evidence indicates that relaxin activity is associated with a water-soluble polypeptide structure, and there have been significant advances in the chemical isolation and purification of the hormone since publication of the first edition of Volume II of this treatise (Doczi *et al.*, 1964; Cohen, 1963; Frieden, 1963; Griss *et al.*, 1962, 1967). The quality of much research for relaxin is directly dependent upon the adequacies (or inadequacies) of the bioassay methods used by the

481

investigator or his suppliers. The classical method of assay employs subjective evaluation of increased flexibility of the pelvic girdle of guinea pigs. With careful control and adequate numbers, reproducibility and statistical validity may be achieved. However, many workers have been content to use a qualitative guinea pig test. More recently, methods employing objective measurement of the interpubic ligament of the mouse have gained favor (Kroc et al., 1959; Steinetz et al., 1960; Cohen, 1963).

Relaxin extracts are generally prepared from pregnant sow ovaries, which have high activity and are commercially available frozen or acetone-dried. Relaxin-like activity has also been found in elasmobranch ovaries, in the ovaries and testes of birds, in pregnant and nonpregnant mammalian ovaries, in placentas, and in blood serum of female mammals including man (for reviews see Hisaw and Zarrow, 1950; Hall, 1960; Steinetz et al. 1959a, 1964).

Experimental studies have established several roles of relaxin in mammalian reproduction. In addition to the softening action of relaxin upon the ligaments of the pelvis, effects on the motility, histology, and composition of the uterus, on the distensibility of the cervix, on parturition and on mammary gland growth have been described (for reviews and recent literature see Hisaw and Zarrow, 1950; Kroc et al., 1959; Steinetz et al., 1959a; Wada and Turner, 1959; Wiqvist, 1959a,b; Zarrow and Yochim, 1961; Rudzik and Miller, 1962a,b; Hisaw and Hisaw, 1964).

The dramatic softening effects of relaxin on the connective tissue of the pubic symphysis have stimulated investigations of its actions on peripheral and cardiovascular connective tissues (Casten et al., 1956; Boucek, 1958; Casten and Gilmore, 1959; Reynolds and Livingood, 1959; Becattini and Cangi, 1962; Mosso et al., 1962; Vedoya et al., 1962) and on glaucoma (Paterson and Miller, 1963). A role of relaxin in the etiology of congenital dislocatability of the hip has been postulated (Wilkinson, 1963; Mannson and Norberg, 1961).

Another significant advance has been the development of potent antisera to porcine relaxin (Cohen, 1963; Steinetz et al., 1964; Dallenbach and Dallenbach-Hellweg, 1964). These antisera cross react with relaxin-like materials obtained from a variety of species and have made possible studies of the localization of relaxin in tissues of the pregnant human by immunofluorescent techniques (Dallenbach and Dallenbach-Hellweg, 1964).

Despite these advances, progress in the field has been hampered by the lack of standardization of relaxin extracts used by different investigators. To date, no bioassay method has been universally accepted, and no U.S.P., B.P., or International Standard has been established.

It is the purpose of the present communication to review the various relaxin assay methods that have been published and to describe in detail those procedures that have proved most useful in the authors' laboratory.

II. Relaxin Standards

In the absence of a national or international standard, an appropriate "house" or "lab" standard may be designated on rather firm criteria, so that potency estimates obtained by various laboratories, using the mouse assay described in Section IV, B, should not differ by more than 2- to 3-fold. At present, discrepancies of 25- to 50-fold are not uncommon when ill-defined standards are employed in different assay designs, or investigators rely on response units.

In 1955, a 130-gm lot of relaxin extracted from selected pregnant sow ovaries (Kroc and Phillips, 1958) was set aside by our laboratory for use as a house reference standard. This material, laboratory number B37-348/8a1α, was designated Warner-Chilcott Relaxin Reference Standard W1164-A, lot 8. Repeated assays against an experience curve by guinea pig pubic symphysis palpation (Kroc et al., 1956a,b, 1959) revealed a potency of approximately 150 guinea pig units per milligram. The activity of 1 mg of Standard is roughly equivalent to the relaxin activity of 15–20 ml. of rabbit serum obtained on day 28 of pregnancy, or to the activity of 250 mg of fresh pregnant sow ovaries obtained when the fetal crown-rump length is 5–7 inches.

Standard W1164-A, lot 8 is a fine white powder, moisture content 6.5%, nitrogen 16.55%, ash 1.6% and soluble up to 6% in 0.9% saline or distilled water at pH 5 or lower.

Because of improvements in the collection of pregnant sow ovaries and in extraction and purification procedures (e.g., Cohen, 1963; Frieden, 1963; Doczi et al., 1964) relaxin extracts with specific activities 3- to 10-fold greater than that of W1164-A, lot 8 were produced. Accordingly, a second house reference standard was designated in 1963. This preparation, W1164, 48E-2103a, was approximately 6.6 times more potent than W1164-A, lot 8 by mouse and guinea pig pubic symphysis assays and by uterine motility inhibition. It was, therefore, judged to have an activity of approximately 1000 guinea pig units/mg.

The term "guinea pig unit" has been discarded since most of our assays are conducted in mice and the unit has been redefined as the activity of 1 μg of this standard preparation. W1164, 48E-2103a is currently used to standardize high potency extracts and relaxin fractions obtained by starch gel electrophoresis.

For those readers who wish to establish a provisional standard in their own laboratory, an extract of frozen or fresh pregnant sow ovaries, of acetone-dried sow ovaries, or of pregnant rabbit serum may be made according to published methods (Albert and Money, 1946; Albert et al., 1947; Frieden and Hisaw, 1950; Frieden et al. 1956; Kroc and Phillips, 1958; Cohen, 1963). The extracts may then be tested at several dose levels using the mouse interpubic ligament method described in Section IV, B. The useful portion of the dose-response curve (2-fold dose increments) for interpubic ligament growth in estrogen-primed mice should occupy the tabulated ranges.

Dose of relaxin	Mean ligament length, 10–20 mice (mm)
No relaxin	0.4–0.8
Low dose	1.0–1.6
Intermediate dose	1.7–2.2
High dose	2.3–3.0

The slope (b) of the dose-response line should be in the range 1.5–2.5 or greater, and λ (s/b values) should be less than 0.4.

If these criteria are met, the investigator may assume that the doses of his standard are roughly equivalent to 0.25, 0.5, and 1 unit of activity.

The use of appropriate standards will be discussed further in Sections III–VI.

III. Guinea Pig Pubic Symphysis Methods of Assay

A. SURVEY OF GUINEA PIG METHODS

Pubic Symphysis Palpation and X-Ray Measurement of Pubic Separation

Experimental relaxation of the symphysis pubic of the spayed guinea pig was described as early as 1929 by Hisaw. A relaxin assay using ovariectomized estrogen-primed guinea pigs was published by Abramowitz and associates (1944). The Abramowitz unit was defined as the dose of relaxin required to induce unmistakable "relaxation" of the pubic symphysis of two-thirds of a group of 12 guinea pigs. "Relaxation" or mobility was determined subjectively by manual palpation of the pubic symphysis. The assay was thus based upon "all or none" criteria. Frieden and Hisaw (1950) added a graded scoring system to Abramowitz' assay. Talmadge and Hurst (1950) described a revised method using a combination of palpation and roentgenographic measurement of the symphysis pubis. A few experiments of this type were attempted in this laboratory (Beach and Kroc, unpublished) but X-ray measurement of pubic separation did not correlate with relaxin dose or palpation score. A quantitative palpation procedure using intact guinea pigs and a relaxin reference standard was summarized by Kroc and associates (1956a,b, 1959). This method will be described in detail:

B. A PUBIC SYMPHYSIS PALPATION ASSAY PROCEDURE EMPLOYING A REFERENCE STANDARD

1. Materials

Guinea pig colony: Virgin female guinea pigs (mixed strains) weighing 300–400 gm are housed in aluminum cages on wood shavings. They are maintained on Rockland or Purina Guinea Pig diet and fresh lettuce, one head lettuce per 5 guinea pigs per day. No supplementary water is necessary.

2. Methods

Estrogen priming consists of one subcutaneous injection per week of 5 μg of estradiol cyclopentylpropionate (Depo®-Estradiol, Upjohn) in 0.1 ml of sesame or corn oil.

Relaxin priming (this procedure was proved necessary) is accomplished by administering 20 μg of relaxin standard (Warner-Chilcott Relaxin Reference Standard W1164A, lot 8) in 1 ml of saline subcutaneously once a week on day 5 after the estrogen injection.

Six hours after relaxin administration the symphysis pubis of the animal is palpated. The animal is held head down, ventral side away, between the thighs of the seated examiner. The ischial crests and symphysis pubis are firmly grasped between the thumbs and forefingers so that the two halves of the pelvis may be moved back and forth alternately. If the pubic symphysis is rigid at this time, the estrogen and relaxin priming are continued weekly until marked mobility of the symphysis is observed. The increased flexibility is transient, the peak response occurring at 6 hours and subsiding 12–24 hours after injection.

Mobility responses are estimated subjectively and scored on an arbitrary scale of 0–6. "Zero" indicates no detectable flexibility of the pubic symphysis, whereas "6" represents extreme softening of the ligament separating the pubic bones. Scores of 4 or higher are regarded as "positive" responses.

During the priming period approximately 5% of the guinea pigs give positive responses to the first dose of relaxin, 33% to the second dose, and the remaining animals require 3–4 weeks of relaxin priming. (Occasionally an animal does not respond during 8 weeks of priming.) Positively responding animals are usually reliable for assay for several weeks (range = 2 to 16 weeks).

Experimental relaxation does not usually result in the magnitude of spread or softness observed at the pubic symphysis of the late-pregnant guinea pig. Scoring gradations can be learned only by experience, but if a beginner starts by gently palpating a pregnant guinea pig once or twice a week from mid-pregnancy on, some concept of degree of relaxation can be learned during this transitional period.

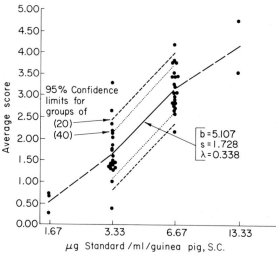

Fig. 1. Variability of absolute response to relaxin standard W1164-A, lot 8 over a period of 3 months and 95% confidence limits for different sized groups of guinea pigs.

One week after an animal has responded positively to 20 μg of relaxin standard, it is added to the assay colony. Before assay time all eligible animals, new and old, are mixed and divided into groups of 10–20 each.

On the day of assay the relaxin extracts are dissolved or suspended in saline in graded dilutions (usually 2-fold apart) and coded. "Unknown" preparations are administered in parallel with relaxin standard, generally in 1-ml doses. All animals are palpated before injection. Only those with no symphyseal movement are used. Two operators palpate and score each animal at the sixth hour after injection. Guinea pigs with scores of 4 or higher may be used for assay the following week. Negative animals must be reprimed with relaxin. Pigs which fail to score positively on two consecutive weeks are discarded.

The loss of sensitivity to relaxin described by Noall and Frieden (1956) was noted during the work described here. In an isolated group of 20 guinea pigs the response to 20 μg of relaxin standard fell from 100% positive to 44% positive in 7 weeks and the drop in response to 3.3 μg was even greater: 50–10% in 3 weeks. This observation points out the need for randomization of new and old guinea pigs.

Figure 1 shows variability of absolute response to Relaxin Standard over a period of 3 months and 95% confidence limits for different sized groups of guinea pigs.

The scores are averaged, and if desired, a median score and percent positive may be calculated (Kroc *et al.*, 1956a). The activity of an

TABLE I

BIOASSAY OF RELEASIN W1164–3, LOT 017, VIALED SOLUTION (U)[a]

Preparation	No. of of pigs	Dose/pig	Average score	SE	Median score	% Positive
1st Assay						
S	20	3.33 μg	1.36	0.35	0.5	15
S	20	6.67 μg	3.21	0.42	4.0	63
U	20	1/6000 ml[b]	1.38	0.36	1.1	10
U	20	1/3000 ml[b]	2.93	0.44	4.0	65
2nd Assay						
S	20	3.33 μg	0.91	0.35	0.0	13
S	20	6.67 μg	3.13	0.44	4.3	65
U	20	1/6000 ml[b]	1.93	0.42	1.0	35
U	20	1/3000 ml[b]	3.01	0.44	4.1	60

Statistical Analysis (based on scores only)

	N[c]	Slope b	Mg S/ml	Range mg S/ml at $P = 0.95$	Limits of error at $P = 0.95$
1st Assay	80	5.65	19.0	13.8–26.2	73–138%
2nd Assay	80	5.48	24.2	17.0–34.6	70–143%
Combined:	160	5.56	21.4	17.0–27.0	79–126%

Conclusion: The observed relative potencies did not differ significantly from the reference standard potency.

[a] Guinea pig pubic symphysis palpation method. Reference standard, S (Lab. No. W1164-A, Lot 8) tested concomitantly on 4 assay days within a 9-day period. All doses administered subcutaneously in volume of 1 ml.

[b] Assumed *activity* equivalents to 3.33 and 6.67 μg reference standard, respectively, based on previous bioassays of constituent purified stock powders.

[c] Total number of animals in completed assay with $N/2$ animals receiving standard (S) and unknown (U), respectively.

unknown is determined by comparison with the dose-response of concomitantly administered relaxin standard.

3. Statistical Evaluation

Statistical analyses are based on scores alone and calculated according to the methods of Bliss (1952) and Snedecor (1940) for a 4- or 6-point balanced assay.

Table I shows two typical bioassays of a relaxin (Releasin®) vialed preparation. The two assays did not differ significantly from the theoretical potency of 20 mg S/ml. The combined results showed a potency of 21.4 mg S/ml and limits of error of 79–126% at the 95% confidence level.

Despite the subjective element of scoring, the use of coded materials and the averaging of the scores of two operators reduce this inherent error. With as few as 20 guinea pigs at each of two dose levels of unknown and standard, the limits of error at $P = 0.95$ are generally within minus 33% to plus 50% of the observed potency. The error may be further reduced by increasing the number of animals per group.

The above-described relaxin assay has advantages over methods previously reported in the literature. The elimination of ovariectomies, the establishment of a relaxin standard and the reduction in the number of estrogen injections to one per week make the method practical for laboratory routine.

IV. Mouse Pubic Symphysis Methods of Assay

A. Survey of Mouse Methods

Interpubic ligament formation in relaxin-treated mice has been studied by many investigators (Hall, 1956; Crelin, 1957; Storey, 1957; Horn, 1958). Several workers have devised bioassay procedures utilizing dose-proportional increases in interpubic ligament length as a measure of potency of relaxin-containing extracts.

1. X-Ray Measurement of Pubic Separation

Hall and Newton (1947) and Hall (1948) described a qualitative assay in which mice were primed with estrone (1.5 μg daily for 2–9 days) and then injected with relaxin. Pubic symphyses were X-rayed before and 24 hours after relaxin injection and the distance between pubic bones was measured after development of the dental X-ray plates. Response was evaluated in terms of increase in width of the pubic gap. The effects of graded doses of relaxin were not investigated. Dorfman et al. (1953)

proposed a quantal assay employing X-ray of the pubic symphysis in ovariectomized adult or intact immature female mice. Using a 4-point assay design with 16 mice at each dose level of "standard" and "unknown," the authors reported limits of error of 65–155% at $P = 0.95$, and a lambda value of 0.375. The chief drawbacks in the assay design of Dorfman and co-workers were the 5 daily estrogen priming injections and the 4 injections of relaxin per mouse required to produce a significant response. Subsequent work has shown that this group was using the lower segment of the potential dose-response curve.

Kliman and co-workers (1953; Kliman and Greep, 1958) also adopted a roetgenographic technique for the measurement of pubic separation in mice. In their study, mice were primed with 1 μg of 17β-estradiol daily for 7 days, and, after a control X-ray of the pelvis, was obtained, animals were injected subcutaneously with graded doses of relaxin and X-rayed again 24 hours later.

Kliman and associates (1953) made use of the long dose-response curve and obtained good precision with their method.

An important contribution to relaxin research was the discovery by Kliman and Greep (1955, 1958) that relaxin activity was markedly enhanced by the use of repository vehicles for injection of the hormone. Thus relaxin, injected as a suspension in beeswax–oil was 65 times more potent than the identical preparation injected in saline solution. The depot principle has been confirmed by a number of investigators (Hall, 1957; Horn, 1958; Kroc et al., 1959; Steinetz et al., 1959a), and will be referred to in Sections VI and VII.

2. Direct Measurement of Interpubic Ligament

Several investigators have reported direct measurement of the interpubic ligament of mice (Crelin, 1954; Kroc et al., 1956b; Steinetz et al., 1957; Horn, 1958).

Kroc et al. (1956b, 1959) and Steinetz et al. (1960) proposed a direct measurement technique involving transillumination of the exposed pubic symphysis. Measurements of ligament lengths were made at 13× magnification using a binocular dissecting scope fitted with an ocular micrometer. These authors also drastically reduced the total number of injections required for priming and dosing, thus permitting a large increase in the number of animals that could be handled in each assay. Kroc et al. (1959) proposed a single subcutaneous injection of 5 μg of estradiol cyclopentylpropionate for estrogen priming. Seven days later, the mice received single subcutaneous injections of relaxin in 1% aqueous benzopurpurine 4-B. This vehicle was found to be twice as effective as beeswax–oil, and offered the usual advantages of making up and injecting a solution rather than a suspension (Steinetz *et al.*, 1959a, 1960).

3. Measurement of Flexibility of the Pelvic Girdle

Crelin (1955) proposed an elegant technique for quantitating changes in the flexibility of the sacroiliac joints and pubic symphyses of mice. The method depends upon the amount of joint flexion produced by a known weight load under standardized conditions of time and positioning of the innominates. Flexion is accurately measured with a protractor viewed through a peep sight. The author has not published bioassay data obtained with the method.

B. A SIMPLE MOUSE INTERPUBIC LIGAMENT DIRECT MEASUREMENT ASSAY EMPLOYING A REFERENCE STANDARD

1. Materials

a. Mice. Virgin female mice weighing 18–20 gm are used for assay. In the experience of the authors, many commercially available strains of mice have proved satisfactory for relaxin assay. Docile, rapidly growing animals appear superior to inherently nervous or slow-growing mice.

Mice are housed in groups of 20 in boxes sufficiently large to prevent crowding. Rockland Mouse Diet is supplemented with whole oats twice per week, and tap water is allowed ad libitum.

b. Solutions for Injection. Estradiol cyclopentylpropionate (Depo®-Estradiol, Upjohn) is diluted with sesame or peanut oil to a concentration of 5 μg/0.1 ml.

Relaxin extracts may be dissolved in 0.9% saline at ten times the desired concentration and then diluted 1:10 with 1.11% aqueous benzopurpurine 4-B (Dykem). Alternatively, relaxin preparations may be dissolved and diluted with distilled water, and 1% (w/v) benzopurpurine 4-B added as a powder.

c. Special Equipment. Binocular dissecting scope fitted with calibrated ocular micrometer. The transilluminating device consists of a "U-shaped" lucite rod affixed to the microscope state as illustrated in Fig. 2. The tip of the rod is beveled to direct light vertically through the objective. A standard Nicholas illuminator is used as light source.

2. Method of Assay

a. On day 0 each assay mouse is primed with a single subcutaneous injection of 5 μg of estradiol cyclopentylpropionate in 0.1 ml of sesame or peanut oil. As 20 mice are generally employed for each of three dose levels of "Standard" (S) and "Unknown" (U), a minimum of 120 mice

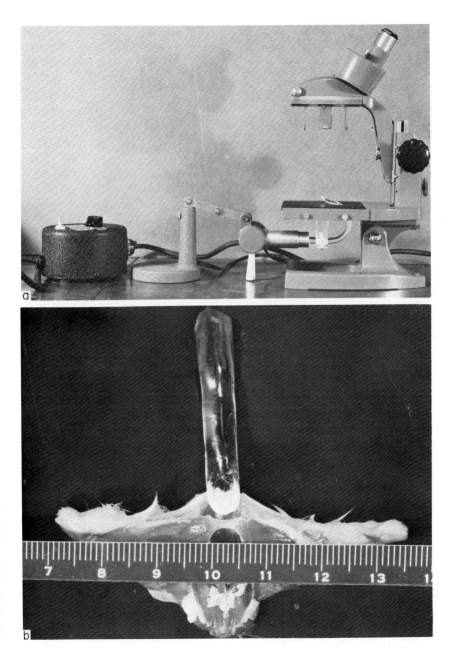

Fig. 2. (a) Dissecting microscope equipped with transilluminating device and ocular micrometer for measuring interpubic ligament length in mice. (b) The ventral view of a dissection of the mouse pelvis with the interpubic ligament positioned on the transilluminator. (From Kroc *et al.*, 1959.)

are primed for each assay. In practice, it is feasible to prime an additional 60 or 120 mice so that 2 or 3 unknowns may be run concomitantly with the standard on a given assay day. (It is also advantageous to run another 10–20 mice as estrogen-primed, untreated controls.)

b. On day 7, the relaxin standard and unknowns are injected, 20 mice per dose level.

c. At 18–24 hours later, the mice are killed (in groups of 10) by exposure to an atmosphere of CO_2 (insulated "Dry Ice" in a closed jar). Mice must weigh at least 20 gm to be eligible for assay.

d. The abdominal cavities are opened, and uteri are examined for evidence of estrogen priming. Mice exhibiting threadlike uteri ("priming failure") are discarded without observation of the pubic symphysis (Steinetz *et al.*, 1960).

e. The anal and vulval areas are then cut away with scissors, and the upper half of the body is cut off to prevent subsequent bleeding at the pubic symphysis. The bony birth canal is freed of skin, vagina, and rectum, and fascia is cleaned off the symphysis pubis.

f. The pelvis is positioned on the transilluminator so that the tip of the lucite rod passes a beam of light vertically through the exposed pubic ligament. The feet are grasped between the thumbs and index fingers, applying a slight lateral traction. Ligaments do not stretch but may tear if too much traction is used.

g. The shortest distance between the edges of the pubes is measured, using the ocular micrometer. Micrometer readings are then converted to millimeters. When practiced, an operator can dissect and measure at a rate of 2–3 mice per minute.

3. Data

These may be handled statistically according to any conventional methods. The authors have employed the methods of Bliss (1952) and Snedecor (1940) for 6-point balanced assays. Potencies of unknowns are expressed in milligram equivalents of the reference standard. In acceptable assays, the limits of error at $P = 0.95$ must fall within minus 33 and plus 50% of the observed potency. Usually, the limits of error at $P = 0.95$ are minus 26 to plus 35% or smaller (Steinetz *et al.*, 1960).

4. Dose-Response Curves

Figure 3 shows curves for a typical mouse assay. Table II illustrates statistical evaluation of results of a completed mouse assay.

Figure 4 illustrates the distribution of lambda values in 21 mouse assays. In two-thirds of the assays lambda was 0.3 or less. Loss of

TABLE II

MOUSE PUBIC LIGAMENT BIOASSAY OF RELEASIN REPOSITORY SUSPENSION W1164–35,
LOT 0729 (U) VERSUS RELAXIN REFERENCE STANDARD W1164-A, LOT 8 (S)[a]

Preparation	No. of mice	Dose (mg or ml/mouse)	Average ligament length (mm ± SE)
S	20	1.67 mg	1.25 ± 0.12
S	19	3.33 mg	1.88 ± 0.11
S	20	6.67 mg	2.81 ± 0.13
U	21	1/12000 ml	1.16 ± 0.10
U	21	1/6000 ml	1.73 ± 0.12
U	19	1/3000 ml	3.14 ± 0.13

Mean observed potency of U: 20.4 mg S/ml

Range of potency (at $P = 0.95$):   17.5–23.7 mg S/ml

Limits of error (at $P = 0.95$):   86–116%

$S = 0.527$ $b = 2.95$ $\lambda = 0.179$

[a] From Steinetz et al. (1960).

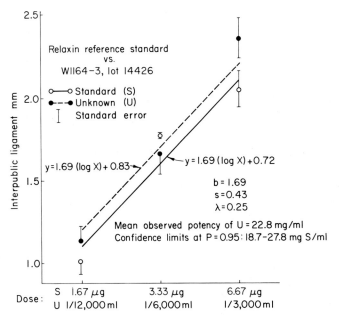

FIG. 3. Mouse interpubic ligament assay of sterile-vialed Releasin solution W1164-3, lot 14426 against reference standard W1164-A, lot 8. The unknown was vialed at a theoretical activity of 20 mg Standard/ml. (From Steinetz et al., 1960.)

precision is almost invariable due to a decrease in slope, as the error, s, remains remarkably constant.

When a high slope value is obtained, fewer observations are required to attain satisfactory limits of error, The predictions in Table III were based on a slope of 2.5 (which is frequently observed). Limits of error as low or lower than those predicted in Table III were obtained in approximately 33% of assays up to 1958. Failure to achieve these limits was generally due to low slope values. Since 1958, the limits shown in Table III have been observed approximately 67% of the time. The improvement is correlated with an increase in slope obtained with mice from a new

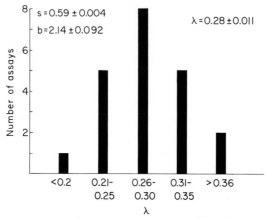

Fig. 4. Distribution of λ values in 21 mouse assays. (From Steinetz et al., 1960.)

TABLE III

RELATIONSHIP OF EXPECTED LIMITS OF ERROR TO THE TOTAL NUMBER OF
OBSERVATIONS IN THE MOUSE ASSAY ASSUMING A CONSTANT SLOPE OF 2.5

Expected % limits of error[a]	Approximate total number of observations
95–105	2745
91–110	686
87–115	308
83–120	177
80–125	116
77–130	82
71–140	48
67–150	32

[a] At $P = 0.95$. At $P = 0.99$ the corresponding limits at each level would naturally cover a greater range.

supplier. It is unwise, however, to attribute the difference solely to strain. Steinetz *et al.* (1960) observed extreme seasonal shifts in slope and dose-response curves obtained with several commercial strains of mice.

TABLE IV

RESULTS OF DUPLICATE MOUSE ASSAYS OF RELAXIN-CONTAINING EXTRACTS
AGAINST REFERENCE STANDARD W1164-A, LOT 8[a]

Type of preparation	Total mice	Potency of U (mg S/ml or mg)	Limits of error at $P = 0.95$ (%)	λ
Sterile vialed solutions				
Lot 22907				
(a)	113	24.2	79–127	0.28
(b)	112	20.6	81–124	0.24
Lot 25367				
(a)	120	23.8	82–123	0.24
(b)	120	26.0	76–131	0.32
Lot 24757				
(a)	119	21.2	71–141	0.41
(b)	120	19.3	80–125	0.27
Lot 35-0729				
(a)	118	19.3	84–119	0.21
(b)	120	20.4	86–116	0.18
Powders				
M-9714				
(a)	121	1.43	74–135	0.36
(b)	117	1.51	78–129	0.31
M-8630				
(a)	117	0.88	80–124	0.25
(b)	115	0.74	77–131	0.30
M-43 (low potent)				
(a)	153	0.13	91–124	0.29
(b)	89	0.12	71–141	0.33
Relaxin reference standard W1164-A, Lot 8				
(a)	123	1.12	77–130	0.31
(b) As above, but with added nonpregnant sow ovarian tissue (2.5 mg/0.2 ml)	139	0.97	80–125	0.26

[a] From Steinetz *et al.* (1960).

According to Steinetz *et al.* (1960) agreement between 9 replicate mouse assays averaged 91%, and the greatest difference between potency estimates was a nonsignificant 16%. Their data are reproduced in Table IV.

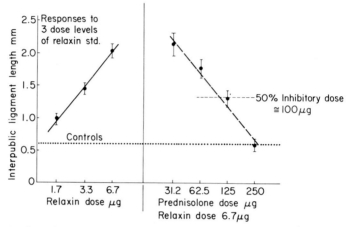

Fig. 5. Quantitative inhibition by prednisolone acetate of the mouse interpubic ligament response to relaxin. All mice were primed with 5 μg of estradiol cyclopentyl-propionate on day zero. On day 7, groups of 10–20 mice were injected subcutaneously with graded doses of relaxin (left side of figure) or 6.7 μg of relaxin plus graded doses of pred-nisolone acete (right side of figure). Controls received only vehicle. Interpubic ligament lengths were measured 24 hours after injection. (From Steinetz *et al.*, 1959a.)

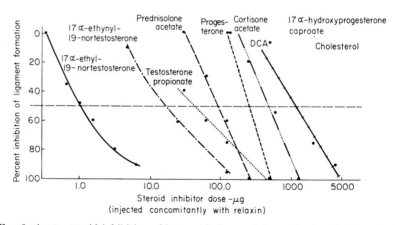

Fig. 6. Acute steroid inhibition of interpubic ligament formation in relaxin-treated estrogen-primed mice. The various inhibitors were evaluated by the method illustrated in Fig. 5. The data are summarized here, plotting inhibition of interpubic ligament formation against steroid dose. (From Steinetz *et al.*, 1959a.)

5. Other Uses or Applications of the Mouse Assay

Hall (1949) and later Kliman (personal communication, 1954) and Crelin and Honeyman (1957) described an inhibitory effect of progesterone and certain other steroids or relaxin-induced growth of the pubic ligament in mice. Steinetz *et al.* (1959a,b) obtained quantitative data on the inhibitory phenomenon, and showed that 19-nortestosterone derivatives were extremely potent in preventing ligament formation due to relaxin treatment. The assay design and results obtained with a number of steroids are illustrated in Figs. 5 and 6. This technique was also found suitable for evaluating activity of ACTH and gonadotropins, as removal of the adrenals or gonads abolished the inhibitory activity of the tropic hormones (Steinetz *et al.*, 1959a,b).

V. Assay of Relaxin by Inhibition of Uterine Motility

Relaxin-containing extracts specifically inhibit the spontaneous motility of the estrogen-dominated uterus *in vivo* and *in vitro* (Felton *et al.*, 1953; Sawyer *et al.*, 1953; Wada and Yuhara, 1956; Miller *et al.*, 1957; Wiqvist and Paul, 1958; Wiqvist, 1959a,b). Several investigators have suggested that there exist marked species differences in uterine response to relaxin (Miller *et al.*, 1957; McGaughey *et al.*, 1958). Progestin domination and pregnancy also importantly modify the effects of relaxin on uterine motility patterns (Posse and Kelly, 1956; Kelly and Posse, 1956; Wiqvist and Paul, 1958; Wiqvist, 1959a,b). Rudzik and Miller (1962a,b) have presented convincing evidence that relaxin inhibits motility by liberating uterine catecholamines. When uterine epinephrine was depleted or absent, relaxin did not inhibit contractions.

Several workers have proposed methods of relaxin assay based upon inhibition of spontaneous uterine contractions. In general, neither the assay designs nor the expenditure of time required for execution make this type of assay attractive for routine use. However, the 4-point balanced assay designed by Wiqvist and Paul (1958) and the screening procedure described by Kroc *et al.* (1959) are well standardized and useful for correlating the uterine motility-inhibiting effects of relaxin with its very different action on the pubic symphysis.

A. *In Vivo* METHODS

Krantz and associates (1950) first described the uterine motility-inhibiting activity of aqueous extracts of sow corpora lutea. In this and a subsequent publication by Felton *et al.* (1953) activity was evaluated *in vivo* in anesthetized guinea pigs. The animals were primed with massive doses of estradiol benzoate (80–100 μg daily for 7–10 days). One uterine horn was exposed and attached to a recording lever, and, after a satisfactory contractile pattern had been established, the test preparation was injected intravenously, and the decrease in amplitude of contractions was observed. The unit was defined as the minimum dose required to induce a 90% reduction in amplitude of contractions for a period of 10 minutes. No reference standard was employed and no statistically analyzable data have been published to date. This method

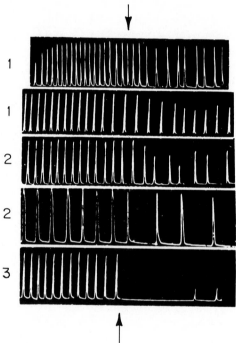

Fig. 7. Uterine motility inhibition scoring system of Wiqvist and Paul (1958). Visual responses are apportioned values of 1 to 3.

has been evaluated in our laboratory, and although qualitatively similar results were observed, variations in sensitivity between guinea pigs were so extreme that no quantitation was possible. This intravenous test in guinea pigs has been routinely used for estimation of potency of a commercial extract of sow ovaries marketed for oral use (Bryant, 1959).

More recently, Griss et al. (1962, 1967) used the method of Krantz et al. (1950) in conjunction with an in vitro uterine motility inhibition test during isolation and purification of a polypeptide from sow ovaries. This material also had high pubic symphysis-relaxing activity (Cohen, personal communication; present authors, unpublished observations).

B. *In Vitro* METHODS

1. *Wiqvist and Paul Method*

Wiqvist and Paul (1958) proposed a relaxin assay based on inhibition of motility of the rat uterus *in vitro*. These authors carefully explored the effects of various environmental variables and set up standardized conditions and criteria that may be duplicated by any laboratory. Ovariectomized rats were primed with 2 μg of estradiol daily for 3 days. On day 4, uterine horns were removed, bisected, and suspended in

TABLE V

SAMPLE ASSAY: 4-POINT ASSAY NUMBER 2 WITH VISUAL CLASSIFICATION OF RESPONSE IN SCORES[a]

| Animal No. | Standard preparation No. 3 Dose (μg) | | Test preparation No. 4 Dose (μg) | | Totals |
	2	4	32	64	
1	0.5	1.0	0	1.5	3.0
2	0	1.0	1.5	1.0	3.5
3	1.0	2.0	3.0	3.0	9.0
4	0.5	2.0	0.5	1.0	4.0
5	0.5	2.5	0	2.5	5.5
6	2.0	2.5	1.0	2.5	8.0
7	0.5	0.5	0	0.5	1.5
8	1.5	3.0	2.0	2.0	8.5
Totals	6.5	14.5	8.0	14.0	43.0
No. of curves	8	8	8	8	32
Means	0.81	1.81	1.0	1.75	—

[a] From Wiqvist and Paul (1958).

Locke's solution with 1% CO_2 in O_2 (pH 7.57–7.60) and a temperature of 37.5 ± 0.5°C. Recordings were made with a heart lever (1.5 gm tension) writing on a smoked drum. A symmetrical 4-point assay design was adopted with 2-fold dose-increments of standard and unknown. Responses were classified visually and assigned values of 1–3 according to the scheme represented in Fig. 7. The subjective element in scoring did not seriously influence potency estimates when 8 examiners independently classified the tracings obtained in a particular assay.

Since all four test doses (2 doses each of standard and unknown) were run simultaneously on the 4 uterine segments obtained from each rat, good precision was obtained with small number of rats. A sample assay is illustrated in Table V, and results and statistical evaluations of this and three other assays are shown in Table VI. Standard preparation number 3 is Standard W1164-A, lot 8, described in Section II. Test preparation number 4 is W1164-A, lot 36, which assayed 0.067 mg Standard W1164-A, lot 8 per milligram by the mouse interpubic ligament procedure (Section IV).

TABLE VI

EXAMPLES OF 4-POINT ASSAYS [a]

Assay No.	Standard preparation	Unknown preparation	Relative potency (%)	Confidence limits, $P = 0.05$	Precision (λ)
1	1	1	1.30	0.84– 2.02	0.24
2	3	4	0.066	0.046–0.096	0.22
3	3	2	0.49	0.31– 0.76	0.22
4	3	2	0.40	0.27– 0.60	0.22

[a] From Wiqvist and Paul (1958).

[b] Slopes significant according to validity tests with no significant deviation from parallelism ($P = 0.05$).

The indices of precision (λ) obtained by Wiqvist and Paul (1958) compare favorably with those generally observed in the mouse interpubic ligament assay.

Griss et al. (1962) successfully used a modified version of this assay for the isolation and purification from swine ovaries of a polypeptide with uterine relaxing activity.

2. Kroc et al. Method

Kroc et al. (1959), described a relaxin assay utilizing inhibition in vitro of motility of uteri obtained from mice in spontaneous estrus. Mice exhibiting cornified vaginal smears were sacrificed, and uteri were removed. Segments of mate horns were suspended in 25 or 50 ml of modified Ringer's solution aerated with oxygen or 5% CO_2 in oxygen, at a temperature of 37°C. Contractions were recorded via a heart lever writing on a smoked drum. After a control period of 10–15 minutes, doses of Standard and Unknown were added to baths containing mate segments. Doses were added to the baths at 5 minute intervals in increments that doubled the concentration, for example, 0.1, 0.1, 0.2, 0.4 ml. Optimal concentrations of Standard and Unknowns did not influence motility patterns until after the second or third addition. Thus, in the majority of tests, Standard W1164-A, lot 8 was used at a concentration of 6.7 μg/ml, and Unknowns, after preliminary test, were adjusted to approximate the activity of this concentration of Standard. Under these conditions a graded response is obtained for Standard and Unknown (Fig. 8). By calculating the minimal total dose required for similar degrees

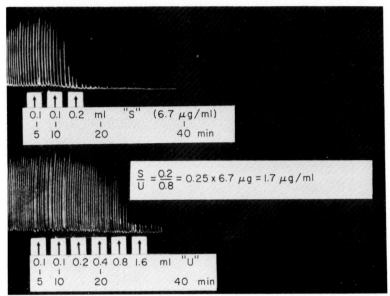

FIG. 8. Kymographic tracing of paired horns of mouse uterus treated with increasing doses of standard (S) and unknown (U) relaxin preparations. Potency ratio was estimated from the 50% inhibiting doses of S and U. (From Kroc *et al.*, 1959.)

of motility inhibition (preferably 50%) by S and U, the ratio S:U times the concentration of S per milliliter yields the relative potency of U per milliliter.

This method has been useful for screening purposes, as only 2 or 3 tests are required to obtain a reasonably good (semiquantitative) potency estimate. This method was not practical for quantitative assay, as only 12–14 segment pairs could be run in one day by a single operator, permitting accurate assessment of only 1 or 2 unknowns.

VI. Comparison of Relaxin Assay Methods

The mouse interpubic ligament direct measurement method offers the most practical means for relaxin bioassay. The direct measurement mouse method is simple, objective, and rapid and is easily learned by laboratory personnel. In contrast to this, the guinea pig pubic symphysis palpation method is subjective, requiring coded samples and independent observations of at least two investigators, and presents the added burden of maintaining a large guinea pig colony. One month of intensive training has generally been required in our laboratories for technicians to become adept at classifying the gradations of mobility of the guinea pig pubic symphysis.

TABLE VII

GUINEA PIG UNIT (gpu) DISCREPANCIES BETWEEN FIVE DIFFERENT LABORATORIES [a]

Laboratory	A	B	C	D	E
Sample designation	Lot No. 017	Control No. 136891	RXP 82/91	R-1	Sample "B"
Labeled potency (gpu)	3000/ml	4000/ml	600–800/ mg	1000/mg	200/mg
Potency vs. W1164-A, lot 8 (gpu)	3200/ml	47/ml	267/mg	196/mg	6.1/mg
Range of potency at $P = 0.95$	2550–4000	33–68	219–326	162–236	4.3–8.7
Relative "size" of gpu $\dfrac{\text{assay potency}}{\text{labeled potency}}$	1.07	0.012	0.382	0.196	0.030

[a] From Steinetz (1963).

The difficulties encountered in trying to set up guinea pig assays have recently been discussed (Steinetz, 1963). Relaxin preparations standardized by guinea pig assay were obtained from five different laboratories. These were assayed against our reference standard W1164-A, lot 8, which has a defined potency of 150 gpu/mg. The results which are reproduced in Table VII, show clearly that no two laboratories agree on what constitutes a guinea pig unit, despite the fact that each is trying to duplicate the original Abramowitz unit. Such evidence favors rejection of the term "guinea pig unit" as a nondefinable and nonreproducible quantity.

Uterine motility inhibition methods are tedious and difficult. The *in vivo* method of Felton, Frieden, and Bryant (1953) does not permit comparison with a reference standard, and no statistically analyzable data obtained with this method have been published to date. *In vitro* methods offer the obvious advantages of a population of segments or strips obtained from the same uterus, thus permitting evaluation of unknowns in terms of a standard. Wiqvist and Paul (1958) proposed a satisfactory 4-point assay design based on inhibition of uterine motility, but the authors themselves called attention to the dangers in subjective scoring of degrees of inhibition. The possibility of nonspecificity of *in vitro* methods has been recognized (Wiqvist and Paul, 1958; Bryant, 1959), but discrete use of this type of assay during fractionation and purification procedures has been justified by experience (Kroc *et al.*, 1959; Griss *et al.*, 1962, 1967).

There has been a question whether the mouse pubic symphysis method measures the same activity as the classical guinea pig palpation method. Thus, Kliman and co-workers (1953) observed that highly purified relaxin of good potency by guinea pig test was relatively ineffective in inducing pubic ligament formation in mice. Conversely, crude preparations, which assayed low in potency by the guinea pig method, were extremely effective in mice. Kliman and Greep (1955, 1959) subsequently showed that the rate of absorption of relaxin from the injection site was critical in the mouse, and that crude preparations were only slowly mobilized, giving a repository effect. The activity of highly purified relaxin was greatly enhanced in mice by use of appropriate retardant vehicles, whereas activity of crude preparations was not influenced by adjuvants.

Roentgenographic pubic symphysis methods offer the possible advantage of pretreatment measurements of pubic separation, but this problem can be circumvented in the direct measurement method by sacrificing a representative control sample of the mouse population. The difficulties encountered in anesthetizing mice, X-raying and measuring pubic separation from developed plates versus the simplicity of direct measurement recommend the latter method.

Kroc *et al.* (1956b, 1959) assayed various relaxin preparations against the *same* reference standard by the guinea pig and mouse methods. Potency estimates obtained by the two methods were in good agreement (Table VIII). Essential agreement was likewise obtained between guinea pig and mouse pubic symphysis methods and *in vitro* uterine motility inhibition methods (Kroc *et al.*, 1959; Wiqvist and Paul, 1958). More recently, relaxin extracts prepared by more sophisticated methods (e.g., Cohen, 1963; Doczi *et al.*, 1964) and exhibiting specific activities in the range 1000–3000 units/mg, also failed to show separation of uterine motility-inhibiting from pubic symphysis-relaxing activities (Turner, Doczi, Beach, Steinetz, to be published, Griss *et al.*, 1967).

Thus, postulates of various different "relaxins" and "uterine relaxing factors" obtained from sow ovaries do not have substantiating evidence in their support. In fact, the proponents of a "uterine relaxing factor" distinct from relaxin did not assay their materials against a reference standard, but relied on end-point units in their respective uterine motility inhibition and pubic symphysis palpation tests (Felton *et al.*, 1953; Frieden *et al.*, 1956).

TABLE VIII

BIOASSAYS OF RELAXIN EXTRACTS AGAINST A REFERENCE STANDARD, BY MOUSE AND GUINEA PIG PUBIC SYMPHYSIS METHODS

Material and method of bioassay	Total animals (S + U)	Potency of U (mg S/ml) or mg)	Limits of error at $P = 0.95$ (%)	λ
Vialed sterile solutions				
Lot 016 (prepared from S)				
Guinea pig	120	17.4	73–137	0.40
Mouse	120	21.6	79–127	0.28
Lot 017				
Guinea pig	80	19.0	73–138	0.41
Mouse	97	22.2	78–128	0.26
Lot 14296				
Guinea pig	108	17.1	70–142	0.40
Mouse	117	17.2	76–132	0.32
Lot 14286				
Guinea pig	88	18.7	70–142	0.36
Mouse	107	14.5	82–122	0.22
Lot 018 (low potent control)				
Guinea pig	60	1.72	70–144	0.40
Mouse	140	1.70	76–132	0.30
Powders				
M30-31				
Guinea pig	85	0.74	77–131	0.27
Mouse	107	0.74	78–128	0.26
M66				
Guinea pig	120	1.06	76–131	0.33
Mouse	140	0.99	72–140	0.33
M36 (low potent control)				
Guinea pig	110	0.07	66–151	0.47
Mouse	69	0.07	81–123	0.21

TABLE VIII (*continued.*)

Material and method of bioassay	Total animals (S + U)	Potency of U (mg S/ml) or mg)	Limits of error at P = 0.95 (%)	λ
Commercially available relaxin Cervilaxin® (list No. 19852) (control No. 13891) (stated to contain 20 mg standard or 4000 guinea pig units/ml)				
Guinea pig	80	0.31	69–144	0.29
Mouse	117	0.32	80–125	0.27
Releasin Lot 13216 (stated to contain 20 mg Warner-Chilcott standard/ml)				
Guinea pig	80	23.0	70–142	0.34
Mouse	116	20.6	76–132	0.33
Crude relaxin Saline homogenates of pregnant sow ovaries				
Guinea pig	156	4 mg/gm fresh	69–144	0.48
Mouse	92	5 mg/gm fresh	75–134	0.30

VII. Assay of Repository Forms of Relaxin

A. POTENTIATION OF RELAXIN

Kliman and Greep (1955) first reported that the action of relaxin on the mouse pubic symphysis was markedly enhanced by suitable repository vehicles. Relaxin activity may be potentiated by mechanical retardation of absorption (beeswax–oil mixtures, protein precipitants) or by biochemical alteration of the injection site (antihyaluronidases). Figure 9 illustrates the potentiating effects of various types of vehicles on the response of the mouse interpubic ligament to single doses of relaxin. Benzopurpurine 4B (L-390) and beeswax in oil are remarkable potentiators as the minimum effective dose of relaxin in these vehicles is 1/150th–1/300th of the dose required in saline solution.

Depot-relaxin may be assayed in mice by testing identical dose levels of the same relaxin preparation in a standard versus an unknown vehicle. Otherwise the standardized procedure described under Section IV is followed.

B. Duration of Pelvic Relaxation in Guinea Pigs

In contrast to the mouse, the guinea pig will not show potentiation of low doses of relaxin administered in repository vehicles. The doses for the guinea pig duration test must be approximately 500 times greater than the relaxin priming dose, i.e., 10 mg versus 0.02 mg. After administration of a single large dose of relaxin in saline solution to guinea pigs,

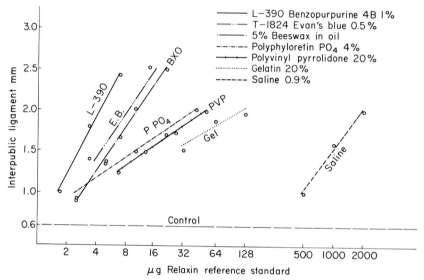

Fig. 9. Influence of vehicle on the 24-hour response of the mouse interpubic ligament to a single subcutaneous injection of relaxin. The curve illustrating relaxin in saline represents a composite of several assays. It is atypical; usually no dose response is obtained. (From Steinetz et al., 1960.)

marked relaxation is observed at 6–24 hours, but this is followed by rapid involution of the interpubic ligament so that little or no innominate mobility is detectable at 48 hours. In contrast, an identical dose injected in an effective repository vehicle will maintain strong relaxation for 1–3 weeks. (The mouse pubic ligament does not regress and therefore cannot be used for a duration test.)

The phenomenon of prolonged relaxation of the pubic symphysis made possible a semiquantitative assay procedure for evaluating long-acting relaxin preparations.

Young responsive guinea pigs (estrogen and relaxin primed as in Section III) are isolated from the regular colony and injected intramuscularly with a single dose of relaxin in depot form. The animals are palpated 6 hours later and daily or every other day thereafter until scores reach zero. (The scoring system is the same as described in

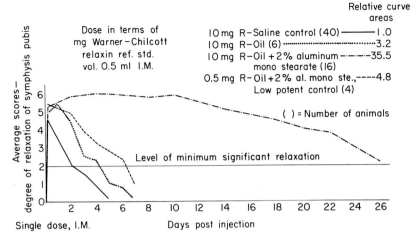

FIG. 10. Effect of relaxin repository preparation on duration of relaxation of the guinea pig symphysis pubis. Semiquantitative estimate of effectiveness was obtained from calculated relative areas under the curve assigning a value of 1 to the area observed with a single injection of relaxin in saline.

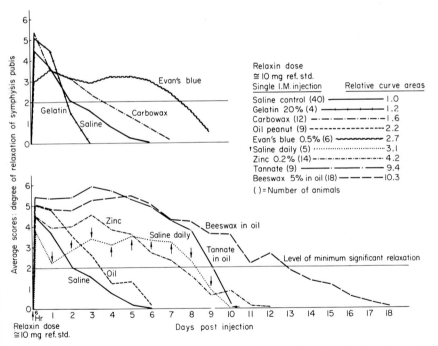

FIG. 11. Effect of relaxin repository preparations on duration of relaxation of the guinea pig symphysis pubis. Multiple injections of relaxin in saline failed to maintain the degree of relaxation observed when animals were treated with effective respository preparations. (From Steinetz et al., 1959a.)

Section III.) The palpation scores are recorded and averaged. The level of minimum significant relaxation is arbitrarily an average score of 2.

Estrogen priming is discontinued when the assay is started. The guinea pigs are not reused after a test.

Figure 10 is a graphic representation of the duration effect of a vialed repository preparation of relaxin (relaxin in oil plus 2% aluminum monostearate) at a dose equivalent to 10 mg relaxin standard W1164-A, lot 8. For purposes of comparison, 10 mg of a low potent powder (equivalent in activity to 0·5 mg relaxin standard W1164-A, lot 8) suspended in the same vehicle was injected in another group of pigs. These preparations are compared to single doses of 10 ml of relaxin standard W1164-A, lot 8 in sesame oil and in saline. The 10 mg standard dose in aluminum monostearate produced a significant level of relaxation for 26 days, whereas an equivalent dose in oil or saline or a low dose (0.5 mg standard activity) in aluminum monostearate did not maintain relaxation after 4, 2, or 6 days, respectively.

Figure 11 depicts the sustained action of single injections of relaxin in different repository forms. In contrast, even repeated daily injections of relaxin in saline solution failed to duplicate the effects of the depot.

This test has been useful and reliable in estimating duration ot effect for clinical trial repository preparations.

VIII. Other Actions of Relaxin Potentially Suitable for Bioassay Work

A. Effects of Relaxin on the Uterus

Zarrow and Brennan (1959) first demonstrated an effect of relaxin on the water content of uteri of weanling rats. Increase in water content was proportional to dose of relaxin administered, and the peak effect was observed 6 hours after injection.

Steinetz et al. (1957) investigated the effects of relaxin on the composition of uteri of estrogen-primed, ovariectomized rats. Uterine weight, nitrogen, and water content were markedly increased in 6–12 hours, and glycogen concentration was doubled 12–24 hours after relaxin injection. All these effects were of sufficient magnitude to warrant exploration of a dose-response curve.

B. Effects of Relaxin on the Cervix

A softening effect of relaxin upon the uterine cervix has been reported by several investigators (Graham and Dracy, 1952; Zarrow et al., 1956; Steinetz et al., 1957; Crelin, 1958; Cullen and Harkness, 1958; Kroc et al.,

1959). Kroc *et al.* (1959), succeeded in obtaining dilatability increments proportional to relaxin dose in spayed, pregnant rats maintained on estrogen and progesterone. Only in such animals was the magnitude of the effect sufficiently great to permit the establishment of a dose-response curve.

C. MISCELLANEOUS EFFECTS

Many other actions of relaxin have been reported in the literature (i.e., induction of mammary gland growth: Hamolsky and Sparrow, 1945; Smith, 1954; Wada and Turner, 1959; influences on parturition: Smithberg and Runner, 1956; Steinetz *et al.*, 1957; effects on the uterine endometrium: Hisaw and Hisaw, 1964). Techniques for the demonstration of such effects, however, are in all probability too difficult or time consuming to be adapted to bioassay procedures.

IX. Notes on the Stability of Relaxin

An important application of the mouse assay of relaxin described in Section IV has been its use in evaluating the stability of preparations manufactured for human use.

Whereas, relaxin activity is lost during incubation with proteolytic enzymes or reducing agents (Frieden, 1951), the hormone is very stable under less drastic conditions.

Relaxin is relatively thermostable and may be autoclaved for 20 or 30 minutes without significant potency loss. Sterile saline solutions of relaxin are likewise stable, but refrigeration is desirable to prevent "shedding." Table IX illustrates the stability of four lots of sterile-vialed relaxin solutions stored at 4°C for 1–2 years. The preparations were in

TABLE IX

STABILITY OF STERILE RELEASIN SALINE SOLUTIONS

Preparation	Original potency mg S/ml (range at $P = 0.95$)	Potency after storage at 4°C 1–2 years mg S/ml (range at $P = 0.95$)
W1164-3		
Lot 07547	18.5 (14.1–24.4)	19.1 (15.3–24.1)
Lot 244482	19.9 (13.9–28.5)	20.2 (16.2–24.8)
Lot 153782	18.1 (14.1–22.8)	19.0 (16.2–22.4)
Lot 13216	20.6 (15.7–27.2)	19.8 (14.7–26.7)

TABLE X

STABILITY OF STERILE RELEASIN REPOSITORY SUSPENSIONS

Preparation W1164-35:	Lot 002088, mg S/ml (range at $P = 0.95$)			Lot 003108 mg S/ml (range at $P = 0.95$)		
Storage temperature:	45°C	Room temp.	4°C	45°C	Room temp.	4°C
Original assay	—	19.3 (15.5–24.1)	—	—	19.9 (17.5–22.7)	—
Months stored						
1	23.7 (18.0–31.0)	25.4 (19.0–34.0)	24.4 (19.5–30.7)	21.4 (17.3–26.5)	18.0 (14.4–22.7)	18.7 (15.5–22.4)
3	18.5 (14.4–23.8)	18.4 (13.8–24.5)	18.3 (14.3–23.6)	20.0 (15.6–26.6)	25.6 (18.9–34.3)	—
6	16.3 (12.5–21.5)	18.9 (14.7–24.2)	—	—	—	—

TABLE XI

RELEASIN HEAT STABILITY TEST (MOUSE INTERPUBIC LIGAMENT ASSAY)
POWDER W1164-A, LOT 30–31

(27.3 mg/ml $\cong$ 20 mg S/ml)

	In 0.9% saline solution			In 20% gelatin solution		
	Observed potency			Observed potency		
Hours heated at 100°C	Mg S/ml	Range at $P = 0.95$	% 0 Hour potency	Mg S/ml	Range at $P = 0.95$	% 0 Hour potency
0	22.7	(17.0–30.3)	100	15.8	(12.6–19.8)	100
1	22.0	(17.0–28.6)	97	11.4	(7.8–16.6)	72
2	16.0	(11.0–23.0)	70	10.6	(7.4–15.4)	67
4	7.8	(5.0–12.4)	34[a]	9.4	(6.8–13.1)	60
8	2.0	(1.2–3.2)	9[a]	3.6	(2.6–5.0)	23[a]
16	0.6	(0.4–0.8)	3[a]	1.4	(1.0–2.0)	9[a]
32	<0.1		<0.4[a]	<0.1		<0.4[a]
	$Y = 1.05 - 0.94 \log X$			$Y = 0.61 - 0.45 \log X$		

[a] Potency loss significant ($P < 0.01$).

each instance assayed against reference standard W1164-A, lot 8, by the mouse pubic ligament direct measurement method.

Table X demonstrates the stability of relaxin respository suspensions stored at room temperature and 45°C for 1–6 months.

Relaxin solutions continuously subjected to a temperature of 100°C undergo a gradual potency loss which is linearly related to the logarithm of the heating time (Table XI). Addition of 20% gelatin delays the loss of potency until the eighth hour of heating (Table XI). This finding is curious, inasmuch as simple addition of gelatin to relaxin solutions is often accompanied by an apparent reduction (20–30%) in potency, which becomes a statistically significant 50% after heating at 100°C for 1 hour. Whether this represents true inactivation or reversible binding, remains an unanswered question.

REFERENCES

Abramowtiz, A. A., Money, W. L., Zarrow, M. X., Talmage, R. V., Kleinholz, L. H., and Hisaw, F. L. (1944). *Endocrinology* **34**, 103.
Albert, A., and Money, W. L. (1946). *Endocrinology* **38**, 56.
Albert, A., Money, W. L., and Zarrow, M. X. (1947). *Endocrinology* **40**, 370.
Becattini, U., and Cangi, G. (1962). *Med.* **18**, 783.
Bliss, C. I. (1952). "The Statistics of Bioassay." Academic Press, New York.
Boucek, R. J. (1958). *Southern Med. J.* **51**, 825.
Bryant, H. H. (1959). Discussion: Part IX. *Ann. N.Y. Acad. Sci.* **75**, 1037.
Casten, G. G., and Boucek, R. J. (1958). *J. Am. Med. Assoc.* **166**, 319.
Casten, G. G., and Gilmore, H. R. (1958). *Circulation* **18**, 702.
Casten, G. G., Boucek, R. J., Noble, N., and Scotti, T. M. (1956). *Am. J. Med.* **20**, 943.
Cohen, H. (1963). *Trans. N.Y. Acad. Sci.* [2] **25**, 313.
Crelin, E. S. (1954). *Am. J. Anat.* **95**, 47.
Crelin, E. S. (1955). *Proc. Soc. Exptl. Biol. Med.* **90**, 236.
Crelin, E. S. (1957). *Science* **125**, 650.
Crelin, E. S. (1958). *Anat. Record* **130**, 401.
Crelin, E. S., and Honeyman, M. S. (1957). *Anat. Record* **127**, 407.
Cullen, B. M., and Harkness, R. D. (1958). *J. Physiol. (London)* **140**, 46 P.
Dallenbach, F., and Dallenbach-Hellweg, G. (1964). *Virchow's Arch. Pathol. Anat.* **337**, 301.
Doczi, J., Blythe, R., Feri, G., Palombo, G., and Phillips, G. E. (1964). *Am. Chem. Soc. Meeting, Denver, Colorado, Jan. 20–23. Div. Biol. Chem., Sect. A, Proteins I, Paper No. 2.*
Dorfman, R. I., Marsters, R. W., and Dinerstein, J. (1953). *Endocrinology* **52**, 204.
Felton, L. C., Frieden, E. H., and Bryant, H. H. (1953). *J. Pharmacol. Exptl. Therap.* **107**, 160.
Frieden, E. H. (1951). *Arch. Biochem.* **30**, 138.
Frieden, E. H. (1963). *Trans. N.Y. Acad. Sci.* [2] **25**, 331.
Frieden, E. H., and Hisaw, F. L. (1950). *Arch. Biochem.* **29**, 166.
Frieden, E. H., Noall, M. W., and de Florida, F. A. (1956). *J. Biol. Chem.* **222**, 611.

Graham, E. F., and Dracy, A. E. (1952). *J. Diary Sci.* **35**, 499.

Griss, G., Keck, J., Engelhorm, R., and Tuppy, H. (1962). *Experientia* **18**, 545.

Griss, G., Keck, J., Engelhorn, R., and Tuppy, H. (1967). *Biochem. Biophys. Acta.* **140**, 45.

Hall, K. (1948). *J. Endocrinol.* **5**, 314.

Hall, K. (1949). *Quart. J. Exptl. Physiol.* **35**, 65.

Hall, K. (1956). *J. Endocrinol.* **13**, 384.

Hall, K. (1957). *J. Endocrinol.* **15**, 108.

Hall, K. (1960). *J. Reprod. Fertility* **1**, 368.

Hall, K., and Newton, W. H. (1947). *J. Physiology* **106**, 18.

Hamolsky, M., and Sparrow, R. C. (1945). *Proc. Soc. Exptl. Biol. Med.* **60**, 8.

Hisaw, F. L. (1929). *Physiol. Zool.* **2**, 59.

Hisaw, F. L., and Hisaw, F. L. (1964). *Am. J. Obstet. Gynecol.* **89**, 141.

Hisaw, F. L., and Zarrow, M. X. (1950). *Vitamins Hormones* **8**, 151.

Horn, E. H. (1958). *Endocrinology* **63**, 481.

Kelly, J. V., and Posse, N. (1956). *Obstet. Gynecol.* **8**, 531.

Kliman, B., and Greep, R. O. (1955). *J. Clin. Endocrinol. Metabolism* **15**, 847.

Kliman, B., and Greep, R. O. (1958). *Endocrinology* **63**, 586.

Kliman, B., Salhanick, H. A., and Zarrow, M. X. (1953). *Endocrinology* **53**, 391.

Krantz, J. C., Jr., Bryant, H. H., and Carr, J. (1950). *Surg. Gynecol. Obstet.* **90**, 372.

Kroc, R. L., and Phillips, G. E. (1958). U.S. Patent No. 2,852,431.

Kroc, R. L., Beach, V. L., and Stasilli, N. R. (1956a). *Federation Proc.* **15**, 113.

Kroc, R. L., Steinetz, B. G., Beach, V. L., and Stasilli, N. R. (1956b). *J. Clin. Endocrinol. Metab.* **16**, 966.

Kroc, R. L., Steinetz, B. G., and Beach, V. L. (1959). *Ann. N.Y. Acad. Sci.* **75**, 942.

McGaughey, H. S., Jr., Corey, E. L., and Thornton, W. N. (1958). *Am. J. Obstet. Gynecol.* **75**, 23.

Mannson, J., and Norberg, I. (1961). *Medlemsblad Sveriges Veterinaerfoerbund* **13**, 330.

Miller, J. W., Kesley, A., and Murray, W. J. (1957). *J. Pharmacol. Exptl. Therap.* **120**, 426.

Mosso, H., Biblioni, A., and Buzzi, A. (1962). *Semana Med. (Buenos Aires)* **120**, 410.

Noall, M. W., and Frieden, E. H. (1956). *Endocrinology* **58**, 659.

Paterson, G., and Miller, S. (1963). *Brit. J. Opthalmal.* **47**, 129.

Posse, N., and Kelly, J. V. (1956). *Surg. Gynecol. Obstet.* **103**, 687.

Reynolds, H., and Livingood, C. S. (1959). *A.M.A. Arch. Dermatol.* **80**, 407.

Rudzik, A. D., and Miller, J. W. (1962a). *J. Pharmacol. Exptl. Therap.* **138**, 82.

Rudzik, A. D., and Miller, J. W. (1962b). *J. Pharmacol. Exptl. Therap.* **138**, 88.

Sawyer, W. H., Frieden, E. H., and Martin, A. C. (1953). *Am. J. Physiol.* **172**, 547.

Smith, T. C. (1954). *Endocrinology* **59**, 54.

Smithberg, M., and Runner, M. N. (1956). *J. Exptl. Zool.* **133**, 441.

Snedecor, G. W. (1940). "Statistical Methods." Iowa State College Press, Ames, Iowa.

Steinetz, B. G. (1963). *Trans. N. Y. Acad. Sci.* [2]. **25**, 307.

Steinetz, B. G., Beach, V. L., and Kroc, R. L. (1957). *Endocrinology* **61**, 271.

Steinetz, B. G., Beach, V. L., and Kroc, R. L. (1959a). *In* "Recent Progress in the Endocrinology of Reproduction" (Charles W. Lloyd, ed.), pp. 389–427. Academic Press, New York.

Steinetz, B. G., Beach, V. L., and Kroc, R. L. (1959b). *Program 41st Meeting Endocrine Soc.* p. 102.

Steinetz, B. G., Beach, V. L., Kroc, R. L., Stasilli, N. R., Nussbaum, R. E., Nemith, P. J., and Dun, R. K. (1960). *Endocrinology* **67**, 102.

Steinetz, B. G., Beach, V. L., Tripp, L. V., and De Falco, R. J. (1964). *Acta Endocrinol.* **47**, 371.

Storey, E. (1957). *J. Pathol. Bacteriol.* **74**, 147.

Talmage, R. V., and Hurst, W. R. (1950). *J. Endocrinol.* **7**, 24.

Vedoya, R., Cintas, J., Rodriguez, P., and Mendelzon, J. (1962). *Semana Med.* (*Buenos Aires*) **120**, 1319.

Wada, H., and Turner, C. W. (1959). *Proc. Soc. Exptl. Biol. Med.* **102**, 568.

Wada, H., and Yuhara M. (1956). *Sci. Rept. Faculty Agr. Okayama Univ.* **9**, 21.

Wilkinson, J. (1963). *J. Bone. Surg.* **45B**, No. 2.

Wiqvist, N. (1959a). *Acta Endocrinol.* **31**, 391.

Wiqvist, N. (1959b). *Acta Endocrinol. Suppl.* **46**, 3.

Wiqvist, N., and Paul, K.-G. (1958). *Acta Endocrinol.* **29**, 135.

Zarrow, M. X., and Brennan, D. M. (1959). *Ann. N.Y. Acad. Sci.* **75**, 981.

Zarrow, M. X., and Yochim, J. (1961). *Endocrinology* **69**, 292.

Zarrow, M. X., Neher, G. M., Sikes, D., Brennen, D. M., and Bullard, J. F. (1956). *Am. J. Obstet. Gynecol.* **72**, 260.

Chapter 14

Thyrotropic Hormone

C. W. TURNER

I. Introduction

Since the review in the first edition concerning thyrotropin, the most important advance has concerned the increase in our knowledge of the role of the hypothalamus in thyrotropin secretion and discharge. For recent reviews of this subject the reader is referred to D'Angelo (1963b), Florsheim *et al.* (1963), Purves (1964), Martini and Ganong (1966), and Guillemin (1967).

The discovery of a lack of neural connections between the hypothalamus and anterior pituitary and of the presence of hypophyseal portal vessels which could transmit substances from the hypothalamus to the anterior lobe set the stage for the intense research of recent years.

Research has indicated that the hypothalamus plays an important role in the secretion and discharge of TSH by the anterior pituitary.

It has been shown that the transplanted pituitary shows marked reduction in TSH secretion as judged by various indices of thyroid function. Similarly, the pituitary cultured *in vitro* soon loses its capacity to secrete TSH unless a hypothalamic extract is added.

Marked progress has been made, also, in the extraction of a factor (hormone) in the hypothalamus which stimulates the release of TSH from the pituitary (TRF).

Progress is reported in the assay of the exophthalmos-producing substance (EPS), its separation from TSH, and its presence in the serum of exophthalmos patients.

The development of sensitive methods of TSH immunoassay of both plasma and pituitary has contributed to our knowledge of factors influencing TSH secretion and discharge.

Finally, great progress has been made in our understanding of the abnormal factor in the serum in hyperthyroidism (Graves' disease) and its source.

Terminology

The thyroid-stimulating hormone of the anterior pituitary has been called thyrotropin, thyrotrophin, thyrotropic hormone, and thyrotrophic hormone. In this chapter the abbreviation TSH will be used.

The hypothalamic factor (peptide) which is active in stimulating the release of TSH from the anterior pituitary has been called TRF.

The exophthalmos-producing substance of the pituitary will be abbreviated EPS. The abnormal factor in human serum in hyperthyroidism is called the long-acting thyroid stimulator or LATS.

II. Hypothalamic Control of TSH Secretion

Recent research has indicated that the hypothalamus plays an important role in the secretion and discharge of TSH by the anterior pituitary. Evidence of this relation has been shown by the effect of lesions in the anterior hypothalamus upon the uptake and release of ^{131}I by the thyroid, by lower PBI levels in blood, and by reduction of TSH in the pituitary and blood.

A second type of evidence is concerned with the extraction of a factor in the hypothalamus which stimulates the release of TSH from the pituitary (TRF).

A. EFFECT OF ELECTROLYTIC LESIONS

Greer (1951) produced bilateral, symmetrical electrolytic lesions in the hypothalamus of rats. These animals failed to show the goitrogenic response to thiouracil feeding. However, the iodide-concentrating capacity of the thyroid was about normal.

Bogdanove and Halmi (1953) repeated Greer's work using propylthiouracil and noted impairment of the hyperplastic response of the thyroid but no interference of the thyroid : serum iodide concentration ratio.

Florsheim (1959) reported that rats with anterior hypothalamic lesions showed lower TSH levels after goitrogen feeding than control animals as measured by bioassay based upon hormonal iodine discharge from chick thyroids. The discharge of labeled hormone from the thyroid of lesioned and control rats was inhibited by equal doses of exogenous thyroid. This was taken to indicate that the thyroid-pituitary feedback system controlling TSH release is independent of the hypothalamus.

Moll et al. (1961) produced electrolytic lesions of the hypothalamic area between the fornix columns at the level of the paraventricular nuclei which inhibited thyroid function as judged by thyroid weight, uptake and release of ^{131}I, and response to methylthiouracil.

Averill et al. (1961) observed a significant and permanent depression of thyroid secretion effective within 6 hours, following anterior ventral hypothalamic lesions in the rat.

van Beugen and van der Werfften Bosch (1961) studied the effect of lesions in the basal midline of the anterior hypothalamus on thyroid activity of rats exposed to temperature of 24 and 4°C. The index of thyroid function was the biological half-life of thyroidal-^{131}I. The $t_{1/2}$ values were $7\frac{1}{2}$ days at 24°C and 4 days at 4°C in intact rats and 13 days at 24°C and 7 days at 4°C in rats with a hypothalamic lesion. This part of the hypothalamus does not seem essential for the response of the pituitary thyroid axis to a low environmental temperature.

van der Werfften Bosch and Swanson (1963) compared the thyroid enlargement caused by 0.15% propylthiourea diet on normal and lesioned rats after 14 and 28 days. It was found that the lesion reduced the thyroid weight to about 75% of the intact rat on either diet. It was concluded that lesions caused a lowered steady state of the pituitary-thyroid feedback system.

de Jong and Moll (1965) made lesions in midline or bilaterally in the hypothalamus of rats. Single midline lesions which destroyed the area between the fornix bundles at the level of the paraventricular nuclei (PVN) resulted in a reduced rate of thyroidal-^{131}I release in rats at room temperature and blocked the thyroidal response to 4°C. Single midline lesions just inferior to the PVN caused inhibition of the response to cold but were less effective at room temperature. Lesions made anterior to the PVN caused partial blocking of the cold response but had no effect at room temperature. No effect was produced by midline lesions either superior or posterior to the PVN or bilaterally placed lesions laterally to the PVN.

Panda and Turner (1967c) placed unilateral and bilateral electrolytic lesions in the supraoptic area of the hypothalamus of female rats. Unilateral lesions after 8 and 48 hours caused a temporary decrease in the percentages of circulating TSH followed by a return to normal. Bilateral lesions caused a fall in plasma TSH to a level 41% below normal at 10 days whereas the pituitary level increased 70%. Rats with bilateral symmetrical supraoptic lesions, kept for 3 days at 4°C, had a lower plasma TSH content (23%) and a higher pituitary TSH content (16%) than the sham-operated control animals, but the levels of pituitary TSH did not show any significant difference ($0.100 > P > 0.050$). Thyroidectomized rats with bilateral lesions kept at 26°C for 3 days had a much lower plasma TSH (39%) and a slightly higher pituitary TSH as compared to the normal intact animals, suggesting that the hypothalamus also influences the synthesis of TSH in the pituitary. Thyroidectomized rats with bilateral lesions kept at 4°C for 3 days showed both a plasma and pituitary TSH increase compared to controls at 26°C, suggesting that when a higher demand for thyroid function is present the pituitary gland has some autonomy for both secretion and release of TSH. This autonomy appears to be slight, as there was no statistically significant difference between the pituitary TSH levels of the thyroidectomized animals bearing similar supraoptic lesions and exposed to 4 and 26°C.

B. EFFECT OF THERMAL LESIONS

Averill *et al.* (1961) placed thermal bilateral lesions in the anterior ventral hypothalamus of female rats. There followed a significant and permanent depression of thyroid function as measured by the rate of loss of ^{131}I. This depression was effective less than 6 hours after the lesions had been made. Rats retained a significant depression of both 24-hour uptake of ^{131}I and rate of release of incorporated ^{131}I when measured 2, 4, and 8 weeks postoperatively. Rats with thyroid-depressing lesions required only 1.0 μg of Na L-thyroxine/100 gm body weight per day to prevent thyroid secretion compared to 3–4 μg daily.

Averill *et al.* (1961) reported that bilateral thermal lesions placed in the anterior ventral hypothalamus resulted in a significant and permmanent depression of thyroid secretion rate.

C. ELECTRICAL STIMULATION OF HYPOTHALAMUS

Harris and Woods (1958) and Campbell *et al.* (1960) reported a change in TSH release caused by hypothalamic stimulation of the rostral portion of the median eminence.

Shizume *et al.* (1962) reported a significant increase in thyroidal-^{131}I secretion after stimulating the anterior hypothalamus or the median eminence of normal dogs.

D'Angelo and Snyder (1963) reported that electrical stimulation of the anterior hypothalamus and rostral portion of the median eminence effected significant increases in serum TSH to levels which were 3–4 times greater than in sham-stimulated controls. These effects were not observed in animals with lesions.

D'Angelo *et al.* (1964) stimulated electrically the preoptic, supra-chiasmatic, and anterior hypothalamic areas for 10 minutes daily for 4–9 days. There was a marked reduction in AP-TSH stores, increased plasma TSH concentration (4–5 times), and histological stimulation of the thyroid gland. Excitation of posterior median eminence and arcuate nuclear regions of the tuberal hypothalamus produced effects of similar magnitude. They suggest that the portions of the hypothalamus involved in the regulation of TSH and ACTH secretion are overlapping and diffuse rather than discrete.

Averill and Salaman (1967) noted that plasma TSH levels increased by 90–600% in 8 of 13 conscious rabbits during electrical stimulation applied through platinum electrodes previously implanted in the ventral anterior hypothalamus. Plasma TSH levels had increased 15–20 minutes from the onset of stimulation, reaching peak values after 30 minutes of excitation in 6 out of 10 times.

D. Cooling of the Hypothalamus

Andersson et al. (1962) observed a rapid release of thyroid hormone due to 6 hours of local cooling of the preoptic area of the anterior hypothalamus of the goat.

Later, Andersson et al. (1963a) again observed an increased thyroidal-^{131}I release due to cooling of this area, but lesions in the median eminence blocked this response. They suggested that "warm detectors" in this "heat loss center" have an inhibitory effect on the release of TSH.

Andersson et al. (1963b) reported that 15 μg T_4 per kilogram body weight in the goat blocked the effects of preoptic cooling after a 2-hour delay. They concluded than an accumulation of thyroxine at some site was necessary before full inhibition of TSH release was obtained.

E. Action of Thyroxine

Scow and Greer (1955) suggested that L-T_4 acts directly on the pituitary of mice and Euler and Holmgren (1956) noted a similar effect in rabbits. In rats, Yamada and Greer (1959a) suggested it acted on the pituitary and on the hypothalamus to prevent release of TSH.

Kendall (1962) showed that L-T_4 injected into the rat pituitary blocked thyroidal-^{131}I release.

Panda and Turner (1968a,b) made intrahypophyseal and hypothalamic thyroid autotransplants into adult female rats and estimated the plasma and pituitary TSH levels. Thyroidectomized rats bearing thyroid autotransplants in the pituitary had.significantly lower plasma TSH levels than that of controls at 26°C but not at 4°C. Thyroidectomized rats bearing thyroid autotransplants in the supraoptic area showed a significantly lower level of plasma TSH and higher pituitary TSH at 4°C but not at 26°C. It was suggested that L-T_4 feedback operates at the pituitary level in normal situations, but at the hypothalamus area of TFR secretion when higher thyroid function is required such as in cold exposure.

Vale et al. (1967) reported that when increasing amounts of L-T_4 are administered to rats given a constant dose of TRF a dose is found to completely inhibit the TSH-releasing activity of that dose. Conversely, when increasing amounts of TRF are administered to rats pretreated with a constant dose of L-T_4, a dose of TRF is reached which will overcome the inhibitory effect of the L-T_4.

Bowers *et al.* (1967) reported that both L-T_4 and L-T_3 inhibited the release of TSH produced by TRF in mice. Complete inhibition of the TRF-TSH release response occurred with 0.3 μg L-T_3 and partial inhibition with 0.03 μg. Similarly, 2.7 μg L-T_4 and 0.9 μg produced complete and partial inhibition. Increasing the dose of TRF overcomes the inhibition of L-T_4.

Intravenous administration of a highly purified TRF of bovine or porcine origin was reported by Redding and Schally (1967) to cause significant depletion of AP-TSH in mice at a level of 4 ng. Pretreatment of the mice with 10 μg L-T_4 prevented the release.

F. Effect of Pituitary Transplants

Greer *et al.* (1953) reported that intraocular AP transplants in hypophysectomized mice did not maintain body weight or the weights of thyroid, ovaries, adrenals, or uterus significantly above those of hypophysectomized controls. Nevertheless, the implants were able to maintain an ^{131}I uptake per unit of thyroid weight and a thyroid/serum iodide ratio at two-thirds the level of the intact controls.

Scow and Greer (1955) extended the above experiments to include a group fed propylthiouracil (then withdrawing it). There was a marked increase in ^{131}I uptake. On the other hand, thyroxine produced a depression of ^{131}I uptake.

Khazin and Reichlin (1961) studied the thyroid response to thyroxine and to hemithyroidectomy in hypophysectomized rats bearing intraocular pituitary transplants. The graft stimulated thyroid ^{131}I uptake and when hemithyroidectomized, showed a more rapid ^{131}I release rate and uptake and caused thyroid enlargement. Thyroxine injection led to thyroid inhibition in experimental and normal animals. These observations suggest that pituitary tissue is capable of autonomous TSH secretory response to alterations in blood thyroid hormone level.

Greer *et al.* (1966) reported that pituitaries from 8- to 23-day-old rats transplanted under the median eminence of hypophysectomized hosts resulted in thyroid hypertrophy nearly equal to that of intact controls when propylthiouracil was fed for 14 days. Transplants slightly to one side of the central median eminence, but in contact with the hypothalamus, supported testicular size and structure but did not result in thyroid hypertrophy.

G. TSH-STIMULATING HYPOTHALAMIC PEPTIDE (TRF)

Guillemin *et al.* (1962) reported the purification of a hypothalamic extract fraction active in stimulating release of TSH *in vivo* preparations.

Justisz *et al.* (1963) showed that the TRF fraction was a peptide and produced a linear response as a function of the log of the dose injected. It was found to be inhibited by administration of large doses of thyroxine and to have no TSH-like activity when injected into hypophysectomized animals.

Schreiber (1964) extracted a peptide type substance from the rat hypothalamus which stimulated TSH release both *in vitro* and *in vivo*. It was shown that this TRF was not a neurohypophyseal hormone, that it did not have thyrotropin activity itself, and that it could be blocked with either thyroxine or triiodothyronine. He suggested that this factor caused both the synthesis and discharge of thyrotropin.

Schally *et al.* (1965) has extracted a polypeptide from the hypothalamus of sheep, cattle, pig, and man which was shown to stimulate release of TSH *in vitro* and *in vivo*. A procedure for its purification was described.

Vale *et al.* (1967) reported that neutron activation of a highly purified preparation of hypothalamic TRF failed to reveal presence of iodine in the molecule.

1. TRF in Man

Bowers *et al.* (1965) reported the extraction and purification of human TRF. Activity was observed by both *in vitro* and *in vivo* methods.

Schally *et al.* (1967b) reported that human hypothalamic and neurohypophyseal tissues (posterior lobe, stalk, and median eminence) contained TRF.

2. TRF in Cattle

Reichlin (1964) gave a preliminary report that a bovine pituitary stalk-median eminence extract purified by gel filtration had TRF activity when assayed in mice.

Schally *et al.* (1966b) described the extraction and purification of TRF from bovine hypothalamus. It emerged from Sephadex just after α-MSH and before arginine vasopressin. Purified TRF was active *in vivo* at a level of 10 μg and *in vitro* at a dose of 1 μg. It is suggested that it is a weakly basic polypeptide. It is different from oxytocin, vasopressin, α- and β-MSH and LRF (LH-releasing factor).

3. TRF in Sheep

Guillemin *et al.* (1963) incubated rat AP *in vitro*. They released minute amounts of TSH into the incubation fluid. Addition of hypothalamic TSH-releasing factor (TRF) of sheep origin increased the amount of TSH present as a linear function of the log of the dose.

The ability of TRF to stimulate TSH release *in vitro* was inhibited by *in vivo* pretreatment or *in vitro* preincubation with L-thyroxine.

The LH-releasing factor, ACTH-releasing factor, lysine-vasopressin, oxytocin, α-MSH and β-MSH were inactive.

Guillemin *et al.* (1965a) further purified the TRF factor from sheep median eminence-stalk fragments and hypothalamus fragments without median eminence. The material obtained at the last stage of purification was active *in vivo* to stimulate release of TSH at <0.1 μg dry weight. Highly purified TRF had no LH- or ACTH-releasing activity.

4. TRF in Swine

Schally *et al.* (1966a) described a method of extraction and purification of TRF from swine hypothalamus. TRF activity was found to emerge between peaks of α-MSH and lysine vasopressin. The extract was active *in vitro* at a dose of 20 μg and *in vivo* at a level of 100 μg.

Schally and Redding (1967) reported that a highly purified swine TRF stimulated the release of TSH from rat AP *in vitro* at doses as small as 0.01 ng. The response is inhibited by small amounts of L-T_3 or L-T_4. Actinomycin D did not abolish the response, indicating that *de novo* synthesis of TSH is not required for TRF to exert its effect. α- and β-MSH do not stimulate the release of TSH *in vitro*.

H. ASSAY OF TRF *in Vitro* AND *in Vivo*

Bowers *et al.* (1965) described an *in vitro* method of assay of TRF. Anterior pituitaries from rats weighing 150–200 gm were cut in halves. These halves were placed in 20-ml beakers and incubated in 1.5 ml Krebs-Ringer bicarbonate for three 60-minute periods. The media used in the first two periods were discarded. In the third incubation period a measured amount of the material being assayed was added to the contents of 1 beaker whereas the contents of the second beaker served as the control. At the end of the incubation period, the medium was free of pituitary tissue. Both media were then assayed for TSH by the method of McKenzie (1958) and by the method of Bowers *et al.* (1959), which is based on the uptake of ^{131}I by the thyroid glands of the tadpole.

1. Mice

Mice on low iodine diet were injected with ^{131}I, 1 μg L-T$_4$ and 1 mg of codeine (Redding *et al.*, 1966). One milligram of codeine was administered 24 and 30 hours later. At 48 hours TSH or TRF was injected intravenously. The effect was measured by the percentage increase in blood ^{131}I. There was a linear relationship between the log-dose of TRF and the increase in blood radioactivity. The sensitivity of the assay was 0.05 mU TSH with an index of precision (λ) of 0.2. Purified preparations of TRF of porcine, ovine, bovine, and human origin which were active in releasing TSH from rat pituitaries were active in mice.

2. Rats

Bowers *et al.* (1965) measured TRF activity by measuring plasma TSH levels before and after the administration of the preparation. Rats weighing 350–400 gm were thyroidectomized. One to 3 months later 1 μg of L-T$_4$ was given intravenously; 2 hours later urethane was given subcutaneously. One hour later 1.5 ml of blood was removed from the jugular vein and the TRF or saline was given intravenously. Fifteen minutes later 1.5 ml of blood was removed. Heparin was added and the plasma was frozen. The TSH levels of the plasma were assayed in the mouse by the method of McKenzie.

I. Effects of TRF

Guillemin *et al.* (1963) reported that rat AP *in vitro* increased the amount of TSH present in the fluid when TRF of sheep origin was added. The release was inhibited when rats were pretreated or when L-T$_4$ was added to the incubation media.

Bowers *et al.* (1965) tested peptide-like releasing factors obtained from cattle, sheep, pig, and human by the *in vitro* and *in vivo* assay methods.

Sakiz and Guillemin (1965) reported that when the pituitary is induced to secrete TSH by TRF it concomitantly secretes less ACTH in response to stress. Conversely, when the secretion of ACTH is inhibited by pretreatment with dexamethasone and Nembutal, the pituitary secretes higher quantities of TSH in response to TRF. It suggests that the pituitary cannot simultaneously secrete elevated amounts of TSH and ACTH.

Ducommun *et al.* (1965) reported that a purified preparation of TSH-releasing factor (TRF) with specific activity of 30 U/mg of sheep hypothalamus, elevated the level of circulating plasma TSH from 21–197 mU/100 ml in 3 minutes after intravenous injection in normal animals. A less marked effect was noted in thyroidectomized animals.

Sinha and Meites (1966) cultured rat pituitaries for 4, 6, or 9 days. Extracts of rat hypothalamic or cerebral cortical tissue were added after 1, 3, or 6 days of culture. Release of TSH in cultures with cerebral extracts fell to low levels by day 3 whereas with hypothalamic extracts, the TSH increased to levels equal to or exceeding the first 3 days. The total amount of TSH in the medium was 50–97% greater than that found in the AP, indicating that TRF increases the synthesis as well as the release of TSH.

Schally and Redding (1967) reported that highly purified porcine TRF stimulated the release of TSH from rat AP *in vitro* at doses as small as 0.01 μg. By increasing the doses of TRF, greater amounts of TSH were released. The pituitary response to TRF was inhibited by small amounts of L-T_3 and L-T_4. Actinomycin D did not abolish the response to TRF, indicating the *de novo* synthesis of TSH was not required for TRF to exert its effect. α- and β-MSH did not stimulate the release of TSH *in vitro*.

Averill and Kennedy (1967) suppressed the endogenous secretion of TSH by phenobarbital and a temperature of 34°C. Intrapituitary infusion for $2\frac{1}{2}$–3 hours of an extract prepared from the hypothalami of rats and sheep increased the ^{131}I level of the blood, and the magnitude of the response increased with increasing dosage. When compared with the intravenous infusion of TSH, it was estimated that intrapituitary infusion of TRF released only about 5% of the TSH present in the AP.

III. Isolation and Purification of Pituitary TSH

Methods of purifying bovine and ovine TSH were developed during the period up to 1960 (Table I). Since that time extraction and purification of human TSH has received much attention (see Bates and Condliffe, 1960).

Elrick *et al.* (1963) described a method of processing human pituitary glands by which the TSH yield was 3 times greater than from acetone-dried glands.

Elrick *et al.* (1964) compared the amount of TSH from human pituitaries, after embalming, with the amount from control glands. The pituitaries from embalmed patients yielded 35–40% less than controls, but the percentage of yield from the 2 groups was similar.

Lepp and Oliner (1967b) compared the yield of human TSH from glands (a) frozen, (b) processed with acetone, or (c) with acetone, 0.1% thioethanol, and 1% acetic acid. They reported that optimal TSH activity was preserved following freezing compared to the other two preservatives.

In contrast to growth hormone which is species specific in man, TSH of bovine origin has been shown to produce typical hormonal response in man. That the two sources of TSH were quantitatively equal was studied by Schneider *et al.* (1965). Human and bovine TSH was assayed in chicks. The human response to each TSH preparation was similar with respect to time course and degree of effect after a single dose and on the basis of log-dose response.

Bakke (1965) reported the results of the assay of crude human pituitary glands and after an extraction procedure by 18 different laboratories using 12 different assay procedures in comparison with the

TABLE I

PURIFICATION OF PITUITARY TSH

Species	Potency	Reference
Bovine		Condliffe and Bates (1956)
		Condliffe and Bates (1957)
		Bates *et al.* (1959b)
		Bates and Condliffe (1960)
		Carsten and Pierce (1960)
Ovine		Ellis (1958)
Human		Heideman *et al.* (1959)
	201 U/mg	Condliffe (1963)
		Elrick *et al.* (1963)
	201 U/mg	Parlow *et al.* (1965a,b)
		Hartree *et al.* (1964)
Comparative		Wallace and Ferguson (1964)

USP bovine standard. Since the TSH activity of the powders remained stable for 9 months, it was suggested that a reference standard of human TSH should be prepared.

Brown and Munro (1967) reported the availability of a Human Thyrotrophin Research Standard A from the Medical Research Council in England. It is supplied as a freeze-dried powder in sealed ampoules.

Hennen (1967) extracted a TSH-like factor from a human bronchial carcinoma which was similar to human TSH both in biological activity and its immunological properties.

Hershman (1967a) reported that the TSH of male rats did not decline significantly for 48 hours at room temperature or for 6 days at 2°C. It was suggested that the surprising stability of TSH was due to the fact that TSH is localized in the small granules of the basophilic cells whereas the proteases are contained within lysosomes that do not interact with secretion granules.

A. IODINATION OF TSH

Utiger et al. (1963) described a method for the iodination of both human and bovine TSH. TSH-^{131}I with specific activities up to 150 mCi/mg have been produced which retained biological activity.

Heideman et al. (1965) reported upon an improved method of TSH-^{131}I preparation which involved a microtechnique of iodine distillation. Biological activity was not significantly less than that of control TSH. In a study of gel electrophoresis of bovine TSH-[131]I (Heideman et al., 1966) the radioactivity and biological activity migrated similarly but with slight dissociation. Increasing quantities of antiserum shifted increasing quantities of radioactivity to slower moving regions. Bovine TSH interfered with TSH-^{131}I binding to antibody in proportion to biological activity.

B. BIOLOGICAL HALF-LIFE ($t_{1/2}$) OF TSH

Bakke et al. (1962) estimated the biological half-life ($t_{1/2}$) of bovine TSH in man. Normal individuals had a $t_{1/2}$ of 35.4 $\pm$ 3.38 minutes, hypermetabolic patients a $t_{1/2}$ of 26.8 $\pm$ 4.05 minutes, and hypometabolic patients of 97.9 $\pm$ 29.1 minutes.

Bakke and Lawrence (1962) reported that the $t_{1/2}$ of bovine TSH in the normal male rat was 13.7 minutes, in hyperthyroid rats 2.2 minutes, and hypothyroid rats 34.0 minutes. When rats were treated with rat or human TSH the $t_{1/2}$ was quite similar to the results with bovine TSH.

Hendrich and Turner (1964) determined the $t_{1/2}$ of bovine TSH-^{131}I in six calves as 72.59 $\pm$ 7.68 minutes in late fall. Unfortunately the iodination process had biologically inactivated the TSH.

C. CRYSTALLIZATION OF BOVINE TSH

Condliffe and Jakoby (1967) claimed that further purification of bovine TSH was effected by crystallization from solutions of 36–50% saturated ammonium sulfate.

D. BIOLOGICAL EFFECTS OF TSH

1. Effect of TSH on Incorporation of Amino Acids by the Thyroid Gland

Debons and Pittman (1962) incubated slices of bovine and dog thyroid glands with TSH. The uptake of α-aminoisobutyric acid-^{14}C was significantly increased over control values.

Nadler and Mitmaker (1961) injected leucine-^{3}H and made radioautographs of the thyroid glands. In hypophysectomized rats the reaction was observed over the cells and later over the colloid but less intense than in controls. TSH reversed the inhibitory effect.

Raghupathy *et al.* (1963) reported that surviving slices of thyroid glands of guinea pigs incorporated ^{14}C of 7 labeled amino acids. The injection of TSH increased the recovery of ^{14}C-labeled protein. Hypophysectomy of rats reduced the incorporation of leucine-^{14}C in their thyroid gland slices, whereas TSH corrected this defect.

Tong *et al.* (1963) injected into adult guinea pigs 15 USP units of TSH in 3 divided doses. After 15 and 20 hours the thyroid glands were sliced and incubated for 2 hours in a solution containing either *l*-leucine-^{14}C or iodide-^{131}I. Slices incorporated 60–100% more ^{14}C into protein than did control animals.

Klitgaard *et al.* (1963) injected 60 one-day-old chicks with 2 injections of 0.8 USP units of TSH on each of 2 days prior to the injection of ^{125}I and ^{14}C-labeled tyrosine. Chicks were sacrificed at 1, 2, 4, 8, 24, and 48 hours later. ^{125}I-injected chicks showed an elevation of ^{125}I between 8 and 24 hours. Tyrosine-^{14}C uptake of TSH was elevated at 2 hours, and at 8 hours it was 3 times the control value. It remained elevated for 24 hours.

Raghupathy *et al.* (1964) reported that sheep thyroid glands or cultured monolayers incorporated ^{14}C-labeled amino acids into protein. TSH had no effect on incorporation of leucine-^{14}C into protein or the uptake of α-aminoisobutyric acid-^{14}C by thyroid slices.

Tong (1964a,b) reported that isolated bovine thyroid cells stimulated with TSH caused the incorporation of *l*-leucine-^{14}C. This suggests that TSH stimulates protein synthesis in the thyroid cell.

Klitgaard *et al.* (1965) studied the effect of TSH in baby chicks on the uptake of ^{125}I, tyrosine-^{14}C, and arginine-^{14}C. A 2-fold increase in uptake was observed. It suggests that TSH stimulates the rate of protein synthesis in the thyroid gland.

Tong (1965) reported that TSH added to isolated thyroid cells stimulated the incorporation of ^{131}I into L-T_4 and iodotyrosine and at the same time stimulated *l*-leucine-^{14}C incorporation into protein. When puromycin was added it depressed protein synthesis but did not alter ^{131}I incorporation. It is suggested that TSH action on L-T_4 production is not dependent on increased synthesis of protein.

Cavalieri and Searle (1967) studied the effect of a single dose of TSH on the incorporation *in vivo* of ^{14}C-labeled amino acids into thyroid proteins of the rat. Soluble thyroid proteins were analyzed by sucrose density gradient ultracentrifugation. TSH injected 2–4 hours before pulse-labeling increased the total amount of ^{14}C in protein and accelerated the appearance of label in 19 S thyroglobulin. When TSH was given within 1 hour of labeling or 2 hours afterward, total ^{14}C incorporation was unaffected, but the label appeared in 18–19 S thyroglobulin at the expense of label in an immature (15–16 S) precursor protein.

2. Effect of TSH on Thyroid Enzymes and Cofactors

De Groot and Dunn (1966) injected bovine TSH into rats and noted the effect upon the thyroid oxidative enzymes. An increase in activity per milligram of protein was observed in NADPH cytochrome c reductase, isocitric dehydrogenase, glucose-6-phosphate dehydrogenase, and NADH-DPIP reductase by 24 hours and increased up to 72 hours. Prior L-T_4 injection diminished the enzyme activity.

Maayan and Rosenberg (1966) measured the oxidized and reduced forms of NAD and NADP in the rat thyroid before and 3 hours after bovine TSH was given intravenously to normal and hypophysectomized animals. In the normal rat TSH increased the total NADP content, particularly the reduced form. Total NAD was unchanged but NADH was significantly increased. In hypophysectomized rats TSH increased NADP with little change in NADPH.

Oka and Field (1967) reported that TSH increased the NADP in dog thyroid slices during 10- and 20-minute periods without incorporation of nicotinic acid-^{14}C. TSH decreased NADPH levels in slices without a significant incorporation of nicotinic acid into this nucleotide. TSH accelerated nicotinic acid incorporation into NADP during the 20- to 30-minute incubation but was diminished later. They suggest that TSH initially stimulates NADPH oxidation followed by increased NADP synthesis.

Graig (1967) reported that exogenous TSH increased the per gram activity and specific activity of creatine phosphokinase and lactic dehydrogenase in rat thyroid glands. Endogenous TSH stimulation similarly enhanced thyroidal activity of both enzymes but had no effect on myocardial enzymes.

Hershman (1967b) perfused intact dog thyroid glands with glucose-^{14}C and ^{131}I. Added TSH increased the production of $^{14}CO_2$ $194 \pm 28\%$, and lactate $159 \pm 20\%$, but did not affect the production of pyruvate, the uptake of glucose, the uptake of ^{131}I, or the MIT:DIT ratio. It is suggested that TSH stimulates the glycolytic pathway in the thyroid.

3. Effect of TSH on Thyroid Hormone Biosynthesis

It has been recognized that following TSH administration there is a latent period before an increased uptake of ^{131}I occurs. This latent period was observed by Shimoda et al. (1966), but a striking alteration in thyroid constituents occurred within 30 minutes. There was a marked stimulation of L-T_4 synthesis and a decrease in DIT. A lesser increase in L-T_3 and a questionable reduction in MIT were observed. Similar results were observed in hypophysectomized rats. They suggest that TSH rapidly stimulates the coupling of iodotyrosines to form iodothyronines.

Bates and Warren (1963) reported that when TSH was injected into chicks with ^{131}I-labeled thyroids there was a depletion of ^{131}I, [127]I, and sialic acid from the thyroid gland during about 24 hours, presumably as components of thyroglobulin. Under fasting conditions the sialic acid content of the thyroid returns to normal levels more rapidly than does the iodine content.

Nataf et al. (1965) cultured the embryonic thyroid glands of 16-day to 17-day rats. The glands made no use of ^{131}I in a synthetic medium. The blood of hypophysectomized rats slightly increased the ^{131}I uptake. When TSH was added ^{131}I was taken up by both media. In the synthetic media MIT and DIT were formed, but little L-T_4. The serum increased the coupling to increase the L-T_4 formed.

Studer and Greer (1967) studied the rebound effect in rats after the withdrawal of propylthiouracil on a low iodine diet; a peak uptake of ^{131}I and maximum thyroid weight was found after 4–5 days. The biosynthesis of labeled amino acids was characterized by very high MIT/DIT and L-T_3/L-T_4 ratios.

Isaacs and Rosenberg (1967) gave a tracer dose of ^{125}I or ^{131}I at 2 hours before cannulation of the arterial and venous thyroid vessels of the dog. In some, stable iodide and [99m]TcO$_4$ was given also. Intravenous injection of 10 U TSH induced a prompt decline in the clearance of pertechnetate in both normal and high iodide dogs. Iodide clearance by the thyroid was unaffected by TSH in the normal iodide group. In the iodide-loaded animals TSH induced an initial decline in iodide clearance, followed in less than 20 minutes by a 50% increase over pre-TSH values. The results suggest that TSH promptly enhances thyroidal organification of iodide, and this may be among the earliest of the glandular responses to TSH.

4. TSH Release of Inorganic Iodine

Recently, it has been reported that TSH releases inorganic iodine in addition to the thyroid hormones in the early phase of its action (Deiss et al., 1959; Nagataki et al., 1959; Rosenberg et al., 1960).

Roche et al. (1953) reported increased deiodination of DIT by thyroid tissue of rats and guinea pigs given daily injections of TSH for 4–10 days.

Nagataki et al. (1961) suggested the following explanation: In the initial phase of TSH action, the rate of iodide production from iodotyrosine exceeds the rate of organic binding, thus permitting the release of iodide production.

Maayan and Rosenberg (1963) reported that intravenous injection of TSH in rats resulted in prompt enhancement of the deiodinating activity of thyroid tissue (within 3 hours) which lasted for at least 24 hours. The effect was enhanced by the addition of NADPH.

5. Effect of TSH on Serotonin

Clayton and Szego (1967) noted enhancement of blood flow and decline of serotonin content of the rat thyroid within minutes after intravenous injection of TSH in intact rats sensitized by thyroxine pre-treatment. The increased vascularity was maintained through at least 4 hours after hormone administration. This was accompanied by an increase in thyroid water within 2 hours.

6. Effect of TSH on Sugar, Sodium and Potassium

Gedda (1960) reported the injection of TSH into guinea pigs induced a 3-fold increase of potassium in the thyroid gland as compared to the plasma. Later the concentration of sodium was increased.

Solomon (1960) reported the uptake of radioactive sodium by the thyroid gland after TSH stimulation. Later Gedda (1964) reported that TSH had no effect on the K or Na content of striated muscle or liver, but increased blood glucose significantly.

Freinkel (1960) reported that the addition of TSH to the medium increased the uptake of glucose and the production of $^{14}CO_2$ and lipid-^{14}C from glucose-U-^{14}C by sheep thyroid slices.

Irie and Slingerland (1963) gave TSH *in vivo* to normal and hypo-physectomized rats. They observed an increase in the uptake of glucose by slices of thyroids from these rats. The $^{14}CO_2$ produced was increased, but not significantly. The lactic acid release was increased, but there was no change in lipid-^{14}C.

7. TSH on O_2 Consumption of Adipose Tissue

Freinkel (1961) reported that TSH stimulated O_2 uptake of rat adipose tissue associated with an increase of glucose uptake. It was suggested that TSH accelerates lipolysis of triglycerides to free fatty acids and glycerol.

Jungas and Ball (1962) reported that purified samples of TSH were very active in increasing O_2 uptake of adipose tissue.

8. Effect of TSH on Release of Thyroid Hormones

It has been suggested that TSH induces an increased rate of proteo-lysis of thyroglobulin. Balasubramaniam et al. (1965) reported studies which support the theory that TSH enhances the migration of protein from the follicular lumen into intracellular particulate droplets as the first step in the release of thyroid hormones. In further study, Deiss et al. (1966) suggested that release of thyroid hormone induced by TSH occurs in intracellular particles containing both substrate and protease.

Taurog et al. (1964) reported that when TSH was administered to rabbits, cats, and dogs, an increase in L-T_4 in the venous blood occurred after 15–30 minutes with a 3- to 10-fold increase between 1 and 2 hours.

Taurog and Thio (1966) showed that puromycin blocked thyroid protein synthesis about 95% when TSH was given. However, it was shown that the release of L-T_4 in rabbits whose thyroid protein synthesis was blocked by puromycin was unaffected. It was suggested that L-T_4 release was not dependent on prior stimulation of protein synthesis.

Dingledine and Egdahl (1967) injected 1 U TSH in the thyroid artery in 8 patients; a significant rise in radioactivity in the thyroid vein was observed in 7 patients. When less than 1 U was administered slight or no response was observed. Peripheral venous samples were negative. The response was observed within 10 minutes and continued to rise for 30–60 minutes.

Row et al. (1967) gave porcine TSH to euthyroid patients. No ^{131}I-labeled iodotyrosines were detected either before or after. Stable iodotyrosine-like compounds were detected both before and after TSH, but no increase was observed. There was an increase of L-T_3 and L-T_4 after TSH. In hyperthyroid patients, TSH had no effect on the iodinated compounds. When large doses of ^{131}I were given ^{131}I-labeled iodotyrosines appeared but were not increased by TSH. They suggest that they might come from an unknown extrathyroidal source.

IV. Exophthalmos-Producing Substance (EPS)

Dobyns (1946) reported that some TSH preparations were more effective in producing exophthalmos than others. These observations were further confirmed by Dobyns and Steelman (1953). They claimed to be able to separate two fractions by their differential solubility in trichloroacetic acid, one of which contained TSH and the second EPS.

Condliffe et al. (1959) and Bates and Condliffe (1960) claimed a separation of EPS and TSH activities by chromatography of TSH concentrates on CM- and DEAE-cellulose. Confirmation was reported by Noguchi et al. (1962). Brunish et al. (1962) reported obtaining an EPS concentrate low in TSH by chromatography on CM-cellulose. Bates et al. (1959a) reported that TSH prepared from transplantable TSH-producing tumors in mice (Furth) were lacking in EPS.

In contrast to these reports, Hennen *et al.* (1965) were unable to confirm these observations. They invariably found both activities in a single fraction. Dedman *et al.* (1967) prepared 7 bovine TSH preparations by a variety of extraction procedures. These preparations were assayed for TSH and EPS. While their TSH potencies varied from 0.14 to 39 IU/mg, the ratio of TSH to EPS activity was quite similar. It was, therefore, concluded that no dissociation of the two biological activities could be demonstrated.

1. Assay of EPS

Schockaert (1932) reported that a crude pituitary extract produced exophthalmos in ducks. In mammals Marine and Rosen (1934) and Smelser (1936) reported the condition could be caused in guinea pigs. Pochin (1944) suggested a weight increase of the Harderian gland in the guinea pig, and Wegelius *et al.* (1959) suggested ^{35}S uptake as being indicative of a response.

Several species of fish have been shown to be very sensitive, including the Atlantic minnow, goldfish, and carp.

Albert (1945) Method. Fundulus heteroclitus Linn. (the common Atlantic minnow) 3–4 inches in length are kept in a tank of running tap water at 10°C in winter and 18°C in summer. To avoid loss of fluids by the intraperitoneal injection route, the needle is inserted into the cloaca, through the rectum, over the pelvic girdle, and into the peritoneal cavity for a distance of about 0.5 inch. The volume of fluid injected should be 0.1–0.5 ml. The effect of the hormone is to cause protrusion of the eyeballs (exophthalmos). A unit of EPS has been defined as that amount of substance which induces proptosis in 25% of a group of 20 fish 6 hours after injection.

Haynie et al. (1962) Method. Carassius auratus, the common goldfish, 4–6 inches in length and weighing 12–15 gm are placed in a tank with water temperature of 72°F. The fish are not fed for 24 hours before or during assay. Baseline eye measurements are made with vernier calipers to the nearest 0.1 mm. The test material is injected intraperitoneally through the vent with a No. 25 gauge needle. The injections are made at 12-hour intervals for 3 days with measurement of the intercorneal distance made prior to each injection. The results are expressed as the maximum percentage increase in the intercorneal distance. The response is linear in the dosage range of 0.125–0.625 USP units. Dedman *et al.* (1967) used goldfish with some modification of the above method.

Der Kinderen Method (see Der Kinderen et al., 1960). Cyprinus carpio, carp weighing 4–14 gm were marked by clipping the tail. The test material was injected through the cloaca into the coelomic cavity at 12-hour intervals. Groups of 5–8 fish were used in each assay. The intercorneal distance was measured with a plastic caliper before and after 24, 48, and 72 hours. The increase in proptosis was expressed as a percentage of the intercorneal distance found at the beginning of the test.

Sobonya and Dobyns (1967) tested 14 species of native Ohio fish, but none was found to surpass *Fundulus heteroclitus* in degree of response to an EPS standard, ease of handling, or hardiness. The response of carp and goldfish was inferior to *Fundulus heteroclitus*.

2. EPS in the Serum

The possible presence of EPS in serum was first studied by Dobyns and Wilson (1954). They found a fair correlation between clinical severity of exophthalmos and the degree of proptosis in *Fundulus*. These observations were confirmed by Canadell and Barraquer (1956) using goldfish. Der Kinderen *et al.* (1960) used small carp as assay animals in a study of EPS in serum. Sera of 9 normal persons caused no increase in the intercorneal distance in the fish. In exophthalmic patients EPS values tended to be higher. Der Kinderen *et al.* believe that TSH and EPS are not identical.

Dobyns *et al.* (1961) assayed EPS in the serum of patients with progressive exophthalmos, using the Atlantic minnow. The serum of some patients produced pronounced exophthalmos in the fish, but there was no strict correlation between the degree of response in fish and the severity of symptoms.

Schwarz *et al.* (1962) reported elevated titers of EPS in sera of 7 patients. Following pituitary surgery or X-ray treatment, the EPS disappeared from the serum, associated with regression of ocular symptoms. Human pituitaries were observed to contain EPS.

Horster and Klein (1964) reported elevated EPS in serum of 81 patients with exophthalmos of up to 2 years. The assays were not correlated with PBI or thyroidal ^{131}I turnover. The highest titers of EPS were found in patients with longest duration and severest symptoms. In 56 euthyroid and hyperthyroid persons without exophthalmos, no EPS could be demonstrated.

Björkman *et al.* (1961) infused the blood of patients with progressive exophthalmos into euthyroid patients. A significant rise in the PBI level of the recipients was observed.

Schwarz *et al.* (1966) reported that only 2 of 64 exophthalmic patients showed no EPS in serum. Of 44 nonexophthalmic patients, only 2 showed EPS. A fair correlation was found between the severity of the disease and EPS levels.

Pimstone *et al.* (1964) ran parallel assays of TSH, LATS, and EPS in plasma from euthyroid and hyperthyroid patients with and without exophthalmos. In all cases of exophthalmos, LATS was elevated, but TSH and EPS were not consistently elevated.

V. Methods of Assay of Pituitary TSH

A. BIOLOGICAL

1. Mouse

McKenzie (1958) Method. Swiss-Webster female mice weighing about 15 gm were used. Eight microcuries ^{131}I were injected to ensure maximum uptake. Ten micrograms thyroxine was then administered, followed by the addition to the ration of 0.066% thyroid powder (USP). After 3 days allowed for clearance of blood iodine, TSH was injected intravenously. Maximum blood ^{131}I was reached in 2 hours. The ^{131}I in blood was counted by plating 0.1 ml on aluminum planchets using either a gas flow or an end-window counter. The lower limit of detection was 0.025 mU with a volume of injection of 0.2–0.5 ml of serum. The average index of precision (λ) was 0.24. A 4-point assay technique was suggested with 6 observations for each of 2 doses of the standard and of the unknown preparations. The error of an assay was calculated to be about 25%.

Sakiz and Guillemin (1964) suggested the following modifications of the McKenzie method. Female mice (10–15 gm) are kept in a temperature-controlled room and fed a low iodine diet for 10 days. They are then injected intraperitoneally with 1.5 μCi ^{131}I, followed 5 hours later by 10 μg L-T_4 subcutaneously. Twenty-four hours later they receive a second injection of 5 μg L-T_4 and are used 48 hours after this last injection. Under ether anesthesia 0.25 ml of blood is withdrawn from the jugular vein in a heparinized syringe. TSH or the releasing factor (TRF) is injected by the same route in 0.3-ml volume. Two hours later a second 0.25-ml sample is taken, and the radioactivity measured. A new method to calculate and analyze the results is presented. However, Becktel (1967) suggests that there is little evidence of any gross difference between the ratio and covariance analysis of TSH assays.

Levy *et al.* (1965) used 22 strains of inbred mice and 2 strains of deer mice to find, if possible, a strain more sensitive to TSH than the Swiss-Webster strain for use in the McKenzie method. While some strains were found to be significantly more sensitive, the increase was not believed to be sufficient to increase the usefulness of the assay.

Rerup and Melander (1965) modified the McKenzie method as follows: female mice weighing 16 ± 2 gm were kept on a normal pellet diet. ^{131}I was injected intraperitoneally (8μCi/mouse in 0.1 ml) followed by 20 μg L-T_4 in 0.1 ml. A second dose of L-T_4 is given 72 hours later.

The mice are ready for TSH assay for 2–6 days after ^{131}I injection.

Good and Stenhouse (1966) suggested a modification of the McKenzie method by the application of a design balanced for residual effects. It is claimed that the modification results in increased sensitivity and an average index of precision (λ) of 0.188.

McKenzie (1967) Method. In the light of 8 years of experience, modification of the method for use of pituitary and serum TSH and LATS is suggested.

Querido et al. (1953) Method. Female mice weighing 20–23 gm are used. A diet containing 25 mg/kg of thyroprotein is fed for 9 days. The TSH is injected intraperitoneally in 4 equal doses at 12-hour intervals. At 36 hours after the first injection, 1 μCi ^{131}I is administered by the same route, and 24 hours later the thyroids are removed and digested and radioactivity is measured as in the Overbeck method. During the 24-hour ^{131}I uptake period, the animals may be fasted. The sensitivity of the method using mice appears to be similar to that of the comparable method using rats, but great strain differences were encountered. TSH in amounts equivalent to 10–250 μg of provisional USP units may be estimated.

Garcia and Selenkow (1964) modified the Querido method as follows: White female mice weighing 15–20 gm were distributed into groups of 10 animals. On day 1, each animal was given intraperitoneally 70 μg of L-T$_4$. On day 3, solutions containing TSH were injected intraperitoneally in two separate doses 8–10 hours apart. On the morning of day 4, 0.05 μCi of ^{131}I was given intraperitoneally. Eight hours later animals were killed and the thyroid glands were excised, dissolved in NaOH, and counted. The Charles River C-D strain of mice showed greater sensitivity to TSH than the Swiss-Webster strain.

Brown and Munro (1967) Method. This method is based upon the *in vivo* labeling of the mouse thyroid gland followed by the *in vitro* discharge of ^{131}I from the gland with and without TSH. The release of ^{131}I from the gland into the medium was then calculated and expressed as a percentage of the total radioactivity in the thyroid at the time it was introduced into the medium at the beginning of incubation. It was reported that there was a significant lack of parallelism between bovine and human TSH; however, LATS gave a parallel dose-response relationship with human TSH.

2. Cattle

Bakke et al. (1957) Method. The observation that TSH influences the osmoregulation of cattle thyroid slices incubated 21 hours at 38°C was used as an index of response. TSH has been shown to induce higher final weights compared to the control group due to the swelling of the follicles resulting from the entry of fluid from the incubation medium. The reader is referred to the original paper for the details of the method. The method is said to be specific, of adequate range, sensitive to <0.01 USP mU of TSH per milliliter, with a median λ of 0.28.

Odell *et al.* (1963) suggested a modification of the Bakke method. He observed that rabbit thyroid glands responded as well as cattle slices. He reported that preparations of ACTH, GH, lactogen, LH, and FSH were without effect.

3. Chicks

Bates and Cornfield (1957) method. New Hampshire chicks, 1-day-old, were kept in a brooder with water available, but no food. They were injected subcutaneously with 2–3 μCi ^{131}I. ^{131}I uptake was measured *in vivo* 24 hours later. Only chicks with at least 15% uptake were included. A solution containing 8 μg thyroxine and 0.5 mg propylthiouracil was then injected daily to block endogenous TSH secretion and ^{131}I recycling. The TSH solution to be assayed was injected subcutaneously in a volume of 0.2 ml daily for 2 or 3 days. Daily thyroidal-^{131}I counts were made. The end point is the relative percent of ^{131}I remaining (RPR) at the end of 1, 2, or 3 days. A linear relation between log dose and the extent of depletion was found with an index of precision, λ, of about 0.20.

B. Immunological

Readers are referred to Ciba Foundation Colloquia on Endocrinology, volume 14, which reviews the earlier methods on TSH immunoassay by Werner (1962), on studies with antiserum to TSH by Beck *et al.* (1962) and immunobiological studies of TSH by Selenkow *et al.* (1966).

Odell *et al.* (1967) has summarized studies of TSH physiology by means of radioimmunoassay.

1. Production of Antibodies to TSH

McKenzie and Fishman (1960) reported that rabbit antisera to commercial and USP TSH were shown to inhibit biological assay of bovine TSH. However, they did not inhibit LATS.

Hayashida *et al.* (1961) produced a potent antiserum against rat pituitary TSH. Rabbits were injected with rat AP for periods of 6–18 months.

Werner *et al.* (1961) produced antisera against purified bovine TSH in rabbits and demonstrated that these antisera could inhibit the biological action of both bovine TSH and human TSH.

Reichlin and Boshans (1964) reported acute inhibition of thyroidal-^{131}I release in the rat following injection of rabbit antibody to cattle TSH.

Baschieri et al. (1962) reported that injection of 0.1 ml of immune rabbit plasma every other day for 10 days led to significant inhibition of ^{131}I uptake by the thyroid and to a decrease in gland size.

Pascasio and Selenkow (1962) produced antiserum to several bovine TSH preparations in rabbits and in guinea pigs. Each was capable of inhibiting the biological effects of bovine TSH as determined by the Querido or McKenzie assays. The antibodies have been shown to be associated with γ-globulins. It was observed that ^{131}I uptake in rats was progressively reduced by the antiserum.

Levy et al. (1962) produced a rabbit antiserum to purified bovine TSH. It was shown that the antiserum neutralized bovine and human TSH, but greater amounts were required for the latter.

Utiger et al. (1963) used the Bates and Cornfield method in estimating the neutralization of TSH by antiserum. The test materials and the thyroxine-propylthiouracil solution were injected subcutaneously, and the animals were counted again 24 hours later. The relative percentage remaining (RPR) was calculated, and then the percentage neutralization of TSH response by the antiserum was calculated from the RPR values. In each assay 5 or 6 chicks were used and 2.0 mU TSH and antisera were injected in separate sites. USP-TSH was run with each assay. The sensitivity of this assay varied from 0.5–1.0 mU TSH.

Garcia and Selenkow (1964) reported that lots of antiserum to bovine TSH have different biological neutralizing capacities which do not parallel their serological titer. They suggest that each lot be assayed for the biological neutralizing dose (BND).

The BND is defined as the minimum volume (ml) of the antiserum which completely neutralizes the biological activity of a known quantity of USP TSH, using the modified Querido assay. Control groups were injected with either physiological saline, propylthiouracil (PTU) alone, normal rabbit serum (NRS), or PTU and NRS. Forty-eight hours after discontinuance of injections, a dose of [131]I (0.25 μCi/100 gm) is administered intraperitoneally to each animal. Eighteen hours later, the animals are killed and the thyroid glands are removed, dissolved in 10% NaOH, and counted.

It was shown that rabbit antiserum neutralized exogenous or endogenous TSH in the guinea pig, rat, and mouse.

Selenkow et al. (1966) reported that the antibodies to TSH and LH appear to be distinct and separable. The biological neutralizing capacity of antibodies to TSH was not altered after removal of antibodies to LH.

Panda and Turner (1966) produced in rabbits anti-TSH plasma by the administration of bovine TSH. Its biological effect upon the endogenous thyroxine secretion rate of rats was shown by its ability to depress ^{131}I uptake by 65% at a level of 2.5 ml and. to block the release rate of thyroidal-^{131}I for a period of 5 days. Lower levels of anti-TSH plasma showed a graded effect upon the release rate.

Hays et al. (1967) reported that antibodies formed to bovine TSH were inhibitory not only to bovine TSH, but also to human TSH and that they partially inhibited the effects of endogenous TSH.

2. Radioimmunoprecipitation Assay of TSH

Utiger et al. (1963) described a method for the assay of TSH to which the reader is referred for the details. It is claimed that this method is capable of detecting as little as 0.01 mU of homologous TSH.

Odell et al. (1965a,b) developed a radioimmunoassay method capable of measuring TSH in human serum. Their results were not reported in terms of bovine USP reference standard, but in terms of their laboratory human TSH standard.

Wilber and Utiger (1967) described an assay method for rat TSH which utilized ^{125}I mouse thyrotropic tumor TSH, antibovine TSH serum and USP bovine TSH as a standard. Serum TSH in normal rats after decapitation ranged from 15–66 mU/ml. During pentobarbital anesthesia, serum TSH was significantly lower (10–37 mU/ml). Mean normal rat pituitary TSH content was 44 mU/gland. After 50 μg L-T$_4$ twice daily for 14 days, serum TSH became undetectable in 5 of 7 rats and HP-TSH fell to 25% of normal. Wilber and Utiger suggested that L-T$_4$ administration inhibits TSH synthesis as well as release.

Panda and Turner (1967a) developed a hemagglutination-inhibition technique for the estimation of TSH in the plasma and pituitary. It is sensitive to detect 0.1–0.2 mU/ml of TSH in USP Reference Standard.

C. TSH-LIKE EFFECTS OF OTHER HORMONES

Administration of α- and β-MSH was reported to increase thyroid activity in rabbits by Courier and Cehovic (1960) and in guinea pigs by Cehovic (1962).

Werner et al. (1964) reported that responses similar to that obtained by TSH by the McKenzie method were observed with β-MSH and ACTH administered in saline but became like LATS when injected in normal human serum.

Bowers et al. (1964–1965) used the McKenzie method of TSH assay. They reported that lysine or arginine vasopressin increased ^{131}I blood levels. Oxytocin and Val-5-angiotensin II were inactive. The greatest effect was elicited with corticotropin A and natural or synthetic α- and β-MSH. α- and β-MSH also increased the uptake of ^{131}I in mice.

Schally *et al.* (1967a) examined 7 synthetic peptides related to α-MSH and ACTH and 11 stereoisomeric fragments of α-MSH for their TSH-like activity in mice injected with ^{131}I and L-T_4. Five synthetic peptides related to ACTH and 4 MSH stereoisomers increased blood ^{131}I levels.

VI. TSH Content of the Pituitaries of Various Species

1. Man

Bakke and Lawrence (1959) reviewed the literature concerning the TSH content of the human pituitary. Since the assay methods were rather insensitive, the data are of doubtful significance.

Bakke and Lawrence (1959) assayed 203 human pituitary glands of which 198 were obtained at autopsy and 5 at operation by their method using bovine thyroid slices. The AP of 44 individual males from 25–86 years of age (mean 60 years) showed a range from 10–477 mU and a mean of 114 $\pm$ 15.9 mU. Five female AP glands removed at operation ranged from 220–1100 mU. In 12 patients less than 51 years of age the mean TSH was 210 mU whereas in 32 patients more than 51 years of age the mean TSH was 82 mU/gland.

Bates and Condliffe (1960) reported the normal human pituitary TSH content to be approximately 2000 mU.

Bakke *et al.* (1964) reported that the TSH content of the pituitaries of 57 euthyroid women was 348 mU/gland. To 5 women 3–5 doses of 25 μg L-T_3 every 8 hours had a mean potency of 333 mU (range 301–639 mU). Three women who received 6–7 doses had pituitary TSH of 7.5 mU/gland (range less than 0.7–11.8 mU).

Kumahara *et al.* (1967) found the TSH of the AP of 4 patients with Grave's disease to be immunologically abnormal. However, the time response for the bioassay was normal. The TSH activity of 3 patients who died in a hyperthyroid state were found to be about 1/25 of normal.

2. Mouse

Bates and Garrison (1961) thyroidectomized 3-month-old mice with ^{131}I. After 12–18 months the pituitaries became greatly enlarged. At this time the blood was collected and the AP assayed for TSH or the AP was transplanted into the leg. The TSH of the AP contained 0.1–0.2 U of TSH/mg dry weight. The mean blood level was 33 mU/ml. A ratio of TSH/ml of blood times 40 gives the amount of TSH in AP. When L-T_4 was given, the blood level of TSH dropped to 10–30% of starting level and the TSH of the tumor dropped to 4% of normal. Since the relation of the blood level to tumor level in the hind leg was the same, it was concluded that the release of TSH from the tumors was independent of any hypothalamic influence.

3. Rat

Bakke and Lawrence (1958) reported that the TSH content of the rat AP fell to 10% of the control values after 7 days of thyroid hormone administration.

D'Angelo (1958) reported that L-T_3 at level of 0.4 µg/day reduced the rat TSH to about 25% of normal and 2 µg caused almost complete loss. Ten micrograms of T_4 was considered equipotent.

D'Angelo (1958) determined the TSH of the pituitaries of 12 rats weighing a mean of 290 gm. The mean TSH/mg was 70 mU USP units (range 60–90) and 875 mU/gland.

D'Angelo (1961) determined the TSH of the AP of rats 4–8 months of age. The mean was 71 ± 17 mU/mg and 690 ± 40 USP mU/gland. In old rats the TSH fell to less than 10% of these values.

Rats on propylthiouracil showed decreased TSH levels with depletion almost complete after 1 month. The hormone level was less than 5% of normal. After goitrogen withdrawal, the TSH level remained low for 3 days, but by 7 days TSH stores had increased 500% of normal and were still above normal on day 20.

It was estimated that the AP of the adult female rat normally possesses the equivalent of several days supply of TSH.

Bakke and Lawrence (1964) gave 0.05% propylthiouracil in the drinking water. Since the rats drank about 30 ml/day they received about 15 mg/day. This treatment produced a progressive and parallel increase in serum TSH over a one-year period. Pituitary TSH declined markedly for 4 weeks, returned to control levels at 10 weeks, then rose until a level 5 times the control was achieved after 32 weeks. Either physiological or toxic doses of DL-T_4 caused a depression of serum TSH as early as 1 hour after administration followed by an increased pituitary TSH content to as much as 8 times the starting level after 10–60 hours. This indicated a net synthesis of 61 mU/hour.

van Rees et al. (1965) noted decreases in both AP and serum TSH levels of castrate male rats. Testosterone propionate (TP) increased serum TSH of castrated males, but on the AP the TP prevented the decrease induced by castration. High doses of TP produced low AP-TSH similar to castrated rats.

Bakke and Lawrence (1965a) reported that pituitary TSH of the rat was at a peak at 8 AM then declined by noon followed by an increase until 8 AM. Serum TSH could not be measured. In PTU-fed rats the serum TSH was lowest at 6 AM.

Singh *et al.* (1967) studied the diurnal variation of plasma and pituitary TSH of rats subject to 14 hours of light and 10 hours darkness. The plasma TSH level rose gradually from 3 AM to 3 PM, then declined. The pituitary TSH was highest at 3 AM and then declined to 3 PM.

D'Angelo (1966) reported a gradual decline in pituitary TSH in normal aging female rats. TSH of 15-month-old animals were about one-third of young adults and dropped to very low levels in animals 22–24 months old. Blood TSH levels in aged rats were maintained with slight fluctuations. Castration in either sex resulted in a significant decrease of TSH in both serum and AP. The reductions after 3 weeks and 1 year were of similar magnitude.

van Rees (1966) determined the TSH level of the AP and blood of thyroidectomized rats after treatment with L-T_3 or L-T_4 for 2 weeks. Low levels of both hormones caused an increase in the AP whereas higher levels showed less effect or a decrease. This decrease was associated with a decrease in TSH serum levels. L-T_3 was about 3 times more active than L-T_4 in producing normal AP and serum levels.

Panda and Turner (1967b) determined the TSH content of the pituitary of female rats from weaning time (24 days) up to 110 days of age. The TSH per pituitary gland increased from 127.2 mU to 834.0 mU/gland at 80 days of age and then declined.

Panda and Turner (1967b) reported mature female rats had a mean pituitary TSH level of 68.26 mU/mg. After thyroidectomy, the TSH/mg was reduced to 40.4 mU after 10 days and to 35.0 mU after 20 days. After 25 days of thyroidectomy L-T_4 at a level of 2.5 μg/100 gm body weight was injected for 1, 3, and 5 days; the pituitary TSH/mg was 37.5, 38.6 and 77.9 mU, respectively. When rats held at 26°C were changed to a temperature of 4.4°C for 10 and 20 days, the pituitary TSH increased to 108.04 and to 240.9 mU/mg, respectively.

The combined effect of thyroidectomy and 4.4°C for 10 and 20 days caused the TSH to decline to 43.79 and 37.58 mU/mg. When these rats were returned to 26°C for 4 days, the TSH remained low, 34.90 mU/mg.

4. Guinea Pig

D'Angelo (1966) reported no change in TSH secretion with age in the guinea pig. Blood levels of TSH in normal and ovariectomized animals were too low to be detected. When propylthiouracil (PTU) was given in the food (0.1%) for 2–5 months serum TSH was elevated markedly (110–120 mU/100 ml) and the TSH of the AP was elevated 800%. Some decline in AP-TSH concentration was noted in spayed animals, but of questionable significance. The combination of ovariectomy and PTU failed to modify the TSH level. The TSH of the normal female guinea pig is only a fraction of that in the rat. It should be noted that the FSH of these animals was studied also.

VII. Determination of TSH Secretion Rate

Crenshaw et al. (1957) blocked the secretion of TSH by the administration of thyroprotein to a dwarf beef animal. Iodine-[131] uptake in the animal was greatly reduced. TSH was then administered in increasing amounts until ^{131}I uptake was restored to normal. It was estimated that the TSH secretion rate of this animal was about 40 USP units/100 lb body weight.

A modification of this method has been suggested by Premachandra and Turner (1960) in which both the thyroxine secretion and TSH secretion could be estimated concurrently. In the determination of thyroxine secretion rate (Chapter 8), the thyroidal-^{131}I release rate with recycling blocked is first determined. Then increasing levels of thyroxine are administered to block TSH secretion and thyroidal-^{131}I release. This level is considered to be the estimated thyroxine secretion rate. By maintaining the block of endogenous TSH secretion, the injection of TSH in amounts sufficient to restore the initial rate of release of thyroidal-. [131]I is then considered to be the estimated TSH secretion rate (TSH-SR).

If one wishes to determine only the estimated TSH secretion rate, the following procedure is suggested. The biological $t_{1/2}$ of thyroidal-^{131}I release under administration of a goitrogen is determined (time required for one-half of thyroidal-^{131}I to be released). Then a level of thyroxine is administered slightly in excess of thyroxine secretion rate to block TSH. TSH is injected for 4 days and the $t_{1/2}$ is again determined. If $t_{1/2}$ is less than original $t_{1/2}$, the amount of TSH is increased; if greater, the amount of TSH is reduced.

By this technique, a group of mature chickens were shown to have estimated TSH secretion rates ranging between 0.05 and 0.075 USP units per 100 gm body weight.

Hendrich and Turner (1964) determined the TSR and TSH-SR of 2-year-old New Hampshire hens. Both indices of thyroid function were observed to be significantly higher during late spring than during late summer to early fall. No significant difference was observed between TSR and TSH-SR of 1- and 2-year old hens tested concurrently during late summer. There was no significant correlation between TSR and TSH-SR.

Hendrich and Turner (1964) compared the TSR and TSH-SR of 7 growing calves during the spring and the following fall. In the spring the TSR was 0.214 mg/L-T_4/100 lb body weight and the TSH-SR was 829 mU TSH/100 lb body weight. In the fall the mean TSR remained the same but the TSH-SR declined to 764 mU TSH/100 lb body weight.

Hendrich and Turner (1967) compared the TSR and TSH-SR of 53 New Hampshire hens ranging from 1–4 years of age. No significant changes occurred with increasing age. The mean TSR was 0.94 μg/L-T_4/100 gm body weight, and the mean TSH-SR was 3.8 mU of TSH/100 gm body weight.

Bakke *et al.* (1962) calculated the TSH secretion rate in normal patients as 260 mU/day; of hypometabolic patients, 2500 mU/day; and of hypermetabolic patients, 10,000 mU/day. Schneider *et al.* (1965) observed that human and bovine TSH were similar in biological activity in man. They accepted the estimated TSH secretion rate in normal man of about 260 mU/day.

VIII. Effect of TSH on Thyroid Glands and Slices

A. SPECIES

1. Human

Hung *et al.* (1966) described a method of incubating human thyroid tissue with [131]I. The histology of the gland was preserved up to 7 days. Labeled MIT, DIT, and L-T_4 was observed on hydrolysis. Addition of TSH accelerated the conversion of MIT to DIT as well as the coupling to form L-T_4 and its release. No labeled amino acids were detected when TSH was not added.

2. Rats

Earlier workers reported that TSH injected into adult animals even as late as 24 hours after the injection failed to augment the ^{131}I uptake of the glands.

Nataf and Chaikoff (1964) prepared thyroid lobes of fetal, newborn, and adult rats and slices of the latter. They were treated with the same dose of TSH. It was observed that uptake of added ^{131}I and its incorporation was greater by the lobes. The thyroids of fetal and newborn rats were much more responsive to TSH than were the adult rats.

Mack and Niccolini (1965) reported that the *in vitro* whole rat thyroids took up ^{131}I to a greater extent than slices.

Shimoda and Greer (1966) fed a low iodine diet for prolonged periods or propylthiouracil for 10 days. The thyroid lobes were markedly stimulated to iodothyronine synthesis. *In vivo* administration of TSH daily for 2 days also improved *in vitro* iodothyronine-^{131}I synthesis in both intact and hypophysectomized rats.

Slingerland *et al.* (1966) fed rats 1 gm of cysteine per 100 gm of diet for 1 week. However, it has no effect on the amount and ratio of MIT-^{131}I or DIT-^{131}I formed *in vivo*.

3. Guinea Pig

Kirkham (1962) Method. The thyroid glands of male guinea pigs treated for about 100 days with methylthiouracil are incubated for 40 hours in Gey's solution with ^{131}I and TSH at 25°C. An aliquot of 0.2 ml of the culture medium is removed for the determination of radio-activity. Then 0.2 ml of a solution of KSCN is added, and a second aliquot of 0.2 ml is removed 4 hours later. The difference in radioactivity between the two samples is inversely related to the amount of TSH in contact with the tissue.

Desbarats-Schönbaum *et al.* (1967) observed erratic responses in the Kirkham assay due to "nonspecific" stimulation. This material can be removed from human serum and other preparations by filtration through Sephadex G-25 medium. Rabbit antibovine TSH abolishes the response to bovine and human TSH. The system does not respond to LATS.

4. Rabbits

Hung *et al.* (1967) showed that rabbit thyroid glands in organ culture were able to concentrate ^{131}I and incorporated the iodine into MIT, DIT, and L-T_4. This process was accelerated by TSH. No evidence for the incorporation of tyrosine-^{14}C or phenylalanine-^{14}C into these iodinated compounds was observed.

5. Bovine and Dog Thyroid Gland Slices

Kogl and van Deenen (1961) reported that TSH increased the uptake of ^{32}P by bovine thyroid slices. [32]P was incorporated into lecithins, cephalins, and an inositol phosphatide. They suggested that the phosphatides contribute to the metabolic activity of the thyroid.

Powell *et al.* (1964) reported that cattle thyroid slices, incubated with TSH, accumulated inorganic iodide-[127] in a rectilinear fashion for up to 8 hours of incubation whereas little change was noted in controls. An oxygen atmosphere was essential. The log-dose response curve was biphasic with hormone concentration ranging from 0.01–100 mU per milliliter of incubation medium, maximum increases were achieved at TSH levels of 1 mU/ml.

Segal *et al.* (1966) studied amino acid uptake by bovine and dog thyroid slices. They included α-aminoisobutyric acid (AIB), cycloleucine, glycine, L-histidine, L-tyrosine, and L-valine. AIB continued a linear uptake curve for 4 hours of incubation whereas the others reached a steady state in 30 minutes. TSH caused a small but significant increase in AIB uptake, but not with the other amino acids studied.

Slingerland *et al.* (1966) reported that the addition of cysteine to the medium of incubated calf thyroid slices reduced the uptake of ^{131}I, the amount of trichloroacetic acid-precipitated ^{131}I, and the amount of MIT-^{131}I and DIT-^{131}I formed. It is suggested that this is due to reducing ability of cysteine.

Ohta and Field (1966) reported the ATP concentration of dog thyroid slices was 319 ± 76 mμmoles/gm wet weight. Incubation with TSH decreased the ATP levels during a 45-minute incubation, and ATP was greater when glucose was omitted. It was not changed when TSH was omitted. There was no correlation between CO_2 production and ATP levels.

B. PREPARATION OF ISOLATED THYROID CELLS

Tong *et al.* (1962) and Tong (1964b) have described a method for the isolation of thyroid epithelial cells of sheep and cattle freed from colloid and released from the follicular organization of the tissue by a trypsinization process. It was shown by Kerkof *et al.* (1964a) that when these cells were cultured as monolayers they remained essentially unchanged for 7 days. The addition of TSH to the culture resulted in a reorganization of the monolayers giving rise to a structural pattern resembling cross sections of the intact thyroid.

Kerkof and Chaikoff (1966) thyroidectomized rats either by surgery or by injection of ^{131}I at birth. When isolated thyroid cells were implanted subcutaneously, they became reorganised into follicles containing colloid. The implants utilized ^{131}I and formed MIT, DIT, L-T_4, and L-T_3. They released L-T_4 into the circulation.

C. EFFECT OF TSH ON ISOLATED THYROID CELLS

Tong *et al.* (1962) reported that isolated sheep thyroid cells cultured as monolayers retained their capacity to concentrate iodide ions, to incorporate the iodide into iodotyrosines and iodothyronines, and to deiodinate iodotyrosines.

Tong (1964a) incubated isolated cattle thyroid cells with 0.2 U of TSH. The cells incorporated ^{131}I into L-T_4 and monoiodo- and diiodo-tyrosine at rates 2- to 4-fold greater than in the controls. No enhancement of iodide concentrating activity was detected.

Tong (1964b) further studied the *in vitro* activity of isolated cattle cells, noting the synthesis of L-T_4, transport of iodide, oxidation of glucose and uptake of α-aminoisobutyrate. TSH added at concentration as low as 10^{-4} U/ml stimulated L-T_4 synthesis and uptake of α-amino-isobutyrate. The conversion of glucose-1-^{14}C to ^{14}CO was stimulated by 0.2 U/ml of TSH. However, TSH depressed iodide concentrating activity. He suggested that TSH has separate and independent stimulatory actions on a number of metabolic pathways in the thyroid cell.

Kerkof *et al.* (1964b) cultured sheep thyroid cells. It was reported that ^{131}I uptake and its incorporation into mono- and diiodotyrosine and L-T_4 decreased after 1 day of culture. The addition of TSH increased the incorporation of ^{131}I from day 3 to day 7 of culture. L-T_4-^{131}I was recovered in free form from the incubation medium and was increased by TSH.

Tong (1964d) reported that perchlorate at a concentration of 2 mm completely eliminated ^{131}I uptake by the cells but did not significantly impair the stimulatory action of TSH on the incorporation of ^{131}I into L-T_4.

Tong (1965) reported that TSH added to isolated cells stimulated 2- to 3-fold incorporation of ^{131}I into L-T_4 and iodotyrosines and a 35% incorporation of ^{14}C leucine into protein. Puromycin depressed the synthesis of protein to less than 2% but did not influence L-T_4 production. Tong suggested that L-T_4 production is not dependent upon increased synthesis of protein.

Dickson (1966) isolated sheep thyroid cells and cultured them in filter wells for 6 days in a medium containing insulin, hydrocortisone, and bovine serum. The cells retained the capacity to concentrate iodide and to form MIT and DIT. When TSH was added there was a 5-fold increase in uptake of ^{131}I and a 2-fold increase of iodotyrosines and L-T_4 formation. CO_2 produced from metabolized glucose-U-^{14}C was doubled. TSH was ineffective when tapazole was added to the medium or when hydrocortisone was omitted.

Kalderon and Wittner (1967) cultured lamb thyroid cells for 190 days. The effect of TSH at various time intervals was studied. It was noted that the ability to form follicle-like spaces persisted up to 30 days but gradually diminished to about 50 days.

D. Function of Isolated Thyroid Cells

Rabin *et al.* (1966) studied the capacity of normal hog isolated thyroid cells to function *in vitro*. Thyroglobulin was synthesized during the first 3 days of *in vitro* growth. Radioactively labeled L-T_3 and L-T_4 were detected during this period. The synthesis of MIT and DIT continued for at least 2 additional days.

IX. Bioassay of TSH in Blood Serum

The methods of assay of TSH in blood serum reported in the previous edition have been superseded largely by immunoassay methods of greater sensitivity (see under pituitary). A number of investigators continue to use the McKenzie method which can distinguish pituitary TSH from LATS and D'Angelo uses the stasis tadpole.

Bottari *et al.* (1963) described a method which utilizes the release of ^{131}I from guinea pig thyroid slices incubated in a nutrient medium in response to the addition of TSH. By taking guinea pigs weighing 600–800 gm and by reducing the initial volume of medium from 1–0.5 ml, Salaman (1964) obtained an uptake of ^{131}I sufficient to allow division of each gland into 18 instead of 8 parts, thus providing more tubes for use in the assay and improving the statistical validity.

Bakke *et al.* (1961) described an acid-salt fractionation method for plasma by which 75% of the protein was removed in the first fraction and 95% in the second fraction without significant loss of TSH.

X. Factors Influencing TSH in Plasma of Various Species

1. *TSH in Human Blood*

Yamazaki *et al.* (1961a,b) detected TSH in the sera of 16 out of 20 euthyroid subjects with a range from 0.084–0.175 mU/ml. They also compared the TSH content of serum of women during labor and from the umbilical cord after delivery in 10 cases, using McKenzie's method. The mean of the maternal blood was 0.124 and 0.112 mU/ml in the cord blood. If TSH does not cross the human placenta, then the fetal hypothalamus and pituitary maintain a concentration of TSH similar to that in the adult.

Pimstone *et al.* (1963) reported a mean normal plasma TSH level of 22.4 mU/100 ml.

D'Angelo (1963a) reported that serum TSH levels were in the normal range in thyrotoxic patients before pituitary removal. In all cases blood TSH could not be detected after hypophysectomy. Yet thyroid function persisted at normal or supranormal levels.

El Kabir *et al.* (1963) reported that patients with mild goitrous lymphoid thyroiditis having an abnormal avid ^{131}I uptake tended to have a depressed serum TSH content.

Wilber and Odell (1965) observed a normal range of serum TSH of 0.6–4 mμg/ml. When 30–45 mg/day of tapazole was administered daily, 4 of 8 subjects showed a rise in serum TSH.

Pinchera *et al.* (1965) detected TSH in the sera of hypothyroid patients with or without a history of thyrotoxicosis. Levels of circulating

TSH ranged between 0.08 and 0.7 mU/ml. None of the sera of euthyroid or hyperthyroid subjects gave TSH responses.

Reichlin and Utiger (1967) followed plasma TSH, PBI, and free L-T$_4$ in hypothyroid patients during therapy with L-T$_4$ increasing from 25 μg/day to 200 μg. As the dose of L-T$_4$ was increased, plasma levels, percentage in the free form, and concentration all increased progressively. At the maximum, free L-T$_4$ increased 12-fold, PBI increased 6-fold, and the percentage of free L-T$_4$ doubled. Plasma TSH levels fell as PBI values rose, and they became undetectable at high PBI levels. Normal levels of TSH with doses of L-T$_4$ of 150–300 μg/day and plasma PBI were between 4.9 and 8.2 μg/100 ml of plasma. It was not possible to determine whether it was free or total L-T$_4$ which was the regulator of TSH secretion.

Sawin and McHugh (1966) described a patient who was believed to lack TSH secretion as indicated by plasma TSH of <1 mμg/ml.

2. TSH in Plasma of the Mouse

Bates and Garrison (1961) thyroidectomized mice. After 12–18 months, the mean blood level was 33 mU/ml. A ratio of TSH/ml of blood times 40 indicated the amount of TSH in the pituitary. When L-T$_4$ was injected, the blood level dropped to 10–30% of the starting level.

Condliffe et al. (1965) studied the TSH in the blood of mice bearing transplantable TSH-secreting tumors (TiT). The plasma and tumor TSH was found to behave similarly by various chemical procedures.

3. TSH in Plasma of the Rat

D'Angelo (1961) reported the TSH in the serum of rats ranged from 67–100 mU/100 ml with a consistent tendency for higher values in older animals with a mean 82.4 $\pm$ 9.4 mU/100 ml of serum. Rats on propylthiouracil showed consistently elevated levels of TSH with a mean of 140 $\pm$ 9 mU/100 ml of serum up to 60 days. Longer treatment further increased the level. After goitrogen withdrawal, the serum TSH level declined and then returned to about normal after 20 days.

Kraicer et al. (1963) reported that neck surgery performed under ether anesthesia had no effect on AP-TSH but produced a 30–40% fall in plasma TSH within 15 minutes, followed by a return to normal within 12 hours. Adrenalectomy had no effect on pituitary or plasma TSH levels.

Bakke and Lawrence (1964) gave rats a goitrogen in the water. This produced a progressive increase in serum TSH over a year period. Either physiological or toxic doses of DL-T$_4$ caused a depression of serum TSH as early as 1 hour after administration.

Good *et al.* (1965) reported that the administration of salicylate, DNP, and V-resorcylate significantly depressed plasma TSH and PBI. It was suggested that these drugs increase the circulation of free-L-T_4 in spite of decreased PBI and this controls the negative feedback system.

Early studies had indicated that 2,4-dinitrophenol (DNP) caused TSH secretion to decline in the face of lowered circulating L-T_4. Since these observations were based on indirect measurements on thyroid function, Bakke and Lawrence (1965a) directly measured serum and pituitary levels following DNP administration to rats. They observed no change in thyroid weight or pituitary or serum TSH titers during 1–8 days of treatment. It did not impair TSH secretion.

After 30 days of DNP, a variable decrease in TSH synthesis occurred without a corresponding decrease in pituitary or serum TSH.

Van Rees *et al.* (1965) noted a decrease of TSH in the serum of castrate male rats. Testosterone propionate (TP) increased the serum TSH of castrate rats.

Ducommun *et al.* (1966) studied the effect of various stimuli on the plasma TSH of male rats by the McKenzie method. Handling, transferring from one room to another, and intraperitoneal injections lead to a rapid decrease of plasma TSH within 15 minutes. In rats kept at 22°C, with rapid decapitation at 7 AM, plasma levels varied from 25–30 mU/100 ml.

D'Angelo (1966) reported that normal aging female rats showed only slight fluctuations in blood TSH. Castration in either sex resulted in a significant decrease in serum TSH.

Van Rees (1966) determined the TSH level of the blood of thyroidec-tomized rats after treatment for 2 weeks of L-T_3 or T_4. There was a decrease in blood TSH.

Singh *et al.* (1967) determined the diurnal variation in the TSH content of the plasma of adult female rats. The plasma TSH level increased gradually from 0.72 mU/ml at 3 AM to a peak of 1.02 mU/ml at 3 PM, then declined.

Boccabella and Alger (1967) determined the TSH serum levels of rats at various stages of the estrus cycle by the McKenzie method. The highest level of 42.2 mU/100 ml was observed in early estrus. Other stages were as follows: diestrus 22.0, proestrus 13.7, late estrus 22.7, and metestrus 16.2. It was suggested that enhanced TSH secretion during early estrus is partially responsible for increases in thyroidal-^{131}I uptake in late estrus.

Ducommun *et al.* (1967) noted that chronic stress of minor intensity prevented the usual inhibition of TSH secretion induced by an acute stressing procedure. Chronic stress leads to increased resting levels of plasma TSH in the rat.

The secretion of TSH is controlled by the serum concentration of thyroid hormones. To determine whether iodide might also play a direct role, Abbassi and McKenzie (1967) measured the concentration of TSH in the blood and AP of rats injected with iodide after surgical thyroidectomy or administration of goitrogens. Iodide failed to decrease TSH levels. When rats given propylthiouracil and low-iodine diet were injected with iodide, there was significantly less increase in thyroid weight, despite unchanged serum and AP TSH concentrations. It is suggested that iodide exerts a direct effect on the thyroid gland.

Panda and Turner (1967b) reported that mature female rats maintained at 26°C had a plasma TSH level of 0.94 mU/ml. After 10 days of thyroidectomy, the plasma increased to 2.15 mU/ml, and to 2.81 after 20 days. After 25 days of thyroidectomy L-T_4 at a level of 2.5 μg/100 gm body weight was injected for 1, 3, and 5 days. The plasma level was reduced to 1.59, 1.48, and 1.06 mU/ml, respectively. When rats held at 26°C were changed to 4.4°C for 10 and 20 days, the plasma TSH increased to 2.15 and 2.69 mU/ml, respectively. The combined effect of thyroidectomy and 4.4°C for 10 and 20 days, caused the plasma TSH to increase to 4.37 after 10 days, then decline to 2.4 mU/ml after 20 days. When such rats were returned to 26°C for 4 days, the plasma level declined to 1.44 mU/ml.

Panda and Turner (1967a) determined the plasma TSH of female rats from weaning time (24 days) up to 110 days of age. The plasma TSH at 24 days was 0.32 mU/ml, then increased gradually to 1.18 mU/ml at 95 days followed by a slight decline to 110 days.

4. TSH in Plasma of the Guinea Pig

D'Angelo (1967) fed late pregnant guinea pigs propylthiouracil (PTU) for several weeks and noted a progressive fetal thyroid hyperplasia (13- to 50-fold). TSH concentrations of plasma and pituitary were significantly elevated after birth. Maternal titers of plasma TSH were also increased. PTU administered during the first 2 weeks postpartum failed to alter TSH levels of blood and pituitary.

Injection of L-T_3 or L-T_4 at high dosage levels into pregnant animals reduced TSH levels in the pituitary. Injection of L-T_4 during the first week in the young suppressed TSH secretion.

D'Angelo (1966) reported that blood levels of TSH in guinea pigs of increasing age and after ovariectomy were too low to be detected. When propylthiouracil (PTU) was given in the food (0.1%) for 2–5 months, serum TSH was elevated markedly (110–120 mU/100 ml).

5. *TSH in Plasma of the Rabbit*

Brown-Grant *et al.* (1954) reported inhibition of TSH release in the rabbit as a result of stressful procedures.

El Kabir (1962), using the Bottari *et al.* (1963) method, found that after thyroidectomy in the rabbit, the plasma TSH concentration remained low for about 10 days before rising to a high level that was maintained for at least 4 weeks.

XI. Abnormal Factor in Serum in Hyperthyroidism (LATS)

In the assay of TSH by methods of Adams and Purves (1957a) and McKenzie (1958) guinea pigs and mice previously injected with ^{131}I show a maximum increase in serum ^{131}I after an interval of 2–3 hours when TSH is administered. In the assay of serum from thyrotoxic patients Adams (1958) noted that the maximum response did not occur until after 16 hours. When USP thyrotropin is added to serum that elicits the abnormal TSH response, the time course of the response induced by the mixture indicates that the two components act independently. It was suggested that the abnormal responses only to sera from cases of thyrotoxicosis makes it seem likely that the abnormal TSH has relationship to this disorder.

McKenzie (1958) noted a delayed response in mice with sera from 9 of 11 thyrotoxic patients and with sera from 3 patients not thyrotoxic. Sera from 4 myxedematous, 2 euthyroid, and 2 thyrotoxic individuals gave no delayed response.

Munro (1959) assayed the serum from 32 patients by the McKenzie method. The 2-hour response was observed in 3 of 6 patients with hypothyroidism, in 1 of 3 patients with simple or nontoxic goiter, and in 1 of 9 normal subjects. Six of 11 patients with hyperthyroidism gave the delayed response, and 1 of 9 normal subjects. Serum from 7 normal subjects did not give either response.

McKenzie (1960b) reported that mice administered thyroid to block TSH secretion showed an increased thyroidal-^{131}I by sera from patients with hyperthyroidism when given 12 hours before ^{131}I injection. TSH produced a maximal increase in ^{131}I uptake when administered 4 hours before ^{131}I. Thus a delayed response both in ^{131}I uptake and release is shown by the sera in hyperthyroidism.

Several additional reports on the presence of this factor have been made (Yamazaki *et al.*, 1961a; Major and Munro, 1960; Pimstone *et al.*, 1963; Noguchi *et al.*, 1964; Pinchera *et al.*, 1965).

McKenzie (1965, 1967) and Adams (1965) have reviewed the role of LATS in the pathogenesis of Graves' disease.

Noguchi *et al.* (1964) reported LATS in serum of 54 of 95 patients with hyperthyroidism. The level of LATS in such patients showed a tendency to decrease after treatment with goitrogens or thyroidectomy, but not after 24 hours.

Kriss et al. (1964) reported oral corticosteroid therapy resulted in a marked fall in plasma LATS, but relapse occurred upon drug withdrawal.

Snyder et al. (1964) reported that 2 of 3 patients showed a reduction in LATS concentration in plasma upon prednisone treatment.

Adams and Kennedy (1965) reported a thyrotoxic patient with a high level of LATS in her serum. It was shown also that her serum contained a high level of TSH. After the patient received 0.4 mg/day of L-T_4 for 2 weeks there was no change in the LATS content but TSH was no longer detectable.

Mosier (1965) detected LATS in the sera of 4 mongoloid females without hyperthyroidism. Three patients had minimal thyroid enlargement.

McCullagh et al. (1960) cited several references concerning the persistence of thyroid function after hypophysectomy. They reported upon a patient who developed hyperthyroidism after section of the stalk and after AP deficiency was evident.

Furth et al. (1962) reported that normal thyroid function persisted in a group of hyperthyroid patients following total surgical hypophysectomy.

Burke (1967b) described a case of a 44-year-old woman in whom hyperthyroidism developed 6 months after subtotal hypophysectomy and pituitary irradiation for a chromophobe adenoma. It was suggested that the production of LATS was the cause.

A. ASSAY OF LATS

McKenzie (1960a) produced evidence for the presence of LATS in the serum of patients with hyperthyroidism by injecting their serum intravenously into mice fed desiccated thyroid. An increased uptake of ^{131}I was observed if the serum was administered 12 hours prior to the iodine. This compares with 4 hours for maximum uptake when TSH was administered.

Adams (1961) presented data showing that the dose-response line for LATS is steeper than for TSH and that the maximal response attainable is much higher. These findings were in accord with the concept that the action of LATS is similar to that of a low concentration of TSH maintained for a long time.

Pimstone et al. (1963) conducted parallel assays of TSH, LATS, and EPS in the serum of patients. Evidence was presented that EPS and

LATS are not the same substance, and further, that the assay of TSH in the presence of LATS may not be valid.

In a further study (Pimstone *et al.*, 1964) these hormones were assayed in plasma and tissue samples from euthyroid and hyperthyroid subjects with and without exophthalmos. In all cases of exophthalmos plasma LATS was elevated, TSH and EPS were not consistently found. In the plasma of some nonexophthalmic patients LATS was also found.

Kriss *et al.* (1964) reported that the TSH response was greatest after 3 hours and very slight after 24 hours. LATS induced a response at 3 hours about equal to TSH but at 24 hours was 3- to 6-fold higher and was still measured at 48 hours. They suggest the 24-hour interval in the assay of LATS.

McKenzie and Williamson (1966) describe the improvement in the assay of LATS as a result of 8 years of experience. The present method used is quicker and more efficient, and about 150 mice may be used in one assay.

Mason *et al.* (1967) modified the assay for TSH described by Good and Stenhouse (1966) for LATS. Their design eliminates the factors of animal and day variation and the residual effects of the initial test dose by use of mice on 2 successive days. Linearity of the dose-response curve was observed over the range of 6.25–400 mU of standard.

McKenzie (1967) Method. Mice maintained on a low-iodine diet for 10 days are injected with 15 μCi ^{125}I and 10 μg Na L-T$_4$. Four days later 0.1 ml of blood is obtained by a retroorbital puncture immediately before the intravenous injection of the test substance and 2 and 9 hours later. Radioactivity in the blood is then measured. Radioactivity which is maximal at 2 hours is indicative of TSH; whereas LATS causes an increase which is greater at 9 hours. Improvements in the statistical analysis of the assay results are presented in the papers cited above.

Lepp and Oliner (1967a) presented data indicating that the baby chick does not respond to LATS in doses 30-fold above that causing a mouse response. No effect was noted at 3, 7, or 18 hours after administration.

B. STANDARD FOR LONG-ACTING THYROID STIMULATOR (LATS)

Dorrington and Munro (1964) have prepared a dry powdered standard for the long-acting thyroid stimulator (LATS). It has been shown to be stable over a period of 18 months. The material was obtained from a patient with thyrotoxicosis. A unit was defined as the amount of LATS contained in 1 ml of original serum. Each ampoule contained 4.0 ml and after freeze-drying contained 236 mg of powder containing 40 mU LATS standard.

C. Half-Life of LATS Compared to TSH

Adams (1960) compared the $t_{1/2}$ of LATS and TSH in rats. LATS had a $t_{1/2}$ of 7.5 hours whereas TSH had fallen to less than 5% of the 2-minute level.

McKenzie (1961) made a similar comparison of the two preparations, using mice. While TSH had a very short $t_{1/2}$, LATS was still high after 8 hours.

D. Physiological Activity of LATS

Munro (1959) and Adams (1961) showed that LATS is active in hypophysectomized mice. It does not act on the thyroid indirectly stimulating the pituitary to secrete TSH.

Scott et al. (1966) reported that LATS increased the uptake and oxidation of glucose and enhanced the formation of lactate by sheep thyroid slices comparable to TSH. It also increased phospholipogenesis, but the specificity of individual phospholipid responses may be different from responses to TSH. In contrast to TSH, LATS increased the labeling of neutral lipids from glucose-U-^{14}C although their effect on decreasing the ratio of radioactive triglyceride/diglyceride were similar.

Shishiba et al. (1967) observed that intracellular colloid droplets were induced in mice by LATS in a manner qualitatively indistinguish-able from the effect of TSH, but with a longer latency. Both LATS and TSH induced release of thyroidal-^{131}I, but again LATS showed a longer latency period.

E. Heat Stability of LATS

McGiven et al. (1965) heated human antibody against thyroglobulin at 70°C for 10 minutes. Its potency was reduced to 2% of the initial value. The potency of LATS was similarly reduced to less than 10% by this treatment. Human TSH was more stable; its potency was reduced only to 45%. The antibody had a $t_{1/2}$ of 10.2 hours.

F. Chemical Identity of LATS

LATS found in the serum of some thyrotoxic patients is associated with the γ-globulin fraction of serum protein (Purves and Adams, 1961; Adams and Kennedy, 1962; McKenzie, 1962). TSH is readily separable from the serum γ-globulins by procedures such as that of Bates et al. (1959a). It has not been possible to extract TSH from sera containing LATS (Purves and Adams, 1961) or to separate LATS from γ-globulins. McGiven et al. (1965) suggested that LATS is a γ-globulin.

Kriss et al. (1964) described a method for the separation of LATS from plasma with an 8-fold increase in purity. A single protein was identified as a 7 S γ-globulin. Incubation of LATS with antihuman 7 S antibody destroyed its biological activity.

Miyai and Werner (1966) increased the potency of LATS 30–37 times over the original sera by means of column chromatography. The protein was identified as YG globulin. Activity was neutralized by anti-YG globulin serum, but not by YA or YM serum.

G. Effect of LATS on TSH Antiserum

McKenzie and Fishman (1960) prepared antiserum to bovine TSH. Although it inhibited the endogenous TSH of patients with myxedema, it did not inhibit LATS. This was taken to indicate that TSH is dissimilar to LATS. Werner and Tierney (1961), however, reported that LATS could be neutralized by TSH antiserum, but about 10 times as much was required.

Beall and Solomon (1966) tested the hypothesis that LATS had antibody function. It was not possible to transfer LATS activity to new immunoglobulin G molecules in a dialysis bath, thus supporting the idea that LATS is an integral part of the molecule. LATS was consistently removed from serum by a thyroid microsomal fraction and eluted from the microsomes under conditions appropriate for dissociation of antigen-antibody complexes. These findings were consistent with the hypothesis that LATS is an antibody.

Kohler et al. (1967) tested the possibility that a complete complement system might be necessary for response to LATS in mice. DBA/2 mice which have a total absence of the fifth component of complement were injected with decomplemented plasma known to contain LATS. The presence of a complete complement system was not necessary for LATS activity, and the response was not increased by passive transfer of a complete complement source.

H. Absorption of LATS by Thyroid Microsomes

Dorrington et al. (1966) reported that LATS had the ability to be absorbed by the endoplasmic reticulum of microsomes of human thyroid tissue. In contrast it failed to absorb human TSH.

Adams and Kennedy (1967) noted that when an extract of the thyroid gland was added to serum containing LATS it was neutralized to varying degrees. When a thyrotoxic serum negative for LATS was added to a highly potent LATS serum, the neutralization by the thyroid extract was inhibited. This material has been called LATS protector. It is present in the γ-globulin fraction. It was not found in normal patients or in 4 with myxedema. It was found in a greater proportion of thyrotoxic sera than was LATS.

Burke (1967a) further studied the interaction of LATS by thyroid microsomes. It was observed that preincubation of thyroid microsomes with TSH significantly limits their inhibition of LATS-Ig G activity. TSH-induced modification of microsomal LATS inhibition is not correlated with the effect on LATS-Ig G absorption. The magnitude of microsomal LATS-Ig G absorption is inconsistent with the small percentage of total Ig G presumably represented by LATS.

I. SOURCE OF LATS SECRETION

McKenzie and Gordon (1965) incubated the white blood cells from a patient with a high LATS titer in her blood. The medium (199) contained 10% fetal calf serum and phytohemagglutinin which is said to stimulate γ-globulin synthesis *in vitro*. It was believed that LATS was synthesized and ^{14}C-labeled amino acids were incorporated.

Miyai *et al.* (1967) cultured peripheral lymphocytes obtained from patients with Graves' disease with phytohemagglutinin. LATS-like activity was detected in the culture media by assay. The activity was found in the YG globulin fraction and was neutralized with anti-YG globulin serum.

XII. Bioassay of TSH in Urine

Gorbman (1945) described a method for the ultrafiltration of urine to recover excreted hypophyseal hormones. After filtration, the 2% collodion membrane is dissolved in alcohol–ether and the dried residue taken up in saline for assay. Kriss and Greenspan (1954) further purified the extract by precipitation with 40% alcohol and reprecipitation with 80% alcohol.

Greenspan and Lew (1959), using the Gorbman (1945) method, reported that the ultrafiltrate residue contained a nonhypophyseal factor which stimulated ^{32}P uptake by the chick thyroid as well as a factor which interferes with the effect of TSH on the release of thyroidal-^{131}I in the chick. They suggested that data on urine levels of TSH reported by Henry and Blocke-Michel (1955) and Currie *et al.* (1956) may have to be corrected for the presence of the interfering substance.

TSH in Urine. The estimation of TSH in urine of normal and pathological cases appears to be of doubtful value at this time. Students of the problem include Savoie (1952), Kriss and Greenspan (1954), Henry and Bloche-Michel (1955), Bloche-Michel and Henry (1955), Currie *et al.* (1956), and Greenspan and Lew (1959).

Burger *et al.* (1965) reported equivocal evidence of TSH in urine. Hennen (1966) and Burger (1967a) reported that HCG showed TSH activity by the McKenzie method similar to bovine TSH. It did not neutralize the antibodies of human TSH or the antibodies against HCG.

Burger (1967b) tested urine extracts from pregnant women and found only a small dose response. It was suggested that urinary TSH is bound to urinary proteins, possibly to uromucoid protein which interferes with its biological activity but is regained by purification.

XIII. TSH in Human Placenta

Hennen (1966) reported evidence of TSH in human placental extract, but Burger (1967a) was not able to confirm it by his extraction procedure.

REFERENCES

Abbassi, V., and McKenzie, J. M. (1967). *Endocrinology* **81**, 871.
Adams, D. D. (1958). *J. Clin. Endocrinol. Metab.* **18**, 699.
Adams, D. D. (1960). *Endocrinology* **66**, 658.
Adams, D. D. (1961). *J. Clin. Endocrinol. Metab.* **21**, 799.
Adams, D. D. (1965). *Brit. Med. J.* **1**, 1015.
Adams, D. D., and Kennedy, T. H. (1962). *Proc. Univ. Otago Med. School* **40**, 6.
Adams, D. D., and Kennedy, T. H. (1965). *J. Clin. Endocrinol. Metab.* **25**, 571.
Adams, D. D., and Kennedy, T. H. (1967). *J. Clin. Endocrinol. Metab.* **27**, 173.
Adams, D. D., and Purves, H. D. (1957a). *Can. J. Biochem. Physiol.* **35**, 993.
Adams, D. D., and Purves, H. D. (1957b). *Metab. Clin. Exptl.* **6**, 26.
Albert, A. (1945). *Ann. N.Y. Acad. Sci.* **50**, 466.
Adersson, B., Ekman, L., Gale, C.C., and Sundsten, J. W. (1962). *Acta Physiol. Scand.* **54**, 191.
Andersson, B., Ekman, L., Gale, C. C., and Sundsten, J. W. (1963a). *Acta Physiol. Scand.* **59**, 12.
Andersson, B., Gale, C. C., and Ohga, A. (1963b). *Acta Physiol. Scand.* **59**, 67.
Averill, R. L. W., and Kennedy, T. H. (1967). *Endocrinology* **81**, 113.
Averill, R. L. W., and Salaman, D. F. (1967). *Endocrinology* **81**, 173.
Averill, R. L. W., Purves, H. D., and Sirett, N. E. (1961). *Endocrinology* **69**, 735.
Bakke, J. L. (1965). *J. Clin. Endocrinol. Metab.* **25**, 545.
Bakke, J. L., and Lawrence, N. (1958). *Clin. Res.* **6**, 244.
Bakke, J. L., and Lawrence, N. (1959). *J. Clin. Endocrinol. Metab.* **19**, 35.
Bakke, J. L., and Lawrence, N. (1962). *Endocrinology* **71**, 43.
Bakke, J. L., and Lawrence, N. (1964). *Acta Endocrinol.* **46**, 111.
Bakke, J. L., and Lawrence, N. (1965a). *Endocrinology* **77**, 382.
Bakke, J. L., and Lawrence, B. (1965b). *Metabolism* **14**, 841.
Bakke, J. L., Roy, S., and Lawrence, N. (1960). *Clin. Res.* **8**, 139.
Bakke, J. L., Heideman, N. L., Jr., Lawrence, N. L., and Wiberg, C. (1957). *Endocrinology* **61**, 352.
Bakke, J. L., Lawrence, N., Arnett, F., and MacFadden, W. (1961). *J. Clin. Endocrinol. Metab.* **21**, 1280.
Bakke, J. L., Lawrence, N., and Roy, S. (1962). *J. Clin. Endocrinol. Metab.* **22**, 352.

Bakke, J. L., Kammer, H., and Lawrence, N. (1964). *J. Clin. Endocrinol. Metab.* **24**, 281.

Balasubramaniam, K., Deiss, W. P., Jr., Tan, W. C., and Powell, R. C. (1965). *Endocrinology* **77**, 54.

Baschieri, L., Negri, M., de Luca, F., Sereno, L., and Cramarossa, J. (1962). *Experientia* **18**, 144.

Bates, R. W., and Condliffe, P. G. (1960). *Recent Progr. Hormone Res.* **16**, 309.

Bates, R. W., and Cornfield, J. (1957). *Endocrinology* **60**, 225.

Bates, R. W., and Garrison, M. M. (1961). *Proc. Soc. Exptl. Biol. Med.* **106**, 435.

Bates, R. W., and Warren, L. (1963). *Endocrinology* **73**, 1.

Bates, R. W., Albert A., and Condliffe, P. G. (1959a). *Endocrinology* **65**, 860.

Bates, R. W., Garrison, M. M., and Howard, T. B. (1959b). *Endocrinology* **65**, 7.

Beall, G. N., and Solomon, D. H. (1966). *J. Clin. Endocrinol. Metab.* **26**, 1382.

Beck, J. C., McKenzie, J. M., Fishman, J., Gosselin, L., and McGarry, E. E. (1962). *Ciba Found. Colloq. Endocrinol.* **14**, 238.

Becktel, J. M. (1967). *Proc. Soc. Exptl. Biol. Med.* **124**, 999.

Björkman, S. E., Denneberg, T., and Hedenskog, I. (1961). *Acta Endocrinol.* **38**, 577.

Bloche-Michel, H., and Henry, R. (1955). *Ann. Endocrinol. (Paris)* **16**, 268.

Boccabella, A. V., and Alger, E. A. (1967). *Endocrinology* **81**, 121.

Bogdanove, E. M., and Halmi, N. S. (1953). *Endocrinology* **53**, 274.

Bottari, P. M., Donovan, B. T., and El Kabir, D. J. (1963). *J. Physiol. (London)* **169**, 278.

Bowers, C. Y., Segaloff, A., and Brown, B. (1959). *Endocrinology* **65**, 882.

Bowers, C. Y., Redding, T. W., and Schally, A. V. (1964). *Endocrinology* **74**, 559.

Bowers, C. Y., Redding, T. W., and Schally, A. V. (1965). *Endocrinology* **77**, 609.

Bowers, C. Y., Schally, A. V., Reynolds, G. A., and Hawley, W. D. (1967). *Endocrinology* **81**, 741.

Brown, J. R., and Munro, D. S. (1967). *J. Endocrinol.* **38**, 439.

Brown-Grant, K., Harris, G. W., and Riechlin, S. (1954). *J. Physiol.* **126**, 41.

Brunish, R., Hayashi, K., and Hayashi, J. (1962). *Arch. Biochem. Biophys.* **98**, 135.

Burger, A. (1967a). *Acta Endocrinol.* **55**, 587.

Burger, A. (1967b). *Acta Endocrinol.* **55**, 600.

Burger, A., Studer, H., and Wyss, F. (1965). *In* "Current Topics of Thyroid Research" (C. Cassano and M. Andreoli, eds.), p. 624. Academic Press, New York.

Burke, G. (1967a). *J. Clin. Endocrinol. Metab.* **27**, 1095.

Burke, G. (1967b). *J. Clin. Endocrinol. Metab.* **27**, 1161.

Canadell, J. M., and Barraquer, J. (1956). *Ann. Endocrinol. (Paris)* **17**, 369.

Cambell, H. J., George, R., and Harris, G. W. (1960). *J. Physiol. (London)* **152**, 527.

Carsten, M. E., and Pierce, J. G. (1960). *J. Biol. Chem.* **235**, 78.

Cavalieri, R. R., and Searle, G. L. (1967). *Proc. Soc. Exptl. Biol. Med.* **126**, 459.

Cehovic, G. (1962). *Compt. Rend. Acad. Sci.* **254**, 1872.

Clayton, J. A., and Szego, C. M. (1967). *Endocrinology* **80**, 689.

Condliffe, P. G. (1963). *Endocrinology* **72**, 893.

Condliffe, P. G., and Bates, R. W. (1956). *J. Biol. Chem.* **223**, 843.

Condliffe, P. G., and Bates, R. W. (1957). *Arch. Biochem. Biophys.* **68**, 229.

Condliffe, P. G., and Jakoby, W. B. (1967). *Endocrinology* **80**, 203.

Condliffe, P. G., Bates, R. W., and Fraps, R. M. (1959). *Biochem. Biophys. Acta* **34**, 430.

Condliffe, P. G., Bates, R. W., Fontaine, Y. A., and Garrison, M. (1965). *Endocrinology* **77**, 745.

Courier, R., and Cehovic, G. (1960). *Compt. Rend. Acad. Sci.* **251**, 832.

Crenshaw, W. W., Pipes, G. W., Ruppert, H. L., Jr., and Turner, C. W. (1957). *Missouri, Univ. Agr. Expt. Sta. Res. Bull.* **621**.

Currie, H. R., Cruickshank, B., Dekanski, J. B., Hewett, C. L., and McGirr, E. M. (1956). *Scot. Med. J.* **1**, 355.

D'Angelo, S. A. (1958). *J. Endocrinol.* **17**, 286.

D'Angelo, S. A. (1961). *Endocrinology* **69**, 834.

D'Angelo, S. A. (1963a). *J. Clin. Endocrinol. Metab.* **23**, 229.

D'Angelo, S. A. (1963b). *In* "Advances in Neuroendocrinology" (A. V. Nalbandov, ed.), Chapter 6. Univ. of Illinois Press, Urbana, Illinois.

D'Angelo, S. A. (1966). *Endocrinology* **78**, 1230.

D'Angelo, S. A. (1967). *Endocrinology* **81**, 132.

D'Angelo, S. A., and Snyder, J. (1963). *Endocrinology* **73**, 75.

D'Angelo, S. A., Snyder, J., and Grodin, J. M. (1964). *Endocrinology* **75**, 417.

Debons, A. F., and Pittman, J. A. (1962). *Endocrinology* **70**, 937.

Dedman, M. L., Fawcett, J. S., and Morris, C. J. O. R. (1967). *J. Endocrinol.* **39**, 197.

De Groot, L. J., and Dunn, A. D. (1966). *Endocrinology* **78**, 1032.

Deiss, W. P., O'Shaughnessy, P. J., and Wynn, J. O. (1959). *J. Clin. Invest.* **38**, 334.

Deiss, W. P., Balasurbramaniam, K., Peake, R. L., Starrett, J. A., and Powell, R. C. (1966). *Endocrinology* **79**, 19.

de Jong, W., and Moll, J. (1965). *Acta Endocrinol.* **48**, 522.

Der Kindern, P. J., Houtstra-Lanz, M., and Schwarz, F. (1960). *J. Clin. Endocrinol. Metab.* **20**, 712.

Desbarats-Schönbaum, M. L., Sellers, E. A., Belzile, A., and Schönbaum, E. (1967). *Acta Endocrinol.* **54**, 282.

Dickson, J. A. (1966). *Endocrinology* **79**, 721.

Dingledine, W. S., and Egdahl, R. H. (1967). *Metabolism* **16**, 1042.

Dobyns, B. M. (1946). *Surg. Gynecol. Obstet.* **82**, 290.

Dobyns, B. M., and Steelman, S. L. (1953). *Endocrinology* **37**, 389.

Dobyns, B. M., and Wilson, L. A. (1954). *J. Clin. Endocrinol. Metab.* **14**, 1393.

Dobyns, B. M., Wright, A., and Wilson, L. (1961). *J. Clin. Endocrinol. Metab.* **21**, 648.

Dorrington, K. J., and Munro, D. S. (1964). *J. Endocrinol.* **31**, 21.

Dorrington, K. J., Carneiro, L., and Munro, D. S. (1966). *J. Endocrinol.* **34**, 133.

Ducommun, P., Sakiz, E., and Guillemin, R. (1965). *Endocrinology* **77**, 792.

Ducommun, P., Sakiz, E., and Guillemin, R. (1966). *Proc. Soc. Exptl. Biol. Med.* **121**, 921.

Ducommun, P., Vale, W., Sakiz, E., and Guillemin, R. (1967). *Endocrinology* **80**, 953.

El Kabir, D. J. (1962). *Nature* **194**, 688.

El Kabir, D. J., Doniach, D., and Turner-Warwick, R. (1963). *J. Clin. Endocrinol. Metab.* **23**, 510.

Ellis, S. (1958). *J. Biol. Chem.* **233**, 63.

Elrick, H., Yearwood-Drayton, V., Arai, Y., Leaver, F., and Morris, H. G. (1963). *J. Clin. Endocrinol. Metab.* **23**, 694.

Elrick, H., Yearwood-Drayton, V., Arai, Y., and Morris, H. G. (1964). *J. Clin. Endocrinol. Metab.* **24**, 910.

Euler, C. von, and Holmgren, B. (1956). *J. Physiol. (London)* **131**, 125.

Florsheim, W. H. (1959). *Proc. Soc. Exptl. Biol. Med.* **100**, 73.

Florsheim, W. H., Austin, N. S., and Velcoff, S. M. (1963). *Endocrinology* **72**, 817.

Freinkel, N. (1960). *Endocrinology* **66**, 851.

Frienkel, N. (1961). *J. Clin. Invest.* **40**, 476.

Furth, E. D., Becker, D. V., Ray, B. S., and Kane, J. W. (1962). *J. Clin. Endocrinol. Metab.* **22**, 518.

Garcia, A. M., and Selenkow, H. A. (1964). *Proc. Soc. Exptl. Biol. Med.* **116**, 467.

Gedda, P. O. (1960). *Acta Endocrinol. Suppl.* **56**.

Gedda, P. O. (1964). *Acta Endocrinol.* **45**, 197.

Good, B. F., and Stenhouse, N. S. (1966). *Endocrinology* **78**, 429.

Good, B. F., Hetzel, B. S., and Hogg, B. M. (1965). *Endocrinology* **77**, 674.

Gorbman, A. (1945). *Endocrinology* **37**, 177.

Graig, F. A. (1967). *Endocrinology* **81**, 708.

Greenspan, F. S., and Lew, W. (1959). *Endocrinology* **64**, 160.

Greer, M. A. (1951). *Proc. Soc. Exptl. Biol. Med.* **77**, 603.

Greer, M. A., Scow, R. O., and Grobstein, C. (1953). *Proc. Soc. Exptl. Biol. Med.* **82**, 28.

Greer, M. A., Matsuda, K., and Stott, A. K. (1966). *Endocrinology* **78**, 389.

Guillemin, R. (1967). *Ann. Rev. Physiol.* **29**, 313.

Guillemin, R., and Sakiz, E. (1965). *Nature (London)* **207**, 297.

Guillemin, R., Yamazaki, E., Jutisz, M., and Sakiz, E. (1962). *Compt. Rend. Acad. Sci.* **255**, 1018.

Guillemin, R., Yamazaki, E., Gard, D. A., Jutisz, M., and Sakiz, E. (1963). *Endocrinology* **73**, 564.

Guillemin, R., Sakiz, E., and Ward, D. N. (1965a). *Proc. Soc. Exptl. Biol. Med.* **118**, 1132.

Guillemin, R., Ward, D. N., and Sakiz, E. (1965b). *Proc. Soc. Exptl. Biol. Med.* **120**. 256,

Harris, G. W., and Woods, J. W. (1958). *J. Physiol. (London)* **143**, 246.

Hartree, A. S., Butt, W. R., and Kirkham, K. E. (1964). *J. Endocrinol.* **29**, 61.

Hayashida, T., Rankin, R., McCleeland, G., and Contopoulos, A. N. (1961). *Endocrinology* **69**, 1036.

Haynie, T. P., Winzler, R. J., Matovinovic, J., Carr, E. A., Jr., and Beierwaltes, W. H. (1962). *Endocrinology* **71**, 782.

Hays, M. T., Solomon, D. H., and Beall, G. N. (1967). *J. Clin. Endocrinol. Metab.* **27**, 1540.

Heideman, M. L., Jr., Bakke, J. L., and Lawrence, N. L. (1959). *Arch. Biochem. Biophys.* **82**, 62.

Heideman, M. L., Jr., Levy, R. P., McGuire, W. L., and Shipley, R. A. (1965). *Endocrinology* **76**, 828.

Heideman, M. L., Jr., McGuire, W. L., Levy, R. P., and Shipley, R. A. (1966). *Proc. Soc. Exptl. Biol. Med.* **122**, 795.

Hendrich, C. E., and Turner, C. W. (1963). *Poultry Sci.* **42**, 1190.

Hendrich, C. E., and Turner, C. W. (1964). *Proc. Soc. Exptl. Biol. Med.* **117**, 218.

Hendrich, C. E., and Turner, C. W. (1967). *Proc. Soc. Exptl. Biol. Med.* **124**, 616.

Hennen, G. (1966). *Ann. Endocrinol. (Paris)* **27**, 242.

Hennen, G. (1967). *J. Clin. Endocrinol. Metab.* **27**, 610.

Hennen, G., Winand, R., and Nizet, H. (1965). *In* "Current Topics in Thyroid Research" (C. Cassano and M. Andreoli, eds.), p. 464. Academic Press, New York.

Henry, R., and Bloche-Michel, H. (1955). *Ann. Endocrinol. (Paris)* **16**, 258.

Hershman, J. M. (1967a). *Endocrinology* **80**, 302.

Hershman, J. M. (1967b). *Metabolism* **16**, 279.

Horster, F. A., and Klein, E. (1964). *Acta Endocrinol.* **46**, 95.

Hung, W., Winship, T., Bowen, K., and Houck, J. C. (1966). *Proc. Soc. Exptl. Biol. Med.* **122**, 121.

Hung, W., Winship, T., Bowen, K., and Houck, J. C. (1967). *Proc. Soc. Exptl. Biol. Med.* **125**, 610.

Irie, M., and Slingerland, D. W. (1963). *Endocrinology* **73**, 265.

Isaacs, G. H., and Rosenberg, I. N. (1967). *Endocrinology* **81**, 981.

Jungas, R. L., and Ball, E. G. (1962). *Endocrinology* **71**, 68.

Justisz, M., de la Llosa, P., Sakiz, E., Yamazaki, E., and Guillemin, R. (1963). *Compt. Rend. Soc. Biol.* **157**, 235.

Kalderon, A. E., and Wittner, M. (1967). *Endocrinology* **80**, 797.

Kendall, J. W. (1962). *Endocrinology* **71**, 452.

Kerkof, P. R., and Chaikoff, I. L. (1966). *Endocrinology* **78**, 1177.

Kerkof, P. R., Long, P. J., and Chaikoff, I. L. (1964a). *Endocrinology* **74**, 170.

Kerkof, P. R., Raghupathy, E., and Chaikoff, I. L. (1964b). *Endocrinology* **75**, 537.

Khazin, A., and Reichlin, S. (1961). *Endocrinology* **68**, 914.

Kirkham, K. E. (1962). *J. Endocrinol.* **25**, 259.

Klitgaard, H. M., Palay, H., and Meade, R. C. (1963). *Federation Proc.* **22**, 622.

Klitgaard, H. M., Meade, R. C., Trocke, D. K., Palay, H. J., and Lorscheider, F. L. (1965). *Proc. Soc. Exptl. Biol. Med.* **119**, 334.

Kogl, F., and van Deenen, L. L. M. (1961). *Acta Endocrinol.* **36**, 9.

Kohler, P. O., Mardiney, M. R., and Ross, G. T. (1967). *Endocrinology* **81**, 671.

Kraicer, J., Ducommun, P., Jobin, M., Berup, C., van Rees, G. P., and Fortier, C. (1963). *Federation Proc.* **22**, 507.

Kriss, J. P., and Greenspan, F. S. (1954). *J. Clin. Endocrinol. Metab.* **14**, 770.

Kriss, J. P., Pleshakov, V., and Chien, J. R. (1964). *J. Clin. Endocrinol. Metab.* **24**, 1005.

Kumahara, Y., Iwatsubo, H., Miyai, K., Masui, H., Fukuchi, M., and Abe, H. (1967). *J. Clin. Endocrinol. Metab.* **27**, 333.

Lepp, A., and Oliner, L. (1967a). *Endocrinology* **80**, 369.

Lepp, A., and Oliner, L. (1967b). *Endocrinology* **81**, 299.

Levy, R. P., McGuire, W. L., and Heideman, M. L., Jr. (1962). *Proc. Soc. Exptl. Biol. Med.* **110**, 598.

Levy, R. P., McGuire, W. L., Shaw, R. K., and Bartsch, G. E. (1965). *Endocrinology* **76**, 890.

Maayan, M. L., and Rosenberg, I. N. (1963). *Endocrinology* **73**, 38.

Maayan, M. L., and Rosenberg, I. N. (1966). *Endocrinology* **78**, 1049.

McCullagh, E. P., Reynolds, C. W., and McKenzie, J. M. (1960). *J. Clin. Endocrinol. Metab.* **20**, 1029.

McGiven, A. R., Adams, D. D., and Purves, H. D. (1965). *J. Endocrinol.* **32**, 29.

Mack, R. E., and Niccolini, R. (1965). *Proc. 47th Meeting Endocrine Soc., New York, New York*, p. 108.

McKenzie, J. M. (1958). *Endocrinology* **63**, 372.

McKenzie, J. M. (1960a). *J. Clin. Endocrinol. Metab.* **20**, 380.

McKenzie, J. M. (1960b). *Physiol. Rev.* **40**, 398.

McKenzie, J. M. (1961). *J. Clin. Endocrinol. Metab.* **21**, 635.

McKenzie, J. M. (1962). *J. Biol. Chem.* **237**, 3571.

McKenzie, J. M. (1965). *J. Clin. Endocrinol. Metab.* **25**, 424.

McKenzie, J. M. (1967). *Recent Progr. Hormone Res.* **23**, 1.

McKenzie, J. M., and Fishman, J. (1960). *Proc. Soc. Exptl. Biol. Med.* **105**, 126.

McKenzie, J. M., and Gordon, J. (1965). *Proc. 47th Meeting Endocrine Soc., N.Y.*, p. 23.

McKenzie, J. M., and Williamson, A. (1966). *J. Clin. Endocrinol. Metab.* **26**, 518.

Major, P. W., and Munro, D. S. (1960). *J. Endocrinol.* **20**, xix.

Marine, D., and Rosen, S. H. (1934). *Am. J. Med. Sci.* **188**, 565.

Martini, L., and Ganong, W. F., eds. (1966). "Neuroendocrinology," Vol. I. Academic Press, New York.

Mason, E. K., Hetzel, B. S., Good, B. F., and Stenhouse, N. S. (1967). *J. Clin. Endocrinol. Metab.* **27**, 1529.

Miyai, K., Fukuchi, M., Kumahara, Y., and Abe, H. (1967). *J. Clin. Endocrinol. Metab.* **27**, 855.

Miyai, K., and Werner, S. C. (1966). *J. Clin. Endocrinol. Metab.* **26**, 503.

Moll, J., de Wied, D., and Kramendonk, G. H. (1961). *Acta Endocrinol.* **38**, 330.

Mosier, H. D. (1965). *J. Clin. Endocrinol. Metab.* **25**, 1005.

Munro, D. S. (1959). *J. Endocrinol.* **19**, 64.

Nadler, N. J., and Mitmaker, B. (1961). *Proc. 43rd Meeting Endocrine Soc.*, p. 31.

Nagataki, S., Shizume, K., Matsuda, K., and Ishii, J. (1959). *Proc. Soc. Exptl. Biol. Med.* **102**, 765.

Nagataki, S., Shizume, K., and Okinaka, S. (1961). *Endocrinology* **69**, 199.

Nataf, B. M., and Chaikoff, I. L. (1964). *Endocrinology* **75**, 547.

Nataf, B. M., Rivera, E. M., and Chaikoff, I. L. (1965). *Endocrinology* **76**, 35.

Noguchi, A., Sato, S., and Yamazaki, E. (1962). *Horumon Rinsho* **10**, 29.

Noguichi, A., Kirihari, H., and Sato, S. (1964). *J. Clin. Endocrinol. Metab.* **24**, 160.

Odell, W. D., Bates, R. W., Rivlin, R. S., Sipsett, M. B., and Hertz, R. (1963). *J. Clin. Endocrinol. Metab.* **23**, 658.

Odell, W. D., Wilber, J. F., and Paul, W. E. (1965a), *J. Clin. Endocrinol. Metab.* **25**, 1179.

Odell, W. D., Wilber, J. F., and Paul, W. E. (1965b). *Metabolism* **14**, 465.

Odell, W. D., Wilber, J. F., and Utiger, R. D. (1967). *Recent Progr. Hormone Res.* **23**, 47.

Ohta, M., and Field, J. B. (1966). *Endocrinology* **79**, 732.

Oka, H., and Field, J. B. (1967). *Endocrinology* **81**, 1291.

Panda, J. N., and Turner, C. W. (1966). *Metabolism* **15**, 1104.

Panda, J. N., and Turner, C. W. (1967a). *Proc. Soc. Exptl. Biol. Med.* **124**, 711.

Panda, J. N., and Turner, C. W. (1967b). *Acta Endocrinol.* **54**, 485.

Panda, J. N., and Turner, C. W. (1967c). *J. Physiol. (London)* **192**, 1.

Panda, J. N., and Turner, C. W. (1968a). *J. Physiol. (London)* **195**, 29.

Panda, J. N., and Turner, C. W. (1968b). *Acta Endocrinol.* **57**, 363.

Parlow, A. F., Condliffe, P. G., Reichert, L. E., Jr., and Wilhelmi, A. E. (1965a). *Endocrinology* **76**, 27.

Parlow, A. F., Wilhelmi, A. E., and Reichert, L. E., Jr. (1965b). *Endocrinology* **77**, 1126.

Pascasio, F. M., and Selenkow, H. A. (1962). *Endocrinology* **71**, 254.

Pimstone, B. L., Hoffenberg, R., and Black, E. (1963). *J. Clin. Endocrinol. Metab.* **23**, 336.

Pimstone, B. L., Hoffenberg, R., and Black, E. (1964). *J. Clin. Endocrinol. Metab.* **24**, 976.

Pinchera, A., Pinchera, M. G., and Stanbury, J. B. (1965). *J. Clin. Endocrinol. Metab.* **25**, 189.

Pochin, E. E. (1944). *Clin. Sci.* **5**, 75.

Powell, R. C., Rahman, M. A., and Deiss, W. P. (1964). *Endocrinology* **74**, 395.

Premachandra, B. N., and Turner, C. W. (1960). *Poultry Sci.* **39**, 1286.

Purves, H. D. (1964). *In* "The Thyroid Gland" (R. Pitt-Rivers and W. R. Trotter, eds.), Vol. 2, Chapter 1. Butterworths, London and Washington, D.C.

Purves, H. D., and Adams, D. D. (1961). *In* "Advances in Thyroid Research" (R. Pitt-Rivers, ed.), pp. 184–188. Pergamon Press, Oxford.

Querido, A., Kassenaar, A. A. H., and Lameyer, L. D. F. (1953). *Acta Endocrinol.* **12**, 335.

Rabin, B. S., Kite, J. H., Jr., and Rose, N. R. (1966). *Proc. Soc. Exptl. Biol. Med.* **121**, 888.

Raghupathy, E., Tong, W., and Chaikoff, I. L. (1963). *Endocrinology* **72**, 620.

Raghupathy, E., Abraham, S., Kerkof, P. R., and Chaikoff, I. L. (1964). *Endocrinology* **74**, 468.

Redding, T. W., and Schally, A. V. (1967). *Endocrinology* **81**, 918.

Redding, T. W., Bowers, C. Y., and Schally, A. V. (1966). *Endocrinology* **79**, 299.

Reichlin, S. (1964). *In* "Brain-Thyroid Relationships," p. 17. Little, Brown, Boston, Massachusetts.

Reichlin, S., and Boshans, R. L. (1964). *Endocrinology* **75**, 571

Reichlin, S., and Utiger, R. D. (1967). *J. Clin. Endocrinol. Metab.* **27**, 251.

Rerup, C., and Melander, A. (1965). *Acta Endocrinol.* **50**, 177.

Roche, J., Michel, O., Gorbman, A., and Lissitzky, S. (1953). *Biochem. Biophys. Acta* **12**, 570.

Rosenberg, I. N., Athaus, J. C., and Behar, A. (1960). *Endocrinology* **66**, 185.

Row, V. V., Kim, R. H., Ezrin, C., and Volpe, R. (1967). *J. Clin. Endocrinol. Metab.* **27**, 1647.

Sakiz, E., and Guillemin, R. (1964). *Proc. Soc. Exptl. Biol. Med.* **115**, 856.

Sakiz, E., and Guillemin, R. (1965). *Endocrinology* **77**, 797.

Salaman, D. F. (1964). *J. Endocrinol.* **29**, 283.

Savoie, I. C. (1952). *Ann. Endocrinol. (Paris)* **13**, 81.

Sawin, C. T., and McHugh, J. E. (1966). *J. Clin. Endocrinol. Metab.* **26**, 955.

Schally, A. V., and Redding, T. W. (1967). *Proc. Soc. Exptl. Biol. Med.* **126**, 320.

Schally, A. V., Redding, T. W., and Bowers, C. Y. (1965). *Federation Proc.* **24**. 191.

Schally, A. V., Bowers, C. Y., and Redding, T. W. (1966a). *Proc. Soc. Exptl. Biol. Med.* **121**, 718.

Schally, A. V., Bowers, C. Y., and Redding, T. W. (1966b). *Endocrinology* **78**, 726.

Schally, A. V., Kastin, A. J., Redding, T. W., Bowers, C. Y., Yajima, H. S., and Kubo, K. (1967a). *Metabolism* **16**, 824.

Schally, A. V., Muller, E. E., Arimura, A., Bowers, C. Y., Saito, T., Redding, T. W., Sawano, S., and Pizzolato, P. (1967b). *J. Clin. Endocrinol. Metab.* **27**, 755.

Schneider, P. B., Robbins, J., and Condliffe, G. (1965). *J. Clin. Endocrinol. Metab.* **25**, 514.

Schockaert, J. A. (1932). *Am. J. Anat.* **49**, 379.

Schrieber, V. (1964). *Ann. Endocrinol. (Paris)* **25**, 26.

Schwarz, F., der Kinderen, P. J., and Houtstra-Lanz, M. (1962). *J. Clin. Endocrinol. Metab.* **22**, 718.

Schwarz, F., der Kinderen, P. J., and Houtstra-Lanz, M. (1966). *Acta Endocrinol.* **51**, 359.

Scott, T. W., Good, B. F., and Ferguson, K. A. (1966). *Endocrinology* **79**, 949.

Scow, R. O., and Greer, M. A. (1955). *Endocrinology* **56**, 590.

Segal, S., Roth, H., Blair, A., and Bertoli, D. (1966). *Endocrinology* **79**, 675.

Selenkow, H. A., Saravis, C. A., and Garcia, A. M. (1966). *Acta Endocrinol.* **51**, 32.

Shimoda, S., and Greer, M. A. (1966). *Endocrinology* **78**, 715.

Shimoda, S., Kendall, J. W., and Greer, M. A. (1966). *Endocrinology* **79**, 921.

Shishiba, Y., Solomon, D. H., and Beall, G. N. (1967). *Endocrinology* **80**, 957.

Singh, D. V., Panda, J. N., Anderson, R. R., and Turner, C. W. (1967). *Proc. Soc. Exptl. Biol. Med.* **126**, 553.

Sinha, D. K., and Meites, J. (1966). *Endocrinology* **78**, 1002.

Slingerland, D. W., Sullivan, J. J., and Mulvey, P. F. (1966). *Endocrinology* **78**, 805.

Smelser, G. K. (1936). *Proc. Soc. Exptl. Biol. Med.* **35**, 128.

Snyder, N. J., Green, D. E., and Solomon, D. H. (1964). *J. Clin. Endocrinol. Metab.* **24**, 1129.

Sobonya, R. E., and Dobyns, B. M. (1967). *Endocrinology* **80**, 1090.

Solomon, D. H. (1960). *Biochem. Biophys. Acta* **43**, 346.

Studer, H., and Greer, M. A. (1967). *Endocrinology* **80**, 52.

Taurog, A., and Thio, D. T. (1966). *Endocrinology* **78**, 103.

Taurog, A., Tong, W., and Chaikoff, I. L. (1958a). *Endocrinology* **62**, 646.

Taurog, A., Tong, W., and Chaikoff, I. L. (1958b). *Endocrinology* **62**, 664.

Taurog, A., Evans, E. S., Potter, G. D., and Chaikoff, I. L. (1960). *Endocrinology* **67**, 609.

Taurog, A., Porter, J. C., and Thio, D. T. (1964). *Endocrinology* **74**, 902.

Tong, W. (1964a). *Federation Proc.* **23**, 148.

Tong, W. (1964b). *Endocrinology* **74**, 304.

Tong, W. (1964c). *Endocrinology* **75**, 527.

Tong, W. (1964d). *Endocrinology* **75**, 968.

Tong, W. (1965). *Endocrinology* **76**, 163.

Tong, W., Kerkof, P. R., and Chaikoff, I. L. (1962). *Biochem. Biophys. Acta* **60**, 1.

Tong, W., Raghupathy, E., and Chaikoff, I. L. (1963). *Federation Proc.* **22**, 563.

Utiger, R. D., Odell, W. D., and Condliffe, P. G. (1963). *Endocrinology* **73**, 359.

Vale, W., Burgus, R., and Guillemin, R. (1967). *Proc. Soc. Exptl. Biol. Med.* **125**, 210.

van Beugen, L., and van der Werfften Bosch, J. J. (1961). *Acta Endocrinol.* **38**, 585.

van der Werfften Bosch, J. J., and Swanson, H. E. (1963). *Acta Endocrinol.* **42**, 254.

van Rees, G. P. (1966). *Acta Endocrinol.* **51**, 619.

van Rees, G. P., Noach, E. L., and van Dieten, J. A. M. A. (1965). *Acta Endocrinol.* **50**, 155.

Wallace, A. L. C., and Ferguson, K. A. (1964). *J. Endocrinol.* **30**, 387.

Wegelius, O., Naumann, J., and Brunish, R. (1959). *Acta Endocrinol.* **30**, 53.

Werner, S. C. (1962). *Ciba Found. Colloq. Endocrinol.* **14**, 225.

Werner, S. C., ed (1963). "Thyrotropin." C. C. Thomas, Springfield, Illinois.

Werner, S. C., and Tierney, J. (1961). *Proc. Soc. Exptl. Biol. Med.* **108**, 780.

Werner, S. C., Seegal, B., and Osserman, E. F. (1961). *J. Clin. Invest.* **40**, 92.

Werner, S. C., Tierney, J., and Tallberg, T. (1964). *J. Clin. Endocrinol. Metab.* **24**, 339.

Wilber, J. F., and Odell, W. D. (1965). *J. Clin. Endocrinol. Metab.* **25**, 1408.

Wilber, J. F., and Utiger, R. D. (1967). *Endocrinology* **81**, 145.

Yamada, T., and Greer, M. A. (1959a). *Endocrinology* **64**, 559.

Yamada, T., and Greer, M. A. (1959b). *Endocrinology* **64**, 920.

Yamazaki, E., Noguchi, A., Sato, S., and Slingerland, D. W. (1961a). *J. Clin. Endocrinol. Metab.* **21**, 1127.

Yamazaki, E., Noguchi, A., and Slingerland, D. W. (1961b). *J. Clin. Endocrinol. Metab.* **21**, 1013.

Author Index

567

Subject Index

A

17α-Acetoxy-6-methyl pregna-4,6-diene-
3,20-dione, as antiestrogen, 140
2-Aetyl-7-oxa1,2,3,4,a,5,6,7,9,10,10a-
dodecahydrophenanthrene, as
antiandrogen, 221
assay of 225, 233, 236–237
Acid phosphatase,
androgen effect on, 204–207
determination of, in prostate secretion,
209–211
prostatic, in androgen assay, 207–212
in inhibition of androgenic activity
(Standard Method), 275
Acne, antiandrogens and, 221
Acromegaly, thyroxine transport in, 326–
327
ACTH,
inhibition activity, assay for (Standard
Method), 270
as standard stimulator in assays for
anti-adrenal activity (Standard
Methods), 276, 277
Adipose tissue, thyrotropic hormone
effects on oxygen uptake by, 531
Adrenal activity, inhibition of, assay for
(Standard Methods), 276, 277
Adrenal hormones, assay, statistics of, 24
Adrenaline,
bioassays of,
by cardiovascular response, 291–292
by electrophysiology, 297
by eye measurements, 294
intestinal muscle use in, 294
methods of, 290–291
nictitating membrane use in, 294
parallel type, 288–289
by perfused rabbit ear, 295
specificity of, 289–290
spleen use in, 296
stomach muscle use in, 295

tissue and fluid purification for, 290
using isolated smooth muscle, 296
using rat uterus, 293
quantitation and functional evaluation,
287–299
biological methods, 287–288
Adrenosterone, assay of, 179, 180, 183,
185, 191–192
Albert method of EPS assay, 533
Allen-Doisy test for vaginal cornification, 67–72
administration methods, 72–73
animal preparation, 69–70
interpretation of, 75–77
intravaginal type, 77–83
modifications of, 72–75
smear test in, 73–75
solution preparation, 68–69
spaying animal, 68
typical test, 70–72
Amphenone B, in assay for anti-adrenal
activity (Standard Method), 277
Anabolic agents, androgens and, 151–220
Androgen(s),
anabolic agents and, 151–220
androgenic and myogenic activity,
Standard Method of assay, 256–257
antiestrogenic activity, 121
assay of, 90, 153–218
bird methods, 153–197
capon comb growth, 153–162
chick comb growth, 162–193,
196–197
sparrow's bill, 193–196
on mammals, 197–218
effect on thyroxine binding, 325
Androgen-anabolic assays, 199–201
Androgenic activity, Standard Method
for assay of, 256–257
Androgenic and myogenic activity, inhibition of, assay (Standard Methods),
273–274, 275

588

transport of thyroid hormones during, 323
thyroid function in, 328
Hypertricosis, antiandrogens and, 221
Hypoglycemic convulsions, blood sugar level in, 367
Hypothalamus, in thyrotropic hormone secretion, 517–525
Hypothyroidism,
  iodinated compounds in blood during, 321, 322
  thyroid function test in, 329–330

I

Immunoassay,
  of glucagon, 426–429
  of insulin, 406–407
  of parathyroid hormone, 449–454
Immunoprecipitation, in insulin radio-immunoassay, 409–410
Infancy, thyroxine-binding globulin in, 330–331
Insecticides, assay of, statistics, 55–56
Insulin, 365–414
  assays for, 367–412
    biological methods, 403–405
      in vitro, 404–405
      in vivo, 403–404
    chromatography methods, 410–412
    mouse method, 391–401
    rabbit method, 367–390
    statistics of, 29
    using insulin antiserum, 405–410
      immunoassay, 406–407
      radio immunoassay, 407–410
    radiolabeled, in assays, 405
    standard preparation, 366–367
Insulin antiserum, assays using, 405–410
  immunoassay, 406–407
  radioimmunoassay, 407–410
Insulin testing cabinet for mice, 399
Interpubic ligament measurement method of relaxin assay, 490–496
Intestinal muscle, in bioassay of adrenaline and noradrenaline, 294
Iodine, inorganic, thyrotropic hormone effects on release of, 530–531
Iodine-131,
  in glucagon immunoassay, 426–429

in insulin assay, 366, 407–410
use in study of thyroidal substances, 302, 304
Isocitric dehydrogenase,
  in antiestrogen activity, 139
  antiestrogen assay using, 145–146
Isoprenaline, in bioassay using rat stomach, 295
3'-Isopropyl-3,5-dihomo-L-thyronine, biological activity of, 347
3'Isopropyldiiodothyroacetic acid, 307
3'-Isopropyldiiodothyronine, biological activity of, 346–347
Isoproterenol, bioassay of by eye measurements, 294

J

Jensen et al., method of, 146

K

6-Ketoestrone, as antiestrogen, 127
6-Ketorstrone-17β, as antiestrogen, 127
11-Keto-17α-methyltestosterone, assay of, 191, 192
11-Ketotestosterone, assay of, 187
Kirk et al., method of, 207–212
Kroc et al., method of, 500–501

L

Lactogenic hormone, thyroxine effects on, 335
LATS, see Long-acting thyroid stimulator
Lee and Williams, method of, 139–140
Lennon and Saunders, method of, 203–204
Lerner, methods of, 138–139, 140–141
Lerner et al., methods of, 125, 126, 226–228
Levator ani muscle, steroid stimulation of, 151–152
Liquid diet, composition of, 202–203
Liver,
  glucagon effects on, 417–418
  glycogen deposition in, in assay for glucocorticoid activity (Standard Method), 266–267